Books are to be returned on or before
the last date below.

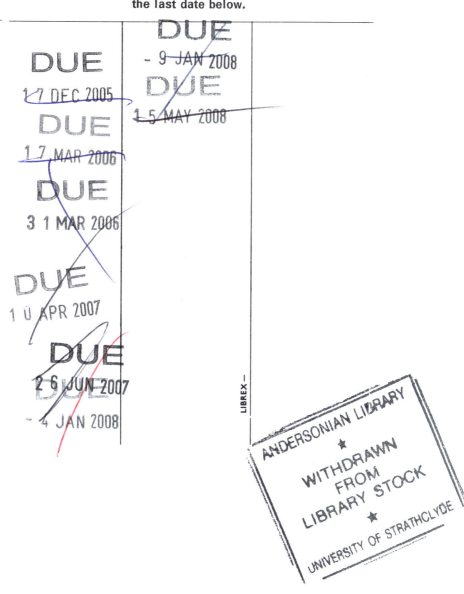

DUE

DUE
- 9 JAN 2008

DUE
1 7 DEC 2005

DUE
1 5 MAY 2008

DUE
1 7 MAR 2006

DUE
3 1 MAR 2006

DUE
1 0 APR 2007

DUE
2 6 JUN 2007

DUE
- 4 JAN 2008

LIBREX —

# Food preservation techniques

## Related titles from Woodhead's food science, technology and nutrition list:

*Natural antimicrobials for the minimal processing of foods* (ISBN: 1 85573 669 1)

Consumers demand products with fewer synthetic additives but increased quality and shelf-life. As a result there has been growing interest in natural antimicrobials. This authoritative collection reviews the practical application of a range of antimicrobials from plant, animal and microbial sources.

*Novel food packaging techniques* (ISBN: 1 85573 675 6)

This comprehensive and authoritative collection summarises key recent developments in packaging. The book first discusses the range of active and intelligent packaging techniques. It then summarises the major trends in modified atmosphere packaging. The final part of the book discusses general issues such as the regulatory context, packaging optimisation and consumer attitudes to novel packaging formats.

*Rapid and on-line instrumentation for food quality assurance* (ISBN: 1 85573 526 1)

With its high volume of production, the food industry has an urgent need for instrumentation which gives rapid results and can be used on-line. This important collection reviews the wealth of recent research in this field. Part I discusses product safety and the use of rapid techniques to identify chemical and microbial contaminants. Part II looks at techniques to monitor product quality.

Details of these books and a complete list of Woodhead's food science, technology and nutrition titles can be obtained by:

- visiting our web site at www.woodhead-publishing.com
- contacting Customer Services (email: sales@woodhead-publishing.com; fax: +44 (0) 1223 893694; tel.: +44 (0) 1223 891358 ext. 30; address: Woodhead Publishing Limited, Abington Hall, Abington, Cambridge CB1 6AH, England)

Selected food science and technology titles are also available in electronic form. Visit our web site (www.woodhead-publishing.com) to find out more.

If you would like to receive information on forthcoming titles in this area, please send your address details to: Francis Dodds (address, tel. and fax as above; e-mail: francisd@woodhead-publishing.com). Please confirm which subject areas you are interested in.

# Food preservation techniques

Edited by
Peter Zeuthen and Leif Bøgh-Sørensen

CRC Press
Boca Raton Boston New York Washington, DC

WOODHEAD PUBLISHING LIMITED
Cambridge England

Published by Woodhead Publishing Limited
Abington Hall, Abington
Cambridge CB1 6AH
England
www.woodhead-publishing.com

Published in North America by CRC Press LLC
2000 Corporate Blvd, NW
Boca Raton FL 33431
USA

First published 2003, Woodhead Publishing Limited and CRC Press LLC
© 2003, Woodhead Publishing Limited
The authors have asserted their moral rights.

British Library Cataloguing in Publication Data
A catalogue record for this book is available from the British Library.

Library of Congress Cataloging-in-Publication Data
A catalog record for this book is available from the Library of Congress.

Woodhead Publishing Limited ISBN 1 85573 530 X (book); 1 85573 714 0 (e-book)
CRC Press ISBN 0-8493-1757-6
CRC Press order number: WP1757

Cover design by The ColourStudio
Project managed by Macfarlane Production Services, Markyate, Hertfordshire
(e-mail: macfarl@aol.com)
Typeset by MHL Typesetting Limited, Coventry, Warwickshire
Printed by TJ International Limited, Padstow, Cornwall, England

# Contents

**18    Pulsed electric fields** ........................................... 360
*L. Picart and J-C. Cheftel, Université des Sciences et Techniques du
Languedoc, France*

**19    High hydrostatic pressure technology in food preservation** .... 428
*Indrawati, A. Van Loey, C. Smout and M. Hendrickx,
Katholieke Universiteit Leuven, Belgium*

**Part IV    Assessing preservation requirements** ...................... 449

**20    Modelling food spoilage** ......................................... 451
*J. Sutherland, London Metropolitan University, UK*

# Contributor contact details

## Chapter 2

Professor P. M. Davidson and
  Dr S. Zivanovic
Department of Food Science and
  Technology
University of Tennessee
2509 River Drive
Knoxville
TN 37996-4539
USA

Tel: 865-974-0098
Fax: 865-974-7332
E-mail: pmdavidson@utk.edu

## Chapter 3

Professor J. Pokorný
Department of Food Chemistry and
  Analysis
Faculty of Food and Biochemical
  Technology
Institute of Chemical Technology
Technicka 5
CZ-166 28 Prague 6
Czech Republic

Tel +4202 2435 3264
Fax +4202 3333 9990
E-mail jan.pokorny@vscht.cz

## Chapter 4

Dr A.S. Meyer
BioCentrum-DTU
Technical University of Denmark
DK-2800 Lyngby
Denmark

E-mail: am@biocentrum.dtu.dk

## Chapter 5

Dr P. Paulsen and Professor F. J. M.
  Smulders
Institute of Meat Hygiene
University of Veterinary Medicine
  Vienna

A1210 Vienna
Austria
Tel 43-1-25077-3318
E-mail: peter.paulsen@vu-wien.ac.at

1428 Buenos Aires
Argentina

E-mail: alzamora@ciudad.com.ar

## Chapter 6

Dr H. Park
Graduate School of Biotechnology
Korea University
5-Ka
Anam-Dong
Sungbuk-Ku
Seoul 136-701
Korea

Fax: 82 2 3290 3450
E-mail: hjpark@korea.ac.kr
E-mail: hjpark@clemson.edu

## Chapter 9

Dr Graham Bown
Retort Product Manager, Food
    Flexibles Europe
Alcan Packaging
PO Box 3
Nightingale Way
Midsomer Norton
Radstock
BA3 4AA
UK

E-mail: graham.bown@alcan.com

## Chapter 7

Professor F.-K. Lücke
Department of Household
    Management, Nutrition, Food
    Quality (FB OE)
University of Applied Sciences
    (Fachhochschule)
Marquardstr. 35
D-36039 Fulda
Germany

E-mail: Friedrich-Karl.Luecke@he.
    fh-fulda.de

## Chapter 10

Dr L. Beney, Dr J. Perrier-Cornet,
    Dr F. Fine, Professor P. Gervais
ENSBANA
1 Esplanade Erasme 21000
Dijon
France

Tel: 03 80 39 66 54
Fax: 03 80 39 66 11
E-mail: gpab@u-bourgogne.fr

## Chapter 11

Dr V. K. Juneja
Food Safety Research Unit
USDA-ARS-ERRC
600 E. Mermaid Lane
Wyndmoor
PA 19038
USA

## Chapter 8

Professor S.M. Alzamora
Department of Industry, FCEyN
Universidad de Buenos Aires
Ciudad Universitaria

Tel: 215-233-6500
Fax: 215-233-6406
E-mail: vjuneja@arserrc.gov


## Chapter 12

Dr C. J. Kennedy
Nutrifreeze Ltd
8 Roland Court
Huntington Road
York, YO32 9PW
UK

Tel: +44 (0)1904 767675
Fax: +44 (0)1904 767505
E-mail: chris.kennedy@nutrifreeze.com


## Chapter 13

Associate Professor
J. Botella
Department of Botany
University of Queensland
Brisbane
Qld 4072
Australia

Tel: 61-7-3365 1128
Fax: 61-7-3365 1699
E-mail: j.botella@botany.uq.edu.au


## Chapter 14

Dr A. Grandison
School of Food Biosciences
The University of Reading
PO Box 226
Reading, RG6 6AP
UK

Tel: + 44 (0)1189 316724
Fax: +44 (0)1189 316649
E-mail: a.s.grandison@reading.ac.uk

## Chapter 15

S. Green, N. Basaran and Professor
    B. G. Swanson
Food Science & Human Nutrition
Washington State University
106K FSHN Building
PO Box 646376
Pullman
WA 99164-6376
USA

Tel: 509 335 3793
Fax: 509 335 4815
E-mail: swansonb@wsu.edu


## Chapter 16

Professor T. J. Mason and Dr L.
    Paniwynk
School of Science and the
    Environment
Coventry University
Priory Street
Coventry CV1 5FB
UK

Tel: +44 (0)24 7688 7688

Dr. F. Chemat
Faculté des Sciences
Université de la Réunion
15 Avenue René Cassin – BP 7151
F-97715 St Denis Messag.
Cedex 9
France

Tel: +33 262 93 81 82


## Chapter 17

Professor B. Ooraikul
Dept of Agricultural, Food and
    Nutritional Science

University of Alberta
Edmonton AB
Canada T6G 2P5

Fax: 780 492 8914
E-mail: ooraikul@ualberta.ca

## Chapter 18

Dr L. Picart and Professor J-C.
  Cheftel
Unité de Biochimie et Technologie
  Alimentaires
Université des Sciences et Techniques
  du Languedoc
F-34095 Montpellier CDX05
France

Tel: +33 (0)4 67 14 33 51
Fax: +33 (0)4 67 63 33 97
E-mail: c.cheftel@univ-montp2.fr

## Chapter 19

Dr Indrawati, Dr A. Van Loey, Dr C.
  Smout and Professor M. Hendrickx
Dept of Food and Microbial
  Technology
Katholieke Universiteit Leuven
Kasteelpark Arenberg 22
B-3001 Leuven
Belgium

Fax: +32 16 321960
E-mail: indrawati.hartono@agr.
  kuleuven.ac.be

## Chapter 20

Dr J. P. Sutherland
Department of Health and Human
  Sciences

London Metropolitan University
166–220 Holloway Road
London N7 8DB
UK

Tel: +44 (0)207 133 2571
Fax: +44 (0)207 133 2571
E-mail: j.sutherland@londonmet.
  ac.uk

## Chapter 21

Dr E. Dens and Professor J. Van Impe
Department of Chemical Engineering
BioTeC-Bioprocess Technology and
  Control
Katholieke Universiteit Leuven
W. de Croylaan 46
B-3001 Leuven
Belgium

Tel: +32-16-321466
Fax: +32-16-322991
E-mail: jan.vanimpe@cit.kuleuven.
  ac.be

## Chapter 22

Professor M. Peleg
Department of Food Science
Chenoweth Laboratory
University of Massachusetts
Amherst
MA 01003-1410
USA

Tel: (413) 545-5852
Fax: (413) 545-1262
E-mail: Micha.peleg@foodsci.umass.
  edu

# Chapter 23

Professor S. Brul, Dr F. Klis,
    Professor D. Knorr, Dr T. Abee and
    Dr S. Notermans
Food Processing Group
Unilever Research
Olivier van Noortlaan 120
3133 AT Vlaardingen
The Netherlands

Tel: 31-10-4604151
Fax: 31-10-4605188
E-mail: Stanley.brul@unilever.com

# Chapter 24

Dr P. Zeuthen*
Hersegade 7 G,
DK-4000
Roskilde
Tel/ Fax: 46355665
E-mail: peter.zeuthen@image.dk

Dr Leif Bøgh-Sørensen
Danish Veterinary and Food
    Administration
Morkhoj Bygade 19
DK-2860 Soborg
Denmark

E-mail: lbs@fdir.dk

# 1

# Introduction

One of the major advances in human history was the ability to preserve food. It was the prerequisite to man settling down in one place, instead of moving from place to place in the never ending hunt for fresh food. The earliest preservation technologies developed were drying, smoking, chilling and heating. Later on the art of controlling these technologies was developed. The work of Pasteur in the nineteenth century then made it possible to understand the real mode of operation of preservation techniques such as heating, chilling and freezing, providing the basis for more systematic monitoring and control.

The use of various compounds such as salt and spices to preserve foods was also used in ancient times. Unfortunately, the gradual use of a wider range of chemicals for preservation such as boron or cumarine sometimes led to misuse. Consumers have developed some suspicion of the use of chemical additives, sometimes with good reason in such cases as antibiotics and materials such as hexamethyltetramine (which during processing and storage develops into formaldehyde).

Consumers have fewer reservations about physical treatments, although one of the oldest technologies, smoking, is now suspected of being carcinogenic. Another more recent physical treatment which is also much under debate is irradiation. Many studies have shown it to be safe and it has been approved for use in food processing in several countries, e.g., the USA, because it has proved to be the best way to kill *Salmonella* and other pathogenic bacteria. However, irradiation of foods is not used in practice in most countries in Europe because of continuing consumer concerns about the safety of the technology.

Recent debate about preservation techniques has focused on ways of preserving foods in a way that is both safe but also preserves the intrinsic nutritional and sensory qualities present in raw and fresh food by minimising the amount and severity of subsequent processing operations. This is why minimally processed foods have gained such great popularity, although they raise new safety risks. As an example, they often rely on an effective cold chain during storage and distribution to prevent microbial growth. This book describes both established and new preservation methods which embrace biotechnology and physics. Both methods offer the possibility of preserving food safely with a minimal impact on quality. The book describes the principles behind individual preservation methods, the foods to which they can be applied, their impact on food safety and quality, their strengths and limitations. It also shows how individual techniques have been combined to achieve the twin goals of food safety and quality. The book tries to describe a *status quo* of where we are in the development of food preservation techniques at the beginning of a new millennium, and some of the things we still need to do.

# Part I

# Ingredients

# 2

# The use of natural antimicrobials

**P. M. Davidson and S. Zivanovic, University of Tennessee, USA**

## 2.1 Introduction

Food antimicrobials are chemical compounds added to or present in foods that retard microbial growth or kill microorganisms. The functions of food antimicrobials are to inhibit or inactivate spoilage microorganisms and pathogenic microorganisms. The latter function has increased in importance in the past 10–15 years as food processors search for more and better tools to improve food safety (Davidson, 2001). Prior to recent approvals of certain compounds to control foodborne pathogens by worldwide regulatory agencies, one of the only uses of antimicrobials to control a pathogen was nitrite or nitrate against *Clostridium botulinum* in cured meats.

A number of compounds are approved by international regulatory agencies for use as direct food antimicrobials (Table 2.1). The question arises as to why, with so many compounds already approved for use in foods, would the food processing industry need a greater number of food antimicrobials? The primary incentive for searching for effective antimicrobials among naturally occurring compounds is to expand the spectrum of antimicrobial activity over that of the regulatory-approved substances. Most of the traditional, currently approved food antimicrobials have limited application due to pH or food component interactions. For example, organic acids function at low concentrations only in high acid foods (generally less than pH 4.5–4.6). This is because the most effective antimicrobial form is the undissociated acid which exists in majority only at a pH below the $pK_a$ of the compound. All regulatory-approved organic acids used as antimicrobials have $pK_a$ values less than 5.0 (Table 2.2) which means their maximum activity will be in high-acid foods. For food products with a pH of 5.5 or greater, there are very few compounds that are effective at low

**Table 2.1**  Current regulatory-approved compounds for use as direct addition food antimicrobials

**Compound or group of compounds**

Alkyl esters of *p*-hydroxybenzoic acid (Parabens; methyl, ethyl, propyl, butyl and heptyl)
Acetic acid and acetate salts, diacetates, dehydroacetic acid
Benzoic acid and benzoate salts
Dimethyl dicarbonate, diethyl dicarbonate
Lactic acid and lactate salts
Lysozyme
Natamycin
Nisin
Nitrites and nitrates
Phosphates
Propionic acid and propionate salts
Sorbic acid and sorbate salts
Sulfite derivatives

**Table 2.2**  pK$_a$ of regulatory-approved organic acids

| Compound or group of compounds | pK$_a$ |
|---|---|
| Acetic acid | 4.75 |
| Benzoic acid | 4.19 |
| Lactic acid | 3.79 |
| Propionic acid | 4.87 |
| Sorbic acid | 4.75 |

concentrations. Another factor leading to reduced effectiveness among food antimicrobials is food component interactions. Most food antimicrobials are amphiphilic. As such, they can solubilize in or be bound by lipids or hydrophobic proteins in foods making them less available to inhibit microorganisms in the food product.

Interest in natural antimicrobials is also driven by the fact that international regulatory agencies are generally very strict about requirements for toxicological evaluation of novel direct food antimicrobials. In many parts of the world, toxicological testing of new synthetic compounds could take many years and many millions of dollars to obtain approval. For some types of food additives a payback may be possible (e.g., artificial sweeteners), but for food antimicrobials it is less likely that obtaining approval would be profitable.

An argument often used to justify natural antimicrobials is that they will produce 'green' labels, i.e., one with few or no 'synthetic' additives in the ingredient list. While this rationale may be true, it must be remembered that many of the antimicrobial compounds approved for use in foods today come from natural sources (Table 2.3). If a truly effective antimicrobial was discovered from a natural source, it may be more economically feasible to synthesize it than to extract it from a natural source. This justification also leads

**Table 2.3**   Natural sources for antimicrobials

| Compound or group of compounds | Natural source |
| --- | --- |
| Acetic acid | Vinegar |
| Benzoic acid | Cranberries, plums, prunes, cinnamon, cloves, and most berries |
| Lactic acid | Lactic acid bacteria |
| Propionic acid | Swiss cheese (*Propionibacterium freudenreichii* ssp. *shermanii*) |
| Sorbic acid | Rowanberries |

consumers to the mistaken belief that food additives currently in use are potentially toxic and should be avoided.

In addition to potential benefits associated with natural antimicrobials in foods, there are a number of potential concerns that need to be examined with respect to food safety. For example, if an antimicrobial is to be used exclusively to inhibit a pathogenic microorganism, it must be uniformly effective, stable to storage, and stable to any processes to which it is exposed. Standardized assays for activity need to be developed to ensure that the antimicrobial compounds retain potency. Finally, producers and users of natural antimicrobials that make claims for efficacy of use will be likely to be liable for any claims they make. In short, natural antimicrobials have excellent potential but probably will not produce miracles.

## 2.2   Natural antimicrobials from animal sources

Naturally occurring antimicrobials may be classified by source. There are compounds from animal, plant and microbial sources. As stated above, some naturally occurring antimicrobials have been approved for direct addition into foods by regulatory agencies including lactoferrin, lysozyme, natamycin and nisin.

### 2.2.1   Chitosan

Chitosan, (1→4)–2-amino-2-deoxy-$\beta$-D-glucan, is a natural constituent of fungal cell walls (Ruiz-Herrera, 1992). It is produced commercially from chitin, a by-product of shellfish processing, by alkaline deacetylation. Chitosan is the designated name for the series of polymers with different ratios of glucosamine (GlcN) and *N*-acetyl glucosamine (GlcNAc). Most commercial chitosans have less than 30% acetylated units (referred to as degree of acetylation less than 30%) and molecular weights between 100 and 1,200 kDa (Li *et al.*, 1997; Onsoyen and Skaugrud, 1990).

Chitosan inhibits growth of foodborne molds, yeasts and bacteria including *Aspergillus flavus, Saccharomyces cerevisiae, Zygosaccharomyces bailii, Mucor racemosus, Byssochlamys* spp., *Botrytis cinerea, Rhizopus stolonifer* and *Salmonella, Staphylococcus aureus, Escherichia coli, Yersinia enterocolitica, Listeria monocytogenes* and *Lactobacillus fructivorans* (Roller and Covill, 2000; Sudarshan *et al.*, 1992; Papineau *et al.*, 1991; Wang, 1992). However, reported minimum inhibitory concentrations for both bacteria and yeasts vary widely from 0.01–5.0% depending on polymer characteristics and pH, temperature, and presence of interfering substances such as proteins and fats (Chen *et al.*, 1998; Rhoades and Roller, 2000; Roller and Covill, 1999; Sudarshan *et al.*, 1992; Tsai and Su, 1999; Tsai *et al.*, 2000). Chitosan may directly affect the microbial cell by interaction with the anionic cell wall polysaccharides or components of the cytoplasmic membrane resulting in altered permeability or prevention of transport (Tsai and Su, 1999; Fang *et al.*, 1994).

Darmadji and Izumimoto (1994) showed that 1% chitosan was necessary for reduction of only 1–2 logs of *Pseudomonas*, staphylococci, and total bacteria count in minced beef patties and lower concentrations (0.2 and 0.5%) had no effect on the microflora. In contrast, fresh strawberries and bell peppers dipped in acidic chitosan solutions and inoculated with *B. cinerea* or *R. stolonifer* were reported to have a shelf life equivalent to that of fruit treated with conventional fungicide (El-Ghaouth *et al.*, 1991; El-Ghaouth, 1997). Roller and Covill (1999) reported that 0.1 to 5 g/l of chitosan glutamate inhibited growth of eight yeast species in apple juice at 25°C. The most sensitive strain was *Z. bailii*, which was completely inactivated by chitosan glutamate at 0.1 g/l. For *S. cerevisiae*, the minimum inhibitory concentration was 0.4 g/l and no resumption of growth was observed after 32 days.

### 2.2.2   Lactoferrin

In milk and colostrum, the primary iron-binding protein is lactoferrin. Lactoferrin has two iron binding sites per molecule. Lactoferrin is inhibitory by itself to a number of microorganisms including *Bacillus subtilis, B. stearothermophilus, Listeria monocytogenes, Micrococcus* species, *E. coli* and *Klebsiella* species (Oram and Reiter, 1968; Korhonen, 1978; Reiter, 1978; Mandel and Ellison, 1985; Payne *et al.*, 1990). The compound has no activity against *Salmonella* Typhimurium, *Pseudomonas fluorescens* and little activity against *E. coli* O157:H7 or *L. monocytogenes* VPHI (Payne *et al.*, 1994). Some gram-negative bacteria may be resistant because they adapt to low iron environments by producing siderophores such as phenolates and hydroxamates (Ekstrand, 1994). Microorganisms with a low iron requirement, such as lactic acid bacteria, would not be inhibited by lactoferrin. Since it is cationic, lactoferrin may increase the outer membrane permeability to hydrophobic compounds, including other antimicrobials. According to Naidu and Bidlack (1998), lactoferrin blocks adhesion of microorganisms to mucosal surfaces, inhibits expression of fimbria and other colonizing factors of enteric pathogens, such as *E. coli*, and inactivates lipopolysaccharides of gram-negative bacteria.

Lactoferricin B or hydrolyzed lactoferrin (HLF) is a small peptide produced by acid-pepsin hydrolysis of bovine lactoferrin (Bellamy *et al.*, 1992). Jones *et al.* (1994) reported that the compound was inhibitory to *Shigella*, *Salmonella*, *Yersinia enterocolitica*, *E. coli* O157:H7, *S. aureus*, *L. monocytogenes* and *Candida*. In contrast, while HLF was effective against *L. monocytogenes*, Enterohemorrhagic *E. coli*, and *Salmonella* Enteritidis in peptone yeast extract glucose broth, it was not active in a more complex medium, trypticase soy broth (TSB) (Branen and Davidson, 2000). The addition of EDTA enhanced the activity of HLF in TSB, indicating that the decreased activity of HLF may have been due, in part, to excess cations in the medium. Venkitanarayanan *et al.* (1999) found that, while 50 or 100 $\mu$g lactoferricin B per ml reduced viable *E. coli* O157:H7 in 1% peptone, it was much less effective as an antimicrobial in ground beef.

### 2.2.3 Lactoperoxidase system

Lactoperoxidase is an enzyme that occurs in raw milk, colostrum, saliva and other biological secretions. Bovine milk naturally contains 10 to 60 mg of lactoperoxidase per liter (Ekstrand, 1994). This enzyme reacts with thiocyanate (SCN$^-$) in the presence of hydrogen peroxide and forms antimicrobial compound(s). This is termed the lactoperoxidase system (LPS). Fresh milk contains 1 to 10 mg of thiocyanate per liter, which is not always sufficient to activate the LPS. Hydrogen peroxide, the third component of the LPS, is not present in fresh milk due to the action of natural catalase, peroxidase or superoxide dismutase. Approximately 8 to 10 mg hydrogen peroxide per liter is required for LPS. In the LPS reaction, thiocyanate is oxidized to the antimicrobial hypothiocyanate (OSCN$^-$) which also exists in equilibrium with hypothiocyanous acid (p$K_a$ = 5.3) (Reiter and Härnulv, 1984; Gaya *et al.*, 1991).

The LPS is generally more effective against gram-negative bacteria, including pseudomonads, than gram-positive bacteria (Björck, 1978). However, it does inhibit both gram-positive and gram-negative foodborne pathogens including salmonellae, *S. aureus*, *Listeria monocytogenes* and *Campylobacter jejuni* (Beumer *et al.*, 1985; Kamau *et al.*, 1990; Siragusa and Johnson, 1989). The LPS system can increase the shelf life of raw milk (Ekstrand, 1994). Inactivation of lactoperoxidase occurs at 80°C in 15 sec whereas residual lactoperoxidase activity is detected following treatment at 72°C. Barrett *et al.* (1999) theorized that lactoperoxidase may have a role in the keeping quality of pasteurized milk treated at 72°C for 15 sec. LPS has also been used as a preservation process in infant formula, ice cream, cream, cheeses and liquid whole eggs (Ekstrand, 1994).

### 2.2.4 Lysozyme

Lysozyme is an enzyme that catalyzes hydrolysis of the $\beta$-1,4 glycosidic bonds between N-acetylmuramic acid and N-acetylglucosamine of the peptidoglycan of bacterial cell walls. It is present in avian eggs, mammalian milk, tears (and other secretions), insects and fish. In hypotonic solutions, the enzyme causes lysis of bacterial cells. The enzyme is most active against gram-positive bacteria because the peptidoglycan of the cell wall is more exposed. It inhibits the foodborne bacteria *Bacillus stearothermophilus*, *Clostridium botulinum*, *C. thermosaccharolyticum* (*Thermoanaerobacterium thermosaccharolyticum*), *C. tyrobutyricum*, *Listeria monocytogenes* and *Staphylococcus aureus* (Hughey and Johnson, 1987; Hughey *et al.*, 1989). There is variation in the susceptibility of gram-positive bacteria to lysozyme probably due to the presence of teichoic acids or other compounds that bind the enzyme. Also, certain species have greater proportions of 1,6 or 1,3 glycosidic linkages in the peptidoglycan which are more resistant than the 1,4 linkage (Tranter, 1994). Lysozyme is less effective against gram-negative bacteria due to reduced peptidoglycan content (5–10%) and presence of the outer membrane of lipopolysaccharide (LPS) and lipoprotein (Wilkins and Board, 1989). Gram negative cell susceptibility can be increased by combination with chelators (e.g., EDTA) that bind $Ca^{++}$ or $Mg^{++}$ which are essential for maintaining integrity of the LPS layer. Lysozyme is used to prevent gas formation ('blowing') in cheeses such as Edam and Gouda by *C. tyrobutyricum*. Cheese manufacturers using eggwhite lysozyme for this purpose generally add a maximum of 400 mg/l. Lysozyme is used in Japan to preserve seafood, vegetables, pasta and salads. Lysozyme has been evaluated for use as an antimicrobial in wines to inhibit lactic acid bacteria and as a component of antimicrobial packaging (Padgett *et al.*, 1998).

## 2.3   Natural antimicrobials from plant sources

Major components of naturally occurring antimicrobials in plants can include those present in the intact plant and those released due to infection or injury. Components present in intact plants include alkaloids, dienes, flavonols, flavones, glycosides, lactones, organic acids, phenolic compounds, and protein-like compounds (López-Malo *et al.*, 2000). Post-infection inhibitors may include isothiocyanates, phenolic compounds, phytoalexins and sulfoxides (López-Malo *et al.*, 2000). Of greatest potential as food antimicrobials are compounds from spices and their essential oils. Additionally, compounds from the *Allium* family, the Cruciferae or mustard family and phenolic compounds have shown some potential.

### 2.3.1   Allium

Onion (*Allium cepa*) and garlic (*Allium sativum*) have been shown to inhibit growth and toxin production of many microorganisms including *B. cereus*, *C. botulinum* type A, *E. coli*, *Lactobacillus plantarum*, *Salmonella*, *Shigella*, and *S. aureus*, and the fungi *A. flavus*, *A. parasiticus*, *Candida albicans*, and species of *Cryptococcus*, *Rhodotorula*, *Saccharomyces*, *Torulopsis* and *Trichosporon*

(Saleem and Al-Delaimy, 1982; Conner and Beuchat, 1984; Beuchat, 1994; González-Fandos *et al.*, 1994). Cavallito and Bailey (1944) isolated the major antimicrobial compounds from garlic by using steam distillation of ethanolic extracts. They identified the antimicrobial component as allicin (diallyl thiosulfinate; thio-2-propene-1-sulfinic acid-5-allyl ester). Allicin is formed by the action of the enzyme, allinase, on the substrate alliin [S-(2-propenyl)-L-cysteine sulfoxide]. The reaction occurs only when cells of the garlic are disrupted, releasing the enzyme to act on the substrate. A similar reaction occurs in onion except that the substrate is [S-(1-propenyl)-L-cysteine sulfoxide] and one of the major products is thiopropanal-S-oxide. The products responsible for anti-microbial activity are also apparently responsible for the flavor of onions and garlic. In addition to antimicrobial sulfur compounds, onions contain the phenolic compounds protocatechuic acid and catechol, which could contribute to their antimicrobial activity (Walker and Stahmann, 1955). The mechanism of action of allicin is most likely inhibition of sulfhydryl-containing enzymes (Beuchat, 1994).

### 2.3.2   Hydroxycinnamic acids and related compounds

Hydroxycinnamic acids include caffeic, *p*-coumaric, ferulic and sinapic acids. These compounds are found in plants and plant foods and they frequently occur as esters and less often as glucosides (Ho, 1992). Herald and Davidson (1983) demonstrated that ferulic acid at $1000 \, \mu g/ml$ and p-coumaric acid at 500 or $1000 \, \mu g/ml$ inhibited the growth of *Bacillus cereus* and *Staphylococcus aureus*. The compounds were much less effective against *Pseudomonas fluorescens* and *E. coli*. In contrast, alkyl esters of hydroxycinnamic acids including methyl caffeoate, ethyl caffeoate, propyl caffeoate, methyl *p*-coumarate and methyl cinnamate were effective inhibitors of the growth of *P. fluorescens* (Baranowski and Nagel, 1983). Stead (1993) determined the effect of caffeic, coumaric and ferulic acids against the wine spoilage lactic acid bacteria *Lactobacillus collinoides* and *L. brevis*. At pH 4.8 in the presence of 5% ethanol, *p*-coumaric and ferulic acids were the most inhibitory compounds at 500 and $1000 \, \mu g/ml$. At $100 \, \mu g/ml$, all three hydroxycinnamic acids stimulate growth of the microorganisms, suggesting that these compounds may play a role in initiating the malolactic fermentation of wines. Baranowski *et al.* (1980) studied the effect of caffeic, chlorogenic, *p*-coumaric, and ferulic acids at pH 3.5 on the growth of *Saccharomyces cerevisiae*. Caffeic and chlorogenic acid had little effect on the organism at $1000 \, \mu g/ml$. In the presence of *p*-coumaric, however, the organism was completely inhibited by $1000 \, \mu g/ml$. Ferulic acid was the most effective growth inhibitor tested. At $50 \, \mu g/ml$, this compound extended the lag phase of *S. cerevisiae* and, at $250 \, \mu g/ml$, growth of the organism was completely inhibited. Chipley and Uraih (1980) found that ferulic acid inhibited aflatoxin $B_1$ and $G_1$ production by *Aspergillus flavus* and *A. parasiticus* by up to 75%. Salicylic and trans-cinnamic acids totally inhibited aflatoxin production at the same level.

Furocoumarins are related to the hydroxycinnamates. These compounds, including psoralen (6-hydroxy-5-benzofuranacrylic acid $\delta$-lactone) and its derivatives, are phytoalexins (compounds produced by plants in response to attacks by fungi and insects) in citrus fruits, parsley, carrots, celery and parsnips. Purified psoralen and natural sources of the compound (e.g., cold pressed lime oil, lime peel extract) have demonstrated antimicrobial activity against *E. coli* O157:H7, *Erwinia carotovora*, *L. monocytogenes* and *Micrococcus luteus* following irradiation with long-wave (365 nm) ultraviolet light (Manderfield *et al.*, 1997; Ulate-Rodriguez *et al.*, 1997).

### 2.3.3  Isothiocyanates

Mustard seed has as a primary pungency component the compound allyl isothiocyanate (AIT). Isothiocyanates (R − N = C = S) are derivatives from glucosinolates in cells of plants of the *Cruciferae* or mustard family (cabbage, kohlrabi, Brussel sprouts, cauliflower, broccoli, kale, horseradish, mustard, turnips, rutubaga). These compounds are formed from the action of the enzyme myrosinase (thioglucoside glucohydrolase EC 3.2.3.1) on the glucosinolates when the plant tissue is injured or mechanically disrupted. In addition to the allyl side group, other isothiocyanate side groups include ethyl, methyl, benzyl and phenyl. These compounds have been reported to be potent antimicrobial agents.

Isothiocyanates are inhibitory to fungi, yeasts and bacteria in the range of 16–110 ng/ml in the vapor phase (Isshiki *et al.*, 1992) and 10–600 μg/ml in liquid media (Mari *et al.*, 1993). Inhibition against bacteria varies but generally gram-positive bacteria are less sensitive to AIT than gram-negative bacteria. Delaquis and Mazza (1995) found a 1–5 log decrease in viable cells of *Escherichia coli*, *Listeria monocytogenes* and *Salmonella* Typhimurium in the presence of 2000 μg AIT per ml of air. Delaquis and Sholberg (1997) examined this effect further and showed that 1000 μg AIT per ml of air apparently decreased viable *E. coli* O157:H7, *Salmonella* Typhimurium, and *L. monocytogenes* by up to 6 logs. However, cells recovered to a large extent if they were exposed to air. *E. coli* O157:H7 was the most resistant. Park *et al.* (2000) evaluated AIT as sanitizer against *E. coli* O157:H7 on alfalfa seeds for sprouting. 50 μl AIT eliminated 2.7 log CFU *E. coli* O157:H7/g of wet seeds but did not eliminate the microorganism on dry seeds. AIT had a detrimental effect on germination of wet alfalfa seeds. AIT was ineffective against *Salmonella* inoculated onto alfalfa seeds and caused sensory problems with treated alfalfa sprouts (Weissinger *et al.*, 2001). Ward *et al.* (1998) prepared horseradish essential oil distillate (ca. 90% AIT) and applied it to the headspace of cooked roast beef inoculated with *E. coli* O157:H7, *L. monocytogenes*, *Salmonella* Typhimurium, *Staphylococcus aureus*, *Serratia grimeseii* and *Lactobacillus sake*. AIT at 20 μl/l of air inhibited the pathogens and spoilage microorganisms on the beef. Delaquis *et al.* (1999) added 20 μl horseradish essential oil per liter of air with pre-cooked roast beef slices. The beef was stored for 28 days at 4°C and inoculated spoilage bacteria monitored. *Pseudomonas* and *Enterobacteriaceae* were inhibited to the greatest extent while lactic acid bacteria were more resistant. The development of off-odors and flavors was delayed and cooked meat color was preserved in the treated roasts. The mechanism by which isothiocyanates inhibit cells may be due to inhibition of enzymes by direct reaction with disulfide bonds or through thiocyanate (SCN⁻) anion reaction to inactivate sulfhydryl enzymes (Delaquis and Mazza, 1995).

### 2.3.4   Spices and their essential oils

Spices and their essential oils have varying degrees of antimicrobial activity. Among the spices, cloves, cinnamon, oregano, thyme, sage, rosemary, basil and vanillin have the strongest antimicrobial activity. The major antimicrobial components of clove (*Syzygium aromaticum*) and cinnamon (*Cinnamomum zeylanicum*) essential oils are eugenol (2-methoxy-4-(2-propenyl)-phenol)) and cinnamic aldehyde (3-phenyl-2-propenal), respectively. Smith-Palmer *et al.* (1998) determined that the 24 hr minimum inhibitory concentrations of cinnamon and clove essential oils against *Campylobacter jejuni*, *Escherichia coli*, *Salmonella* Enteritidis, *Listeria monocytogenes*, and *Staphylococcus aureus* were 0.05, 0.04–0.05, 0.04–0.05, 0.03, and 0.04%, respectively, in an agar dilution assay. Cinnamic aldehyde or thymol (600 mg/liter of air) significantly reduced *Salmonella* populations on alfalfa seeds used for sprouting and did not affect germination (Weissinger *et al.*, 2001). Azzouz and Bullerman (1982) evaluated 16 ground herbs and spices at 2% (wt/vol) against nine mycotoxin producing *Aspergillus* and *Penicillium* species. The most effective antimicrobial spice evaluated was clove which inhibited growth initiation at 25°C by all species for over 21 days. Cinnamon is the next most effective spice inhibiting three *Penicillium* species for over 21 days. Bullerman (1974) determined that 1.0% cinnamon in raisin bread inhibits growth and aflatoxin production by *A. parasiticus*. López-Malo *et al.* (2002) confirmed growth inhibition of the related mold, *A. flavus*, by eugenol, thymol ((5-methyl-2-(1-methylethyl) phenol)) and carvacrol ((2-methyl-5-(1-methylethyl)phenol)). Eugenol (200 µg/ml) increased the lag time and decreased the growth rate of *P. citrinum* while 100 µg/ml delayed production of the mycotoxin, citrinin, by the mold (Vazquez *et al.*, 2001). The compound also prevented growth of the mold at 200 µg/ml in one type of cheese. Smid and Gorris (1999) reported that cinnamic aldehyde inhibited growth of both bacteria and fungi on and increased shelflife of treated packaged tomatoes.

The antimicrobial activity of oregano (*Origanum vulgare*) and thyme (*Thymus vulgares*) has been attributed to their essential oils which contain the terpenes carvacrol and thymol, respectively. Both compounds have inhibitory activity against a number of bacteria, molds and yeasts including *Bacillus subtilis*, *E. coli*, *Lactobacillus plantarum*, *Pediococcus cerevisiae*, *Pseudomonas aeruginosa*, *Proteus* species, *Salmonella* Enteritidis, *S. aureus*, *Vibrio parahaemolyticus*, and *A. parasiticus* (Davidson and Naidu, 2000). Firouzi *et al.* (1998) showed that thyme essential oil was the most effective antimicrobial against *L. monocytogenes* 4b growth compared to other spice and herb extracts. Similarly, thyme essential oil was the most effective antimicrobial among 15 spice essential oils tested by Smith-Palmer *et al.* (1998) against *C. jejuni*, *E. coli*, *Salmonella* Enteritidis, *L. monocytogenes* and *S. aureus*. Aligiannis *et al.* (2001) found that a species of oregano with a high concentration of carvacrol (*Origanum scabrum*) had significantly greater antimicrobial activity than a species (*Origanum microphyllum*) with no carvacrol. This demonstrates that not all herb or spice sources of such essential oils are equivalent in their antimicrobial activity. Pol and Smid (1999) and Periago and Moezelaar (2001) determined that the interactive inhibitory effect of carvacrol and nisin was synergistic against *L. monocytogenes* or *B. cereus*. Ultee and Smid (2001) found that 0.06 mg/ml of carvacrol inhibited growth and diarrheal toxin production of *B. cereus*. Ultee *et al.* (2000) and Ultee and Smid (2001) further determined that carvacrol in combination with cymene (methyl-isopropylbenzene) and soy sauce inhibited *B. cereus* growth in rice and carvacrol alone inhibited toxin production by the microorganism in soup. Inhibition was dependent upon initial inoculum. Ultee *et al.* (1999, 2002) determined that carvacrol depletes intracellular ATP, reduces the pH gradient across the cytoplasmic membrane and collapses the proton motive force of *B. cereus* leading to eventual cell death.

Rosemary (*Rosmarinus officinalis*) contains primarily borneol (endo-1,7,7-trimethylbicyclo[2.2.1] heptan-2-ol) along with pinene, camphene, camphor while sage (*Salvia officinalis*) contains thujone ((4-methyl-1-(1-methylethyl)bicyclo[3.1.0]-hexan-3-one)). At 2% in growth medium, sage and rosemary are more active against gram-positive than gram-negative bacterial strains (Shelef *et al.*, 1980). The inhibitory effect of these two spices at 0.3% is bacteriostatic while at 0.5% they are bactericidal to gram-positive strains. Of 18 spices tested against *L. monocytogenes* in culture medium, Pandit and Shelef (1994) found the most effective compound to be rosemary. The most inhibitory fraction of the rosemary was $\alpha$-pinene. Smith-Palmer *et al.* (1998) demonstrated that rosemary (0.02–0.05%) and sage (0.02–0.075%) were inhibitory to *L. monocytogenes* and *S. aureus* but not to gram-negative bacteria. Hefnawy *et al.* (1993) evaluated ten herbs and spices against two strains of *L. monocytogenes* in tryptose broth. The most effective spice was sage which at 1% decreased viable *L. monocytogenes* by 5–7 logs after one day at 4°C. Allspice was next most effective inactivating the microorganism in four days. In foods, both rosemary and sage have significantly reduced activity. *L. monocytogenes* Scott A growth in refrigerated fresh pork sausage was delayed by 0.5% ground rosemary or 1% rosemary essential oil (Pandit and Shelef, 1994). Sensitivity of *B. cereus*, *S. aureus* and *Pseudomonas* to sage was greatest in microbiological medium and significantly reduced in rice and chicken and noodles (Shelef *et al.*, 1984).

Sweet basil (*Ocimum basilicum*) essential oil has limited antimicrobial activity with linalool and methyl chavicol the primary antimicrobial agents. Against 33 bacteria, yeasts and molds in an agar well assay, basil essential oil extract was active against certain fungi, including *Mucor* and *Penicillium* species, but had little activity against bacteria (Lachowicz *et al.*, 1998). Wan *et al.* (1998) screened the essential oil components of sweet basil, linalool and methyl chavicol, against 35 strains of bacteria, yeasts and molds. Again, the compounds demonstrated limited activity against most microorganisms except *Mucor* and *Penicillium*. In contrast, methyl chavicol (0.1%) in filter-sterilized fresh lettuce supernatant reduced viable *Aeromonas hydrophila* by 5 logs and, as a wash for lettuce leaves, the compound was as effective as 125 $\mu$g/ml chlorine (Wan *et al.*, 1998). Smith-Palmer *et al.* (1998) reported minimum inhibitory concentrations for basil essential oil of 0.25, 0.25, 0.1, 0.05, and 0.1% for *C. jejuni, E. coli, Salmonella* Enteritidis, *L. monocytogenes* and *S. aureus*, respectively.

Vanillin (4-hydroxy-3-methoxybenzaldehyde) is a major constituent of vanilla beans, the fruit of an orchid (*Vanilla planifola, Vanilla pompona*, or *Vanilla tahitensis*). Vanillin is most active against molds and non-lactic gram-positive bacteria (Jay and Rivers, 1984). López-Malo *et al.* (1995) prepared fruit-based agars containing mango, papaya, pineapple, apple and banana with up to 2000 $\mu$g vanillin per ml and inoculated each with *A. flavus, A. niger, A. ochraceus*, or *A. parasiticus*. Vanillin at 1500 $\mu$g/ml significantly inhibited all strains of *Aspergillus* in all media. Cerrutti and Alzamora (1996) demonstrated complete inhibition of growth for 40 days at 27°C of *Debaryomyces hansenii, S. cerevisiae, Z. bailii* and *Z. rouxii* in laboratory media and apple puree at a$_w$ of 0.99 and 0.95 by 2000 $\mu$g/ml vanillin. In contrast, 2000 $\mu$g/ml vanillin was not effective against the yeasts in banana puree. Cerrutti *et al.* (1997) utilized vanillin with calcium lactate, ascorbic acid and citric acid to produce a shelf-stable strawberry puree.

Delaquis *et al.* (2002) demonstrated that oil of cilantro (leaves of *Coriandrum sativum* L.) were effective in inhibiting the growth of *L. monocytogenes*. The inhibitory activity was attributed to presence of alcohols and aldehydes (C6–C10). Many other spices have been tested and shown to have limited or no activity. They include anise, bay (laurel), black pepper, cardamom, cayenne (red pepper), celery seed, chili powder, coriander, cumin, curry powder, dill, fenugreek, ginger, juniper oil, mace, marjoram, nutmeg, orris root, paprika, sesame, spearmint, tarragon, and white pepper (Marth, 1966; Davidson and Naidu, 2000).

## 2.4   Natural antimicrobials from microbial sources

### 2.4.1   Natamycin (Pimaricin)

Natamycin ($C_{33}H_{47}NO_{13}$; MW 665.7 Da) or pimaricin is an antifungal agent. It was first isolated from *Streptomyces natalensis*, a microorganism found in soil from Natal, South Africa (Anonymous, 1991). Natamycin is active against nearly all molds and yeasts, but has little or no effect on bacteria or viruses. Most molds are inhibited by 0.5 to 6 $\mu$g/ml natamycin while some species require 10–25 $\mu$g/ml. Most yeasts are inhibited by 1.0 to 5.0 $\mu$g/ml natamycin. Natamycin inhibits the production of mycotoxins by molds. Ray and Bullerman (1982) reported that 10 $\mu$g/ml natamycin inhibited aflatoxin B$_1$ production of *Aspergillus flavus* by

62.0%, penicillic acid production by *Penicillium cyclopium* by 98.8% and eliminated ochratoxin production by *A. ochraceus* and patulin production by *P. patulum.* Lodi *et al.* (1989) found that natamycin was effective in preserving seven types of Italian cheeses with no detrimental effect on ripening. Natamycin (100 $\mu$g/ml) added in the wash water was effective in increasing the time to spoilage of uninoculated cottage cheese by up to 13.6 days over the control (Nilson *et al.*, 1975). Adding natamycin to the cottage cheese dressing was even more effective in extending shelf life. In addition to cheese, research with natamycin has shown it to be effective to inhibit fungal growth on fruits, meats and baked goods (Ayres and Denisen, 1958; Shirk and Clark, 1963; Ayres *et al.*, 1956; Van Rijn *et al.*, 1999; Ticha, 1975).

### 2.4.2 Nisin

Nisin is a 34 amino acid peptide produced by a strain of the dairy starter culture, *Lactococcus lactis* ssp. *lactis*. Nisin has a narrow spectrum inhibiting only gram-positive bacteria, including *Alicyclobacillus*, *Bacillus cereus*, *Brochothrix thermosphacta*, *Clostridium botulinum*, *C. sporogenes*, *Desulfotomaculum*, *Enterococcus*, *Lactobacillus*, *Leuconostoc*, *Listeria monocytogenes*, *Micrococcus*, *Pediococccus*, *Sporolactobacillus*, and *Staphylococcus* (Thomas *et al.*, 2000). Against bacterial spores, nisin is sporostatic rather than sporicidal (Delves-Broughton *et al.*, 1996). Nisin does not generally inhibit gram-negative bacteria, yeasts, or molds. The spectrum of activity of nisin can be expanded to include gram-negative bacteria when it is used in combination with chelating agents (e.g., EDTA), heat, or freezing (Delves-Broughton and Gasson, 1994; Carneiro de Melo *et al.*, 1998). Nisin activity generally increases with decreasing pH and decreased initial numbers of microorganisms. The presence of food components such as lipids and protein influence nisin activity (Scott and Taylor, 1981). Nisin was less active against *L. monocytogenes* in milk (Jung *et al.*, 1992) and ice cream (Dean and Zottola, 1996) with increasing fat concentrations. This was probably due to binding of nisin to fat globules (Jung *et al.*, 1992); this binding was overcome by adding emulsifiers (e.g., Tween 80). The primary mechanism of nisin is believed to be the formation of pores in the cytoplasmic membrane that result in depletion of proton motive force and loss of cellular ions, amino acids, and ATP (Crandall and Montville, 1998).

   The application of nisin as a food preservative has been studied extensively (Hurst and Hoover, 1993; Montville *et al.*, 2001; Cleveland *et al.*, 2001). Based upon its target microorganisms, nisin application falls into one of three categories: (1) prevent spoilage by sporeforming bacteria, (2) prevent spoilage by lactic acid bacteria and related microorganisms or (3) kill or inhibit gram-positive pathogenic bacteria, e.g., *Bacillus cereus*, *C. botulinum* or *L. monocytogenes* (Thomas *et al.*, 2000). Somers and Taylor (1981, 1987) studied the use of nisin to prevent *C. botulinum* outgrowth in processed cheese spread formulated to have higher than normal moisture content and/or lower salt content. Nisin was an effective antibotulinal agent at 12.5–250 $\mu$g/g. The higher nisin levels allowed for the safe formulation of cheese spreads with higher moisture content and lower salt concentration. Delves-Broughton (1990) reported that nisin levels of 6 to 12.5 $\mu$g/g controlled non-*C. botulinum* spoilage in processed cheese. Dean and Zottola (1996) found that nisin decreased *L. monocytogenes* cells to undetectable levels in 3% and 10% fat ice cream stored at $-18$°C. Budu-Amoako *et al.* (1999) found that heating canned lobster in brine at 60 or 65°C for 5 or 2 min, respectively, in combination with 25 $\mu$g/g nisin reduced *L. monocytogenes* by 3–5 logs. They proposed that using nisin could reduce the commercial thermal process for this product (13–18 min at 65.5°C) with equivalent lethality and reduced drained weight loss.

Nisin has shown some potential for use in selected meat products. For example, Scannel *et al.* (1997) found that 2% lactate combined with 12.5 $\mu$g/g nisin was superior to nisin alone at controlling growth of total aerobes, *S. aureus*, and *S.* Kentucky in fresh pork sausage stored at 4°C for 10 days. Nisin also has been suggested as an adjunct to nitrite in cured meats for the purpose of preventing the growth of clostridia (Caserio *et al.*, 1979; Holley, 1981). Although nisin appears to be more effective than nitrites at preventing the growth of some pathogenic and spoilage microorganisms in cured meats, it is yet to be shown to prevent *C. botulinum* growth in cured meats. Since nisin is effective against most lactic acid bacteria but is inactive against yeasts, there is potential use for nisin in alcoholic beverages to prevent growth of spoilage lactic acid bacteria (Ogden *et al.*, 1988, Radler, 1990). Choi and Park (2000) used nisin at 100 IU/ml to inhibit lactobacilli responsible for spoilage of kimchi, traditional Korean fermented vegetables. Nisin has been evaluated for use as a component of antimicrobial packaging (Ming *et al.*, 1997; Padgett *et al.*, 1998). Two limitations for the application of nisin to foods are losses during processing and during storage (Thomas *et al.*, 2000).

### 2.4.3   Bacteriocins and culture products

Bacteriocins with potential for use in foods are produced by strains of *Carnobacterium, Lactobacillus, Lactococcus, Leuconostoc, Pediococcus*, and *Propionibacterium* (Montville *et al.*, 2001; Chikindas and Montville, 2002). Many of these compounds could potentially be used as food antimicrobials but, at the present time, few are approved by regulatory agencies to be added to foods in their purified form. One approach to using these compounds has been to grow bacteriocin-producing starter cultures in a medium such as whey, non-fat dry milk or dextrose. The fermentation medium is then pasteurized and spray-dried which kills the starter culture but retains the active antimicrobial. These products act as antimicrobial additives but are generally considered toxicologically acceptable and, depending upon the country, may be listed as 'cultured whey' or 'cultured non-fat dry milk' on the food label. Examples of such products are Microgard®, Alta™, and Perlac™. Alta™ at 0.1–1.0% was shown to decrease the growth rate of *Listeria monocytogenes* on vacuum-packaged smoked salmon stored at 4 or 10°C (Szabo and Cahill, 1999). Degnan *et al.* (1994) inoculated fresh blue crab (*Callinectes sapidus*) with a 3 strain mixture of *L. monocytogenes* (ca. 5.5 log CFU/g) and washed with various fermentation products (2,000–20,000 arbitrary units [AU]/ml of wash) and stored at 4°C. Counts of *Listeria monocytogenes* decreased 0.5–1.0 log with Perlac or MicroGard and 1.5–2.7 logs with Alta.

## 2.5   Evaluating the effectiveness of antimicrobials

### 2.5.1   Methods for determining the *in vitro* antimicrobial activity of natural compounds

To apply a naturally occurring antimicrobial to a food requires that one determine the efficacy of the compound *in vitro* (i.e., microbiological media) and in a food product. In an *in vitro* system, a number of variables or factors concerning the antimicrobial can be evaluated. It is very important to evaluate the activity of a potential antimicrobial against multiple strains of pathogen since strain variation may occur. Another important variable is the initial number of microorganisms in the system. Since most antimicrobials are bacteriostatic rather than bactericidal, the higher the initial number, the shorter the shelf life of the product.

The agar diffusion method has probably been the most widely used method for determination of antimicrobial activity throughout history. In the test, antimicrobial compound is added to an agar plate on a paper disk or in a well. The compound diffuses through the agar resulting in a concentration gradient which is inversely proportional to the distance from the disk or well. Degree of inhibition, which is indicated by a zone of no growth around the disk or well, is dependent upon the rate of diffusion of the compound and cell growth (Barry, 1986). Therefore, the antimicrobial evaluated should not be highly hydrophobic, as the compound will not diffuse and little or no inhibition will be detected. Results of this test are generally qualitative.

Agar and broth dilution assays are generally used when quantitative data are desired. In both methods a single statistic, known as the minimum inhibitory concentration (MIC), is generated. In the dilution assays, a number of containers are prepared to contain a single concentration of antimicrobial in a microbiological medium. A test microorganism is exposed to the antimicrobial and incubated for a specified period, usually at least 24 hr. The MIC is generally defined as the lowest concentration of an antimicrobial that prevents growth of a microorganism after the specified incubation period.

These methods provide little information concerning the effect of an antimicrobial on the growth or death kinetics of a microorganism. Concentrations of an antimicrobial which are below the MIC may still cause an increased lag phase, reduced growth rate or even initial lethality followed by growth. In food products, total inhibition of a pathogen or spoilage microorganism is not always required. An increased lag phase, especially under conditions of severe abuse, is often sufficient to protect the consumer. Therefore, to determine the effect of a compound on the growth (or death) kinetics of a microorganism, a method is required that produces an inhibition curve using a colony count procedure. In clinical microbiology, these inhibition curves are known as 'time-kill curves' (Schoenknecht *et al.*, 1985). This method is versatile but has some disadvantages including the fact that no single statistic is produced to compare treatments such as MIC and it is labor intensive and expensive. Progress made in modeling of the growth kinetics of microorganisms (Whiting and Buchanan, 2001) has allowed for improved statistical analysis of growth/inhibition curves in the presence of food antimicrobials.

A second method for determining antimicrobial effectiveness over time is to measure turbidity increases with a spectrophotometer. A major disadvantage to this type of analysis is sensitivity of the instrument. Spectrophotometers generally require log 6.0–7.0 CFU/ml for detection (Piddock, 1990). This may create a situation in which no growth (i.e., no absorbance increase) is observed when, in fact, undetectable growth is occurring at levels below log 5.0 CFU/ml. An erroneous interpretation of 'lethality' could result (Parish and Davidson, 1993).

### 2.5.2    Aspects of determining efficacy of natural antimicrobials in foods

If a compound is to be useful as a natural food antimicrobial, it must function in a food system. Many researchers have made claims concerning the potential effectiveness of natural antimicrobials based solely upon data from testing in microbiological media only to find that a compound is much less effective or ineffective in a food system. Application testing can be very complex and include a number of variables including microbial, food-related (intrinsic), environmental (extrinsic) and process (Gould, 1989).

Because of the variation in characteristics and activities among naturally occurring compounds, it is somewhat difficult to generalize regarding methods for applying the compounds. Even among regulatory-approved antimicrobial compounds, such as benzoic acid or sorbic acid, there are no standard methods for evaluating activity or application procedures. Applying the antimicrobial to a food involves either a model food system or the actual food. A great deal of information can be gained by using model systems that contain a percentage of a food in a buffer or microbiological medium. These systems demonstrate potential interferences by food components but allow for easier sampling by the researcher. The microorganism or microorganisms utilized should be a natural contaminant (bioburden) or a pathogen of interest and incubation conditions should reflect use and abuse. Success of application testing may be determined by increased shelf life or reduction of potential health hazards.

## 2.6    Key issues in using natural antimicrobials

### 2.6.1    Activity spectra and application data

Despite major interest in naturally occurring antimicrobials, there is still research needed on their spectrum of action, especially in food products. Much of the early research, particularly on microbially derived antimicrobials focused on activity in microbiological media only. As has been stated previously, many compounds are effective in microbiological media but have reduced or no activity in foods. Therefore, an expanded database on activity of antimicrobials against foodborne pathogens and spoilage microorganisms in food products is needed.

### 2.6.2    Purification
Food additives in general, and preservatives in particular, are regulated in the United States by the Food and Drug Administration (FDA) and Department of Agriculture's Food Safety and Inspection Service (USDA-FSIS). One of the alleged attractions of naturally occurring antimicrobials is their reduced impact on the labeling of foods. Consumers are reportedly concerned about the presence of synthetic chemicals in their foods and would prefer natural compounds. A potential problem with natural antimicrobials is, if they are highly purified, they may need to be approved as food additives. This would involve very expensive and time-consuming toxicological testing. In addition, the compound would probably have to be listed using a chemical name on a food label. This of course would defeat the purpose of using a natural compound. For that reason, less purification may be better. If a product is simply an 'extract of' a commonly consumed plant or animal food product, it is much less likely to require complex regulatory approval for use. This of course is possible only if the product from which the extract is taken is known to be non-toxic.

### 2.6.3    Combinations
Likely the best method for determining what type of antimicrobial to use would be based upon its mechanism of action and/or target in the cell. The exact mechanisms through which antimicrobials affect microbial growth are complex and difficult to elucidate. Mechanisms of action of food antimicrobials generally are classified as reaction with the cell membrane causing permeability changes or interference with uptake and transport, inactivation of essential enzymes, interference with genetic mechanisms or inhibition of protein synthesis (Branen, 1993). Unfortunately, few targets even for the regulatory-approved food antimicrobials such as organic acids, have actually been fully elucidated. If the mechanism of the compound is known, combinations of antimicrobials with different mechanisms could be utilized against the microorganisms in the food product.

### 2.6.4    Resistance development
Potential food antimicrobials should not contribute to the development of resistant strains nor alter the environment of the food in such a way that growth of another pathogen is selected. There has been much interest in the effect of

environmental stress factors (e.g., heat, cold, starvation, low pH/organic acids) on developed resistance of microorganisms to subsequent stressors. This developed resistance is termed tolerance, adaptation, or habituation depending upon how the microorganism is exposed to the stress and the physiological conditions that lead to enhanced survival (Foster, 1995; Buchanan and Edelson, 1999). It has been demonstrated that pathogens can develop a tolerance or adaptation to organic acids following prior exposure to low pH. While this increased resistance may be a problem in application of organic acids for controlling pathogens, it has not been demonstrated that this is a problem in actual food processing systems (Davidson and Harrison, 2002).

### 2.6.5   Toxicological data and regulatory approval

Perhaps the most important aspect of any compound proposed for use as a food preservative would be the toxicological characteristics. Because they occur in nature, it is often thought that naturally occurring antimicrobials are less toxic than synthetic compounds. Obviously, this is not always true. A naturally occurring antimicrobial must be shown to be non-toxic either by animal testing or by its continuous consumption as a food over a long period. The latter may be problematic even for some common potential natural antimicrobials such as spice extracts. This is because, while spices have been consumed for centuries, they are not normally consumed in the concentrations necessary to achieve antimicrobial activity. In addition to lack of toxicity, naturally occurring compounds must be able to be metabolized and excreted so as not to lead to residue build-up (Branen, 1993). In addition, they should be non-allergenic (Harlander, 1993). Food antimicrobials should not bind nor destroy important nutrients in a food product.

### 2.6.6   Cost

Perhaps the greatest roadblock to the use of naturally occurring antimicrobials may be cost. For example, the only antimicrobial enzymes produced at a cost to be useful in food preservation are lysozyme and glucose oxidase (Fuglsang *et al.*, 1995). There are a number of potential costs associated with natural antimicrobials including cost of the source material, extraction and purification costs and packaging. A potential antimicrobial must pay for itself by extending shelf life and/or minimizing chances for foodborne illness. Depending upon the perishability of a food product, even an additional 2–3 days of shelf life can significantly offset the cost of an antimicrobial (Branen, 1993).

### 2.6.7   Activity validation methods

At the present time, there are few standardized methods for validation of the activity of regulatory-approved food antimicrobials. While, in the US, there are methods for the determination of the activity of lysozyme (U.S. *Code of Federal*

*Regulations*, 21*CFR* 184.1550) and nisin (U.S. *Code of Federal Regulations*, 21*CFR* 184.1538), there are no other activity assays specified or required for food antimicrobials. If natural antimicrobials are to be used exclusively as inhibitors of pathogens in food products, assays need to be developed that evaluate the activity of these compounds against the pathogen they are designed to kill. The reason for these assays is that various conditions of process or storage could reduce the effectiveness of the compound. For example, it is known that peptides, such as nisin, are susceptible to inactivation by enzymes in foods. Therefore, just as thermal processes need validation, so should there be validation for the activity of food antimicrobials.

### 2.6.8   Sensory effects
Another major factor that needs to be addressed prior to applying naturally occurring antimicrobials is their potential impact on the sensory characteristics of a food. Many naturally occurring antimicrobials must be used at high concentrations to achieve antimicrobial activity against microorganisms. Obviously, compounds that negatively impact flavor and odor or contribute inappropriate flavors and odors would be unacceptable. For example, many spice extracts have antimicrobial activity but, at the concentration required for antimicrobial activity, would cause a food to be inedible to most consumers. In addition to adverse effects on flavor, odor or texture, it would be unacceptable for a food antimicrobial to mask spoilage as this could protect consumers from ingesting foodborne pathogens.

### 2.6.9   Summary
To summarize, an ideal naturally occurring antimicrobial would be effective enough to be added as a whole food or as an edible component (e.g., a herb or spice). Few, if any, antimicrobials are present in foods at concentrations great enough to be antimicrobials without purification or concentration. Often, even if purification of the antimicrobials is possible, adding them to another food may lead to undesirable sensory changes. The ultimate challenge is to find a naturally occurring antimicrobial which can be added to a 'microbiologically sensitive' food product in a non-purified form from another non-sensitive food. The non-purified food would have to contain an antimicrobial which is completely non-toxic and is highly effective in controlling the growth of microorganisms. This may well be impossible. Beuchat and Golden (1989) may have summarized it best when they said that 'the challenge is to isolate, purify, stabilize, and incorporate natural antimicrobials into foods without adversely affecting sensory, nutritional, and safety characteristics ...' and '... without increased costs for formulation, processing or marketing.'

## 2.7   Future trends

The future of research in the area of food antimicrobials will probably be on two fronts. First, is the expansion of information on the antimicrobial spectrum of natural antimicrobials. This research will be more focused on the appropriate use of natural antimicrobials or utilization of compounds in situations that they are compatible. For example, certain compounds, such as thymol, carvacrol, and AIT, are not compatible with certain foods. Appropriate or compatible use would involve using these compounds in foods in which they add to the positive sensory characteristics of the product in addition to improving food safety or increasing shelf life.

A second major area of research involves use of natural antimicrobials in combinations with each other and with other traditional food antimicrobials or processing methods. To more effectively apply natural antimicrobials so that synergistic activity is possible will require knowledge of the mechanisms of action of the compounds. To attain synergistic activity with antimicrobial combinations requires that the components have different mechanisms. In addition, natural antimicrobials will be increasingly looked upon as adjuncts in hurdle technology and used with milder non-sterilizing non-thermal processing methods such as high hydrostatic pressure or pulsed electric fields (Smid and Gorris, 1999).

## 2.8   Sources of further information and advice

DAVIDSON PM and BRANEN AL (1993), *Antimicrobials in Foods*, 2nd edn Marcel Dekker, New York.

DAVIDSON PM (2001), 'Chemical preservatives and natural antimicrobial compounds', in Doyle MP, Beuchat LR and Montville TJ, *Food Microbiology, Fundamentals and Frontiers*, 2nd edn, American Society for Microbiology, Washington, DC.

DILLON VM and BOARD RG (1994), *Natural Antimicrobial Systems and Food Preservation*, CAB Intl, Wallingford, UK.

LÓPEZ-MALO A, ALZAMORA SM and GUERRERO S (2000), 'Natural antimicrobials from plants', in Alzamora S M, Tapia M S and López-Malo A, *Minimally Processed Fruits and Vegetables*, Aspen Publ.

NAIDU AS (2000), *Natural Food Antimicrobial Systems*, CRC Press, Boca Raton, FL.

SOFOS JN, BEUCHAT LR, DAVIDSON PM and JOHNSON EA (1998), 'Naturally occurring antimicrobials in food', Task Force Report No. 132, Council for Agricultural Science and Technology, Ames, IA.

## 2.9   References

ALIGIANNIS N, KALPOUTZAKIS E, MITAKU S and CHINOU IB (2001), 'Composition and antimicrobial activity of the essential oils of two *Origanum* species', *J Ag Food Chem*, 49, 4168–70.

ANONYMOUS (1991), 'Delvocid® Technical Bulletin', Gist-brocades Food Ingredients Inc. King of Prussia, PA.

AYRES JC and DENISEN EL (1958), 'Maintaining freshness of berries using selected packaging materials and antifungal agents', *Food Technol*, 12, 562.

AYRES JC, WALKER HW, FANELLI MJ, KING AW and THOMAS F (1956), 'Use of antibiotics in prolonging storage life of dressed chicken', *Food Technol*, 10, 563.

AZZOUZ MA and BULLERMAN LB (1982), 'Comparative antimycotic effects of selected herbs, spices, plant components and commercial fungal agents', *J Food Sci*, 45, 1298–301.

BARANOWSKI JD and NAGEL CW (1983), 'Properties of alkyl hydroxycinnamates and effects on *Pseudomonas fluorescens*', *Appl Environ Microbiol*, 45, 218–22.

BARANOWSKI JD, DAVIDSON PM, NAGEL CW and BRANEN AL (1980), 'Inhibition of *Saccharomyces cerevisiae* by naturally occurring hydroxycinnamates', *J Food Sci*, 45, 592–4.

BARRETT, NE, GRANDISON AS and LEWIS MJ (1999), 'Contribution of the lactoperoxidase system to the keeping quality of pasteurized milk', *J Dairy Res*, 66, 73–80.

BARRY AL (1986), 'Procedure for testing antimicrobial agents in agar media: theoretical considerations', in Lorian V, *Antibiotics in Laboratory Medicine*, 2nd edn, Williams & Wilkins, Baltimore, MD.

BELLAMY W, TAKASE M, WAKABAYASHI H, KAWASE K and TOMITA M (1992), 'Antibacterial spectrum of lactoferricin B, a potent bactericidal peptide derived from the *N*-terminal region of bovine lactoferrin', *J Appl Bacteriol*, 73, 472–9.

BEUCHAT LR (1994), 'Antimicrobial properties of spices and their essential oils', in Dillon VM and Board RG, *Natural Antimicrobial Systems and Food Preservation*, CAB Intl., Wallingford, England.

BEUCHAT LR and GOLDEN DA (1989), 'Antimicrobials occurring naturally in foods', *Food Technol*, 43(1), 134–42.

BEUMER RR, NOOMEN A, MARIJS JA and KAMPELMACHER EH (1985), 'Antibacterial action of the lactoperoxidase system on *Campylobacter jejuni* in cow's milk', *Neth Milk Dairy J*, 39, 107–14.

BJÖRCK, L (1978), 'Antibacterial effect of the lactoperoxidase system on psychrotrophic bacteria in milk' *J Dairy Res*, 45, 109–18.

BRANEN AL (1993), 'Introduction to use of antimicrobials', in Davidson PM and Branen AL, *Antimicrobials in Foods*, 2nd edn Marcel Dekker, New York.

BRANEN JK and DAVIDSON PM (2000), 'Activity of hydrolysed lactoferrin against foodborne pathogenic bacteria in growth media, The effect of EDTA', *Lett Appl Microbiol*, 30, 233–7.

BUCHANAN RL and EDELSON SG (1999), 'pH-dependent stationary-phase acid resistance response of enterohemorrhagic *Escherichia coli* in the presence of various acidulants', *J Food Prot*, 62, 211–18.

BUDU-AMOAKO E, ABLETT RF, HARRIS J and DELVES-BROUGHTON, J (1999), 'Combined effect of nisin and moderate heat on destruction of *Listeria monocytogenes* in cold-pack lobster meat', *J Food Prot*, 62, 46–50.

BULLERMAN LB (1974), 'Inhibition of aflatoxin production by cinnamon', *J Food Sci*, 39, 1163–5.

CARNEIRO DE MELO AMS, CASSAR CA and MILES RJ (1998), 'Trisodium phosphate increases sensitivity of gram-negative bacteria to lysozyme and nisin', *J Food Prot*, 61, 839–44.

CASEIRO G, STECCHINI M, PASTORE M and GENNARI M (1979), 'Effect of nisin and nitrite, separately and together, on the spore germination of *Clostridium perfringens* in meat mixture subjected to heating', *Industrie Alimentari* (Italy), 18: 894–7, 900.

CAVALLITO CJ and BAILEY JH (1944), 'Allicin, the antibacterial principle of *Allium sativum*. I. Isolation, physical properties and antibacterial action', *J Amer Chem Soc*, 16, 1950–1.

CERRUTTI P and ALZAMORA SM (1996), 'Inhibitory effects of vanillin on some food spoilage yeasts in laboratory media and fruit purées', *Intl J Food Microbiol*, 29, 379–86.

CERRUTTI P, ALZAMORA SM and VIDALES SL (1997), 'Vanillin as an antimicrobial for producing shelf-stable strawberry puree', *J Food Sci*, 62, 608–10.

CHEN CS, LIAU WY and TSAI GJ (1998), 'Antibacterial effects of N-sulfonated and N-sulfobenzoyl chitosan and application to oyster preservation', *J Food Prot*, 61, 1124–8.

CHIKINDAS ML and MONTVILLE TJ (2002), 'Perspectives for application of bacteriocins as food preservatives', in Juneja VK and Sofos JN, *Control of Foodborne Microorganisms*, Marcel Dekker, New York.

CHIPLEY JR and URAIH N (1980), 'Inhibition of *Aspergillus* growth and aflatoxin release by derivatives of benzoic acid', *Appl Environ Microbiol*, 40, 352.

CHOI MH and PARK YH (2000), 'Selective control of lactobacilli in kimchi with nisin', *Lett Appl Microbiol*, 30, 173–7.

CLEVELAND J, MONTVILLE TJ, NES IF and CHIKINDAS ML (2001), 'Bacteriocins: safe, natural antimicrobials for food preservation', *Intl J Food Microbiol* 71, 1–20.

CONNER DE and LR BEUCHAT (1984), 'Effects of essential oils from plants on growth of food spoilage yeasts', *J Food Sci*, 49, 429–34.

CRANDALL AD and MONTVILLE TJ (1998), 'Nisin resistance in *Listeria monocytogenes* ATCC 700302 is a complex phenotype', *Appl Environ Microbiol*, 64, 231–7.

DARMADJI P and IZUMIMOTO M (1994), 'Effect of chitosan in meat preservation', *Meat Sci*, 38, 243–54.

DAVIDSON PM (2001), 'Chemical preservatives and natural antimicrobial compounds', in Doyle MP Beuchat LR and Montville TJ, *Food Microbiology, Fundamentals and Frontiers*, 2nd edn, American Society for Microbiology, Washington, DC.

DAVIDSON PM and HARRISON MA (2002), 'Resistance and adaptation to food antimicrobials, sanitizers and other process controls', *Food Technol*, 56(11), 69–78.

DAVIDSON PM and NAIDU AS (2000), 'Phyto-phenols', in AS Naidu, *Natural Food Antimicrobial Systems*, CRC Press, Boca Raton, FL.

DEAN JP and ZOTTOLA EA (1996), 'Use of nisin in ice cream and effect on the survival of *Listeria monocytogenes*', *J Food Prot*, 59, 476–80.

DEGNAN AJ, KASPAR CW, OTWELL WS, TAMPLIN ML and LUCHANSKY JB (1994), 'Evaluation of lactic acid bacterium fermentation products and food-grade chemicals to control *Listeria monocytogenes* in blue crab (*Callinectes sapidus*) meat', *Appl Environ Microbiol*, 60, 3198–203.

DELAQUIS PJ and MAZZA G (1995), 'Antimicrobial properties of isothiocyanates in food preservation', *Food Technol*, 49(11), 73–84.

DELAQUIS PJ and SHOLBERG PL (1997), 'Antimicrobial activity of gaseous allyl isothiocyanate', *J Food Prot*, 60, 943–7.

DELAQUIS PJ, STANICH K, GIRARD B and MAZZA G (2002), 'Antimicrobial activity of individual and mixed fractions of dill, cilantro, coriander and eucalyptus essential oils', *Intl J Food Microbiol* 74, 101–9.

DELAQUIS PJ, WARD SM, HOLLEY RA, CLIFF MC and MAZZA G (1999), 'Microbiological, chemical and sensory properties of pre-cooked roast beef preserved with horseradish essential oil', *J Food Sci*, 64, 519–24.

DELVES-BROUGHTON J (1990), 'Nisin and its uses as a food preservative', *Food Techol*, 44, 100–12, 117.

DELVES-BROUGHTON J and GASSON MJ (1994), 'Nisin', in Dillon VM and Board RG, *Natural Antimicrobial Systems and Food Preservation*, CAB International, Wallingford, Oxon, UK.

DELVES-BROUGHTON J, BLACKBURN P, EVANS RJ and HUGENHOLTZ J (1996), 'Applications of the bacteriocin, nisin', *Antonie van Leeuwenhoek*, 69, 193–202.

EKSTRAND B (1994), 'Lactoperoxidase and lactoferrin', in Dillon VM and Board RG, *Natural Antimicrobial Systems and Food Preservation*, CAB Intl, Wallingford, UK.

EL-GHAOUTH A (1997), 'Biologically-based alternatives to synthetic fungicides for the control of postharvest diseases', *J Ind Microbiol Biotechnol*, 19, 160–2.

EL GHAOUTH ARUL A, PONNAMPALAM J and BOULET RM (1991), 'Chitosan coating effect on storability and quality of fresh strawberries', *J Food Sci*, 56, 1618–20.

FANG SW, LI CJ and SHIN DYC (1994), 'Antifungal activity of chitosan and its preservative effect on low-sugar candied kumquat', *J Food Prot*, 56, 136–40.

FIROUZI R, AZADBAKHT M and NABINEDJAD A (1998), 'Anti-listerial activity of essential oils of some plants', *J Appl Ani Res*, 14, 75–80.

FOSTER JW (1995), 'Low pH adaptation and the acid tolerance response of *Salmonella typhimurium*', *Crit Rev Microbiol*, 21, 215–37.

FUGLSANG CC, JOHANSEN C, CHRISTGAU S and ADLER-NISSEN J (1995), 'Antimicrobial enzymes: applications and future potential in the food industry', *Trends Food Sci. & Technol* 6, 390–6.

GAYA P, MEDINA M and NUNEZ M (1991), 'Effect of the lactoperoxidase system on *Listeria monocytogenes* behavior in raw milk at refrigeration temperatures', *Appl Environ Microbiol*, 57, 3355–60.

GONZÁLEZ-FANDOS E, GARCÍA-LÓPEZ ML, SIERRA ML and OTERO A (1994), 'Staphylococcal growth and enterotoxins (A-D) and thermonuclease synthesis in the presence of dehydrated garlic', *J Appl Bacteriol*, 77, 549–52.

GOULD GW (1989), *Mechanisms of Action of Food Preservation Procedures*, Elsevier Appl Sci, London.

HARLANDER SK (1993), 'Regulatory aspects of bacteriocin use', in Hoover DG and Steenson LR, *Bacteriocins of Lactic Acid Bacteria*, Academic Press, San Diego, CA.

HEFNAWY YA, MOUSTAFA SI and MARTH EH (1993), 'Sensitivity of *Listeria monocytogenes* to selected spices', *J Food Prot*, 56, 876–8.

HERALD PJ and DAVIDSON PM (1983), 'The antibacterial activity of selected hydroxycinnamic acids', *J Food Sci*, 48, 1378–9.

HO CT (1992), 'Phenolic compounds in food. An overview', in Ho CT, Lee CY and Huang MT, *Phenolic Compounds in Food and Their Effects on Health. I. Analysis, Occurrence, and Chemistry*, Amer Chem Soc Symp Ser 506, Amer Chem Soc, Washington, DC.

HOLLEY RA (1981), 'Review of the potential hazard from botulism in cured meats', *Can Inst Food Sci Technol J*, 14, 183.

HUGHEY VL and JOHNSON EA (1987), 'Antimicrobial activity of lysozyme against bacteria involved in food spoilage and food-borne disease', *Appl Environ Microbiol*, 53, 2165–70.

HUGHEY VL, WILGER RA and JOHNSON EA (1989), 'Antibacterial activity of hen egg white lysozyme against *Listeria monocytogenes* Scott A in foods', *Appl Environ Microbiol*, 55, 631–8.

HURST A and HOOVER DG (1993), 'Nisin', in Davidson PM and Branen AL, *Antimicrobials in Foods*, 2nd edn Marcel Dekker, New York.

ISSHIKI K, TOKUORA K, MORI R and CHIBA S (1992), 'Preliminary examination of allyl isothiocyanate vapor for food preservation', *Biosci Biotechnol Biochem*, 56, 1476–7.

JAY JM and RIVERS GM (1984), 'Antimicrobial activity of some food flavoring compounds', *J Food Safety*, 6, 129–39.

JONES EM, SMART A, BLOOMBERG G, BURGESS L and MILLAR MR (1994), 'Lactoferricin, a new antimicrobial peptide', *J Appl Bacteriol*, 77, 208–14.

JUNG D, BODYFELT FW and DAESCHEL MA (1992), 'Influence of fat and emulsifiers on the efficacy of nisin in inhibiting *Listeria monocytogenes* in fluid milk', *J Dairy Sci*, 75, 387–93.

KAMAU DN, DOORES S and PRUITT KM (1990), 'Antibacterial activity of the lactoperoxidase system against *Listeria monocytogenes* and *Staphylococcus aureus* in milk', *J Food Prot*, 53, 1010–14.

KORHONEN H (1978), 'Effect of lactoferrin and lysozyme in milk on the growth inhibition of *Bacillus stearothermophilus* in the Thermocult method', *Suomen Eläinläährilehti*, 84, 255–67.

LACHOWICZ KJ, JONES GP, BRIGGS DR, BIENVENU FE, WAN J, WILCOCK A and COVENTRY MJ (1998), 'The synergistic preservative effects of the essential oils of sweet basil (*Ocimum basilicum* L.) against acid-tolerant food microflora', *Lett Appl Microbiol*, 26, 209–14.

LI Q, DUNN ET, GRANDMAISON EW and GOOSEN MFA (1997), 'Application and properties of chitosan', in Goosen MFA, *Applications of Chitin and Chitosan*, Technomic Publishing, Lancaster, PA.

LODI R, TODESCO R and BOZZETTI V (1989), 'New applications of natamycin with different types of Italian cheese', *Microbiol Aliments, Nutr*, 7, 81.

LÓPEZ-MALO A, ALZAMORA SM and ARGAIZ A (1995), 'Effect of natural vanillin on germination time and radial growth of moulds in fruit-based agar systems', *Food Microbiol*, 12, 213–19.

LÓPEZ-MALO A, ALZAMORA SM and GUERRERO S (2000), 'Natural antimicrobials from plants', in Alzamora SM, Tapia MS and López-Malo A, *Minimally Processed Fruits and Vegetables*, Aspen Publ.

LÓPEZ-MALO A, ALZAMORA SM and PALOU E (2002), '*Aspergillus flavus* dose-response curves to selected natural and synthetic antimicrobials', *Intl J Food Microbiol*, 73, 213–18.

MANDEL ID and ELLISON SA (1985), 'The biological significance of the nonimmunoglobulin defense factors', in Pruitt KM and Tenovuo JO, *The Lactoperoxidase System: Its Chemistry and Biological Significance*, Marcel Dekker Inc., New York.

MANDERFIELD MM, SCHAFER HW, DAVIDSON PM and ZOTTOLA EA (1997), 'Isolation and identification of antimicrobial furocoumarins from parsley', *J Food Prot*, 60, 72–7.

MARI M, IORI R, LEONI O and MARCHI A (1993), '*In vitro* activity of glucosinolate derived isothiocyanates against postharvest fruit pathogens', *Ann Appl Biol*, 123, 155–64.

MARTH EH (1966), 'Antibiotics in foods – naturally occurring, developed and added', *Residue Rev*, 12, 65–161.

MING X, WEBER GH, AYRES JW and SANDINE WE (1997), 'Bacteriocins applied to food packaging materials to inhibit *Listeria monocytogenes* on meats', *J Food Sci*, 62, 413–15.

MONTVILLE TJ, WINKOWSKI K and CHIKINDAS ML (2001) in Doyle MP, Beuchat LR and Montville TJ, *Food Microbiology: Fundamentals and Frontiers* 2nd edn, American Society for Microbiology, Washington, DC.

NAIDU AS and BIDLACK WR (1998), 'Milk lactoferrin – Natural microbial blocking agent (MBA) for food safety', *Environ Nutr Interactions*, 2, 35–50.

NILSON KM, SHAHANI KM, VAKIL JR and KILARA A (1975), 'Pimaricin and mycostatin for retarding cottage cheese spoilage', *J Dairy Sci*, 58, 668.

OGDEN KM, WEITES J and HAMMOND JRM (1988), 'Nisin and brewing', *J Inst Brew*, 94, 233.

ONSOYEN E and SKAUGRUD O (1990), 'Metal recovery using chitosan', *J Chem Technol Biotechnol*, 49, 395–404.

ORAM JD and REITER B (1968), 'Inhibition of bacteria by lactoferrin and other iron chelating agents', *Biochim Biophys Acta*, 170, 351–65.

PADGETT T, HAN IY and DAWSON PL (1998), 'Incorporation of food-grade antimicrobial compounds into biodegradable packaging films', *J Food Prot*, 61, 1330–5.

PANDIT VA and SHELEF LA (1994), 'Sensitivity of *Listeria monocytogenes* to rosemary (*Rosmarinus officianalis* L.)', *Food Microbiol*, 11, 57–63.

PAPINEAU AM, HOOVER DG, KNORR D and FARKAS DF (1991), 'Antimicrobial effect of water-soluble chitosans with high hydrostatic pressure', *Food Biotechnol*, 5, 45–57.

PARISH ME and DAVIDSON PM (1993), 'Methods for evaluation', in Davidson PM and Branen AL, *Antimicrobials in Foods*, 2nd edn Marcel Dekker, New York.

PARK CM, TAORMINA PJ and BEUCHAT LR (2000), 'Efficacy of allyl isothiocyanate in killing enterohemorrhagic *Escherichia coli* O157:H7 on alfalfa seeds', *Intl J Food Microbiol*, 56, 13–20.

PAYNE KD, DAVIDSON PM, OLIVER SP and CHRISTEN GL (1990), 'Influence of bovine lactoferrin on the growth of *Listeria monocytogenes*', *J Food Prot*, 53, 468–72.

PAYNE KD, DAVIDSON PM and OLIVER SP (1994), 'Comparison of EDTA and apo-lactoferrin with lysozyme on the growth of foodborne pathogenic and spoilage bacteria', *J Food Prot*, 57, 62–5.

PERIAGO PM and MOEZELAAR R (2001), 'Combined effect of nisin and carvacrol at different pH and temperature levels on the viability of different strains of *Bacillus cereus*', *Intl J Food Microbiol*, 68, 141–8.

PIDDOCK LJ (1990), 'Techniques used for the determination of antimicrobial resistance and sensitivity in bacteria', *J Appl Bacteriol* 68, 307.

POL IE and SMID EJ (1999), 'Combined action of nisin and carvacrol on *Bacillus cereus* and *Listeria monocytogenes*', *Lett Appl Microbiol* 29, 166–70.

RADLER F (1990), 'Possible use of nisin in winemaking. II. Experiments to control lactic acid bacteria in the production of wine', *Am J Enol Vitic*, 41, 7–11.

RAY LL and BULLERMAN LB (1982), 'Preventing growth of potentially toxic molds using antifungal agents', *J Food Prot*, 45, 953.

REITER B (1978), 'Review of the progress of dairy science, Antimicrobial systems in milk', *J Dairy Res*, 45, 131–47.

REITER B and HÄRNULV BG (1984), 'Lactoperoxidase antibacterial system, natural occurrence, biological functions and practical applications', *J Food Prot*, 47, 724–32.

RHOADES J and ROLLER S (2000), 'Antimicrobial actions of degraded and native chitosan against spoilage organisms in laboratory media and foods', *Appl Environ Microbiol*, 66, 80–6.

ROLLER S and COVILL N (1999), 'The antifungal properties of chitosan in laboratory media and apple juice', *Intl J Food Microbiol*, 47, 67–77.

ROLLER S and COVILL N (2000), 'The antimicrobial properties of chitosan in mayonnaise and mayonnaise-based shrimps salads', *J Food Prot*, 63 (2), 202–9.

RUIZ-HERRERA J (1992), *Fungal Cell Wall, Structure, Synthesis, and Assembly*, CRC Press, Boca Raton, FL.

SALEEM ZM and AL-DELAIMY KS (1982), 'Inhibition of *Bacillus cereus* by garlic extracts', *J Food Prot*, 45, 1007–9.

SCANNEL AGM, HILL C, BUCKLEY DJ and ARENDT EK (1997), 'Determination of the influence of organic acids and nisin on shelf-life and microbiological safety aspects of fresh pork sausage', *J Appl Microbiol*, 83, 407–12.

SCHOENKNECHT FD, SABATH LD and THORNSBERRY C (1985), 'Susceptibility tests: special tests', in Lennette E, *Manual of Clinical Microbiology*, American Society for Microbiology. Washington, DC.

SCOTT VN and TAYLOR SL (1981), 'Effect of nisin on the outgrowth of *Clostridium botulinum* spores', *J Food Sci*, 46, 117–20.

SHELEF LA, JYOTHI EK and BULGARELLI MA (1984), 'Growth of enteropathogenic and spoilage bacteria in sage-containing broth and foods', *J Food Sci*, 49, 737–40.

SHELEF LA, NAGLIK OA and BOGEN DW (1980), 'Sensitivity of some common foodborne bacteria to the spices sage, rosemary, and allspice', *J Food Sci*, 45, 1042–4.

SHIRK RJ and CLARK WL (1963), 'The effect of pimaricin in retarding the spoilage of fresh orange juice', *Food Technol*, 17, 1062.

SIRAGUSA GR and JOHNSON MG (1989), 'Inhibition of *Listeria monocytogenes* growth by the lactoperoxidase-thiocyanate-$H_2O_2$ antimicrobial system', *Appl Environ Microbiol*, 55, 2802–5.

SMID EJ and GORRIS LGM (1999), 'Natural antimicrobials for food preservation', in Rhaman MS, *Handbook of Food Preservation*, Marcel Dekker, New York.

SMITH-PALMER A, STEWART J and FYFE L (1998), 'Antimicrobial properties of plant essential oils and essences against five important food-borne pathogens', *Lett Appl Microbiol*, 26, 118–22.

SOMERS EB and TAYLOR SL (1981), 'Further studies on the antibotulinal effectiveness of nisin in acidic media', *J Food Sci*, 46, 1972–3.

SOMERS EB and TAYLOR SL (1987), 'Antibotulinal effectiveness of nisin in pasteurized process cheese spreads', *J Food Prot*, 50, 842–8.

STEAD D (1993), 'The effect of hydroxycinnamic acids on the growth of wine-spoilage lactic acid bacteria', *J Appl Bacteriol*, 75, 135–41.

SUDARSHAN NR, HOOVER DG and KNORR D (1992), 'Antibacterial action of chitosan', *Food Biotechnol* 6(3), 257–72.

SZABO EA and CAHILL ME (1999), 'Nisin and ALTA™ 2341 inhibit the growth of *Listeria monocytogenes* on smoked salmon packaged under vacuum or 100% $CO_2$' *Lett Appl Microbiol* 28, 373–7.

THOMAS, LV, CLARKSON MR and DELVES-BROUGHTON J (2000), 'Nisin', in Naidu AS, *Natural Food Antimicrobial Systems*, CRC Press, Boca Raton, FL.

TICHA J (1975), 'A new fungicide, pimaricin, and its application in the baking industry', *Mlynsko-Pekarensky Prumysl*, 21, 225. [*Food Sci Technol Abst* 8, 163.]

TRANTER HS (1994), 'Lysozyme, ovotransferrin and avidin', in Dillon VM and Board RG, *Natural Antimicrobial Systems and Food Preservation*, CAB Intl, Wallingford, UK.

TSAI GJ and SU WH (1999), 'Antibacterial activity of shrimp chitosan against *Escherichia coli*', *J Food Prot*, 62, 239–43.

TSAI GJ, WU ZY and SU WH (2000), 'Antibacterial activity of chitooligosaccharide mixture prepared by cellulase digestion of shrimp chitosan and its application to milk preservation', *J Food Prot*, 63, 747–52.

ULATE-RODRIGUEZ J, SCHAFER HW, ZOTTOLA EA and DAVIDSON PM (1997), 'Inhibition of *Listeria monocytogenes*, *Escherichia coli* O157, H7 and *Micrococcus luteus* by linear furocoumarins in a model food system', *J Food Prot*, 60, 1050–4.

ULTEE A and SMID EJ (2001), 'Influence of carvacrol on growth and toxin production by *Bacillus cereus*', *Intl J Food Microbiol*, 64: 373–8.

ULTEE A, KETS EPW and SMID EJ (1999), 'Mechanisms of action of carvacrol on the food-borne pathogen *Bacillus cereus*', *Appl Environ Microbiol*, 65, 4606–10.

ULTEE A, SLUMP RA, STEGING G and SMID EJ (2000), 'Antimicrobial activity of carvacrol toward *Bacillus cereus* on rice', *J Food Prot*, 63, 620–4.

ULTEE A, BENNIK MHJ and MOEZELAAR R (2002), 'The phenolic hydroxyl group of carvacrol is essential for action against the food-borne pathogen *Bacillus cereus*', *Appl Environ Microbiol*, 68, 1561–8.

VAN RIJN FTJ, STARK J and GEIJP EML (1999), 'Antifungal complexes', U.S. Patent 5,997,926.

VAZQUEZ BI, FENTE C, FRANCO CM, VAZQUEZ MJ and CEPEDA A (2001), 'Inhibitory effects of eugenol and thymol on *Penicillium citrinum* strains in culture media and cheese', *Intl J Food Microbiol*, 67, 157–63.

VENKITANARAYANAN KS, ZHAO T and DOYLE MP (1999), 'Antibacterial effect of lactoferricin B on *Escherichia coli* O157, H7 in ground beef', *J Food Prot*, 62, 747–50.

WALKER JC and STAHMANN MA (1955), 'Chemical nature of disease resistance in plants', *Ann Rev Plant Physiol*, 6, 351–66.

WAN J, WILCOCK A and COVENTRY MJ (1998), 'The effect of essential oils of basil on the growth of *Aeromonas hydrophila* and *Pseudomonas fluorescens*', *J Appl Microbiol*, 84, 152–8.

WANG GH (1992), 'Inhibition and inactivation of five species of foodborne pathogens by chitosan', *J Food Prot*, 55, 916–19.

WARD SM, DELAQUIS PJ, HOLLEY RA and MAZZA G (1998), 'Inhibition of spoilage and pathogenic bacteria on agar and pre-cooked roast beef by volatile horseradish distillates', *Food Res Intl*, 31, 19–26.

WEISSINGER WR, MCWATTERS KH and BEUCHAT LR (2001), 'Evaluation of volatile chemical treatments for lethality to *Salmonella* on alfalfa seeds and sprouts', *J Food Prot*, 64: 442–50.

WHITING RC and BUCHANAN RL (2001), 'Predictive modeling and risk assessment', in Doyle MP, Beuchat LR and Montville TJ, *Food Microbiology, Fundamentals and Frontiers*, 2nd edn, American Society for Microbiology, Washington, DC.

WILKINS KM and BOARD RG (1989), 'Natural antimicrobial systems', in Gould GW, *Mechanisms of Action of Food Preservation Procedures*, Elsevier Appl Sci, London.

# 3

# Natural antioxidants

**J. Pokorný, Prague Institute of Chemical Technology, Czech Republic**

## 3.1 Introduction

Foods containing fats and other lipids, terpenes and branched hydrocarbons are not stable on long storage or intensive heating. Unsaturated, and particularly, polyunsaturated fatty acids bound in lipids are oxidized following different mechanisms with formation of free radicals, which are further converted into hydroperoxides. Hydroperoxides are odourless and tasteless, but they decompose with formation of volatile compounds, such as alkanals, alk-2-enals, alka-2,4-dienals, different ketones, alcohols and hydrocarbons. These products give rise to specific objectionable off-flavours, called rancid flavour notes. The sensory value, and thus the food acceptability, is substantially deteriorated by rancidification. The rancidification can be prevented by different methods, such as by using fat materials poor in polyenoic (polyunsaturated) fatty acids, by protecting food products against the access of oxygen or, most often, by adding inhibitors of oxidation. The most important inhibitors are antioxidants, which are able to inactivate free radicals formed during the autoxidation.

Most antioxidants are phenolic substances, more rarely nitrogen heterocycles. The most active antioxidants contain *ortho* or *para* disubstituted hydroxyl groups. In case of synthetic substances, *para* disubstituted derivatives are preferred because of lower toxicity, but among natural antioxidants the *ortho* disubstitution prevails. In the food industry, synthetic antioxidants are mostly used as they are pure, cheap, safe, and readily available. However, modern consumers are afraid of any synthetic chemicals. They feel natural antioxidants are safer and more acceptable to the human body. Therefore food producers try to add natural antioxidants when possible.

## 3.2   Classifying natural antioxidants

Natural antioxidants occur mainly in plants but also in fungi and microorganisms and to lesser extent in animal tissues. They are mostly disubstituted phenolic derivatives, most often 1,2-dihydroxybenzene, more rarely 1,4-dihydroxybenzene derivatives. A hydroxyl group or both can be replaced with a methoxy, ester or another active group. However, cholesteryl esters of ferulic or caffeic acids are less active than the respective free acids (Marinova *et al.*, 1998). Phenolic acids are the most widely occurring antioxidants in higher plants, especially in those used as food. They belong to derivatives of either benzoic acid or cinnamic acid. Gallic acid (3,4,5-trihydroxy-benzoic acid) is a typical example of the benzoic acid group, while caffeic acid (3,4-dihydroxy-1-acryloyl-benzoic acid) is the most important derivative of the cinnamic acid series (Fig. 3.1). Caffeic acid is frequently esterified with quinoic acids, forming chlorogenic acid isomers.

Another important class of antioxidants are flavonoids. They consist of 3 cycles: A = an aromatic ring, containing one or several substituents; cycle A is condensed with cycle B – a heterocyclic group containing oxygen; the third aromatic cycle C is bound to cycle B via a C-C bond, and is substituted usually with 2 or 3 hydroxyl goups (Fig. 3.2). The phenolic hydroxyls can be substituted with gallic acid in cycle C, while the hydroxylic groups in cycle A are often substituted with a glycosyl group, forming glycosides. Several structurally related classes of compounds are present in plant food materials, such as

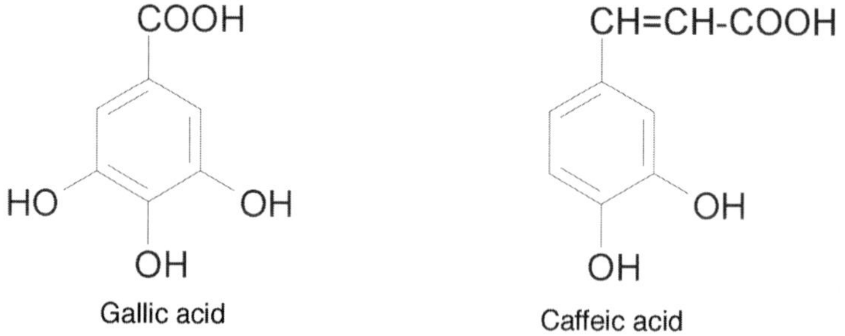

**Fig. 3.1**   Typical representatives of antioxidants of the benzoic and cinnamic acid series.

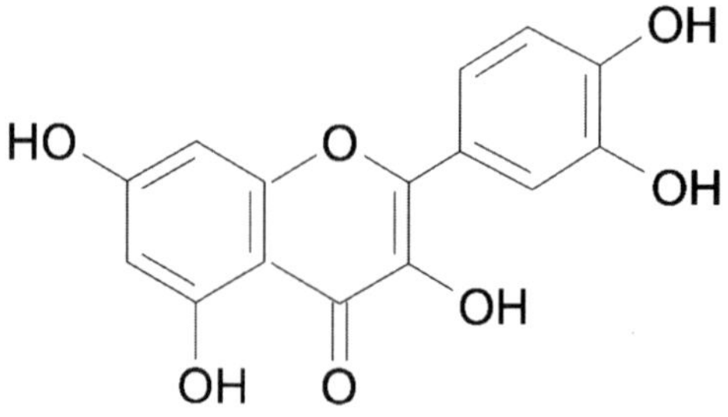

**Fig. 3.2**   Quercetine as an example of flavonoids.

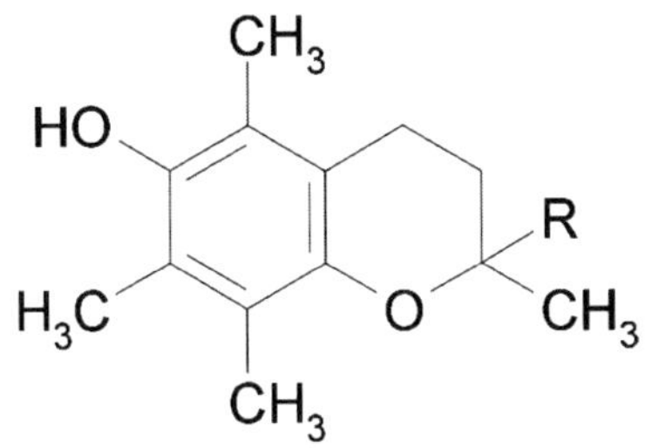

**Fig. 3.3**   α-Tocopherol (R = phytol side chain).

anthocynanins or their polymers. The antioxidant activity is related to the chemical structure (Fig. 3.2).

Tocopherols and the closely related tocotrienols are the most widely occurring plant antioxidants as they have been detected, at least in minute traces, in all plant materials, and at least in small amounts, in all animal food products. They are derivatives of chroman, with a diterpenic phytol side chain (Fig. 3.3). The antioxidant activity resides in the phenolic group, located in the *p*-position to the C-O bond in the adjacent ring. There exist four tocopherols, differing in their degree of substitution on the aromatic ring. The fully substituted d-α-tocopherol, containing three methyl groups on the aromatic ring, is the most active antioxidant *in vivo*, but it is less active *in vitro*, i.e. in bulk oils. The double methyl substituted γ- or β-tocopherols are more active antioxidants in fats and oils. The single methyl substituted δ-tocopherol has the highest antioxidant activity in fats and oils. Synergistic effects exist between γ- and δ-tocopherols; the activity increases only to a certain maximum, which depends on the tocopherol structure (Wagner and Elmadfa, 2000).

Antioxidant activities of tocotrienols (containing three double bonds in the side chain) are similar to those of the respective tocopherols. The ratios of different tocopherols depend on the plant source more than on the factors of plant cultivation. The tocopherol content decreases during oil refining by about 30% (Gogolewski *et al.*, 2000), and their ratios also change.

In addition to phenolic antioxidants, most plants also contain other types of oxidation inhibitors. Synergists have no antioxidant activity of their own, but they can enhance the antioxidant activity of phenolic antioxidants. Polyvalent organic acids or hydroxy acids, such as citric or tartaric acids, phospholipids and amino acids belong to this group of compounds. Transient valency metals are powerful catalysts of lipid oxidation, therefore compounds able to bind metals into inactive complexes (chelating substances) can reduce the rate of oxidation. Among metal chelates, phytates (salts of phytic – inositolhexaphosphoric acid) are widely distributed in many plants.

### 3.2.1   Prooxidants in lipid systems

Contrary to antioxidants, prooxidants decrease the stability of food lipids on storage. The most important prooxidants are heavy metals of transient valency, especially copper, manganese and iron ions or complexes. They catalyze the decomposition of lipid hydroperoxides into free radicals, which initiate further oxidation of unsaturated fatty acid derivatives. Another type of prooxidants are photosensitizers. Green parts of plant material always contain chlorophyll pigments, which are photosensitizers in presence of light, catalyzing the oxidation of polyunsaturated lipids by converting the triplet oxygen into substantially more reactive singlet oxygen. The presence of carotenoids can transform the singlet oxygen back into its less reactive triplet form. Stability against oxidation is thus much improved. Carotenes and different carotenoids have thus an antioxidative activity, at least in the presence of light.

## 3.3    Antioxidants from oilseeds, cereals and grain legumes

Most oilseeds contain tocopherols, which are extracted from seeds with triacylglycerols so they are present in crude oil during oil processing. About a third of the amount originally present is lost during oil refining, mainly deodorization, but synthetic $\alpha$-tocopherol is sometimes added to refined oils, usually bound as acetate as it is more resistant against oxidation than tocopherol. Corn, soybean and rapeseed oils are particularly rich in $\gamma$-tocopherol, contributing to relatively good oxidative stability of those oils.

Olive oil is very stable against oxidation, not only because of low linoleic acid content, but also because of a group of natural antioxidants, derived from hydroxytyrosol. Oleuropein aglycone belongs to this group of antioxidants. The oxygen radical absorbance capacity of extra-virgin olive oils is related to the content of total phenolics (Ninfali et al., 2001). The same antioxidants were detected in olive leaf and olive fruit extracts.

Another interesting group of phenolic antioxidants is present in sesame seed. They belong to lignans, which are decomposed during roasting of sesame seeds, and some decomposition products are extracted from seeds into oil during oilseed processing, such as sesamol, possessing substantial antioxidant activity even in polyenoic edible oils (Fukuda et al., 1988).

Traditional cottonseed contained gossypol and related pigments, imparting high stability to cottonseed oil. As gossypol is toxic both for humans and animals, new glandless varieties free of gossypol are now produced, but even the glandless cottonseed oil contains different phenolic components of antioxidant activity. Evening primrose seeds, used for the small-scale production of some dietetic oils, contain antioxidants active even in polyunsaturated edible oils, which are otherwise difficult to stabilize (Niklová et al., 2001).

After removal of oil from oilseeds, most phenolic antioxidants still remain in extracted oilseed meal, but their use as a source of natural antioxidants is limited to oilseed meals as phenolic antioxidants are not tranferred into edible oils during extraction. They are sometimes used as human food, such as soybeans (*Esaki et al.*, 1990) or tempeli (Murata, 1998). Miso has a similar effect (Santiago *et al.*, 1992). Isoflavones and their glycosides are efficient antioxidants in deoiled soybean meal. Similarly, peanut, sunflower, almond and mustard oilseed meals could be used as sources of antioxidants. If seeds are dehulled before processing, hulls can be used as rich sources of phenolic substances, e.g., rapeseed or canola hulls are rich in tannins – about 128–296 mg/g of sinapic acid equivalents (Amarowicz *et al.*, 2000).

### 3.3.1   Antioxidants from cereals and grain legumes

Cereals belong to the most voluminous components of the diet. They contain several classes of phenolic compounds, possessing antioxidant activity (Zieliński, 2002). The relevant phenolic compounds are mainly soluble in water or in polar organic solvents, such as ethanol, but some phenolics are oil soluble, such as tocotrienols or phenolic acids bound to diacylglycerols. Buckwheat and oat flours (Xing and White, 1997) are the most active source of antioxidants and they were proposed for the stabilization of food before the Second World War. Most phenolics are concentrated in hulls and in bran. Rice bran is commercially used for the production of oil as it contains oryzanol and related phenolic antioxidants. Cereal flours contain both reducing sugars and free amino acids, both precursors of Maillard reactions. An addition of D-glucose enhances the protective effect on lipids in extruded products (Yokata *et al.*, 1987). During heating they interact with the formation of brown macromolecular products, called melanoidins. They possess moderate antioxidant activities, which is important in baked or roasted products (Elizalde *et al.*, 1991). The activity is partially due to their metal chelating activity, but the presence of reductones and interactions of free radicals with imines – the most important intermediary products of Maillard reactions – and other functional groups play their role here, too.

Grain legumes are far less important food components than cereals. The content of phenolic substances is relatively low, about of the same order as in cereals but nevertheless, they may stabilize foods if added in substantial amounts as an ingredient. Legume hulls are particularly rich in phenolic substances, such as flavanols, but they have a bitter taste, which is objectionable for most consumers. Other phenolic substances, such as tannins or lignins, are mostly insoluble, but some decomposition products are partially soluble in oil, therefore they are sometimes efficient in stabilizing the lipid fractions in foods or meals. They are also active in the inhibition of lipoxygenases.

## 3.4   Antioxidants from fruits, vegetables, herbs and spices

All fruits and vegetables contain antioxidants; their high consumption, and therefore, high intake of antioxidants, are the main advantages of the Mediterranian diet (Visioli and Galli, 2001). The most important group of active antioxidants in fruits and vegetables are various flavones, anthocyanins and related compounds (Zhang, 1999). Some compounds of these groups are able to increase vitamin C activity, protecting it against oxidative degradation. They are called bioflavonoids. In red wine and deep-red coloured fruit juices, various anthocyanins and their polymers are present, which are soluble in the aqueous phase, and possess moderate antioxidant activity. In addition to these compounds, various terpenic derivatives could act as potent inhibitors of lipid oxidation (see more in the next section). Another group of active compounds are carotenoids (Stahl and Sies, 1999), e.g., lycopene present in tomatoes. They possess antioxidant activities as mentioned in section 3.3.1.

The best investigated fruit components active as antioxidants are those isolated from citrus fruits. Their activity is stronger in aqueous emulsions because of their prevailing hydrophilic character. For this reason, ethanolic or aqueous extracts containing mostly flavones and their glycosides – i.e., hydrophilic substances – are more active than hexane or diethyl ether extracts. They impart higher inhibition activities to emulsions and other polar food systems, while hexane or ethyl acetate extracts are more active in bulk oils. The most active antioxidants from fruits and vegetables are extracts or materials containing pyrocatechol derivatives. Onion and garlic also contain efficient inhibitors, mainly based on the presence of thiol or sulphide groups. Potent inhibitors can be obtained from plant sources other than food products but in such cases they should be tested for their safety before application, even if they have been used in some countries as a drug for a long time.

### 3.4.1   Herbs and spices as sources of antioxidants

Herbs are stems or leaves from various plants, used for the preparation of infusions, extracts, dressings, soups or sauces. Many species of this class of food ingredients are active antioxidants, mainly because of the content of phenolic compounds. The most important representatives of this group are tea leaves obtained from both green or fermented tea (*Camellia sinensis* L. or *Camellia assamica* L.) or dust left after their preparation. Green tea is particularly rich in catechins and related compounds, usually more than 20% (Yamamoto *et al.*, 1997). Phenolics obtained from tea contain not only catechins, but also epicatechin, gallocatechin and the respective gallates. They were active for the protection of meat lipids against oxidation (Shahidi and Alexander, 1998). Extracts from fermented (black) tea leaves are less active antioxidants because a substantial part of the catechin has been oxidized during the fermentation and converted into tea pigments, especially theaflavins and thearubigins, which are formed from the intermediary quinones by dimerization.

Wastes left over after the preparation of commercial tea infusions or after the production of instant teas, are used for the subsequent extraction of antioxidants, or may be used directly as food ingredients. The antioxidant activity may be ranked in descending order as follows: epigallocatechin gallate > epigallocatechin > epicatechin gallate > epicatechin > theaflavins > therubigins. Leaves used for the preparation of herbal teas in Central European infusions are less efficient. Various herbs used in China, Japan, Korea and other East

Asian countries in folk medicine contain potent antioxidants but they have been generally not sufficiently tested for their safety. Also gingko leaves, containing strong antioxidants and used in East-Asian medicine, have not been sufficiently tested for safety, and should be thoroughly investigated before they are allowed for food use.

The antioxidant activity of spices has been known for 50 years (Chipault *et al.*, 1956). Spices from other parts of plants than leaves are used for conditioning meats and bakery products; some among them are efficient inhibitors of oxidation, such as savory, oregano, spearmint, lavender, nutmeg, allspice, etc. The most active substances are produced from rosemary – *Rosmarinus officinalis* L. (Chang *et al.*, 1978), which is the only commercially available antioxidant from spices, and from sage (*Salvia officinalis* L.). Both of them contain carnosol and carnosic acid as active substituents (Cuvelier *et al.*, 1996; Richheimer *et al.*, 1996). Herbs and leaves efficiently stabilize French fries (Korczak, 1992). Not only non-volatile resins from spices, but also volatile essential oils from different spices are active as antioxidants. After their removal, the remaining non-volatile fraction (a resin) has mainly lower antioxidant activity than the original material. Gingseng and sweetgrass, possessing antioxidant activities, are used as spices not in food, but in alcoholic beverages.

The composition of spices is well known, and most active substances have been identified. However, it is not recommended to use pure components as food additives (even if they have been isolated from materials applied in the food industry). The application of pure natural substances is subject to legal restrictions, and many among them could be found toxic under strict safety checks. Some spices change the flavour of food products, if added for their stabilization against oxidation, but the deodorized materials could be added without affecting the flavour. The antioxidant activity of spices or spice extracts is often combined with antimicrobial activity.

## 3.5   Using natural antioxidants in food

The main guideline is that natural antioxidants are preferred to synthetic antioxidants only insofar as the consumers prefer them, and people feel that humans became adapted to them over the many generations they were consumed. Only food components, and not all natural substances should be accepted for use in foods. Material Generally Regarded As Safe (GRAS) can be added to foods without limitations. The best application of antioxidants is the direct addition of the respective ingredients, found as active antioxidants, to food without any previous fractionation or concentration; herbs and spices belong to this group. Some simple fractionation could be used, e.g., extraction of the oil fraction and utilization of the extracted meal, or distillation of the volatile essential oils, and the use of the nonvolatile residue.

The application of extracts obtained with acetone, methanol and other organic solvents, have to be avoided, as the extracts are rather expensive, and high concentrations of active substances could become a health risk. The use of supercritical carbon dioxide for extraction of antioxidants is a very safe process. It may be expensive to use, but there should be no problems with residues or by-products. Pure substances obtained from natural materials may be slightly toxic. Their addition in high amounts, in order to achieve good stability against oxidation, could easily exceed safe limits in foods. Therefore, they should be subject to similar safety tests as synthetic antioxidants. Antioxidant activity depends on the food composition, and antioxidants active in fats and oils could become less active in emulsions, and vice versa. Different nonlipidic food components also affect the antioxidant activity therefore the test for activity should differ as little as possible from storage conditions, and special tests should be used for frying oils or other lipid foods heated to high temperatures.

### 3.5.1   Applications for the stabilization of lard and meat products

Animal fats contain no natural antioxidants or only traces, therefore the application of antioxidants is very useful. Fortunately, the content of oxylabile (sensitive of oxidation) polyunsaturated fatty acids is relatively low, at least in fats of land mammals, so that even small amounts of antioxidants are very efficient. Butter is among the fats very sensitive to off-flavours. Even when the content of polyunsaturated fatty acids does not exceed 4–8%, their oxidation would deteriorate the flavour. Tocopherols may be added to cream before churning or may even be added to the feed to enrich milk fat with tocopherols. Other efficient antioxidants are spice extracts, especially rosemary oleoresin or ethanolic extract of rosemary leaves, Even essential oils from thyme, cumin and other spices act as preservatives against both oxidation and microorganisms (Farag *et al.* 1988). Maillard products, which are often naturally present in foods containing butter, can improve oxidative stability under certain circumstances.

Pork lard is very unstable against oxidation as unsaturated fatty acids are bound at 1- or 3-positions of the glycerol residue. Its bland flavour may be easily deteriorated even by traces of rancidity. The stabilization of lard by natural antioxidants was reported before the Second World War. In the postwar period numerous papers were published on the subject and only a few examples will be given. Saito *et al.* (1976) tested 27 ground spices in lard, and observed very good antioxidant activities in the cases of sage, rosemary and mace. Methanol extracts from spices synergistically increased the effect of citric acid or ascorbyl palmitate. Flavonoids act as efficient antioxidants in lard, which may explain the effect of herbs and leave spices (Yanishlieva and Marinova, 1996).

The stabilization of meat products is similar to that of lard. Only a few examples of application will be given here. Tocopherols have a pronounced effect on the stability of beef patties stored at 4°C, if they have been added at the concentration of 200 mg/kg or more (Lee and Lillard, 1997). The effect of spices in ground pork has been known for several decades. The application of ground spices would be objectionable in lard because of atypical appearance and flavour notes but they may be added to meat products with success (Shahidi *et al.*,

1995). They are active in cooked meat products and even in raw. The most widely used natural antioxidant is ground rosemary leaves or rosemary oleoresin. Only a few examples suffice. Rosemary antioxidant was found to be active during storage of cooked minced pork meat or in frozen pork sausage (Ho *et al.*, 1995). Restructured meat is very sensitive to oxidation as it produces off-flavours. Rosemary oleoresin was found to be active in restructured raw or cooked pork steaks or restructured chicken nuggets. Tripolyphosphate was added in both cases as a metal chelating agent. Green tea catechins were also found to be efficient in stabilizing meat lipids,

    Smoke is traditionally used as a preservative for meat products. Smoke preparations from ash and beech wood are rich in phenolics so that they may prolong the stability of lard or pork meat, which is important in the production of smoked meat products. Sodium nitrite, added in curing preparations, inhibits the oxidation of pork meat, but its activity decreases with increasing cooking time as it reacts with other meat components. The antioxidant activity was higher in cooked ground pork and beef treated with nitrite, during cold storage, compared to untreated meat (Zubillaga and Marker, 1987). Maillard products also protect sausages against oxidative degradation during frozen storage (Lingnert and Lundgren, 1980) and in cookies (Lingnert, 1980). The antioxidant activity of soy sauce in ground pork fat patties is probably due to free amino acids present in soy sauce.

### 3.5.2    Application of natural antioxidants for the stabilization of fish and fish oil

Fish oils are very sensitive to oxidation as they contain fatty acids with four to six double bonds, therefore it is rather difficult to stabilize them against rancidification. The most common natural antioxidants are tocopherols. At low concentrations (about 100 mg/kg), $\alpha$-tocopherol is more active than $\gamma$- and $\delta$-tocopherols while at high concentrations (about 1000 mg/kg) it is the reverse, and $\delta$- and $\gamma$-tocopherols are more active than $\alpha$-tocopherol. The same could be said in the case of vegetable oils (see below).

    Lecithin and ascorbyl palmitate are synergists in fish oils enriched with tocopherols. Both choline and ethanolamine bound in phospholipids inhibit the accumulation of hydroperoxides in sardine oil. Different flavonoids, especially quercetin, stabilize fish oils against rancidification, shown as synergism with $\alpha$-tocopherol under conditions of the Schaal Oven Test at 60°C and in glass bottles at 2.5°C. The most efficient derivative was 5,3′,4′-trihydroxy-7-methyl-(O)-flavanone. Flavonoids, such as myricetin, quercetin and morin, were found to be more active than synthetic antioxidants in seal blubber and menhaden oils. Extracts from herbs, such as rosemary and oregano, were found to be very active in mackerel oil (Tsimidou *et al.*, 1995).

    The stabilization of fish muscle against rancidification is still more important than the stabilization of oils as unpleasant off-flavours are rapidly produced by interaction of fish lipid oxidation products with proteins. Viscera lipids are more susceptible to oxidation than muscle or skin lipids (Ohshima *et al.*, 1993). The chloroform-methanol extracts of sardine meal possessed antioxidant activity, mainly due to phospholipids, particularly phosphatidylcholine. Phosphatidyl-ethanolamine showed synergistic activity with $\alpha$-tocopherol. Metal chelating agents, such as sodium phosphate, glutamate or citric acid actively protected refrigerated herring against flavour deterioration. Rosemary extract was also efficient as a synergist in stabilizing frozen-crushed fish meat against rancidification. Similar activity was observed in dried sardine (Wada and Fang, 1994). Rosemary oleoresin stabilized lipids of rainbow trout during refrigeration at 4°C or frozen storage (at $-20$°C) for several months (Akhtar *et al.*, 1998). Other ground spices have antioxidant effects in sardine muscle, such as garlic, basil, oregano, parsley, rosemary, sage and thyme, at both 40°C and at 0°C. The addition of ground spices is more acceptable than that of plant extracts as the additives are cheaper and are not objectionable from the standpoint of safety.

### 3.5.3    Applications for the stabilization of vegetable oils and plant foods

Vegetable oils are mainly rather polyunsaturated so that they are less stable against oxidation than animal fats but they usually contain natural antioxidants, in most cases tocopherols, almost in optimum concentrations. At low levels (up to 50 mg/kg) $\alpha$-tocopherol was found more active than $\gamma$-tocopherol, but at high levels (more than 100 mg/kg), on the contrary, $\gamma$-tocopherol was found more active than $\alpha$-tocopherol, when tested at 40°C in the dark (Lampi *et al.*, 1999). Even when considerable losses (higher than 30%) of tocopherols occur during crude oil refining (Gogolewski *et al.*, 2000), stability against oxidation is not much affected by refining. A synergism was observed between $\gamma$- and $\delta$-tocopherols (Wagner and Elmadfa, 2000), but the contents of the latter are very low compared to the former. Tocopherols present in frying oils stabilize fried potatoes (Márquez Ruiz *et al.*, 1999).

Carotenoids (see 3.2.1), particularly $\beta$-apo-8′-carotenoic acid, were reported as synergists of tocopherols in sunflower oil both at 4 and 100°C (Yanishlieva *et al.*, 2001). Carotene was found efficient only at very high concentrations of 500 mg/kg, which do not occur in refined oils but may be extracted from other food components.

Phospholipids are natural constituents of crude edible oils, but they are almost completely removed in the course of their refining in the stage of degumming. However, they may be present in mixtures of oils with other food components. Phosphatidylethanolamine is active as a synergist of tocopherols in soybean oil while phosphatidylcholine was less efficient, and phos-phatidylinositol completely inefficient. They were tested, however, at much higher concentrations than are likely to occur in refined edible oils. Olive oil contains other antioxidants in addition to tocopherols (mostly hydroxytyrosol derivatives) which contribute to its resistance against oxidation (Salvador *et al.*, 1999). Antioxidants extracted from olive leaves and green olive fruits exhibited moderate antioxidant activities in olive and sunflower oils at 30 and 80°C (Hartzallah and Kiritsakis, 1999).

The effect of many other natural antioxidants in edible oils was recently reviewed (Yanishlieva *et al.*, 2001). The most active are extracts from rosemary leaves as they possess about the same activity as synthetic phenolic antioxidants (Gordon and Kourimska, 1995a, b). They are active even in less polyunsaturated oils, such as palmolein, showing synergism with sage extract and citric acid. They were found active in extruded cereal products on storage (Berset *et al.*, 1989) and in edible oils under conditions of both the Schaal Oven Test or during deep frying (Réblová *et al.*, 1999). Many other spice extracts were found moderately active at temperatures up to 100°C and in emulsions, especially allspice extracts. Evening primrose oil is now used as a dietetic oil, but the seed also contains active phenolic substances applicable as antioxidants (Niklová *et al.*, 2001).

### 3.5.4  Applications of natural antioxidants for the stabilization of essential oils and cosmetics against oxidation

Essential oils are not lipids because they do not contain bound fatty acids, but they are as easily oxidized as lipids are and their oxidation proceeds along similar lines. Many essential oils contain components resistant to oxidation or even possessing antioxidant properties, but other essential oils are very sensitive to oxidation, especially citrus essential oils. During their oxidation, citrus odour notes disappear, and intensities of woody, acidic and heavy odour notes develop (Pokorný *et al.*, 1998). Limonene was found to be the most sensitive compound and herbal oleoresins were efficient in its stabilization (Lee and Widmer, 1994). During the oxidation of bergamot oil at 40–60°C, sensory acceptability decreased but rosemary extracts inhibited oxidation and minimized the odour changes (Pudil *et al.*, 1998). Similar activity was also observed in *Citrus hystrix* essential oil, where the rosemary extracts were also found to be efficient. Methanolic extracts of herbs and spices were active in other applications in cosmetics (Betes and Armengol, 1995). Rosemary extracts could be incorporated into liposomes to stabilize different cosmetics and pharmaceuticals (Nguyen and Ribier, 1992).

## 3.6  Improving antioxidant functionality

### 3.6.1  Use of mixtures of inhibitors

The application of high concentrations of an antioxidant is limited for several reasons. Antioxidant activity generally decreases with increasing concentration of the antioxidant so that the optimum concentration should not be exceeded. The maximum concentration is most often regulated by legislation from safety concerns, by the effect on sensory properties or by the price therefore other ways are sought to improve stability against oxidation.

The application of mixtures of antioxidants is advantageous in the case of synthetic antioxidants as it allows some countries to increase the addition of a mixture of antioxidants above the 0.01 or 0.02% permitted for a single antioxidant. Activity is, however, raised only moderately, as all antioxidants compete for the same free radicals. The synergism between $\alpha$-tocopherol with rosemary extracts was observed in systems containing ferrous ions and hemoprotein (Fang and Wada, 1993). Synergism also exists between rosemary and sage extracts, even when the antioxidant composition is rather similar, especially in the presence of citric acid.

### 3.6.2    Application of mixture consisting of antioxidants and synergists

A more efficient solution is to add mixtures of antioxidants and synergists. Synergists have no antioxidant activity of their own in the absence of phenolic antioxidants but they increase the activity of phenolic antioxidants if they are present. Polyvalent organic acids (such as succinic acid), hydroxy acids (such as citric or tartaric acids), amino acids, peptides (Park *et al.*, 2001) or phospholipids belong to this group (see also 3.3). The synergism is based on various mechanisms, and the same synergist may act following several mechanisms. They may convert the oxidized compounds, such as tocopheryl quinones, back to the respective original antioxidants, such as tocopherols.

The main sources of free radicals in oxidizing lipids are hydroperoxide decomposition products – free R-O* and R-OO* radicals. The decomposition is efficiently catalyzed by transient valency heavy metal ions or complexes, such as copper, iron, cobalt or manganese. Therefore, metal chelating agents, such as citric, tartaric, malic or ascorbic acids, phosphoric acid or phosphates, including phytic acid, ethylene diamino tetraacetate (EDTA) belong to this class of synergists. They are also often common food components. Ascorbyl palmitate acted as a synergist of tocopherols of potato chips in peanut oil (Satyanarayana *et al.*, 2000). On the other hand, various substances stabilize hydroperoxides against decomposition, thus reducing the formation of free radicals, e.g., tocopherols stabilize methyl linoleate hydroperoxides (Mäkinen *et al.*, 2001) and even fish oil hydroperoxides. However, ascorbic acid and ascorbyl palmitate have an only minor effect from this standpoint.

Synergistic activity depends on storage conditions, ratio of antioxidants and synergists, and on other factors. The most important mechanism of synergistic activity may depend on the concentration. Most food materials contain several different synergists, including chelating agents, so that the stability of foods is sometimes higher than the stability expected from experiments based on simple models, e.g., in bulk fats and oils.

### 3.6.3    Other ways of improving antioxidant functionality

During food storage, oxygen penetrates into food material by diffusion from air and therefore food lipids are oxidized from the surface. In some cases it is sufficient to apply antioxidants, especially spices, only on the surface. The process is particularly useful in the case of oxylabile (sensitive to oxidation) material, such as fish muscle. Food may be packaged, e.g. vacuum packed in plastic materials with a low or very low Oxygen Transmission Rate (O-TR) thus reducing or inhibiting oxygen diffusion from the air into the package. Food may also be packaged in an active packaging where antioxidants are incorporated in the packaging material with a controlled release of antioxidants to the surface of the food during the storage period.

During storage, free radicals are slowly produced in food even at low temperatures and react with antioxidants, which are thus gradually consumed. The antioxidant functionality can be improved by reduction of the rate of free radical production. The safest way is to use stable lipids in the recipe. Instead of traditional edible oils rich in oxylabile polyunsaturated fatty acids, new modified high-oleic acid oils may be used, such as modified sunflower, soybean, peanut or rapeseed oils. They are very resistant against oxidation even in the absence of antioxidants because of their low polyunsaturated acid content. The stability is good not only on storage but also during deep frying. Another method for the elimination of prooxidants (see 3.2.1) from food is by modifying the recipe. The most active prooxidants are haem compounds, such as muscle myoglobin therefore dry meat is often substituted by meat flavour substances, such as sodium glutamate, in dry soups. The presence of salt increases the oxidation rate of meat lipids therefore salt may be added in the encapsulated form. The protecting layer is dissolved and salt released only during meat cooking so that the contact of salt with meat lipids is only short.

## 3.7   Combining antioxidants with other preservation techniques

The amount of antioxidants necessary for efficient stabilization may be reduced if food preservation by means of antioxidants is combined with another preservation technique. Cold storage is a typical example as the rate of free radical formation and thus also of antioxidant destruction is much lower under refrigeration. Refined rapeseed oil containing about 500 mg of tocopherols per kg is stable only for 2–4 weeks at 40°C, when the concentration of tocopherols approaches zero. If the same oil is stored at 10°C, no perceptible deterioration of sensory quality was observed even after 15 months of storage. On the contrary, frozen storage is not always preferable in foods containing water, such as meat or fish, as water crystallizes out of the hydrated protein layer protecting lipids against access of oxygen, and air has then free access to lipids. Natural antioxidants present are then rapidly consumed in spite of low temperature.

Another factor catalyzing the formation of free radicals and of the reactive singlet oxygen is sunlight, especially in the presence of photosensibilizing pigments. The packaging in protecting materials, such as amber glass or multilayer plastic packaging (depending on O-TR) protect antioxidants against oxidative damage. Autoxidation does not proceed in the absence of air so that the removal of air or its replacement with inert gas is an excellent additional method for food preserved with antioxidants; it would save at least 50% of antioxidants. Packaging in material impermeable to oxygen is another alternative, preferably in sealed metallic cans or in specially designed multilayer plastics (with low or very low O-TR).

Fresh foods of both animal and plant origin contain lipoxygenases and other enzymes catalyzing oxidation and decomposition of hydroperoxides formed as primary reaction products. These precursors can then destroy antioxidants. Antioxidant stability may be enhanced by rapid heating in hot water or by steam, under conditions of blanching vegetables. Foods rich in natural phenolic antioxidants, such as potatoes, apples or bananas, usually contain active enzymes, especially polyphenol oxidases, able to oxidize antioxidants into the respective quinones. Quinones polymerize or are decomposed by reaction with other food components, mainly amine and sulphur groups. The antioxidant activity is thus substantially reduced, and brown discolouration appears. Tea fermentation is a typical example, as the content of catechin is reduced to a half or a third by enzymic fermentation, and the dimeric tea pigments – theaflavin and thearubigin – have only low activities. Polyphenol oxidases can be rapidly inactivated by steam or hot water, at the same time as lipoxygenases.

## 3.8    Future trends

The trend to substitute synthetic antioxidants with natural antioxidants will continue in future in spite of its irrationality, as it is based on consumers' emotions. There will persist objections against antioxidants generally so that even the addition of natural antioxidants would be avoided. Essentially, they are slightly more dangerous for health than synthetic antioxidants so that such a trend (to avoid antioxidants) is correct. Natural antioxidants from foods consumed for thousands of years are considered as less dangerous than antioxidants from different herbs used only in medicine, especially herbs from the Far East, where the health risks are checked inadequately.

Food components with high antioxidant content, such as herbs and spices, will be preferred to extracts and pure natural antioxidants as the latter are served in higher concentrations than the body is familiar with. Food additives rich in natural antioxidants will be available on the market, obtained by conventional breeding or by genetic manipulations. The necessity to add natural antioxidants to foods will be eliminated, at least partially, by the use of recipes applying more oxidation-stable components, requiring no addition of antioxidants. For those cases when antioxidants would remain necessary, the requirements would be optimized, and their total content in foods minimized by their use in mixtures with synergists. Suitable packaging could prevent the diffusion of oxygen, and thus to save further addition of antioxidants.

## 3.9    Sources of further information and advice

ARUOMA O I, CUPPETT S L, *Antioxidant Methodology: In vivo and in vitro concepts*, Champaign, IL, AOCS Press, 1997.

BASU T K, TEMPLE N J, GARG M L, *Antioxidants in Human Health and Disease,* Wallingford, CABI Publishing, 1999.

CHAN H W S, *Autoxidation of Unsaturated Lipids*, London, Academic Press, 1987.

DECKER E A, FAUSTMAN C, LOPEZ-BOTE C J, *Antioxidants in Muscle Foods*, New York, Wiley, 2000.

DENISOV E T, DENISOVA T G, *Handbook of Antioxidants*, 2nd edn, Boca Raton, CRC Press, 2000.

LARSON R A, *Naturally Occurring Antioxidants*, Boca Raton, Lewis Publishing, 1997.

LÖLIGER J, 'The use of antioxidants in foods', *Free Radicals Food Additives*, London, Taylor and Francis, 1991.

MADHAVI D L, DESHPANDE S S, SALUNKHE D K, *Food Antioxidants*, New York, Decker, 1995.

MADSEN H L, BERTELSEN G, 'Spices as antioxidants', *Trends Food Sci Technol*, 1995 **6** (8) 271–7.

PACKER L, HIRAMATSU M, YOSHIKAWA T, *Antioxidant Food Supplements in Human Health*, San Diego, London, Academic Press, 1999.

PACKER L, TRABER M G, XIN W, *Proceedings of the International Symposium on Natural Antioxidants*, Champaign, IL, AOCS Press, 1996.

POKORNÝ J, YANISHLIEVA N, GORDON M, *Antioxidants in Food*, Cambridge, Woodhead Publishing, 2001.

RAHMAN M S, *Handbook of Food Preservation*, New York, Basel, Dekker, 1999.

SHAHIDI F, *Natural Antioxidants*, Champaign, IL, AOCS Press, 1996.

SHAHIDI F, NACZK M, *Food Phenolics*, Lancaster, PA, Technomic Publishers, 1993.

YANISHLIEVA N V, MARINOVA E M, 'Stabilisation of edible oils with natural antioxidants', *Eur J Lipid Sci Technol*, 2001 **103** (11) 752–67.

## 3.10    References

AKHTAR P, GRAY J I, BOOREN A M, GARLING D L, 'Effect of dietary components and surface application of oleoresin rosemary on lipid stability of rainbow trout muscle during refrigerated and frozen storage', *J Food Lipids*, 1998 **5** 43–58.

AMAROWICZ R, NACZK M, SHAHIDI F, 'Antioxidant activity of crude tannins of canola and rapeseed hulls', *JAOCS*, 2000 **77**(9) 957–61.

BERSET C, TROUILLER J, MARTY C, 'Protective effect of the oleoresin rosemary and on several other antioxidants on $\beta$-carotene in extrusion cooking', *Lebensm-Wiss Technol*, 1989 **22**(1) 15–19.

BETES C, ARMENGOL R, 'Antioxidant activity of natural extracts. Cosmetic applications', *Cosmet Toiletries, Ed Ital*, 1995 **16**(2) 11–19.

CHANG S S, OSTRIC-MATIJASEVIC B, HSIEH O A L, HUANG C-L., 'Natural antioxidants from rosemary and sage', *J Food Sci*, 1978 **42** 1102–6.

CHIPAULT J R, MIZUNO G R, LUNDBERG W O, 'The antioxidant properties of spices and foods', *Food Technol*, 1956 **10** 203–11.

CUVELIER M-E, RICHARD H, BERSET C, 'Antioxidative activity and phenolic composition of pilot-plant and commercial extracts of sage and rosemary', *JAOCS*, **73**(5) 645–52.

ELIZALDE B, DALLA ROSA M, LERICI C R, 'Effect of Maillard reaction volatile products on lipid oxidation', *J Am Oil Chem Soc*, 1991 **68**(10) 758–62.

ESAKI H, NOHARA Y, ONOZAKI H, OSAWA T, 'Antioxidative activity of natto', *Nippon Shokuhin Kogyo Gakkaishi*, 1990 **37**(6), 474–7.

FANG X, WADA S, 'Enhancing the antioxidant effect of $\alpha$-tocopherol with rosemary in inhibiting catalyzed oxidation caused by $Fe^{2+}$ and hemoprotein', *Food Res. Int.*, 1993 **26** 405–11.

FARAG R S, ALI M N, TAHA S H, 'Use of some essential oils as natural preservatives for butter', *Grasas Aceites*, 1988 **39**(1) 28–31.

FUKUDA Y, OSAWA T, KAWAGISHI S, NAMIKI M, 'Oxidative stability of foods fried with sesame oil', *Nippon Shokuhin Kogyo Gakkaishi*, 1988 **35**(1), 28–32.

GOGOLEWSKI M, NOGALA-KALUCKA M, SZELIGA M, 'Changes of the tocopherol and fatty acid contents in rapeseed oil during refining', *Eur J Lipid Sci Technol*, 2000 **102** 618–23.

GORDON M H, KOURIMSKA L, 'Effect of antioxidants on losses of tocopherols during deep-fat frying', *Food Chem*, 1995a **52** 175–7.

GORDON M H, KOURIMSKA L, 'The effects of antioxidants of changes in oils during heating and deep frying', *J Sci Food Agric*, 1995b **68** 347–53.

HARTZALLAN H, KIRITSAKIS A, 'Antioxidant effect of olive oil leaf and olive fruit extracts', *Olivae*, 1999 **77** 47–9.

HO C-P, HUFFMAN D L, BRADFORD D D, EGBERT W R, MIKEL W B, JONES W R, 'Storage stability of vacuum packaged frozen pork sausage containing soy protein concentrate, carrageenan or antioxidants', *J Food Sci*, 1995 **60** 257–61.

KORCZAK J, 'Ocena właściwości przeciwutleniajaczych przypraw ziolowych w prazynkach ziemniaczanych', *Roczn Akad Roln Poznaniu, Technol Zywności*, 1992 **233**(17) 63–73.

LAMPI A-M, KATAJA L, KAMAL-ELDIN A, PIIRONEN V, 'Antioxidant activities of $\alpha$- and $\gamma$-tocopherols in the oxidation of rapeseed oil triacylglycerols', *JAOCS*, 1999 **76**(6) 749–55.

LEE H S, WIDMER W W, 'Evaluation of commercial oleoresins for inhibition of limonene oxidation', *Proc Fla State Hortic Soc,* 1994 **107** 281–4.

LEE K-T, LILLARD D-A, 'Effects of tocopherols and $\beta$-carotene on beef patties oxidation', *J Food Lipids*, 1997 **4**(4) 261–8.

LINGNERT H, 'Antioxidative Maillard reaction products, II. Application in cookies', *J Food Proc Preserv*, 1980 **4** 219–33.

LINGNERT H, LUNDGREN B, 'Antioxidative Maillard reaction products, IV. Application in sausage', *J Food Process Preserv*, 1980 **4**(4) 235–46.

MÄKINEN M, KAMAL-ELDIN A, LAMPI A-M. HOPIA A, '$\alpha$-, $\gamma$- and $\delta$-Tocopherols as inhibitors of isomerization and decomposition of *cis,trans* methyl linoleate hydroperoxides', *Eur J Lipid Sci Technol*, 2001 **103**(5) 286–91.

MARINOVA E M, YANISHLIEVA N V, RANEVA V G, TODOROVA D I, 'Antioxidative action of the cholesteryl esters of ferulic and caffeic acids and of their isomers', *Riv Ital Sost Grasse*, 1998 **75**(1) 11–14.

MÁRQUEZ RUIZ G, MARTÍN POLUILLO M, JORGE N, RUIZ MÉNDEZ M V, DOBARGANES M C, 'Influence of used frying oil quality and natural tocopherol content on oxidative stability of fried potatoes', *JAOCS*, 1999 **76**(4) 421–5.

MURATA K, 'Antioxidative stability of tempeh', *J Am Oil Chem Soc,* 1988 **65**(5) 799–800.

NGUYEN Q L, RIBIER A, 'Liposome-incorporated rosemary extract as an antioxidant for cosmetics and pharmaceuticals', *Fr Demande FR*, 1992 2,676,361.

NIKLOVÁ I, SCHMIDT Š, HABALOVÁ K, SEKRETÁR S, 'Effect of evening primrose extracts on oxidative stability of sunflower and rapeseed oils', *Eur J Lipid Sci Technol*, 2001 **103**(5) 299–306.

NINFALI P, ALUIGI G, BACCHIOCCA M, MAGNANI M, 'Antioxidant capacity of extra-virgin olive oils', *JAOCS*, 2001 **78**(3) 243–7.

OHSHIMA T, FUJITA Y, KOIZUMI C, 'Oxidative stability of sardine and mackerel lipids with reference to synergism between phospholipids and $\alpha$-tocopherol', *J Am Oil Chem Soc*, 1993 **70** 269–76.

PARK P-J, JUNG W-K, NAM K-S, SHAHIDI F, KIM S-K, 'Purification and characterization of antioxidative peptides from protein hydrolysate of lecithin-free egg yolk', *JAOCS*, 2001 **78**(6) 651–6.

POKORNÝ J, PUDIL F, VOLFOVÁ J, VALENTOVÁ H, 'Changes of the flavor of monoterpenes during their auto-oxidation under storage conditions', *Food Flavors: Formation, Analysis and Packaging Influences*, eds E T Contis *et al.*, Elsevier, Amsterdam, 1998, pp. 667–78.

PUDIL F, VOLFOVÁ J, JANDA V, VALENTOVÁ H, POKORNÝ J, 'Effect of rosemary and 1,4-dihydropyridines on oxidative and flavour changes of bergamot oil', *Food Flavors: Formation, Analysis and Packaging Influences*, eds. E T Contis *et al.*, Elsevier, Amsterdam, 1998, pp. 679–87.

RÉBLOVÁ Z, KUDRNOVÁ J, TROJÁKOVÁ L, POKORNÝ J, 'Effect of rosemary extracts on the stabilization of frying oil during deep fat frying', *J Food Lipids, 1999* **6** 13–23.

RICHHEIMER S L, BERNARTI M W, KING G A, KENT M C, BAILEY D T, 'Antioxidant activity of lipid soluble phenolic diterpenes from rosemary', *JAOCS*, 1996, **73**(4) 507–14.

SAITO Y, KIMURA Y, SAKAMOTO T, 'Studies on the antioxidant properties of spices. II. The antioxidative effect of some spices', *Eiyo to Shokuryo*, 1976 **29** 404–8.

SALVADOR M D, ARANDA F, FREGAPANE, 'Contribution of chemical components on Corniabra virgin olive oils to oxidative stability. A study of three successive crop seasons', *JAOCS*, 1999 **76**(4) 427–32.

SANTIAGO L A, HIRAMATSU M, MORI A, 'Japanese soybean miso scavenges free radicals and inhibits lipid peroxidation', *J Nutr Sci Vitaminology*, 1992 **38** 297–304.

SATYANARAYANA A, GIRIDHAR N, JOSHI G J, RAO D G, 'Ascorbyl palmitate as an antioxidant for deep fat frying of potato chips in peanut oil', *J Food Lipids*, 2000 **7**(1) 1–10.

SHAHIDI F, ALEXANDER D M, 'Green tea catechins as inhibitors of oxidation of meat lipids', *J Food Lipids*, 1998 **5**(2) 125–33.

SHAHIDI F, PEGG R B, SALEEMI Z O, 'Stabilization of meat lipids with ground spices', *J Food Lipids*, 1995 **2** 145–53.

STAHL W, SIES H, 'Carotenoids: occurrence, biochemical activities, and bioavailability', *Antioxidant Food Supplements in Human Health*, eds L Packer, M Hiramatsu, T Yoshikawa, Academic Press, San Diego, 1990, pp. 183–202.

TSIMIDOU M, PAPAVERGOU E, BOSKOU D, 'Evaluation of oregano antioxidant activity in mackerel oil', *Food Res Int*, 1995 **28** 431–3.

VISIOLI F, GALLI C, 'The role of antioxidants in the Mediterranean diet', *Lipids*, 2001, **36**(Suppl.) 349–52.

WADA S, FANG X, 'The synergistic antioxidant effect of rosemary extract and $\alpha$-tocopherol in sardine oil model system and frozen-crushed fish meat', *J Food Process Preserv*, 1992 **16** 263–74.

WAGNER K-H, ELMADFA I, 'Effects of tocopherols and their mixtures on the oxidative stability of olive oil and linseed oil under heating', *Eur J Lipid Sci Technol*, 2000 **102**(10) 624–9.

XING Y, WHITE P, 'Identification and function of antioxidants from oat groats and hulls', *JAOCS*, 1997 **74**(3) 303–7.

YAMAMOTO T, JUNEJA L R, CHU D C, KIM M, *Chemistry and Application of Green Tea*, Berlin, Boca Raton, Springer (CRC Press), 1997.

YANISHLIEVA N V, MARINOVA E M, 'Antioxidative action of some flavonoids at ambient and high temperatures', *Riv Ital Sostanze Grasse*, 1996 **73**(10) 445–9.

YANISHLIEVA N V, MARINOVA E M, 'Stabilization of edible oils with natural antioxidants', *Eur J Lipid Sci technol*, 2001 **103**(11) 752–67.

YANISHLIEVA N V, MARINOVA E M, RANEVA V G, PARTALI V, SLIWKA H R, '$\beta$-Apo-8'-carotenoic acid and its esters in sunflower oil oxidation', *JAOCS*, 2001 **78**(6) 641–4.

YOKATA A, MIYATA K, MURAGUCHI H, TAKAHASHI A, 'Effect of glucose on the antioxidative activity of Maillard reaction products during extrusion cooking', *Nippon Nogei Kagaku Kaishi,* 1987 **61**(10) 1273–8.

ZHANG H., 'Theoretical elucidation of structure-activity relationship of flavonoid antioxidants', *Sci China*, 1999 **B 42**(1) 107–12.

ZIELIŃSKI H, 'Low molecular weight antioxidants in the cereal grains', *Pol J Food Nutr Sci*, 2002 **11**(1) 3–9.

ZUBILLAGA M P, MARKER G, 'Antioxidant activity of polar lipids from nitrite-treated cooked and processed meats', *J Am Oil Chem Soc*, 1987 **64**(5) 757–60.

# 4

# Antimicrobial enzymes

**A. S. Meyer, Technical University of Denmark**

## 4.1  Introduction

This chapter focuses on the antibacterial action mechanisms and bacteriocidal effects of enzymes that have been investigated as possible preservative agents in different foods and beverages. Various enzyme preparations have been added routinely for decades – or even longer – in food processing. Important examples include addition of rennet in cheese making, amylases in bread baking, and pectinases in fruit juice production. Obviously, the purpose of these conventional enzyme additions is to promote specific transformations of crucial technological significance, e.g., to accelerate the clotting of milk during cheese manufacture or to improve the baking performance of flour in bread making. At present, the applications of enzymes in food processing constantly expand and today the addition of exogenous enzymes is employed in a very large number of different food and beverage processes and several new applications of enzymes in food ingredient manufacture and food processing are projected for the future (Godfrey, 2003). Nevertheless, only relatively few types of enzymes have been investigated for their antimicrobial activities as food preservative agents and only a couple of enzymes are currently employed as preservative agents in foods.

The most studied enzymatic preservative agents include hen egg white lysozyme and other lytic enzymes, glucose oxidase, and different carbohydrate hydrolysing enzymes. In addition, the boosting of naturally occurring lactoperoxidase in milk has been intensively examined. In section 4.2 the mode of antimicrobial action of lysozyme and various other lytic enzyme systems will be reviewed with particular emphasis on their action mechanisms and efficacy when evaluated in genuine food products. The activity mechanisms and antibacterial efficacies of the lactoperoxidase and glucose oxidase systems are then discussed in sections 4.3 and 4.4, respectively. In section 4.4.2 the focus is directed towards a number of other enzyme activities that have been explored for their antimicrobial effects. Section 4.5 summarises the reported combined effects of enzymatic and physicochemical factors and reviews novel techniques for improved antimicrobial potency of enzymes, with particular focus on lysozyme. Section 4.6 presents a brief introduction to the legislation on use of enzymes in foods, and gives a view on the future needs, trends and challenges in the practical exploitation of enzyme-based food preservation systems. Finally section 4.7 gives suggestions for further reading.

### 4.1.1   The use and effect of enzymes as antibacterial agents

Enzymes may exert antibacterial activity by a number of different mechanisms (Table 4.1). Lysozymes and other antimicrobial, lytic enzymes mainly elicit their antibacterial activity by inducing bacteriolysis via catalytic cleavage of cell-surface polymers or cell-wall junctions. As will be discussed later in this chapter, lysozyme may also work bacteriocidally by mechanisms that are independent of its catalytic activity. Lactoperoxidase, and other peroxidase systems, work antimicrobially via oxidative catalysis that releases or produces toxic or inactivating products given that the right substrates are present. In contrast, the antibacterial effect of glucose oxidase is categorised as an oxidative catalysis mechanism that both removes essential substrates (e.g., oxygen) and produces antibacterial products. However, as will be more apparent later, when the mechanisms of each of these enzyme systems is discussed in more detail, these categorisations may be too narrow to describe fully the antibacterial

**Table 4.1**  Proposed antimicrobial enzyme mechanisms and enzymes with known antibacterial effects

| Type of mechanism | Enzyme type | Enzyme source | Effect |
|---|---|---|---|
| Catalytic cleavage of peptidoglycan or cell wall junctions | Lysozyme | Hen egg white | Bacteriolysis (Gram$^+$ organisms)[1] |
| Channel formation and membrane destabilisation | Lysozyme as a cationic peptide | Hen egg white | Increased membrane permeability |
| Oxidative catalysis releasing or producing toxic or inactivating products | Lactoperoxidase Glucose oxidase | Cow's milk *A. niger* | Growth inhibition Growth inhibition |
| Oxidative catalysis removing essential substrates or nutrients | Glucose oxidase | *A. niger* | Growth inhibition |
| Enzyme catalysed degradation of extracellular polysaccharides | Hydrolases | Several different | Biofilm degradation |

[1] Gram positive organisms are more susceptible to enzyme catalysed peptidoglycan degradation.

mechanisms of the enzyme systems. Lastly, a number of hydrolases, in effect mixed carbohydrate hydrolysing activities, can induce accelerated depolymerisation of bacterial polysaccharides and hence exert antibacterial action by causing partial degradation of bacterial biofilms (Table 4.1).

The efficacy of different enzyme systems depends strongly on the physicochemical conditions, i.e., the microenvironment in the system. Furthermore, the response of different enzymatic principles to the intrinsic resistance factors of different bacteria also vary markedly. As highlighted in the following sections, the antibacterial efficacy of these different types of action mechanisms therefore differ markedly in different food systems. Hence, in analogy to other food preservatives, the applicability of different enzyme systems as preservative agents in different foods and against different types of bacteria vary significantly in different systems.

## 4.2    Lysozymes and other lytic enzyme systems

Lysozymes are 1,4-$\beta$-N-acetylmuramidases (EC 3.2.1.17), which catalyse the degradation of bacterial cell wall peptidoglycan by catalysing the hydrolysis of the $\beta$-1,4-glycosidic bonds between $N$-acetylmuramic acid (NAM) C1 and the $N$-acetylglucosamine (NAG) C4 of peptidoglycan (Jollés and Jollés, 1984). Different types of lysozymes are present in tears, mammalian milk, insects, and avian eggs. Lysozyme activities can also be found in a number of other natural sources including in, e.g., vira, where notably the lysozyme activity produced by the T4 bacteriophage has been intensively studied (Tranter, 1994). Today, hen egg white is the major source of the enzyme for commercial extraction, where the enzyme product is a byproduct of egg albumen manufacture (Wigley, 1996). Purification protocols for hen egg white lysozyme were reported as long ago as 1945–46 and the complete sequence of the 129 amino acid residues in the egg white enzyme's single polypeptide chain, which is c type lysozyme, was published about 40 years ago (Jollés et al., 1963). Furthermore, lysozyme was the first enzyme ever to have its structure solved by protein chrystallography (Jollés and Jollés, 1984). A comprehensive account of the structural traits and the catalytic mechanism of the hen egg white lysozyme have been given by Tranter (1994).

The primary antibacterial mechanism of lysozyme is presumably based on the muramidase catalysed cleavage of glycosidic bonds in peptidoglycan, but as discussed below, lysozyme may also work by other mechanisms as inactivated lysozyme also exerts antibacterial effects. The biosynthesis and the dynamics of the cell wall peptidoglycan are a requirement for bacterial growth, and, as is known, the inhibition of peptidoglycan biosynthesis is the mechanism of action of several antibacterial agents including the $\beta$-lactam penicillins and the vancomycin group of glycopeptides (Bugg, 1999). The lysozyme catalysed cleavage of the peptidoglycan polysaccharide results in a punctured cell wall which eventually leads to lysis of the bacterial cell membrane and consequently cell death or, at least, growth inhibition. This mode of action is assumed to explain the efficacy of lysozyme addition to cheese milk in preventing outgrowth from spores of *Cl. tyrobutyricum* and in turn prevent 'late blowing' in cheeses (Wasserfall and Teuber, 1979). Likewise, it is the mechanism proposed to account for the inhibitory action of hen egg white lysozyme on undesirable lactic acid bacteria in wine (Gao *et al.*, 2002; Gerbaux *et al.*, 1997). As expounded further below, enzyme catalysed peptidoglycan hydrolysis leading to bacteriolysis has also been evoked as the mechanism explaining the antibacterial activity of lysozyme on several other spoilage and pathogenic bacteria in food systems (Fuglsang *et al.*, 1995, Hughey *et al.*, 1989; Proctor and Cunningham, 1988). Accordingly, the sensitivity of bacterial cells to lysozyme activity is determined by their cell-wall structure, and notably by the accessibility, thickness and composition of their peptidoglycan.

Both Gram-positive and Gram-negative bacteria contain peptidoglycan in the cell wall. As is well known, the peptidoglycan layer of Gram-positive bacteria is generally much thicker than that of Gram-negative organisms. In Gram-positive cells the peptidoglycan may thus constitute ~50% of the dry weight of the cell wall (Schleifer and Kandler, 1972). Even though the peptidoglycan layer is thinner in Gram-negatives, their peptidoglycan is less accessible as it is sandwiched between the cytoplasmic membrane and an outer membrane composed of lipopolysaccharides, phospholipids, and protein (ratio approximately 1:1:1) (Proctor and Cunningham, 1988). The presence in Gram-negative cells of this outer membrane offers Gram-negative bacteria an effective barrier to lysozyme action. In turn, this barrier renders Gram-negative bacteria intrinsically more resistant than Gram-positive organisms to lysozyme attack and bacteriolysis (Proctor and Cunningham, 1988). In other words, the difference in the cell wall layer structures explains why lysozyme is especially active against Gram-positive organisms including clostridia, listeria, staphylococci, bacilli, and lactic acid bacteria. Perturbation of the outer membrane of Gram-negative bacteria by chemical or physical means may render Gram-negative organisms more susceptible to peptidoglycan degrading enzymes, however (Proctor and Cunningham, 1988).

In Gram-positive bacteria teichoic and lipoteichoic acids intertwine the peptidoglycan and thus confer differences in the detailed peptidoglycan composition in different bacteria. Differences in lipoteichoic acids also affect the potential of bacteria to induce inflammation; with *Staphylococcus aureus* it has been shown that copresence of lipoteichoic acid and peptidoglycan can induce a vigorous, synergistic inflammatory response in rats (de Kimpe *et al.*, 1995). On the other hand, teichoic acid, being negatively charged, may be envisaged to be able to bind lysozyme and thus prevent its motion and in turn diminish its hydrolytic action on the peptidoglycan (Proctor and Cunningham, 1988).

Although the action of lysozyme may be dampened if bound to teichoic acids, the main differences in the sensitivity of different Gram-positive bacteria to lysozyme appear to be caused by variations in the short peptide bridges in the peptidoglycan (Jollés and Jollés, 1984; Proctor and Cunningham, 1988). Data obtained with different types of lysozyme on *S. aureus* (Wecke *et al.*, 1982) as well as with the cell wall lysis system of *Clostridium perfringens* bacteriophage ϕ3626 on different clostridia and other bacteria (Zimmer *et al.*, 2002) suggest that Gram-positive bacteria having highly substituted peptidoglycan may be more resistant to enzymatic hydrolysis of peptidoglycan than those having less substituted peptidoglycan. At present, however, only little is known about the cellular consequences of differences in the cross linking peptide sidechains as knowledge on the specificities of the peptidases which can catalyse the hydrolysis of these peptidoglycan peptide side chains is sparse (Harding *et al.*, 2002). The variations among different bacteria in the interpeptide bridge that connects the pentapeptide bridges in peptidoglycan may also be thought to confer variation in the overall peptidoglycan robustness to hydrolytic enzymes attack. It has long been known that very significant differences in the peptidoglycan structure of Gram-positive organisms occur from variations in the interpeptide bridge between the pentapeptide branches in peptidoglycan (Schleifer and Kandler, 1972). Although lysozyme does not exert any peptidolytic or proteolytic activity, it can be speculated that the physical accessibility and flexibility of the NAG-NAM $\beta$-1,4-glycosidic bonds which constitute the lysozyme substrate, may be influenced from differences in the interpeptide bridges. However, it is presently unknown if interpeptide variations influence the sensitivity of bacteria to lysozyme or other enzyme induced bacteriolysis.

### 4.2.1  Non-enzymic action of lysozyme

Surprisingly, partially heat-denatured lysozyme exerts antibacterial activity on a number of microorganisms (Ibrahim *et al.*, 1996a and b). The antimicrobial activity of such thermally inactivated lysozyme extends to Gram-negative organisms and appears independent of the lysozyme muramidase activity (Ibrahim *et al.*, 1996a). Two mechanisms have been proposed for this non-enzymic action of lysozyme. The first is that lysozyme acts as a cationic protein that induces cell lysis via puncturing of the cell membrane through a protein-phospholipid interaction mechanism (Ibrahim *et al.*, 1996a and b; Pellegrini *et al.*, 1992). The second mechanism is that the lysozyme protein may activate so-called autolysin enzymes in the bacterial cell wall that in turn induce cell lysis (Ibrahim *et al.*, 1996a). Autolysins include N-acetylmuramoyl-L-alanine amidase enzymes that catalyse the cleavage of the amide bonds between the N-acetylmuramic acid lactyl side chain and the amino acid residue at position 1 of the pentapeptide sidechain, i.e., the bond that links the short peptides to the NAG-NAM backbone in peptidoglycan (Bierbaum and Sahl, 1987; Harding *et al.*, 2002). The peptidase induced hydrolysis of the peptidoglycan peptide sidechains have long been suspected to promote lysis of undesirable Gram-positive organisms, and the influence of cationic peptides on the activity of N-acetylmuramoyl-L-alanine amidase was studied 15 years ago (Bierbaum and Sahl, 1987). Amidase enzyme activities are found among bacteriolytic enzymes in bacteriophages; the bacteriophage T7 lysozyme, for example, is actually a bifunctional protein incorporating such an amidase activity (Cheng *et al.*, 1994). Furthermore, the *ply* genes encoding N-acetylmuramoyl-L-alanine amidase were recently identified in the *Bacillus cereus* bacteriophages 12826 and TP21 (Loessner *et al.*, 1997). Despite this, detailed knowledge on the molecular enzymology and practical implications of the action of the peptide sidechain hydrolases in medicine and food science is still limited as substrate analogues for their assay have only recently been synthesised (Harding *et al.*, 2002). Even though the antimicrobial actions of denatured lysozyme are well described (Ibrahim *et al.*, 1996a and b; Pellegrini *et al.*, 1992) and even though very recent data demonstrate that partial denaturation of lysozyme may enhance its activity against *Listeria monocytogenes* (Pszczola, 2002), the significance of these non-enzymic antibacterial effects of lysozyme in the applications where active lysozyme is added in food processes is unknown.

It has been speculated for some time, that chemical modification of lysozyme by covalent attachment of fatty acids might facilitate the penetration of lysozyme through the outer membrane of Gram-negative organisms. Recently, it was proven, that such lipophilisation of hen egg white lysozyme with caproic acid (C6:0), capric acid (C10:0), or myristic acid (C14:0) enhance the bacteriocidal activity of lysozyme against *Escherichia coli* K-12 in a phosphate buffered test medium (Liu *et al.*, 2000). Furthermore, chemical reduction of disulphide bonds in hen egg white lysozyme by reaction with either cysteine or glutathione, has been demonstrated recently to increase the antimicrobial activity of lysozyme against *Salmonella enteritidis* in a phosphate buffer test system (pH 7.2, 30°C) (Touch *et al.*, 2003). Evaluation of the leakage of liposomes obtained after contact with the chemically reduced lysozymes indicated that the bacteriocidal action was mainly attributable to the hydrophobic and cationic properties of the modified lysozymes rather than to the lysozymes' muramidase activity (Touch *et al.*, 2003).

### 4.2.2.   Effects of lysozyme in real food product trials

The presence of egg white lysozyme inhibits the outgrowth of *C. tyrobutyricum* in ripened, yellow cheeses such as Edam or Gouda (Bester and Lombard, 1990; Wasserfall and Teuber, 1979). When the lysozyme is added just before the addition of rennet in cheese making, lysozyme both kills resting vegetative *C. tyrobutyricum* cells, delaying the outgrowth of spore cells into vegetative cells, and retards proliferating vegetative cells (Wasserfall and Teuber, 1979). As discussed in more detail in section 4.6. this effect uniquely permits the use of hen egg white lysozyme as a food additive in cheese in the European Union, E-number 1105 (Directive 95/2/EC). In Gouda cheese lysozyme supplementation has also been suggested as a safeguard against growth of *L. monocytogenes* (Bester and Lombard, 1990). In general, the available data are very difficult to evaluate and compare, as the experimental details vary markedly among different reports and notably because the addition levels of lysozyme are reported as amounts, e.g., mg/kg, rather than in activity units. Thorough quantitative studies and descriptions of the antibacterial efficacies of lysozyme on undesirable bacterial growth in cheese and in other foods are very sparse.

In wines, addition of lysozyme, with dose given as $\sim 250$ mg/L, inhibits growth of *Leuconostoc oenos*, and lysozyme supplementation can consequently control the onset of malolactic fermentation and stabilise the wine after completion of the malolactic conversion (Gerbaux *et al.*, 1997; Pitotti *et al.*, 1991). This successful effect of lysozyme has been highlighted as a possible substitute for sulphite use in wines (Pitotti *et al.*, 1991). A recent report has demonstrated that addition of 125 or 250 mg/L of hen egg white lysozyme during alcoholic fermentation in wine inhibits the proliferation of *Lactobacillus kunkeei, L. brevis, Pediococcus parvulus*, and *P. damnosus*, that are known as lactic acid spoilage bacteria in wines (Gao *et al.*, 2002).

Various Japanese reports and patents from the early 1970s have also claimed preservative effects of lysozyme in several different foods and beverages including sake, fresh vegetables, fish, tofu bean curd, seafoods, and various meat products; an account and discussion of these reported data are given in Proctor and Cunningham (1988). Hughey *et al.* (1989) reported that sprinkling with hen egg white lysozyme (at a dose of 100 mg/kg) retarded, but did not completely inhibit, growth of inoculated populations of *L. monocytogenes* Scott A in shredded lettuce, shredded cabbage, fresh corn, green beans, and shredded carrots during storage at 5°C, while control incubations without lysozyme supported growth of *L. monocytogenes*.

Akashi and Oono (1972) reported lysozyme to exert a weakly preservative effect in lightly salted fish, when lysozyme was employed as a dipping treatment in 1% gelatin–0.05% lysozyme solution, but treatment with sorbic acid consistently resulted in a better preservative effect than lysozyme in these fish products (Akashi and Oono, 1972). Later reports have confirmed that lysozyme exerts only weak antibacterial potency in animal products such as pork sausage (bratwurst) and Camembert cheese (Hughey *et al.*, 1989). In Camembert cheese lysozyme by itself or together with EDTA reduced an inoculated *L. monocytogenes* population by ten-fold during the first 3–4 weeks of the ripening period, but the effect of lysozyme decreased with longer storage, where *L. monocytogenes* was found to grow unhindered in the artificially inoculated, lysozyme-containing cheeses (Hughey *et al.*, 1989). A lysozyme dip treatment (3 mg/mL) of cod fillets spiked with *L. monocytogenes* resulted in retarded growth of listeria during storage at 20°C for 3 days or at 5°C for 17 days, but did not exert a completely inhibitory effect (Wang and Shelef, 1992). However, the lysozyme dip treatments suppressed growth of *L. monocytogenes* more effectively when combined with EDTA (5–25 mM) (Wang and Shelef, 1992).

In whole milk, *L. monocytogenes* is resistant to added hen egg white lysozyme – which has been shown with different strains of *L. monocytogenes* – however, if heat treated, at 62°C for 15 seconds, the *L. monocytogenes* cells become more sensitive to lysozyme, albeit not enough to achieve total growth inhibition from added lysozyme in milk (Carminati and Carini, 1989; Kihm *et al.*, 1994). In an anaerobic meat medium, representing a vacuum-packed product, lysozyme (2,400 Units/ml equivalent to $\sim$50 $\mu$g lysozyme/mL) has been shown to prevent growth and toxin production of heat-treated *Clostridium botulinum* spores for up to three months provided that the storage temperature was below 8°C (Fernandez and Peck, 1999). A study of the available data therefore confirms that the antibacterial activity of neat hen egg white lysozyme is efficient only against a limited number of bacteria, notably Gram-positive organisms, and that the bacteriocidal effect is sufficiently potent in real food products only under particular conditions. Despite its long application as a food preservative in specific products very little is known on the quantitative aspects of enzyme dosage versus bacterial growth inhibition in real food systems. The boosting of lysozyme potency by co-addition of other substances or by manipulations of physicochemical parameters is discussed in section 4.5.

### 4.2.3    Other lytic enzymes

Apart from lysozyme, two other types of hydrolytic enzymes may work bacterio-lytically. Firstly, as already covered above, the N-acetylmuramoyl-L-alanine amidases catalyse cleavage of the junction between the peptidoglycan poly-saccharide backbone and the peptide crosslinks; additionally certain endopep-tidases are known to catalyse the hydrolysis of the peptide sidechains. Knowledge is lacking on enzymatic cleavage of the interpeptide bridges in peptidoglycan, however. *Streptomyces* spp. express an array of cell wall degrading activities that appear to comprise N-acetylmuramoyl-L-alanine amidase activity and/or endopeptidases that presumably act in cooperation to lyse sensitive organisms (Hayashi *et al.*, 1981; Brönneke and Fiedler, 1994). Notably, the so-called mutanolysin from *Streptomyces globisporus*, presumably comprised of L-alanine amidase and N-acetylmuramoyl-L-alanine amidase, exerts bacteriolytic activity on a number of bacteria in model systems and addition of bacterial cell walls to the *Streptomyces globisporus* growth medium has been shown to stimulate the production of the bacteriolytic activities (Brönneke and Fiedler, 1994). Recently, *Streptococcus milleri* was demonstrated to produce an endopeptidase, 'millericin B', which was shown to cleave the last residue in the interpeptide crosslink of peptidoglycan of susceptible strains, and that displayed bacteriolytic activity against several Gram-positive bacteria, except for *Bacillus subtilis* (Beukes *et al.*, 2000). Clearly, these more recent data confirm that hydrolytic enzyme activities other than lysozyme may show promise as preservative agents in foods. However, much more research remains to be done before any firm conclusions can be drawn regarding safety and efficacy of these enzyme systems in genuine food products.

## 4.3    Lactoperoxidase

As the name 'lacto' implies, the enzyme lactoperoxidase (EC 1.11.1.7) occurs in milk, where it contributes to milk's natural, antibacterial defence system by catalysing the net formation of hypothiocyanite ($OSCN^-$) via oxidation of thiocyanate ($SCN^-$) by hydrogen peroxide ($H_2O_2$) – see reaction, below. Lactoperoxidase activity has also been detected in other animal secreta, e.g., in saliva, tears, and nasal fluid (Ekstrand, 1994). Since the presence of lactoperoxidase in milk can be exploited for milk preservation, the milk lactoperoxidase system has been intensively studied and several reviews exist (see e.g., Daeschel and Penner, 1992; Ekstrand, 1994). The antibacterial reaction occurs by direct lactoperoxidase catalysed oxidation of $SCN^-$ to thiocyanogen

$(SCN)_2$ that in turn hydrolyses spontaneously to hypothiocyanite $(OSCN^-)$ as schematised below. At low pH the hypothiocyanous acid, HOSCN, is produced. Lactoperoxidase may also catalyse the direct oxidation of $SCN^-$ to $OSCN^-$ or HOSCN (Daeschel and Penner, 1992):

Lactoperoxidase:    $2\ SCN^- + H_2O_2 + 2\ H^+ \longrightarrow (SCN)_2 + 2\ H_2O$

$(SCN)_2 + H_2O \longrightarrow OSCN^- + SCN^- + 2\ H^+$

Net reaction:    $SCN^- + H_2O_2 \longrightarrow OSCN^- + H_2O$

Although the thiocyanate concentration in milk varies depending on the feed, $SCN^-$ is ususally naturally present in cow's milk in sufficient concentrations to enter as the principal electron donor in the enzymatic reaction (Björck et al., 1979). $H_2O_2$ is generated by catalase negative lactic acid bacteria, and may therefore also be naturally present in milk (Ekstrand, 1994), but, as discussed below, the antibacterial effect of the lactoperoxidase system in milk can be enhanced by co-addition or individual addition of one of the substrates $SCN^-$ and $H_2O_2$. The antibacterial effect is presumably caused by $OSCN^-$, which oxidises protein sulfhydryl groups to disulphides, e.g., of accessible cysteine groups in bacterial proteins. This oxidising effect is assumed to result in inactivation of vital bacterial enzyme systems, notably of enzymes having cysteine residues in their active sites, leading to inhibition of bacterial metabolic functions and consequently cell death (Daeschel and Penner, 1992). The antimicrobial potency of $OSCN^-$ is higher than that of $H_2O_2$. However, proteinaceous systems rich in oxidisable protein groups will scavenge the activity of the lactoperoxidase system (Fuglsang et al., 1995).

At pH values below 5 the HOSCN may exert an inhibitory effect against microorganisms by entering cells as the undissociated acid. In the cytoplasm of the microbial cell, the equilibrium will favour the undissociated acid, and – in analogy to the mechanism behind the the ability of organic acids to inhibit microbial growth – this generation of protons inside the cells is then assumed to be responsible for the antibacterial activity of lactoperoxidase at low pH (Ekstrand, 1994). Furthermore, the bovine milk lactoperoxidase has an apparent activity maximum at pH 5, and this combined with the relatively elevated concentrations of HOSCN at this pH value are in accordance with practical experience that the lactoperoxidase system works optimally at $\sim$ pH 5 (Ekstrand, 1994; Fuglsang et al., 1995).

### 4.3.1   Effects of the lactoperoxidase system in food products

The most widely studied effects of the lactoperoxidase system have been carried out in bovine milk, and in various dairy products. The lactoperoxidase system has been demonstrated to work efficiently to preserve raw milk without refrigeration. The strategy, involving addition of low levels of $H_2O_2$, was advanced as a method for temporary preservation of raw milk in developing countries (Björck et al., 1979). Later, co-addition of equimolar concentrations of 0.25 mM $SCN^-$ and $H_2O_2$ to milk, was found to maximise the activation of the lactoperoxidase system in preservation of unrefrigerated fresh milk (Wang et al., 1987). Other studies have indicated that use of 0.4 mM $H_2O_2$ and extra lactoperoxidase or addition of both lactoperoxidase (370 Enzyme Units/L), KSCN (0.3 mM), and $H_2O_2$ (0.3 mM) are required for optimal mobilisation of the lactoperoxidase system in milk (Siragusa and Johnson, 1989). However, in the latter case, the co-addition only delayed, but did not prevent the growth of, L. monocytogenes in milk stored at 20°C (Siragusa and Johnson, 1989). The keeping quality of milk is known to be better for milk pasteurised at 72°C for 15 seconds than at 80°C for 15 seconds, which has been attributed to the heat shocking of spores at the higher temperature. However, since pasteurisation of milk at 80°C (15 seconds) completely inactivates bovine lactoperoxidase, while the residual lactoperoxidase is ~70% in low-pasteurised milk (72°C, 15 seconds), it has been proposed that the lactoperoxidase system has a role in the shelf-life quality of pasteurised milk, and therefore that pasteurisation at a temperature of 72°C may be a critical factor determining this effect (Barrett et al., 1999).

Addition of glucose with glucose oxidase to produce $H_2O_2$ (see enzymatic reaction in section 4.4) was used to boost the lactoperoxidase system to delay the onset of growth of Salmonella typhimurium in infant formula milk (Earnshaw et al., 1990). Similarly, in cottage cheese inoculated with Pseudomonas fragi, P. fluorescens, E. coli, and S. typhimurium, the addition of glucose and glucose oxidase activated the lactoperoxidase system to kill these organisms that were not detected in the cottage cheese during a 21-day storage period (Earnshaw et al., 1989). Equimolar addition of 25 mM KSCN and $H_2O_2$ as substrates for lactoperoxidase in pasteurised ewe's milk resulted in total inhibition of Aeromonas hydrophila, inoculated at $10^2$ cfu/mL, and reduced the level of psychrotrophs by more than 6 log cfu/g during 48 hours of refrigerated storage of fresh Spanish Villalón cheese (Santos et al., 1995). Other studies have shown that the lactoperoxidase system is not suitable to safeguard the preservation of cheese as activation of the naturally occurring lactoperoxidase in the cheese milk can result in decreased acidity production and prolonged coagulation time of the cheese as a result of inhibition of the lactic acid starter bacteria (Valdez et al., 1988).

An exogenous lactoperoxidase system treatment, comprising bovine lacto-peroxidase (1 $\mu$g/mL), KSCN (5.9 mM), $H_2O_2$ (2.5 mM) exerted antibacterial activity on S. typhimurium and psychrotrophic bacteria on Salmonella inoculated chicken legs in response to the time and temperature extension of the treatment (Wolfson et al., 1994). Maximum growth reduction achieved was a five-fold reduction – but not complete inhibition – of S. typhimurium cfu/g; this was achieved with 15 min. immersion of chicken legs into a 60°C water bath containing the lactoperoxidase system, which is thermostable at this temperature (Wolfson et al., 1994). Compared to lysozyme, the antibacterial spectrum is thus much wider for the lactoperoxidase system because of the lower specificity of the antibacterial mechanism. However, the antibacterial activity of the lactoperoxidase system, especially against Gram-positive organisms, appears strongly dependent on the relative amounts of available substrate, the pH, the medium, and also on the growth phase of the target organisms (Fuglsang et al., 1995). Streptococci appear to be relatively resistant to the antibacterial activity of the lactoperoxidase system compared to other bacteria, and it has been suggested that *Streptococcus* spp. may be able to reduce the oxidation products or repair the damage (Reiter and Härnulv, 1984). As will be discussed in section 4.5 the bacteriocidal activity of the lactoperoxidase system can be enhanced by combinatory strategies. In analogy to the comments given for the effects of lysozyme in food products (section 4.2.2) some more general, quantitative approaches to assess and model the antibacterial efficacy of lactoperoxidase are scarce. At present, it is therefore difficult to predict firmly how efficient the lactoperoxidase system is on specific types of bacteria in dairy foods.

## 4.4    Glucose oxidase and other enzyme systems

Glucose oxidase (EC 1.1.3.4) catalyses the oxidation of $\beta$-D-glucose by $O_2$ producing $\delta$-D-gluconolactone and $H_2O_2$. Since $\delta$-D-gluconolactone hydrolyses spontaneously to D-gluconic acid (or rather, D-gluconate + $H^+$), the net reaction catalysed becomes:

$$O_2 + C_6H_{12}O_6 + H_2O \longrightarrow H_2O_2 + C_6H_{12}O_7$$

Glucose oxidase is produced by fungi of the genera *Penicillium* and *Aspergillus*. *Aspergillus niger* strain NRRL 3 (ATCC 9029) is traditionally the most common source for the commercial production of glucose oxidase as the enzyme is a side-product of gluconic acid production by *A. niger* (Crueger and Crueger, 1990). Glucose oxidase has been employed industrially, notably in the US, since the early 1950s for removal of glucose in eggs prior to spray drying to prevent Maillard browning reactions (Szalkucki, 1993). Furthermore, in conjunction with catalase, glucose oxidase has been used as a flavour-protecting measure in citrus juices via removal of oxygen, but not as a bacteriocidal agent on a commercial scale (Szalkucki, 1993). The potential antibacterial effect of glucose oxidase action has nevertheless received steady research attention. The observed antibacterial action has been widely suggested to be primarily based on the production of $H_2O_2$ (Fuglsang *et al.*, 1995). However, since catalase catalyses the disproportionation of $H_2O_2$ to water and oxygen, the antibacterial activity of glucose oxidase preparations should hence be strongly dependent on the (non)presence of catalase as side activity. Catalase is usually present as an impurity in commercial glucose oxidase preparations, as the coupled removal of $H_2O_2$ is often a prerequisite in non-antibacterial food processing applications of glucose oxidase (Szalkucki, 1993).

Since catalase is one of the fastest enzymes known with a hydrogen peroxide rate constant close to $10^7$ seconds$^{-1}$ mole$^{-1}$, even low levels of catalase can retard the generation of $H_2O_2$ by glucose oxidase preparations. Likewise, in case $H_2O_2$ was the main antibacteriocidal effect, the susceptibility of various microorganisms to inhibition by glucose oxidase should depend on their ability to produce catalase (Fuglsang *et al.*, 1995). However, an evaluation of the data obtained in various systems with commercial glucose oxidase preparations does not confirm these hypotheses. Rather, the data suggest, that especially the decrease in pH caused by the gluconate generation, perhaps coupled with the micro-anaerobic environment generated by the catalysed oxygen removal that may retard obligate aerobes, are more important to the antibacterial activity of glucose oxidase than $H_2O_2$ production (Dobbenie *et al.*, 1995; Dondero *et al.*, 1993). Again, some more thorough quantitative evaluations of the enzyme kinetics versus the antibacterial effects of glucose oxidase with or without catalase would improve our understanding of the mechanisms involved, and presumably allow a more focused approach to employing glucose oxidase as an antibacterial enzyme system.

### 4.4.1    Antibacterial efficiency of glucose oxidase in model systems and real foods

Addition of glucose and a commercial enzyme preparation containing glucose oxidase as well as catalase was shown to suppress significantly the growth of *Pseudomonas fragi*, a common fish spoilage organism, in both nutrient broth and in a fish extract medium inoculated at ambient temperature (26°C) (Yoo and Rand, 1995). Dosage of more than 2.0 Enzyme Units/mL of the glucose oxidase preparation with 16 mg/mL glucose in the fish extract medium lowered the pH to approximately pH 4 due to gluconic acid production (Yoo and Rand, 1995). Similarly, the growth of *Pseudomonas fluorescens* on shrimp kept in a glucose oxidase-glucose solution has been reported to be inhibited (Kantt *et al.*, 1993). In both of the cited studies the glucose oxidase was a commercial preparation containing catalase activity (Kantt *et al.*, 1993; Yoo and Rand, 1995).

In experiments with liquid whole egg, co-addition of 5 Enzyme Units/mL glucose oxidase and 5 mg/mL glucose killed *Salmonella enteritidis*, *Micrococcus luteus*, and *Bacillus cereus* inoculated at $10^3$ cfu/mL after five days of storage of the eggs at 7°C (Dobbenie *et al.*, 1995). The addition also exerted a weak bacteriostatic effect on *Pseudomonas fluorescens* (Dobbenie *et al.*, 1995); in that study the glucose oxidase preparation was also a commercial preparation from *A. niger* and the preparation was stated to contain a maximum of 1% catalase impurity but a statement of the exact catalase activity content was lacking, however (Dobbenie *et al.*, 1995). If the antibacterial mechanism of glucose oxidase is based on $H_2O_2$ production, the observed antibacterial efficiency of the glucose oxidase preparations containing catalase are surprising considering that the catalase removes the $H_2O_2$. The available data therefore support the proposition that the lowering of pH achieved from gluconate production may in fact be the main antibacterial principle of the glucose oxidase in these tests. The preservative potential of glucose oxidase has also been tested on poultry products, legs and chicken breasts, but in these products no convincing antibacterial effects of the glucose oxidase treatments were found (Frels *et al.*, 1984; Jeong *et al.*, 1992).

### 4.4.2    Other enzyme systems

Extracellular polysaccharides of bacteria are composed of a number of different homo- and heteropolysaccharides that are of prime importance in the attachment of bacteria to surfaces and in the formation of bacterial biofilms. Enzyme catalysed removal of biofilms has been studied very little and only a few reports are available. A distinction can be made between the enzymatic release of microorganisms from biofilms and the bacteriocidal activity of different enzymes (Brisou, 1995). Due to the heterogeneity of the extracellular polysaccharides, an enzyme cocktail comprising several different enzyme activities appears necessary for sufficient removal and killing of bacterial biofilms. Glucose oxidase combined with lactoperoxidase was shown to exert bacteriocidal activity on a mixture of Gram-positive and Gram-negative biofilm bacteria, but did not release the biofilm from the model surfaces (Johansen *et al.*, 1997). In contrast, a multicomponent polysaccharide hydrolysing enzyme preparation (comprising pectinase, arabinase, cellulase, *β*-glucanase, and xylanase activities) released bacterial biofilm from steel and polypropylene model surfaces but did not kill the bacteria in the biofilm. The combination of the oxidoreductases and the polysaccharide hydrolysing enzyme preparation, caused both removal and a bacteriocidal effect on the biofilms (Johansen *et al.*, 1997). At present, the identity of the polysaccharide hydrolysing enzymes that are most important for the enzymatic degradation of biofilms is largely unknown.

## 4.5   Combining antimicrobial enzymes with other preservation techniques

The concept of combining several factors to enhance microbiological safety of foods was advanced by Leistner several years ago (Leistner and Gorris, 1995). The strategy of designing a series of hurdles – or rather to combine several factors to obtain synergistic effects – has also proved fruitful in improving the efficiency of enzymes as antibacterial food preservatives. In this section, particular focus will be directed towards the efforts aimed at improving the antibacterial potency of lysozyme; data on boosting the activity of lactoperoxidase will also be briefly summarised.

### 4.5.1   Factors that improve the efficiency of lysozyme

Apart from the effects of neat lysozyme on *Cl. tyrobutyricum* in cheese and on undesirable lactic acid bacteria in wines, as discussed above, it has generally been found that the antibacterial efficacy of lysozyme requires enhancement. In accordance with the notion that peptidoglycan is more accessible to lysozyme catalysed degradation in Gram-positive bacteria, the reported food applications all concern activity of lysozyme against Gram-positive bacteria. Since the antibacterial activity of lysozyme thus mainly targets a narrow bacterial spectrum, native lysozyme works efficiently only in products where spoilage is due to a few, specific, Gram-positive organisms or in cases where extra safeguards are required to control specific Gram-positive pathogens such as, e.g., *L. monocytogenes* or *Cl. botulinum*. In contrast, the oxidoreductase systems, including the lactoperoxidase and glucose oxidase enzyme systems, require availability of specific substrates for the generation of antibacterial reaction products.

The combination of lysozyme with other substances notably with EDTA, glycine, salt (NaCl), or other preservatives such as sorbate or ethanol have shown promise (Proctor and Cunningham, 1988). Use of lysozyme together with other antimicrobial enzymes or in combination with physico-chemical stressing of the cells, such as decreased pH and temperature, also enhance the bacteriocidal effects of lysozyme (Johansen et al., 1994; Proctor and Cunningham, 1988). Several approaches have been attempted in order to render hen egg white lysozyme more active against Gram-negative bacteria. EDTA addition, in particular, has been claimed – and widely investigated – to increase the permeability of the outer membrane, and thereby increase the accessibility of lysozyme to the peptido-glycan of Gram-negative organisms (Proctor and Cunningham, 1988). The exact mechanism by which EDTA may destabilise the outer lipopolysaccharide layer and perturb the membrane has not been fully clarified, however.

With respect to efficacy in food products, the co-addition of EDTA (0.02% by weight) with lysozyme (50 $\mu$g/mL) was shown to significantly inhibit growth of shrimp microflora in model systems comprising 2% by weight of shrimp homogenate (Chander and Lewis, 1980). Apparently EDTA did not induce bacteriocidal effects, but only inhibited the multiplication of the bacterial flora (Chander and Lewis, 1980). Combination of lysozyme with EDTA also improved the antibacterial activity of lysozyme on inoculated populations of L. monocytogenes Scott A in freshly prepared vegetable products stored at 5°C (Table 4.2) (Hughey et al., 1989). Co-addition of glycine (e.g. 0.1% by weight) and/or lysine (e.g. 0.1% by weight) with lysozyme have also been found to result in markedly enhanced potency of lysozyme in different product trials, but mainly against Gram-positive bacteria (Proctor and Cunningham, 1988). The combination of lysozyme with polyphosphates did not improve the antibacterial activity of lysozyme on L. monocytogenes growth in nutrient broth (tryptone soya broth), but the addition of lipase, at the same incubation conditions as with polyphosphates, was found to significantly enhance the bacteriocidal effect of lysozyme (Liberti et al., 1996). In milk, addition of lysozyme together with a bacteriocin (acidocin CH5) from Lactobacillus acidophilus produced a synergistic inhibitory effect against Lactobaccillus delbrueckii subsp lactis used as an indicator organism as the inhibition obtained was significantly larger than that obtained with either of the components alone (Chumchalová et al., 1998). The latter results indicate that the combination of lysozyme with novel bacteriocins may show promise as new, 'natural' preservation principles. More research is clearly warranted on the combined antibacterial efficacies of lysozyme and bacteriocins in real food systems. A more quantitative as well as detailed mechanistic insight into the enhancement of the antibacterial effects of lysozyme by other additives would improve our foundation for rationally designing potent antibacterial cocktails comprising lysozyme as a main preservation principle.

**Table 4.2**    Examples of EDTA enhancement of hen egg white lysozyme's antibacterial effect against *Listeria monocytogenes* Scott A in food products. Data are given as log cfu/ g product (adapted from Hughey *et al.*, 1989). All samples, including the control samples were inoculated with $10^4$/g *L. monocytogenes*. Controls had no lysozyme or EDTA added[1]

| Food system and conditions | Control | Lysozyme (100 mg/kg) | Lysozyme (100 mg/kg) + EDTA (25 mM)[2] |
|---|---|---|---|
| Shredded cabbage Stored in closed containers for 20 days at 5 °C | 6.2 | 4.8 | 1.4 |
| Shredded lettuce Stored in closed containers for 5 days at 5 °C | 4.8 | 3.7 | 1.0 |
| Sausage ('bratwurst') Stored in closed containers for 20 days at 5 °C | 7.0 | 6.8 | 3.7 |

[1] Growth of *L. monocytogenes* in controls with EDTA added alone was similar to that in controls with no EDTA or lysozyme additions.
[2] In sausages only 5 mM EDTA was added.

Taken together, the available data confirm that the bacteriolytic activity of hen egg white lysozyme differs in various food systems and against different bacteria and that various additives can boost the efficiency of lysozyme addition through additive or synergistic effects. The available reports on trials in real foods as compared to the many studies done with nutrient broths or reaction media (not reviewed here), also indicate that the efficiency of lysozyme usually decreases in multi-component food systems.

As mentioned above, partial thermal inactivation of hen egg white lysozyme, where the lysozyme retains ~50% of its native activity, confers potent bacteriocidal effects of this lysozyme against Gram-negative as well as Gram-positive bacteria in nutrient broth systems (Ibrahim *et al.*, 1996a and b). Such partially denatured lysozyme was shown to exhibit enhanced interaction with the bacterial membranes and was also demonstrated to result in increased membrane permeabilisation. The reported preservative efficacy of ultrasonic treatment combined with lysozyme may be a result of the same bactericidal mechanism (Pszczola, 2002). Addition of sucrose and NaCl was found to suppress the enhanced bacteriocidal action of partially denatured lysozyme against *Escherichia coli*, while glycine addition produced a synergistic effect with this partially denatured enzyme (but not with native lysozyme) to inhibit *E. coli* – the synergistic effect of glycine penetrated even in the presence of antagonistic levels of NaCl and sucrose (Ibrahim *et al.*, 1996c). Synthesised lysozyme conjugates, where lysozyme had been modified by the covalent attachment of caffeic acid and cinnamic acid, respectively, have been demonstrated to result in reduced lytic activity of lysozyme and reduced inhibitory efficacy against

*Staphylococcus aureus* (Bernkop-Schnürch *et al.*, 1998). In contrast, especially the lysozyme-caffeic acid conjugates were found to exhibit strongly improved inhibitory action on the growth of *E. coli* (Bernkop-Schnürch *et al.*, 1998)

### 4.5.2   Factors that influence the efficiency of the lactoperoxidase system

Addition of nisin together with lactoperoxidase and glucose/glucose-oxidase to pre-sterilised milk inoculated with *L. monocytogenes* was demonstrated to exert a pronounced synergistic and lasting bacteriocidal effect on *L. monocytogenes* as no cells were detected in the inoculated milk during 15 days of incubation of the milk at 25°C (Boussel *et al.*, 2000). Likewise, designed additions of nisin and bacteriocin-producing lactic acid bacteria in conjunction with activation of the lactoperoxidase system gave a more pronounced decrease of *L. monocytogenes* counts in skim milk and raw milk than those observed for the activated lactoperoxidase system alone (Zapico *et al.*, 1998; Rodriguez *et al.*, 1997). Addition of monolaurin and concomitant activation of the lactoperoxidase system resulted in improved growth inhibition of foodborne pathogens including *Escherichia coli* 0157:H7 and *Staphylococcus aureus* by lactoperoxidase in milk (McLay *et al.*, 1998).

As already highlighted above, pasteurisation of milk at 72°C for 15 seconds versus at 80°C for 15 seconds gave more residual lactoperoxidase activity in milk, suggesting that the lactoperoxidase system may be active in ensuring a better keeping quality of low-pasteurised milk as compared to milk pasteurised at higher temperatures (Barrett *et al.*, 1999). In contrast, a high hydrostatic pressure treatment of milk combined with lactoperoxidase addition to milk was shown to result in an improved bacteriocidal effect on *Escherichia coli* strains and *Listeria innocua* in milk (Garcia-Graells *et al.*, 2000).

## 4.6   Future trends

As with other food-processing aids and additives, the application of enzymes in food manufacture is obviously limited by safety and toxicology requirements and therefore strongly regulated by legislation. It is beyond the scope of this chapter to discuss the general legal aspects of the use of enzymes in production of foods and beverages but a few key points deserve mention: In the United States, several enzyme preparations have GRAS status, where GRAS designates *Generally Recognized As Safe*. The GRAS enzyme preparations may be used as catalysts in several different food and beverage processes. European food legislation on enzyme applications, however, differentiates between the use of enzymes as processing aids and as food additives, respectively (AMFEP 2001; Directive 95/2/EC). When enzymes are employed as processing aids it implies that the added enzymes do not exert any activity nor any technological function in the final product. Each approval concerns the use of a certain type of enzyme preparation for one (or more) specific type of application (AMFEP, 2001).

Recently, the European Commission proposed to clarify this legislation by laying down specific provisions with respect to the use of enzymes as food additives and processing aids (Commission of the European Communities, 2000 and 2002). Despite this proposal and other recent harmonisation efforts at the EU level, there is at present no harmonised EU legislation on the use of enzymes as processing aids in food and beverage manufacture. Notable differences in the legislation on application of enzymes thus exist at the National levels in Europe and between the US and Europe. However, even though some differences in enzyme approvals remain at the national levels in Europe, a large number of enzyme preparations have obtained general approval for use as food processing aids with each enzyme preparation being allowed for use in specific types of processes (AMFEP, 2001).

In the EU, lysozyme from hen egg white is the only enzyme that has status as a food additive and hence has an E-number, E 1105 (Directive 95/2/EC). As a food additive, lysozyme has been permitted for use since 1995 as a preservative agent in ripened cheeses to prevent 'gas blowing' from growth of *Clostridium tyrobutyricum* (Directive 95/2/EC). Recently, the Commission proposed also that the addition of lysozyme to wine to prevent growth of lactic acid bacteria should be included as an authorised use of lysozyme (E 1150) (Commission of the European Communities, 2002).

Food quality and safety are an increasingly important concern. In particular, the apparent rise in cases of foodborne illness and the scale of outbreaks of foodborne illness underline the need to ensure that the available food preservation principles and antibacterial safeguards are employed optimally in all steps of food manufacture. The trend in consumption and availability of more industrially processed food, including meals manufactured on a larger scale in catering businesses and restaurants, only strengthens the need for careful selection and rational development of efficient food preservation methods. Paradoxically, consumers demand more 'natural' and 'minimally processed' foods, that are able to remain 'fresh' for extended periods of time! As a result there is great interest in naturally produced antimicrobial agents in both industry and academia.

Enzymes represent one type of natural food preservative agent. If employed as antibacterial agents, enzymes may most likely be used as extra safeguards in hurdle approaches, to preserve foods effectively. These applications will involve selected, optimised combinations of the enzyme and additional additives, e.g., bacteriocins, and specific treatments and combinations of physicochemical parameters that impart the highest antibacterial potency of the combination. The future challenges will involve continued research on the efficacy of rational combinations of new food preservative agents against spoilage and pathogenic bacteria in foods. Notably, a more quantitative approach, rather than the present empirical avenue, is warranted in the future investigations of enzyme-based food-preservation principles.

## 4.7    Sources of further information and advice

Many new results are currently achieved in research laboratories all over the world. Although it is advisable to keep an eye on new patents in the field, monitoring of the research literature is especially recommended. As is obvious from the reference list to this chapter, data on the efficacy of novel food preservatives are published in many different scientific journals, and it is recommended to attempt to evaluate all the available information critically and carefully. Additional information on the antibacterial mechanism of lysozyme and lactoperoxidase can be found in:

Natural Food Antimicrobial Systems (Naidu, N, ed) Woodhead Publishers, 2000
Natural Antimicrobial Systems and Food Preservation (V.M. Dillon, R.G Board, eds) CAB Intl. 1994

While a broader view on minimal processing of foods can be found in:

Minimal Processing Technologies in the Food Industry (Ohlsson T and Bengtsson N, eds) Woodhead Publishing Ltd (2002).

## 4.8    References

AKASHI A, OONO A (1972), 'The preservative effect of egg-white lysozyme on non-packaged kamaboko' [English abstract], *J Agric Chem Sci Japan*, 46, 177–83.
AMFEP (Association of Manufacturers of Fermentation Enzyme Products) (2001), 'Regulatory aspects of microbial food enzymes': Website: *http://www.amfep.org*. List of enzymes: http://www.amfep.org/enzymes/list01.html, Bruxelles, Belgium.
BARRETT N E, GRANDISON A S, LEWIS M J (1999), 'Contribution of the lactoperoxidase system to the keeping quality of pasteurised milk', *J Dairy Res*, 66, 73–80.
BERNKOP-SCHNÜRCH A, KRIST S, VEHABOVI M, VALENTA C (1998), 'Synthesis and evaluation of lysozyme derivatives exhibiting an enhanced antimicrobial action', *Eur J Pharmaceutical Sci*, 6, 301–6.
BESTER B H, LOMBARD S H (1990), 'Influence of lysozyme on selected bacteria associated with Gouda cheese', *Food Prot*, 53, 306–11.
BEUKES M, BIERBAUM G, SAHL H-G, HASTINGS J W (2000), 'Purification and particle characterization of a murein hydrolase, Millericin B, produced by *Streptomyces milleri* NMSCC 061', *Appl Environ Microbiol*, 66, 23–8.
BIERBAUM G, SAHL H G (1987), 'Autolytic system of *Staphylococcus simulans*: Influence of cationic peptides on activity of N-acetyl-L-alanine amidase', *J Bacteriol*, 169, 5452–8.
BJÖRCK L, CLAESSON O, SCHULTHESS W (1979), 'The lactoperoxidase/thiocyanate/ hydrogenperoxide system as a temporary preservative for raw milk in developing countries', *Milchwiss*, 34, 726–9.
BOUSSOUEL N, MATHIEU F, REVOL-JUNELLES A-M, MILLIÈRE J-B (2000), 'Effects of combinations of lactoperoxidase system and nisin on the behaviour of Listeria monocytogenes ATCC 15313 in skim milk', *Int J Food Microbiol*, 61, 169–75.

BRISOU J F (1995), 'Biofilms. Methods for enzymatic release of microorganisms', CRC Press Inc., Boca Raton FL.

BRÖNNEKE V, FIEDLER F (1994), 'Production of bacteriolytic enzymes by *Streptomyces globisporus* regulated by exogenours bacterial cell walls', *Appl Environ Microbiol*, 60, 785–91.

BUGG T D H (1999), 'Comprehensive Natural Products Chemistry vol 3.' (Pinto M, ed.), pp. 241–94, Elsevier Sc. Ltd., Oxford.

CARMINATI D, CARINI S (1989), 'Antimicrobial activity of lysozyme against *Listeria monocytogenes* in milk', *Microbiologie-Aliments-Nutrition,* 7, 49–56.

CHANDLER R, LEWIS N P (1980), 'Effect of Iysozyme and sodium EDTA on shrimp microflora', *Eur J Appl Microbiol Biotechnol*, 10, 253–58.

CHENG X, ZHANG X, PFLUGRATH J W, STUDIER F W (1994), 'The Structure of Bacteriophage T7 Lysozyme, a Zinc Amidase and an Inhibitor of T7 RNA Polymerase', *Proc Natl Acad Sci USA*, 91, 4034–8.

CHUMCHALOVÁ J, JOSEPHSEN J, PLOCKOVÁ M (1998), 'The antimicrobial activity of acidocin CH5 in MRS broth and milk with added NaCl, $NaNO_3$, and lysozyme', *Intl J Food Microbiol*, 43, 33–8.

COMMISSION OF THE EUROPEAN COMMUNITIES (2000), 'White Paper on Food Safety' (*http://europa.eu.int/comm/dgs/health_consumer/library/pub/pub06_en.pdf* )

COMMISSION OF THE EUROPEAN COMMUNITIES (2002), 'Proposal for a Directive of the European Parliament and of the Council amending Directive 95/2/EC on food additives other than colours and sweeteners'. (*http://europa.eu.int/comm./food/fs/ sfp/addit_flavor/additives/proposal_2002_0662_en.pdf*)

CRUEGER A, CRUEGER W (1990), 'Glucose transforming enzymes' In: *Microbial Enzymes and Biotechnology* 2nd edition, pp. 178–226, Fogarty W M and Kelly C T, eds, Elsevier Applied Science, London and New York.

DAESCHEL M A, PENNER M H (1992), 'Hydrogen peroxide, lactoperoxidase systems, and reuterin'. In: *Food Biopreservatives of Microbial Origin*, pp. 207–57, Bibek R and Daeschel M, eds, CRC Press, London.

DE KIMPE S J, KENGATHARAN M, THIEMERMANN C, VANE J R (1995), 'The cell wall components peptidoglycan and lipoteichoic acid from *Staphylococcus aureus* act in synergy to cause shock and multiple organ failure', *Proc Natl Acad Sci USA*, 92, 10359–63.

DIRECTIVE 95/2/EC (1995), 'European Parliament and Council Directive 95/2/EC of 20 February 1995 on Food additives other than colours and sweeteners', as amended by Directives 96/85/EC, 98/72/EC and 2001/5/EC (*http://europa.eu.int/eur-lex/en/ consleg/pdf/1995/en_1995L0002_do_001.pdf*)

DOBBENIE D, UYTTENDAELE M, DEBEVERE J (1995), 'Antibacterial activity of the glucose oxidase/glucose system in liquid whole egg', *J Food Prot*, 58, 273–9.

DONDERO M, EGANA W, TARKY W, CIFUENTES A, TORRES J A (1993), 'Glucose oxidase/ catalase improves preservation of shrimp (*Heterocarpus reedi*), *J Food Sci*, 58, 774–9.

EARNSHAW R G, BANKS J G, DEFRISE D, FRANCOTTE C (1989), 'The preservation of cottage cheese by an activated lactoperoxidase system', *Food Microbiol*, 6, 285–8.

EARNSHAW R G, BANKS J G, FRANCOTTE C, DEFRISE D (1990), 'Inhibition of *Salmonella typhimurium* and *Escherichia coli* in an infant milk formula by an activated lactoperoxidase system', *J Food Prot*, 53, 170–2.

EKSTRAND B (1994), 'Lactoperoxidase and lactoferrin'. In: *Natural Antimicrobial Systems and Food Preservation*, pp. 15–63, Dillon V M and Board R G, eds, CAB

International, Wallingford, UK.

FERNÁNDEZ P S, PECK M W (1999), 'A Predictive Model That Describes the Effect of Prolonged Heating at 70 to 90°C and Subsequent Incubation at Refrigeration Temperatures on growth from Spores and Toxigenesis by Nonproteolytic *Clostridium botulinum* in the Presence of Lysozyme', *Appl Environ Microbiol*, 65, 3449–57.

FRELS J M, SAMUELSON K J, FRONING G W, RUPNOW J H (1984), 'Evaluation of glucose oxidase-catalase treatment to improve the microbiological quality of poultry meat', *Poultry Sci*, 63, 841–3.

FUGLSANG C C, JOHANSEN C, CHRISTGAU S, ADLER-NISSEN J (1995), 'Antimicrobial enzymes: Applications and future potential in the food industry', *Trends Food Sci Technol*, 6, 390–6.

GAO Y C, ZHANG G, KRENTZ S, DARIUS S, POWER J, LAGARDE G (2002), 'Inhibition of spoilage lactic acid bacteria by lysozyme during wine alcoholic fermentation', *Austr J Grape & Wine Res*, 8, 76–83.

GARCIA-GRAELLS C, VALCKX C, MICHIELS C W (2000), 'Inactivation of *Escherichia coli* and *Listeria innocua* in Milk by Combined Treatment with High Hydrostatic Pressure and the Lactoperoxidase System', *Appl Environ Microbiol*, 66, 4173–9.

GERBAUX V, VILLA A, MONARNY C, BERTRAND A (1997), 'Use of lysozyme to inhibit malolactic fermentation and to stabilize wine after malolactic fermentation', *Am J Enol Vitic*, 48, 49–54.

GODFREY T (2003), 'The industrial enzymes market: A summary', web article located Jan 08 2003 at: *http://www.biocatalysts.com/frames/biocatalysts_01.html*

HARDING R L, HENSHAW J, TILLING J, BUGG T D H (2002), 'Thioester analogues of peptidoglycan fragment MurNAc-L-Ala-gamma-D-Glu as substrates for peptidoglycan hydrolase MurNac-L-Ala amidase', *J Chem Soc Perkin Trans*, 1, 1714–22.

HAYASHI K, KASUMI T, KUBO N, TSUMURA N (1981), 'Purification and characterization of the lytic enzyme produced by *Streptomyces rutgersensis* H-46', *Agric Biol Chem*, 45, 2289–300.

HUGHEY V L, WILGER P A, JOHNSON E A (1989), 'Antibacterial activity of hen egg white lysozyme against *Listeria monocytogenes* Scott A in foods', *Appl Environ Microbiol*, 55, 631–8.

IBRAHIM H R, HIGASHIGUCHI S, JUNEJA L R, KIM M, YAMAMOTO T (1996a) 'A structural phase of heat-denatured lysozyme with novel antimicrobial action', *J Agric Food Chem*, 44, 1416–23.

IBRAHIM H R, HIGASHIGUCHI S, KOKETSU M, JUNEJA L R, KIM M, YAMAMOTO T, SUGIMOTO Y, AOKI T (1996b), 'Partially unfolded lysozyme at neutral pH agglutinates and kills Gram-negative and Gram-positive bacteria through membrane damage mechanism', *J Agric Food Chem*, 44, 3799–806.

IBRAHIM H R, HIGASHIGUCHI S, SUGIMOTO Y, AOKI T (1996c), 'Antimicrobial synergism of partially-denatured lysozyme with glycine: Effect of sucrose and sodium chloride', *Food Res Intl*, 29, 771–7.

JEONG D K, HARRISON M A, FRANK J F, WICKER L (1992), 'Trials on the antibacterial effects of glucose oxidase on chicken breast skin and muscle', *J Food Safety*, 13, 43–9.

JOHANSEN C, GRAM L, MEYER A S (1994), 'The combined inhibitory effect of lysozyme and low pH on growth of *Listeria monocytogenes*', *J Food Prot*, 57, 561–6.

JOHANSEN C, FALHOLT P, GRAM L (1997), 'Enzymatic removal and disinfection of bacterial biofilms', *Appl Environ Microbiol*, 63, 3724–8.

JOLLÉS P, JOLLÉS J (1984), 'What's new in lysozyme research?', *Mol Cell Biochem*, 63, 165–89.

JOLLÉS J, JAUREQUI-ADELL J, BERNIER I, JOLLÉS P (1963), 'The chemical structure of hen's egg white lysozyme: the detailed study', *Biochim Biophys Acta*, 78, 668–89.

KANTT C A, BOUZAS J, DONDERO M, TORRES J A (1993), 'Glucose oxidase/catalase solution for on board control of shrimp microbial spoilage: Model studies, *J Food Sci*, 58, 104–7.

KIHM D J, LEYER G J, GIL-HWAN A, JOHNSON E A (1994), 'Sensitization of heat-treated *Listeria monocytogenes* to added lysozyme in milk', *Appl & Environ Microbiol*, 60, 3854–61.

LEISTNER L, GORRIS L G M (1995), 'Food preservation by hurdle technology', *Trends Food Sci Technol*, 6, 41–6.

LIBERTI R, FRANCIOSA G, GIANFRANCESCHI M, AURELI P (1996), 'Effect of combined lysozyme and lipase treatment on the survival of *Listeria monocytogenes*', *Intl J Food Microbiol*, 32, 235–42.

LIU S-T, SUGIMOTO T, AZAKAMI H, KATO A (2000), 'Lipophilization of lysozyme by short and middle chain fatty acids', *J Agric Food Chem*, 48, 265–9.

LOESSNER M J, MAIER S K, DAUBEK-PUZA H, WENDLINGER G, SCHERER S (1997), 'Three Bacillus cereus bacteriophage endolysins are unrelated but reveal high homology to cell wall hydrolases from different bacilli', *J Bacteriol*, 179, 2845–51.

MCLAY J C, KENNEDY M J, O'ROURKE A-L, ELLIOT R M, SIMMONDS R S (2002), 'Inhibition of bacterial foodborne pathogens by the lactoperoxidase system in combination with monolaurin', *Int J Food Microbiol*, 73, 1–9.

PELLEGRINI A, THOMAS U, VON FELLENBERG R, WILD P (1992), 'Bactericidal activities of lysozyme and aprotinin against Gram-negative and Gram-positive bacteria related to their basic character', *J Appl Bacteriol*, 72, 180–7.

PITOTTI A, ZIRONI R, BO A, AMATI A (1991), 'Possible application of lysozyme in wine technology', *Med Faculteit Landb. Rijksuniv. Gent,* 56, 1697–9.

PROCTOR V A, CUNNINGHAM F E (1988), 'The chemistry of lysozyme and its use as a food preservative and a pharmaceutical', *Crit Rev Food Sci Nutr*, 26, 359–95.

PSZCZOLA, D E (2002), 'Antimicrobials: Setting up additional hurdles to ensure food safety', *Food Technol*, 56, 99–107.

REITER B, HÄRNULV G (1984), 'Lactoperoxidase antibacterial system: Natural occurrence, biological functions, and practical applications', *J Food Prot*, 47, 724–32.

RODRIGUEZ E, TOMILLO J, NUÑEZ M, MEDINA M (1997), 'Combined effect of bacteriocin-producing lactic acid bacteria and lactoperoxidase system activation on *Listeria monocytogenes* in refrigerated raw milk', *J Appl Microbiol*, 83, 389–95.

SANTOS J A, LÓPEZ-DÍAZ T M, GARCÍA-FERNÁNDEZ M C, GARCÍA-LÓPEZ M L, OTERO A (1995), 'Antibacterial effect of the lactoperoxidase system against *Aeromonas hydrophila* and psychrotrophs during the manufacturing of the Spanish sheep fresh cheese Villalón', *Milchwiss*, 50, 690–2.

SCHLEIFER K H, KANDLER O (1972), 'Peptidoglycan types of bacterial cell walls and their taxonomic implications', *Bacteriol Rev*, 36, 407–77.

SIRAGUSA G R, JOHNSON M G (1989), 'Inhibition of *Listeria monocytogenes* growth by the lactoperoxidase-thiocyanate-$H_2O_2$ antimicrobial system', *Appl Environ Microbiol*, 55, 2802–5.

SZALKUCKI T (1993), 'Applications of oxidoreductases' in: *Enzymes in food processing* 3rd edn (Nagodawithana T, Reed G, eds), pp. 279–91, Academic Press Inc., San Diego, California.

TOUCH V, HAYAKAWA S, FUKUDA K, ARATANI Y, SUN Y (2003), 'Preparation of antimicrobial reduced lysozyme compatible in food applications', *J Agric Food Chem*, 51, 5154–61.

TRANTER H S (1994), 'Lysozyme, ovotransferrin and avidin' in: *Natural Antimicrobial Systems and Food Preservation* (Dillon V M, Board R G, eds), 65–97, CAB International, Wallingford, UK.

VALDEZ G F, DE BIBI W, BACHMANN M R (1988), 'Antibacterial effect of the lactoperoxidase/thiocyanate/hydrogen peroxide (LP) system on the activity of thermophilic starter cultures', *Milchwiss*, 43, 350–2.

WANG P, LIN C, WU K, LU Y (1987), 'Preservation of fresh milk by its natural lactoperoxidase system', *Sci Agric Sin*, 20, 76–81.

WANG C, SHELEF L A (1992), 'Behaviour of *Listeria monocytogenes* and the spoilage microflora in fresh cod fish treated with lysozyme and EDTA', *Food Microbiol*, 9, 207–13.

WASSERFALL F, TEUBER M (1979), 'Action of egg white lysozyme on *Clostridium tyrobutyricum*', *Appl Environ Microbiol*, 38, 197–201.

WECKE J, LAHAV M, GINSBURG I, GIESBRECHT P (1982), 'Cell wall degradation of *Staphylococcus aureus* by lysozyme, *Arch Microbiol*, 131, 116–23.

WIGLEY R C (1996), 'Cheese and whey' in: *Industrial Enzymology* 2nd edn, pp. 143–5, T Godfrey and S West eds, Macmillan Press Ltd, London UK.

WOLFSON L M, SUMNER S S, FRONING G W (1994), 'Effects of the lactoperoxidase system to inhibit *Salmonella typhimurium* on poultry', *J Food Safety*, 14, 53–62.

YOO W, RAND A G (1995), 'Antibacterial effect of glucose oxidase on growth of *Pseudomonas fragi* as related to pH', *J Food Sci*, 60 (4), 868–71.

ZAPICO P, MEDINA M, GAYA P, NUÑEZ M (1998), 'Synergistic effect of nisin and the lactoperoxidase system on *Listeria monocytogenes* in skim milk', *Int J Food Microbiol*, 40, 35–42.

ZIMMER M, VUKOV N, SCHERER S, LOESSNER M J (2002), 'The murein hydrolase of the Bacteriophage $\phi$3626 dual lysis system is active against all tested *Clostridium perfringens* strains', *Appl Environ Microbiol*, 68, 5311–17.

# 5

# Combining natural antimicrobial systems with other preservation techniques: the case of meat

**P. Paulsen and F.J.M. Smulders, University of Veterinary Medicine Vienna, Austria**

## 5.1 Introduction

In this chapter, 'natural antimicrobial systems' are defined primarily as agents which are natural meat constituents (Naidu, 2000), especially 'acid- antimicrobials' (organic acids), and compounds produced by (meatborne) bacteria (probiotics, nisin, pediocin, reuterin, sakacins). Organic acids will be discussed in detail (largely based on papers by Smulders, 1995, and Smulders and Greer, 1998), focusing on fresh red meat (carcasses and cuts), as for both most accurate scientific data and practical experience exist. Other decontamination or preservation agents and other commodities will be reviewed in brief.

'Spoilage' is a state of a particular food in which this food is offensive to consumers' senses. This is often caused by metabolites of contaminant bacteria. The preferred substrate, low molecular carbohydrates, are not necessarily degraded into spoilage relevant compounds, but could just lower the pH. However, carbohydrates are present only in low concentrations in meat, while the main constituents of meat are proteins and other nitrogenous compounds (Lawrie, 1998). These are broken down into amino acids, amines, esters, thiols and finally ammonia and sulphur hydrogen. This holds especially true when meat is totally carbohydrate depleted (DFD condition of beef), where the onset of spoilage is more rapid than that of normal pH meat. Nychas *et al.* (1998) provide a detailed view on the physico-chemical changes associated with bacterial growth in meat. With the exception of 'bone taint', as reviewed by James *et al.* (1997), microbial meat spoilage is a surface phenomenon, the risk of which increases with the increase of surface:volume ratio during cutting and

**Table 5.1**  Meatborne pathogenic and spoilage microorganisms (selected after Jay, 1996) and their growth requirements (after ICMSF, 1996; James *et al.*, 1997; Upmann *et al.*, 2000)

| Microorganism | S/P | min. Temp. | pH Range | Atmosphere |
|---|---|---|---|---|
| *Aeromonas* sp. | P | 0 to 4 | 5.5 to 9 | f |
| *Bacillus cereus* | P | 4 | 4.3 to 9.3 | f |
| *Brochothrix th.* | S | 0 | 4.6 to 9.0 | f |
| *Campylobacter jej.* | P | 32 | 4.9 to 8.0 | m |
| *Clostridium* sp. | P | 3.3 to 10 | 4.5 to 8.5 | a |
| *Escherichia* (path.) | P | 7 to 8 | 4.4 to 8.5 | f |
| *Listeria monocytogenes* | P | −0.4 | 5 to 9 | f |
| *Pseudomonas* | S | −0.5 | 5 to 8.5 | s |
| *Salmonella* | P | 5.2 to 7 | 4 to 8 | f |
| *Staphylococcus* | P | 6.7 | 4 to 9.8 | f |
| *Yersinia* | P | 0 | 4.5 to 9 | f |

f . . . facultative anaerobic, m . . . micro-aerophilic, a . . . anaerobic, s . . . strictly aerobic

mincing. The contaminating flora is derived from various sources (see below). Pathogenic bacteria are usually present in lower numbers and uneven distribution (ICMSF, 1996, 1998, Mead and Hinton, 1996, Upmann *et al.*, 2000; see Table 5.1).

The gross composition in terms of protein, mineral and water content (Lawrie, 1998) makes meat an ideal nutrient for many organisms. However, the effective availability of these nutrients is limited, namely by (a) anatomical/ histological barriers, keeping bacteria from deep tissues, (b) antibacterial activities in residual blood, (c) the fact that the preferred low molecular substrates for growth of microbes on the surfaces of meat are limited by the diffusion of the substrates from the core to the surface. Surface desiccation during the chilling process depletes bacteria of water (ICMSF, 1998; Upmann *et al.*, 2000). These limitations make meat an 'ecological niche' (Labadie, 1999). Hence, some microbial species are specialised on meat, such as *Pseudomonas fragi*, *Brochothrix thermosphacta* (Labadie, 1999). Pathogenic bacteria closely linked to meat are, e.g., *Yersinia* in pig tonsils (Schiemann, 1989).

## 5.2  Microbial contamination of meat

The preservation techniques discussed in this chapter are intended either to destroy, remove or to inhibit microbes attached to surfaces of meat and meat products. Therefore, microbial contamination of meat is reviewed in brief (see also Smulders, 1987, 1995; ICMSF, 1998; Upmann *et al.*, 2000; Borch and Arinder, 2002), by addressing four distinct factors: 'material' (i.e., the animal); 'man' (i.e., workers in the meat industry); 'machine' (i.e., equipment used) and 'method' (i.e., the slaughter, chilling and cutting process).

### 5.2.1   The live aminal

Muscle tissue of healthy animals is considered essentially sterile, with the exception of lymph nodes (Romans *et al.*, 1994). However, all meat-producing animals harbour large numbers of various microorganisms on their surfaces exposed to the environment, i.e., skin/fleece, hooves, and mucosal membranes of the digestory and respiratory tracts, with relatively high microbial concentrations of $10^6$cfu/cm$^2$ skin or g faeces, respectively. Pathogenic bacteria excreted in stables may be ingested orally and so reinfection of animals may occur, namely the colonisation of the guts of very young animals with immature gut flora. Use of contaminated feedstuff has been addressed as an important factor, transportation of the animal, insufficient disinfection of transportation vehicles and extended lairage time at the slaughterhouse allow excretion of pathogenic bacteria, and psychogenic stress may release microbes arrested in hepatic mesenteric lymph nodes. Both factors have been addressed as a source of cross-infections (Smulders, 1995).

Removing the bacterial load from the outer as well as the mucosal surfaces of the live animal would be a promising idea. To date, showering of pigs is a successful technique (Smulders, 1995), as well as the 'clean livestock (cattle) policy'. James *et al.* (1997) briefly review trials in pre-slaughter cleaning of animals and Huffmann (2002) concisely reviews pre-harvest experiments (composition of the diet, competitive exclusion cultures, drinking-water treatment, immunisation) with special regard to the reduction of *E. coli* O157.

### 5.2.2   The equipment

By using captive bolt stunners and sticking knives, microbes are introduced into blood vessels and consecutively spread via the bloodstream. However, only a limited number of bacteria can be introduced and the antimicrobial activity of the blood is likely to inactivate them. Knives, steels and aprons of slaughter personnel and meat inspectors may be a source of contamination. Protective gloves, used either to cover wounds on the workers' hands, and in the cutting and dressing area, may act as a vehicle for cross-contamination.

### 5.2.3   The process

For cattle slaughter, removing horns and the manual skinning of the distal parts of the legs and ventral part of the body have been found to be critical for microbial contamination (Smulders, 1995). Dehiding by machines results in lower bacterial loads of meat surfaces than manual dehiding. For pigs, vat scalding at ca. 60°C has been found to contribute to microbial contamination not only of the skin, but also of the lung and stick wound. After de-hairing, singeing of the bodies will effectively reduce their microbial load, but the subsequent polishing process may nullify this effect. Evisceration is critical for both pigs and cattle, especially the removal of the rectum and the opening of the abdominal cavity. After meat inspection – which may include incisions in lymph nodes and other organs harbouring bacteria – the carcasses and organs are chilled. Temperatures around 2°C will prevent most pathogenic bacteria from growing and will substantially retard multiplication of spoilers. Low water partial pressure causes evaporation of water (ICMSF, 1998; Upmann *et al.*, 2000). Provided that this water is adequately removed from the chilling room and the carcasses are not too densely packed, desiccation of the carcass surfaces will occur, which effectively suppresses bacterial growth (ICMSF, 1998). However, this is not true for spray chilling, as applied in the US (Smulders and Greer, 1998). The following (subsequent) cutting and deboning procedures introduce no principally new contamination factors or bacterial genera in the processing line.

### 5.2.4    The personnel
Meat animals, as well as workers in the meat industry, carry bacteria in their nasal and oral cavity and on their skin. Workers' hands have been found to be contaminated with enterobacteriaceae, such as salmonallae or coliform bacteria, which is attributed to the extensive contact with animal tissues. Generally, this flora is 'transient', and can easily be removed by appropriate cleaning, but for enterococci and coliforms, it is proved that this flora may become permanent. In turn, human handling leads to more intensive contamination of meat (see ICMSF, 1998).

### 5.2.5    Intervention strategies
The conversion of fresh meat cuts to meat products is characterised by (a) the introduction of non-meat compounds or additives, some of which may have antimicrobial potential, (b) the production process and associated risks for microbial contamination and simultaneously applied physical measures with a more or less microbicidal effect, as heat treatment. Hygiene is the primary factor for controlling the initial microbial contamination of fresh meat surfaces. The likelihood of contamination with humans pathogenic bacteria, especially by faecal contamination of the carcasses (see ICMSF, 1998; Upmann *et al.*, 2000; Borch and Arinder, 2002) necessitates additional measures, as a terminal treatment of meat carcasses or cuts, with the aim of reducing or eliminating pathogens, and increasing shelf life (Smulders, 1995).

Possible methods for microbial decontamination of fresh meat (see James *et al.*, 1997; Corry and Mead, 1996) may be: (a) application of chemical agents, including those produced *in situ* by bacteria, (b) physical methods, as washing with water, air ionisation, or the application of energy to the meat surfaces and thus to the contaminating bacteria by ionising radiation, ultraviolet radiation, infra-red radiation, steam and high pressure, see also Table 5.2. To date, only the first group of methods seems sufficiently advanced for immediate commercial application (Corry and Mead, 1996). Washing of carcasses with potable water is currently performed but in the EU this is explicitly intended as a means of

**Table 5.2**  Systematics and efficacy of selected decontamination procedures (after Corry and Mead, 1996; James *et al.*, 1997; Lawrie, 1998)

| Type | Method | Typical reduction ($\log_{10}$) |
|---|---|---|
| Chemical | Organic acids | 1.2 to 3.5 |
| | Chlorine | <2 |
| | Ozone | 0.3 to 3 |
| Physical | Water wash | <0.5 up to 1.4 |
| | Water wash, 50–80°C | <0.5 up to >3 |
| | Steam | 3 to 6 |
| | UV radiation | 2 to 3 |
| | Infra-red radiation | ~1.7 |
| | Microwave | ~2 |
| | Irradiation | ~6 (dose dependent) |

removing blood traces and bone fragments and not bacteria. Notably, fresh meat is defined by EC authorities as meat which has not undergone any treatment other than cold treatment (and/or vacuum or modified atmosphere packing) to ensure preservation.

For meat products, a variety of food-technology measures with antimicrobial effects are legally accepted. Some of the more common methods are: the removal of water by drying, heat treatment (pasteurisation or sterilisation), addition of nitrites (Singhal and Kulkarni, 1999), sodium chloride (see Brewer, 1999; Ravishanka and Juneja, 2000) and polyphospates (see Prakash, 2000). In fermented meat products, the *in-situ* formation of lactic acid (lowering the pH) and bacteriocins, together with reduction of the water activity and oxygen consumption form a cascade, see Leistner (1995). Quite recently, high-pressure treatment and application of bacteriocins to meat products have successfully been combined on an industrial scale (Hugas *et al.*, 2002). Antimicrobial packaging films for meat have been developed, but obviously are not adaequately covered in EC food legislation (Quintavalla and Vicini, 2002).

## 5.3    Using organic acids to control microbial contamination

Organic acids are natural constituents of a variety of raw (vegetables, fruits, meat) and processed foods (fermented meat products, sauerkraut, several milk products; see Bogaert and Naidu, 2001). While concentrations of organic acids in fruits decrease with ageing (Stratford, 1999), accumulation of lactic acid in muscle tissue occurs *post mortem* due to glycolysis, with a lactic acid concentration of ca. 0.9%, contributing both to flavour (Lawrie, 1998) and keeping quality. This results in a pH fall of 1–2 units from initially 7.2 (Church and Wood, 1992). Other acids of interest are acetic, tartric, fumaric, sorbic and adipic acids (Stratford, 1999).

### 5.3.1  Organic acids: mode of action

The principal mode of action of organic acids is the release of protons from carboxylic groups, thus lowering the pH of their environment. Proton release means dissociation of the acid molecule, with the degree of dissociation depending on the $pK_a$ value. Strong acids tend to be fully dissociated and thus produce a strong drop in pH, while weak acids are only partially dissociated. This has two important consequences: (a) organic acids with two or three carboxylic groups react on changes of pH by changes in protonation of their carboxylic groups, i.e., they may 'buffer', and (b), in their undissociated state, some of these acids can pass through lipophilic cell membranes. Consequently, on a molar basis, the antibacterial efficacy of weak acids is stronger than that of strong acids. Table 5.3 reviews properties of selected organic acids. Kation effects are reported also. Protons may change the conformation of polar membrane proteins. Binding metal ions ($Fe^{3+}$, $Cu^{++}$, $Mn^{++}$, $Ca^{++}$, $Mg^{++}$) by chelation is relevant only for di- and tricarboxylic acids, especially citric acid (Stratford, 1999).

Organic acids will readily lower the 'environmental' pH, and also lower the growth limits of meatborne microbes (see above), but only temporarily. Woolthuis et al. (1984), having immersed liver in 0.2M lactic acid and effecting an immediate pH drop of 0.6 units, saw the original pH restored after 5 h. Van der Marel et al. (1988) observed no pH drop of broiler carcasses treated with 2% lactic acid. Apparently, this effect is dependent on the substrate also. Hence Rohrbacher (2001) showed that after having sprayed acetic acid (0.3M) and lactic acid (0.2M), onto pork cuts (M. longissimus), these acids are nearly completely buffered within 3 h, whereas on pig skin the pH was significantly lowered (2 units) for as long as 30 h.

The effect on interior cell structures is described by the 'weak acid theory'. The principal idea is that organic acids may pass cell membranes in their undissociated form and in cytoplasm with ca. neutral pH, readily dissociate and

**Table 5.3**  Properties of some organic acids used as additives (after Smulders, 1987; Stratford, 1999, Saltmarsh, 2000; Naidu, 2000)

| Acid | COOH* | pKa | acid.** | taste | 'weak acid'*** | spec. effect**** |
|------|-------|-----|---------|-------|----------------|------------------|
| Acetic | 1 | 4.74 | 1.4 | ++ | yes | Membrane diffusion |
| Lactic | 1 | 3.66 | 2.5 | ~ | yes | Membrane diffusion |
| | | | | | | Water activity reduction |
| | | | | | | 'Specific anion effect' |
| Malic | 2 | 4.7/3.3 | 2.7 | + | no | (Chelation) |
| Tartric | 2 | 3.9/2.8 | 2.9 | + | no | (Chelation) |
| Citric | 3 | 5.7/4.3/2.9 | 2.6 | ++ | no | Chelation |

* Number of carboxylic groups; ** pH fall of a 1% bacteriological peptone solution (pH 6.2), when acids (0.5%, compared on a weight basis, Stratford, 1999) are added; this represents the strength of the acidulant effect on 'environmental pH'; *** Lipophilic character; ability to depress intracellular pH; **** Effects other than acidulant; ~/+/ ++ . . . no/weak/marked generic taste.

thus lower interior pH. This has a direct effect on proteins and nucleic acids (Smulders, 1987; Stratford, 1999), overloads membrane located 'pumps' trying to remove excess protons, thus consuming ATP and effecting energy depletion. This mechanism assumes acid molecules with lipophilic character, as is the case for acetic and to a lesser extent, lactic acid. The extracellular pH has to be near to the $pK_a$ of the acid. Values of pH $< 5.5$ have been found sufficient (Corry and Mead, 1996), ensuring that at least $\sim 10\%$ of the lactic or acetic acid molecules are undissociated, and therefore, diffusible (see Table 5.3; Stratford, 1999; Bogaert and Naidu, 2000; Marshal et al., 2000, Sharma, 2000).

### 5.3.2   Modes of application

Organic acids may be sprayed onto surfaces either by (a) hand-held (mostly experimental) devices or (b) machines equipped with fixed or moving spaying nozzles. Spray pressure, flow rate and time of application, design of the nozzle, spraying angle (at low pressure) and configuration have been found to be of special relevance. Spraying cabinets, and more economical water flood cabinets have been proposed as well as spraying units moving along the carcass. The latter unit has been proved successful to study the efficacy of combined cold water-hot water-acid treatment of veal carcasses (Smulders, 1995).

Immersion is a possible technique for treating smaller parts, such as slaughter byproducts and primal and subprimal cuts. Generally, the whole surface is covered and via blood vessels or bile ducts (liver), the agent can reach the inner parts of the tissue. Organic matter, either covering the surface of organs or released into the immersion tanks, will bind the acid anions, thus decreasing the effective concentration (see Smulders, 1995). This makes immersion techniques more suitable for experimental rather than commercial use (Smulders and Greer, 1998).

Two further approaches have been suggested: firstly, to apply lactic acid to pig carcasses by electrostatic dispersion, and, secondly, an in-situ production of acetic acid and other natural antimicrobial compounds by bacteria. Unlike the spray and the immersion technique, no 'washing effect' of the agent is to be expected (Smulders, 1995). The addition of lactic acid producing starter cultures is well-known in fermented meat products (Leistner, 1995) and has been used for other comminuted meats and meat cuts. Lactobacillus and Streptococcus cultures were found to effectively suppress gram-negative and some gram-positive genera of spoilage bacteria on mutton (Murali et al., 1985), but there is evidence of deterioriation of flavour and odour of vacuum packed lamb meat inoculated with protective Lactobacillus cultures during extended storage (Gill and Penney, 1985).

### 5.3.3   Factors influencing the antibacterial efficacy of organic acids

*The substrate effect*

The nature of the meat surface obviously influences the antibacterial efficacy of organic acids. This may be attributed to the structure of the tissue, the chemical composition and other organic matter and debris covering the surfaces. Bacteria hidden in crevices on pork skin (Prasai *et al.*, 1992) or poultry skin may be inaccessible for organic acid sprays. In the reduction of *Salmonella typhimurium*, *Listeria monocytogenes*, *Escherichia coli* O157:H7 (Dickson, 1991, 1992) and *Pseudomonas fragi* and *Brochothrix thermosphacta*, acid treatment was found to be more effective on fat than on lean meat. This was explained by the relatively low buffering capacity of fat compared to muscle tissue (Greer, 1993).

*The number and composition of bacterial load*
There is evidence both that the microbial reduction by organic acids is proportional to the initial load (Dickson, 1992) and that there is a maximum of reduction that can be achieved. An explanation for this may be the microbial species-specific acid susceptibility. For instance, Greer and Dilts (1992) found that the reduction of a variety of pathogenic and spoilage bacteria on acid treated lean beef slices was affected by the initial level of bacterial contamination and by the bacterial genera under study. The acid sensitivity of bacteria has been the subject of numerous studies which were compiled by Smulders (1995).

*Factors related to the technology of application*
These factors comprise: the mode of application, type of acid, concentration and temperature of acid, contact time of the acid and the meat surface and the time of application. Typically, organic acid concentrations in rinse or immersion solutions are reported to be 1–5% (James *et al.*, 1997). With respect to chilling technology, it was shown that acid application plus surface desiccation ('air chilling') gives higher microbial reduction (Dickson, 1990) and that spray chilling of beef carcasses impairs the effect of acid application (Dickson, 1991; Dickson and Anderson, 1991). Higher acid temperatures tend to yield better microbial reduction, with temperatures of about 55°C being very effective (reviewed by Smulders, 1995).

Bacteria coming in contact with meat surfaces are primarily retained in surface water films or entrapped in crevices but quite soon stronger attachment mechanisms emerge and tissues are colonised. Consequently, acid treatment should be performed before microbial colonisation of the surfaces occurs. While 'early' application of organic acids had both immediate and delayed effects on microflora (Smulders and Woolthuis, 1985), 'late' application of organic acids had either no delayed effect (Acuff *et al.*, 1987) or no significant effect at all (Mulder and Krol, 1975).

The contact time of the acid with the meat surface can be extended in two ways: (a) replicate treatments and (b) application of organic acids using alginate gels (Siragusa and Dickson, 1992, 1993). Replicate acid treatments have been successfully applied in sub-primals (Smulders and Woolthuis, 1985), in the slaughtering process of cattle (Prasai *et al.*, 1992) and for beef sides (Hamby *et al.*, 1987).

The general question, where the most efficient point of intervention by organic acids would be, has been raised by Smulders and Greer (1998).

Considering the nature of microbial contamination (see above), acid treatment would be most promising for retail cuts immediately before vacuum packaging. However, in this processing stage, colour and odour changes are far more critical in terms of consumers' acceptance than they are at the stage of carcass halves or primal cuts. For these parts, further cutting would allow removal of discoloured surfaces.

*Maximum reduction achievable*
The effect of organic acids on contaminant microbes may lead to immediate reduction, or delayed moderation of number and composition of the remaining microflora. As this is influenced by the various factors addressed in this chapter, it is possible to give only a rough outline. Hence, an overall reduction of 1.5 $log_{10}$ units can be expected under industrial conditions (Smulders and Greer, 1998), and for total aerobic counts a reduction of 1–3 $log_{10}$ units (Corry and Mead, 1996). A number of experimental studies have reported up to 6 $log_{10}$ reductions (see Smulders, 1995; James *et al.*, 1997; Naidu, 2000), but these findings are likely to apply to laboratory and not field conditions.

### 5.3.4    Effects on sensory and other meat quality traits
Meat quality traits affected by lactic and acetic acid can be conveniently divided into three groups: colour, odour/flavour, drip loss (Smulders, 1995). It should be noted that application of lactic and acetic acid in concentrations of 1 to 3% on the carcass has practically no impact on sensory properties of the resultant meat cuts. Discolouration of carcasses can be observed, which mostly reverts within 24 h, and is not detectable in meat cuts originating from treated carcasses. Direct treatment of meat cuts, especially when immersed and not sprayed, may often be detrimental to colour and odour (Smulders and Greer, 1998). Findings from the literature are summarised in Table 5.4.

Lowered intracellular pH may result in myofibrillar shrinkage and therefore loss of intracellular liquid (Offer and Trinick, 1983), which means increased drip loss. In principle, this was affirmed in several experiments (e.g. Mendonca *et al.*, 1989); however, muscle tissue excised from acid treated carcasses showed no increased thaw and cook loss after frozen vacuum storage (Jeremiah *et al.*, 1991). Denaturation of myofibrillar proteins may occur, but no increase of toughness in terms of shear force was observed (Mikel *et al.*, 1996).

### 5.3.5    Salts of lactic and acetic acid
The nature of salts of acetic and lactic acid is influenced by the cation, usually calcium, sodium, potassium ions. At present, the significance of these compounds can be summarised as follows (Smulders and Greer, 1998): (a) some of the compounds have 'salty' taste (calcium lactate), (b) the antibacterial activity on meat carcasses is considered rather limited, (c) the mode of action is bacteriostatic rather than bactericidal, (d) in contrast to lactic acid, sodium and

**Table 5.4**  Effects on meat quality traits by lactic and/or acetic acid application (compiled after Smulders, 1995; Smulders and Greer, 1998; Bogaert and Naidu, 2000)

| Acid | Appl. | Conc. | Substrate | Changes | Reference |
|------|-------|-------|-----------|---------|-----------|
| A | S | 2% | Beef carcass | Col. | Osthold *et al.* (1983) |
| L | S | 1% | Beef carcass | Col. | Osthold *et al.* (1983) |
| L | S | 1.25% | Veal carcass | None | Smulders and Woolthuis (1985) |
| L | S | 1% | Pork carcass | None | Prasai *et al.* (1992) |
| L | S | 2.4% | Pork carcass* | Col. | Labots *et al.* (1983) |
| A | S | 2% | Pork loin | Col. | Cacciarelli *et al.* (1983) |
| A/L/M | S | 1% | Beef steak | None | Dixon *et al.* (1987) |
| A/L/M | S | 1% | Beef strip loins | None | Acuff *et al.* (1987) |
| M | S | 2% | Beef strip loins | None | Mikel *et al.* (1996) |
| A | I | 1.2% | Beef cubes | Flavour, col. | Bell *et al.* (1986) |
| A/L/M | I | 1% | Pork chops | Exudate, col. | Mendonca *et al.* (1989) |
| L/A | I | 2% | Beef steaks | Col. | Kotula and Thelappurate (1994) |
| L | I | 3% | Pork discs | Col. | Greer and Dilts (1995) |

L ... lactic acid, A ... acetic acid, M ... mix of lactic and acetic acid; () ... reversible changes; * ... applies only to meat surfaces and surfaces of body cavities; I ... Immersion, S ... Spray; Col. ... colour.

potassium lactates have either no or even stabilising effects on colour of meat, pork sausages, meat mince and flavour of meat products (reviewed by Bogaert and Naidu, 2000), when used in concentrations of 1 to 3%. It was concluded, therefore, that lactates are more promising for treatment of meat cuts immediately before packaging and as an additive to meat products rather than a carcass decontaminant.

## 5.4  Regulatory and safety issues

In the European community, the legal basis for organic acids as food additives is the directive 87/107/EEC. Lactic acid (European designation: E270), acetic acid (E260), and acetates, such as potassium acetate (E261), calcium acetate (E263) and sodium acetates (E262) are generally permitted food additives under EC directive 95/2/EC. Sodium lactate (E325), potassium lactate (E326) and calcium lactate (E327) are food additives, which may be added on a *quantum satis* basis to foods (Directive 92/5 EC annex 1). Sodium lactate and potassium lactate are used in meat products (Barlow, 2000, Saltmarsh, 2000).

The definition of organic acids and their salts as 'food additives' in the EU makes it presently impossible to use them as a 'processing aid' for 'fresh meat' (see above). In contrast, US FDA distinguishes food additives from 'generally regarded as safe' (GRAS) substances. The FDA (2002) specifies the following limits for meat products: sodium acetate 0.12%; sodium diacetate 0.1%; acetic acid 0.6%; for other commodities, addition of these substances is restricted by good manufacturing practice only.

### 5.4.1  Public health concerns

Three concerns have been raised against the application of organic acids on meat surfaces:

- selection for acid tolerant bacteria
- a parallel reduction of competitive flora
- the toxicology of these acids.

*Acid tolerance*

Acid tolerance of pathogenic bacteria may be an important virulence factor, as demonstrated for *Yersinia enterocolitica* by De Koning-Ward and Robins-Browne (1995). However, recent studies by Van Netten *et al.* (1997) showed that adaptation of *Yersinia enterocolitica* (and also *Listeria monocytogenes*) to low temperature and acids did not constitute a health risk. For decontamination of artificially inoculated beef muscle slices, Dickson and Kunduru (1995) showed, that acid adapted *Salmonella* strains were as sensitive to lactic acid rinses as parental strains. For *E. coli* O157:H7, the situation is different. This microorganism combines unfavourable characteristics (summarised by Samelis *et al.*, 2002): (a) high acid tolerance, (b) adaptation to lactic and acetic acids, with a low intracellular pH, (c) the ability to survive under acidic conditions and low temperature, (d) the possible virulence enhancement by acid adaptation, with a low oral infective dose of $\sim$100 cells and (e) transmission via bovine faeces, which can occur during the slaughter process. The implications of these properties have been addressed by Smulders (1995), and Smulders and Greer (1998). The reduction of *E. coli* O157:H7 on meat by acid treatment may be in the range of 0.3–2.0 $\log_{10}$ units (data compiled by Smulders and Greer, 1998), but after attachment – presumably to collagen – Fratamico *et al.* (1996) found a 2% acetic acid rinse ineffective. Most recently, combined multiple intervention strategies with acid sensitising effect (non-acid pre-wash) have been evaluated to control this pathogen on meat (Samelis *et al.*, 2002).

*Competitive flora*

As the application of organic acids will effectively reduce the meatborne spoilage bacterial genera *Pseudomonas* sp. and *Brochothrix thermosphacta* (Smulders and Greer, 1998), there could be a concern that this might pave the way for pathogenic bacteria (Jay, 1996). While psychrophilic meatborne pathogenic bacteria (*Listeria monocytogenes, Yersinia enterocolitica, Aeromonas hydrophila*) are very sensitive to organic acids, with a reduction of 6.5–7.0 $\log_{10}$ units (lean meat) and 2.0–4.5 for fat after 3% lactic acid dips, 55°C, mesophilic enterobacteria are far less sensitive to organic acids (Greer, 1993; Greer and Dilts, 1995). However, it is more likely that lactobacilli, which are resistant to organic acids (Quattara *et al.*, 1997), and – in contrast to *Pseudomonas* – do not require oxygen for growth, will occupy this niche. Furthermore, a residual antimicrobial activity of organic acids on meat cut surfaces was demonstrated for up to three weeks under anaerobic storage (Dorsa *et al.*, 1997). In general, the microbial shift by the application of organic acids is considered beneficial (Corry and Mead, 1996).

*Health aspects*

Provided that general rules of good hygienic practice are observed, no adverse health effects for consumers are to be expected. ADI levels for pure L(+) lactic acid are above 1500 mg/kg body weight (Bogaert and Naidu, 2000). As there seems to be only weak hepatic metabolisation of D(−) lactic acid in humans, but mainly excretion via urine, FAO recommends the daily intake should be limited to 100 mg/kg; this has also to be considered for L(+) / D(−) racemic mixtures. D(−) lactic acid is not to be used in infant food, as adverse health effects, namely on liver function, and acidosis have been discussed, but are not fully substantiated. For acetic acid, such ADI limits have not been proposed, most likely because the sensory properties will limit acetic acid intake. Furthermore, it is estimated that the daily intake of acetic acid via food and beverages is 1g/person, without any evidence of adverse health effects, and feeding experiments indicate that the ADI would be in the order of that of lactic acid (for details, see Elias, 1987). From Dutch data compiled by Smulders (1987), it can be estimated that the daily intake of lactic acid via food and beverages is ~3g/person.

## 5.5   Combining organic acids with other preservation techniques

### 5.5.1   Water

Cold water washes or sprays are an accepted means of cleaning carcasses from organic matter, such as blood, bone fragments, etc. This may be an additional source of contamination (Upmann *et al.*, 2000), but also contributes to the removal of bacteria, provided it is performed before bacterial attachment occurs. However, cold water washes provide no perspective for effective reduction of microbial loads (James *et al.*, 1997). The mode of application is similar to that of organic acid sprays and consequently, water sprays have been used as a reference when the efficacy of organic acid sprays was to be evaluated. In contrast to organic acids, no delayed antimicrobial effect is observed. The immediate reduction by water at 55°C (Wellm, 2000) or 70°C (Anderson and Marshall, 1989) is 1 to 0 log units below the immediate reduction by organic acids applied at the same temperature (Dorsa *et al.*, 1997). Applications of 'hot' (55–95°C) water prove to be more effective than of 'cold' (below 20°C) water (Huffmann, 2002), with (experimental) overall microbial reductions of 1 to 3 log units.

Thermal destruction of microbes attached to meat surfaces can be accomplished by the use of condensing steam. Huffmann (2002) distinguishes steam 'pasteurisation' from 'steam-vacuum' combinations. The latter method consists of steam treatment, followed by vacuuming. Both functions can be integrated in hand-held devices for treatment of small contaminated spots on the carcass, and microbial reductions of 1.1–4 log units have been reported (see

Huffmann, 2002). Similarly, steam treatment can be combined with vacuum cooling. A prototype of a reaction chamber for treatment of meat cuts was developed at the FRPERC, Bristol. Steam condensation with surface temperatures of 70–75°C for 10–20 seconds was followed by lactic or acetic acid sprays or dips. Microbial reductions on lean pork meat and pork skin surfaces of 1–3 $\log_{10}$ units could be achieved, with acid application (0.2–0.3 M, 55°C) contributing an additional 1–1.5 $\log_{10}$ unit reduction (Wellm, 2000). This effect was additive, and not synergistic, and delayed antimicrobial activity of organic acids was less pronounced than expected. Clearly, more research in this field is necessary.

### 5.5.2    Other natural antimicrobial systems

Antimicrobial compounds, such as sakacin, nisin and reuterin are small proteins produced by gram-positive bacteria and are effective against gram-positive (typically those closely related to the producer strain) and some gram-negative bacterial species (James *et al.*, 1997; Naidu, 2000). In contrast to antibiotics, no residue problems are to be expected (Luecke, 1992). Of particular interest is the anti-listerial activity of nisin and sakacin, and the anti-*Salmonella* effect of reuterin. In combination with chelating agents, nisin may reduce *E. coli* O157:H7 (James *et al.*, 1997), but a single application of nisin on beef inoculated with *E. coli* O157:H7 will give a mere 0.4 $\log_{10}$ unit reduction (Cutter and Siragusa, 1995). Nisin is an accepted food additive in various countries (Saltmarsh, 2000). The anti-listerial impact of nisin is also dependent on technology, e.g., high-temperature fermented (US style) sausages (ICMSF, 1998). Nisin as an additive to canned food products aids the suppression of Clostridias and thermophilic spores.

There is strong evidence that production by starter cultures is effective – albeit not fully compensatory for hygienic failures – but is not the sole addition of these compounds. Promising fields of application have recently been addressed by Hugas *et al.* (2002): combining high-pressure treatment with bacteriocins gives a synergistic antimicrobial effect for both bacteriocin insensitive (e.g., *E. coli*) microbes and bacteria which are only moderately sensitive (*Staphylococcus*) to pressure. Bacteriocins integrated in food packaging material exert a measurable antimicrobial effect during prolonged storage periods (Quintavalla and Vicini, 2002). In addition, physical treatments have to be considered. The main advantage is that these methods *per se* leave no residues. Hot water or steam (see above) and high pressure treatment (Knorr, 1995) have been employed successfully for microbial reduction, allowing for combined treatments with minimal alteration of the 'freshness' properties of meat.

### 5.5.3    Fresh meat and meat products

For fresh meat, it was estimated that combinations of condensing steam plus an organic acid spray could improve microbial reduction substantially (James *et al.*,

1997). For pork skin inoculated with *Yersinia enterocolitica* and *Pseudomonas fragi*, Wellm (2000) reported microbial reductions of 4.2 and 3.7 $\log_{10}$ units, respectively (see section 5.5.1). The results were largely influenced by steam condensation temperature and the contact time of the acid. Further research in this field is necessary.

Microbial growth in food is influenced by various factors. Mossel *et al.* (1995) classified them as 'extrinsic' (i.e., environmental factors, such as temperature, atmosphere), 'intrinsic' (i.e., properties of the food under study, such as pH, water activity), process-related (such as nitrite, heat treatment), or related to the properties of the microflora ('implicit'). For suppression or reduction of microbial growth, at least some of these factors have to be at sub-optimum or even lethal level for bacteria, thus constituting a 'hurdle' for microbial growth (Leistner and Gorris, 1994). In general, it is not feasible to rely on a single sub-optimum or lethal factor, as this influences the sensory quality of the food and limits further use. Preservation by water reduction only (either by drying or salting) results in food which is microbiologically stable but only in a few cases a ready-to-eat food. It is more appropriate to combine several factors at sub-optimum level ('mild hurdles') either in parallel or sequentially ('hurdle technology', Leistner, 1995). This concept enabled both a better understanding of the safety of traditional, 'ethnic' food and allows for estimation of the safety of new formulations of meat products ('food design', Leistner, 1995). Leistner and Gorris (1994) provide a comprehensive overview on other applications.

While 'hurdle technology' is a more semi-quantitative concept to understand and operate microbial food safety, exact numerical data on microbial growth as a response to environmental factors can be provided by 'mathematical modelling'. Furthermore, the relative contribution of environmental factors on microbial growth can be assessed and interactions become more clear. Within given limits, these 'models' have predictive quality (see e.g., McClure and Roberts, 1992, Ross *et al.*, 1999, Baranyi, 2000).

## 5.6   Conclusion

Natural antimicrobial agents are present both during meat production and meat processing and also may be introduced as an 'additional line of defence'. With good hygiene practice strictly observed, application of 1–3% lactic or acetic acid on carcasses and meat cuts allows for an (additional) microbial reduction of 1,5 or more $\log_{10}$ units, with observed prolonged antibacterial effects. Hot water washes of carcasses may give similar immediate microbial reduction, but lack prolonged effects; the same holds true for steam application. These measures can effectively be introduced in HACCP systems. Hygienic failures during the following processing steps can jeopardise this reduction, and acid-resistant pathogenic bacteria, such as *E. coli* O157:H7 indicate the necessity for combined treatments. Light sensory changes may be perceived as a consequence of treatment with organic acids. Application to carcasses and 'fresh meat' is not allowed in all countries, nor is steam treatment of meat cuts and carcasses. However, at slaughterhouse and cutting-plant level, these techniques combine practicality with sufficient antimicrobial effect and therefore are still the most promising 'natural antimicrobial system' for the near future.

Various natural compounds are legally accepted additives to meat products and their interactions are well described as 'combined processes' or 'hurdle technology'. It has been demonstrated that even on a commercial basis, sublethal antimicrobial measures can effectively be combined (e.g., high-pressure treatment and bacteriocin) without compromising consumers' expectations in terms of sensory food quality. The bottom line in food safety considerations is that any possible treatment should be acceptable in both scientific and political/societal terms. It seems there is still some way to go before this is achieved. By the same token, compelling evidence is available that such treatments could indeed serve a useful function in rendering meat and meat products safe for human consumption.

## 5.7   References

ACUFF G R, VANDERZANT C, SAVELL J W, JONES D K, GRIFFIN D B and EHLERS J G (1987), 'Effect of acid decontamination of beef subprimal cuts on the microbiological and sensory characteristics of steaks', *Meat Sci*, 19, 207–229.

ANDERSON M E and MARSHALL R T (1989), 'Interaction of concentration and temperature of acetic acid solution on reduction of various species of microorganisms on beef surfaces', *J Food Prot*, 52, 312–315.

BARANYI J (2000), 'Predictive microbiology for the meat industry', Proc. 46th ICoMST, Buenos Aires, 684–688.

BARLOW S M (2000): 'Safety of food additives in Europe', in Saltmarsh M, *Essential guide to food additives*, Leatherhead, Leatherhead Publishing, 43–59.

BELL M F, MARSHALL R T and ANDERSON M E (1986), 'Microbiological and sensory tests of beef treated with acetic and formic acids', *J Food Prot*, 49, 207–210.

BOGAERT J C and NAIDU, A S (2000), 'Lactic acid', in Naidu A S, *Natural Food Antimicrobial Systems*, Boca Raton, CRC Press, 613–636.

BORCH E and ARINDER P (2002), 'Bacteriological safety issues in red meat and ready-to-eat meat products, as well as control measures', *Meat Sci*, 62, 381–390.

BREWER M S (1999), 'Traditional preservatives – Sodium chloride', in Robinson R K, Batt C A and Patel P A, *Encyclopedia of food microbiology*, San Diego, Academic Press, 1723–1728.

CACCIARELLI M A, STRINGER W C, ANDERSON M E and NAUMANN H D (1983), 'Effects of washing and sanitizing on bacterial flora of vacuum-packaged pork loins', *J Food Prot*, 46, 231–234.

CHURCH P N and WOOD J M (1992), *The manufacturing of meat quality*, London, Elsevier.

CORRY J E L and MEAD G C (1996), *Microbial control in the meat industry. 3. Decontamination of meat*, Bristol, University of Bristol.

CUTTER C N and SIRAGUSA G R (1995), 'Treatment with nisin and chelators to reduce *Salmonella* and *Escherichia coli* on beef', *J Food Prot*, 58, 1028–1030.

DE KONING-WARD T F and ROBINS-BROWNE R M (1995), 'Contribution of Urease to Acid

Tolerance in *Yersinia enterocolitica'*, *Inf Immun*, 63, 3790–3795.

DICKSON J S (1990), 'Surface moisture and osmotic stress as factors that affect the sanitizing of beef tissue surfaces', *J Food Prot*, 51, 869–873.

DICKSON J S (1991), 'Control of *Salmonella typhimurium*, *Listeria monocytogenes*, and *Escherichia coli* O157:H7 on beef in a model spray chilling system', *J Food Sci*, 56, 191–193.

DICKSON J S (1992), 'Acetic acid action on beef tissue surfaces contaminated with *Salmonella typhimurium'*, *J Food Sci*, 57, 292–301.

DICKSON J S and ANDERSON M E (1991), 'Microbiological decontamination of food animal carcasses by washing and sanitizing systems: a review', *J Food Prot*, 55, 133–140.

DICKSON J and KUNDURU M (1995), 'Resistance of acid-adapted salmonellae to organic acid rinses on beef', *J Food Prot*, 58, 973–976.

DIXON Z, VANDERZANT C, ACUFF G, SAVELL J and JONES D (1987), 'Effect of acid treatment on beef strip loin steaks on microbiological and sensory characteristics', *Int J Food Microbiol*, 5, 181–186.

DORSA W, CUTTER C and SIRAGUSA G (1997), 'Effects of acetic acid, lactic acid and trisodium phosphate on the microflora of refrigerated beef carcass surface tissue inoculated with *Escherichia coli* O157:H7, *Listeria innocua* and *Clostridium sporogenes'*, *J Food Prot*, 60, 619–624.

ELIAS P S (1987), 'The public's response to decontamination', in Smulders F J M, *Elimination of pathogenic organisms from meat and poultry*, Amsterdam, Elsevier, 345–361.

FDA (2002): at the internet location: www.cfsan.fda.gov/~dms/opa-noti.html.

FRATAMICO P, SCHULTZ F, BENEDICT R, BUCHANAN R and COOKE P (1996), 'Factors influencing attachment of *Escherichia coli* O157:H7 to beef tissues and removal using selected sanitizing rinses', *J Food Prot*, 59, 453–459.

GILL C O and PENNEY N (1985), 'Modification of in-pack conditions to extend the storage life of vacuum packaged lamb', *Meat Sci*, 14, 43–60.

GREER G (1993), 'Control of meat spoilage bacteria by lactic acid', *Meat Focus Int*, 2, 207–208.

GREER G G and DILTS B D (1992), 'Factors affecting the susceptibility of meatborne pathogens and spoilage bacteria to organic acids', *Food Res Int*, 25, 355–364.

GREER G and DILTS B (1995), 'Lactic acid inhibition on the growth of spoilage bacteria and cold tolerant pathogens on pork', *Int J Food Microbiol*, 25, 141–151.

HAMBY P L, SAVELL J F, ACUFF G R, VANDERZANT C and CROSS H R (1987), 'Spray-chilling and carcass decontamination systems using lactic and acetic acid', *Meat Sci*, 21, 1–14.

HUFFMAN (2002), 'Current and future technologies for the decontamination of carcasses and fresh meat', *Meat Sci*, 62, 285–294.

HUGAS M, GARRIGA M and MONFORT J M (2002): 'New mild technologies in meat processing: high pressure as a model technology', *Meat Sci*, 62, 359–371.

ICMSF (1996), *Microorganisms in Foods 5: Characteristics of Microbial Pathogens*, London, Blackie A.&P.

ICMSF (1998), *Microorganisms in Foods 6: Microbial Ecology of Food Commodities*, London, Blackie A.&P.

JAMES C, GOKSOY E O and JAMES S J (1997), *Past present and future methods of meat decontamination*, Bristol, University of Bristol.

JAY J M (1996),'Microorganisms in fresh ground meats: the relative safety of products with low versus high numbers', *Meat Sci*, 43, 674–677.

JEREMIAH L, GREER G and GIBSON L (1991), 'Effects of lactic acid and postmortem ageing on sensory and cooking properties of bovine longissimus muscle', *J Muscle Foods*, 2, 119–131.

KNORR D (1995), 'Hydrostatic pressure treatment of food: microbiology', in Gould G W, *New methods of food preservation*, London, Blackie Academic & Professional, 159–175.

KOTULA K L and THELAPPURATE R (1994), 'Microbiological and sensory attributes of retail cuts of beef treated with acetic and lactic acid solutions', *J Food Prot*, 57, 665–670.

LABADIE J. (1999), 'Consequences of packaging on bacterial growth: meat is an ecological niche', *Meat Sci*, 52, 299–305.

LABOTS H, LOGTENBERG H, STEKELENBURG F K and SNIJDERS J M A (1983), *Study into the possibilities to reduce the Salmonella colony count on pig carcasses under practical conditions. Report T 83-183/100 264*, Zeist, Central Institute for Nutrition and Food Research, TNO.

LAWRIE R A (1998), *Lawrie's meat science*, 6th edn, Cambridge, Woodhead.

LEISTNER L (1995), 'Principles and applications of hurdle technology', in Gould G W, *New methods of food preservation*, London, Blackie Academic & Professional, 1–21.

LEISTNER L and GORRIS L G M (1994), *Food preservation by combined processes, final report FLAIR concerted action No.7, subgroup b*, European Community.

LUECKE F K (1992), 'Prospects for the use of bacteriocins against meat-borne pathogens', in Smulders F J M, Toldrá F, Flores J and Prieto M, *New technologies for meat and meat products*, Nijmegen, Audet Publishing, 37–52.

MCCLURE P J and ROBERTS T A (1992), 'Predictive modelling and meat processing: assessment of product safety', in Smulders F J M, Toldrá F, Flores J and Prieto M, *New technologies for meat and meat products*, Nijmwegen, Audet Publishing, 273–288.

MARSHAL D L, COTTON L N and BAŁA F A (2000), 'Acetic acid', in Naidu A S, *Natural Food Antimicrobial Systems*, Boca Raton, CRC Press, 661–688.

MEAD G C and HINTON M H (1996), *Microbial control in the meat industry. 7. Bacterial pathogens on raw meat and their properties*, Bristol, University of Bristol.

MENDONCA A F, MOLINS R A, KRAFT A A and WALKER A W (1989), 'Microbiological, chemical, and physical changes in fresh, vacuum-packaged pork treated with organic acids and salts', *J Food Sci*, 54, 18–21.

MIKEL W, GODDARD B and BRADFORD D (1996), 'Muscle microstructure and sensory attributes of organic acid-treated beef strip loins', *J Food Sci*, 61, 1058–1061.

MOSSEL D A A, CORRY J E L, STRUIJK C B and BAIRD R M (1995), *Essentials of the microbiology of foods*, Chichester, Wiley.

MULDER S J and KROL B (1975), 'Der Einfluss der Milchsaeure auf die Keimflora und die Farbe frischen Fleisches', *Fleischwirtsch*, 55, 1255–1258.

MURALI H S, LEELA R K, SANKARAN R and SHARMA T R (1985), 'Effect of some lactic cultures on the natural microflora of mutton', *Chem Mikrobiol Technol Lebensmittelhyg*, 9, 19–23.

NAIDU A S (2000), *Natural food antimicrobial systems*, Boca Raton, CRC Press.

NYCHAS G-J E, DROSINOS E H and BOARD R G (1998), 'Chemical changes in stored meat', in Davies A and Board R, *The microbiology of meat and poultry*, London, Blackie Academic & Professional, 288–326.

OFFER G and TRINICK J (1983), 'On the mechanism of water holding in meat: the swelling and shrinking of myofibrils', *Meat Sci*, 8, 245–281.

OSTHOLD W, SHIN H K, DRESEL J and LEISTNER L (1983), 'Verbesserung der Haltbarkeit von Schlachttierkoerpern, herbeigefuehrt durch Oberflaechenbehandlung mit einem Saeurespray', *Fleischwirtsch*, 63, 603–605.

PRAKASH A (2000), 'Polyphosphates', in Naidu A S, *Natural food antimicrobial systems*, Boca Raton, CRC Press, 725–738.

PRASAI R K, ACUFF G R, LUCIA L M, MORGAN, J B, MAY S G and SAVELL J W (1992), 'Microbiological effects of acid decontamination of pork carcasses at various locations in processing', *Meat Sci*, 32, 413–423.

QUATTARA B, SIMARD R, HOLLEY R, PIETTE G and BAGIN A (1997), 'Inhibitory effect of organic acids upon meat spoilage bacteria', *J Food Prot*, 60, 246–253.

QUINTAVALLA S and VICINI L (2002), 'Antimicrobial food packaging in the meat industry', *Meat Sci*, 62, 373–380.

RAVISHANKA S and JUNEJA V K (2000), 'Sodium chloride', in Naidu A S, *Natural food antimicrobial systems*, Boca Raton, CRC Press, 705–724.

ROHRBACHER I (2001), *Dekontamination von Schweinefleisch unter Anwendung von Wasserdampfkondensation bei sub-atmosphärischem Druck und organischen Säuren unter besonderer Berücksichtigung von sensorischen Veränderungen*, Thesis, Vienna, University of Veterinary Medicine.

ROMANS J R, COSTELLO W J, CARLSON C W, GREASER M L and JONES K W (1994), *The meat we eat*, 13th edn, Danville, IL USA, Interstate Publ.

ROSS T, MCMEEKIN T A and BARANYI J (1999), 'Predictive microbiology and food safety', in Robinson R K, Batt C A and Patel P A, *Encyclopedia of food microbiology*, San Diego, Academic Press, 1699–1710.

SALTMARSH M (2000), *Essential guide to food additives*, Leatherhead, Leatherhead Publishing.

SAMELIS J, SOFOS J N, IKEDA J S, KENDALL P A and SMITH G C (2002), 'Exposure to non-acid wash fluids sensitizes *Escherichia coli* O157:H7 to organic acids', *Lett Appl Microbiol*, 34, 7–12.

SCHIEMANN D A (1989), '*Yersinia enterocolitica* and *Yersinia pseudotuberculosis*', in Doyle M P, *Foodborne bacterial pathogens*, New York, Marcel Dekker, 601–671.

SHARMA R K (2000), 'Citric acid', in Naidu A S, *Natural food antimicrobial systems*, Boca Raton, CRC Press, 689–704.

SINGHAL R S and KULKARNI P R (1999), 'Permitted preservatives – Nitrate and Nitrite', Robinson R K, Batt C A and Patel P A, *Encyclopedia of food microbiology*, San Diego, Academic Press, 1762–1769.

SIRAGUSA G and DICKSON J (1992), 'Inhibition of *Listeria monocytogenes* on beef tissue by application of organic acids immobilized in a calcium alginate gel', *J Food Sci*, 57, 293–296.

SIRAGUSA G and DICKSON J (1993), 'Inhibition of *Listeria monocytogenes*, *Salmonella typhimurium* and *Escherichia coli* O157:H7 on beef muscle by lactic or acetic acid contained in calcium alginate gels', *J Food Safety*, 13, 147–158.

SMULDERS F J M (1987), 'Prospects for microbial decontamination of meat and poultry by organic acids with special reference to lactic acid', in Smulders F J M, *Elimination of pathogenic organisms from meat and poultry*, Amsterdam, Elsevier, 319–344.

SMULDERS F J M (1995), 'Preservation by microbial decontamination; the surface treatment of meats by organic acids', in Gould G W, *New methods of food preservation*, London, Blackie Academic & Professional, 253–282.

SMULDERS F J M and GREER G G (1998), 'Integrating microbial decontamination with organic acids in HACCP programmes for muscle foods: prospects and controversies', *Int J Food Microb*, 44, 149–169.

SMULDERS F J M and WOOLTHUIS C H J (1985), 'The immediate and delayed microbiological effects of lactic acid decontamination of calf carcasses. The influence of conventionally boned vs. hot boned and vacuum packaged cuts', *J Food Prot*, 48, 838–847.

STRATFORD M (1999), 'Traditional preservatives – Organic acids', in Robinson R K, Batt C A and Patel P A, *Encyclopedia of food microbiology*, San Diego, Academic Press, 1729–1737.

UPMANN M, PAULSEN P, JAMES S and SMULDERS F J M (2000), 'The microbiology of refrigerated meat', *Fleischwirtsch. Internat.*, 3, 38–45.

VAN DER MAREL G M, VAN LOGTESTIJN J G and MOSSEL D A A (1988), 'Bacteriological quality of broiler carcasses as affected by in-plant acetic acid decontamination', *Int J Food Microbiol*, 6, 31–42.

VAN NETTEN P, VALENTIJN A, MOSSEL D A A and HUIS IN'T VELD J (1997), 'Fate of low temperature and acid-adapted *Yersinia enterocolitica* and *Listeria monocytogenes* that contaminate lactic acid decontaminated meat during chill storage', *J Appl Microbiol*, 82, 769–779.

WELLM G (2000), *Dekontamination von Schweinefleisch unter Anwendung von Wasserdampfkondensation bei subatmosphärischem Druck und organischen Säuren unter besonderer Berücksichtigung mikrobieller Aspekte und einiger Umweltaspekte*, Thesis, Vienna, University for Agriculture.

WOOLTHUIS C H J and SMULDERS F J M (1985), 'Microbial decontamination of calf carcasses by lactic acid sprays', *J Food Prot*, 48, 832–837.

WOOLTHUIS C H J, MOSSEL D A A, VAN LOGTESTIJN J G, DE KRUIJF J M and SMULDERS F J M (1984), 'Microbial decontamination of porcine liver with lactic acid and hot water', *J Food Prot*, 47, 220–226.

# 6

# Edible coatings

**H. J. Park, Korea University**

## 6.1   Introduction: the development of edible coatings

Major losses in quality and quantity of fresh fruits occur between harvest and consumption (Sparks, 1976). Savings obtained through reduction of post-harvest fruit losses are regarded as 'a hidden harvest' (Spurgeon, 1976). Several techniques have been developed which are successful in extending shelf-life, through a better understanding of the respiration process in fresh fruits. Controlled atmosphere storage and modified atmosphere storage have been used for preserving fruits by reducing their quality changes and quantity losses during storage. Edible coatings on fresh fruit can provide an alternative to modified atmosphere storage by reducing quality changes and quantity losses through modification and control of the internal atmosphere of the individual fruits.

### 6.1.1   A historical view of edible coatings

Wax was the first edible coating used on fruits and vegetables. The Chinese applied wax coatings to oranges and lemons in the twelfth and thirteenth centuries (Hardenburg, 1967). Although the Chinese did not realize that the full function of edible coatings was to slow down respiratory gas exchange, they found that wax coated fruits could be stored longer than non-waxed fruits. In the 1930s hot-melt paraffin waxes became commercially available as edible coatings for fresh fruits such as apples and pears. Erbil and Muftugil (1986) reported that coating peach surfaces with wax emulsions decreased water vapor and oxygen transmission thus, diminishing the respiration rate and increasing shelf-life of the fruit. Nisperos-Carriedo *et al.* (1990) observed that oils or waxes and cellulose had similar effects in preventing spoilage and retaining the fresh-picked quality for tropical fruits.

Several attempts have been made to develop other materials that could be used to coat produce and modify internal gas composition for short-term storage. Zhang and Quantick (1997) suggested that chitin and chitosan (deacetylated chitin) from marine invertebrates could be used to make a transparent film for application as an edible coating on fruits and vegetables. In 1982, Lowings and Cutts (1982) reported an edible coating material that is non-phytotoxic, tasteless, odorless and effective in preserving fruits. This coating material is a mixture of sucrose fatty acid esters (SFAE), sodium carboxymethyl cellulose and mono- and diglycerides. SFAE was originally developed as an emulsifier. However, it has been established that the ripening of fruits can be retarded by a coating of SFAE. SFAE mixtures have been commercially available for coating fruits and vegetables since the 1980s, under the trade names 'TAL Pro-long' and 'Semperfresh' (Banks, 1984; Chu, 1986; Santerre *et al.*, 1989). Park *et al.* (1994b, c) applied zein coating to the surface of tomatoes and reported that the film coating delayed color change, weight loss and maintained firmness during storage.

### 6.1.2 Problems associated with edible coatings

Even though some edible coatings have been successfully applied to fresh produce, other applications adversely affect quality. Modification of the internal atmosphere by the use of edible coatings can increase disorders associated with high carbon dioxide or low oxygen concentration (Ben-Yehoshua, 1969). Smock (1940) indicated that waxing apples and pears inhibited normal ripening rate and if sufficient wax was applied, respiration was greatly inhibited and alcoholic flavors were developed by anaerobic fermentation. Smith and Stow (1984) reported that apples (cv. Cox's Orange Pippin) coated with sucrose fatty acid ester had fewer detrimental changes in terms of fruit firmness, yellowing and weight loss but had increased incidence of core flush. Park *et al.* (1994c) reported that tomatoes coated with 0.6 mm zein film produced alcohol and off-flavors inside the tomatoes which were attributable to an internal gas composition that was too low in oxygen and too high in carbon dioxide. Smith *et al.* (1987) summarized the effects on physiological disorders associated with modification of internal atmosphere by use of coatings, as core flush, flesh breakdown and accumulation of ethanol and alcoholic off-flavors.

Wax and SFAE mixtures are the most widely used edible coatings for fruits and vegetables. But, they are not equally effective for all produce. Another problem is that consumers tend to be wary of waxy coatings. Therefore, development of alternative edible coatings which do not impart a waxy taste are desirable. The effects of edible coatings on internal gas composition and their interactions with quality parameters must be determined for coated fresh produce. For example, color change and firmness are very important quality parameters in fruits. Shewfelt *et al.* (1987) stated that color change, loss of firmness, ethanol fermentation, decay ratio and weight loss of edible-film coated fruits are all important qualities for various products.

## 6.2   How edible coatings work: controlling internal gas composition

Edible coatings can provide protection for fresh products and can also give the same effect as modified atmosphere storage with respect to modifying internal gas composition. The success of edible coatings for fruits depends mainly on selecting films or coatings which can give a desirable internal gas composition that is appropriate for a specific product.

## 6.3   Selecting edible coatings

If a coating is too thick, detrimental effects can result because the internal oxygen concentration is below a desirable and beneficial level and there is an associated increased carbon dioxide concentration which is above a critical tolerable level. These conditions lead to anaerobic fermentation. This can be remedied by: (1) developing several edible coatings, (2) controlling wettability of edible coatings, (3) measuring gas permeation properties of selected coatings, (4) measuring diffusion properties of skin and flesh of selected fruits, (5) predicting internal gas compositions for the fruits coated with edible films, and (6) observing coating effects on the quality changes of fruits.

## 6.4   Gas permeation properties of edible coatings

There are several possible edible coatings for fruits such as cellulose, casein, zein, soy protein and chitosan. These were chosen because they have the desirable characteristics of generally being odorless, tasteless and transparent. It is not easy to measure the gas permeation properties of the coatings after they have been applied to fruits. Therefore, separate flat films are prepared and tested. Two known primary methods of preparation of flat films were described by Kamper and Fennema (1984) and Aydt *et al.* (1991). An OX-TRAN 1000[TM] (Mocon Modern Control, Minneapolis, MN) was used to measure oxygen permeability (OP), and water vapor permeability (WVP) was measured using a variation of the ASTM Standard Method E 96 (ASTM, 1987), known as the 'cup method'. Carbon dioxide $CO_2$ permeability was measured using a modified permeability cell designed by Gilbert and Pegaz (1969). WVP and gas permeabilities of the coatings can be calculated as shown in Box 1.

OP, WVP and carbon dioxide permeabilities of edible coatings reported in the literature are presented in Table 6.1 and compared with other conventional plastic films. The oxygen permeabilities of most edible coatings were lower than the conventional plastic films. The oxygen permeability (OP) of sucrose polyester (SPE) coatings was 1–3 times higher than that of polyethylene film and was 4–10 times higher than that of polypropylene film. The OPs of SPE coatings were similar to cellulose film values but were higher than those of edible protein

## Box 1   Gas permeability

The permeation process can be described mathematically by Fick's first law. The flux ($J$) which is proportional to the concentration gradient can be defined in one direction as follows:

$$J = -D\partial C/\partial X \tag{6.1}$$

where $J$ is the flux, the net amount of solute that diffuses through unit area per unit time ($g\,m^{-2}\,s^{-1}$ or $ml\,m^{-2}\,s^{-1}$), $D$ is the diffusivity constant ($m^2\,s^{-1}$), $C$ is the concentration gradient of the diffusing substance and $X$ is the thickness of the film (m) (Chang, 1981; Crank, 1975; Jost, 1960; Landrock and Proctor, 1952).

With two assumptions, (1) that the diffusion is in a steady state and (2) that there is a linear gradient through the film, the flux ($J$) is given by:

$$J = D(C_2 - C_1)/X = Q/(At) \tag{6.2}$$

where $Q$ is the amount of gas diffusing through the film (g or ml), $A$ is the area of the film ($m^2$) and $t$ is the time (s). After application of Henry's law, the driving force is expressed in terms of the partial pressure differential of gas and a rearrangement of terms yield the following equation in terms of permeability:

$$Q/(At) = DS(p_2 - p_1)/X = P\Delta p/X \tag{6.3}$$

where $S$ is the Henry's law solubility coefficient (mol atm$^{-1}$), $\Delta p$ is partial pressure difference of the gas across the film (Pa) and $P$ is the permeability ((ml or g) m m$^{-2}$ s$^{-1}$ Pa$^{-1}$).

Then, the permeabilities of $O_2$, $CO_2$ and $H_2O$ vapor can be calculated from equation [6.4]:

$$P = QX/(At\Delta p) \tag{6.4}$$

coatings such as zein. The OP permeabilities of protein films were lower than those of polyethylene (low density), polyethylene and polyvinyl chloride, and were close to that of polyester film. The OP permeabilities of protein films, corn-zein and wheat were also lower than those of cellulose films, methyl cellulose MC(L) and hydroxypropyl cellulose HPC(L) both with low levels (L) of plasticizer. The addition of lipid (Myvacet 7-00$^{TM}$) into HPC film decreased the OP permeability only slightly.

The $CO_2$ permeabilities of protein films, corn-zein and wheat were lower than those of plastic films, polyethylene (low density), polyethylene and polyvinyl chloride, with the exception of polyester film which exhibits a greater barrier to $CO_2$ permeation (Table 6.1). $CO_2$ permeabilities of cellulose films, MC(L) and HPC(L), were higher than those of plastic films. The addition of

**Table 6.1**    $O_2$, $CO_2$ and $H_2O$ vapor permeabilities of edible coatings

| Film | Permeability | | |
|------|--------------|---|---|
| | $^bO_2$ | $^bCO_2$ | $^cH_2O$ Vapor |
| SPE | $2.10 \pm 0.0001$ | – | $0.00042 \pm 0.04$ |
| Chitosan (15 cp) | 0.0014 | – | 0.49 |
| Zein | $0.36 \pm 0.16$ | $2.67 \pm 1.09$ | $0.116 \pm 0.019$ |
| Wheat gluten | $0.20 \pm 0.09$ | $2.13 \pm 1.43$ | $0.616 \pm 0.013$ |
| MC (L) | $2.17 \pm 0.45$ | $69.0 \pm 19.33$ | $0.092 \pm 0.003$ |
| HPC (L) | $3.57 \pm 0.03$ | $143.9 \pm 3.76$ | $0.110 \pm 0.004$ |
| HPC/lipid | $3.44 \pm 0.06$ | $81.7 \pm 4.58$ | $0.082 \pm 0.003$ |
| Cozeen | 0.89 | $5.25 \pm 26.10$ | 0.407 |
| PE | 8.30 | 26.1 | – |
| PP | $0.55 \pm 0.005$ | – | $0.00065 \pm 0.06$ |
| PVC | $0.09 - 17.99$ | $1.35 - 26.98$ | 0.00071 |
| PET | $0.13 - 0.30$ | $0.67 - 1.12$ | – |

PE is polyethylene, PP is polypropylene, PVC is polyvinyl chloride, PET is polyester (Aydt *et al.*, 1991; Kamper and Fennema, 1984; Park, 1999; Park and Chinnan, 1995a, 1995b; Park *et al.*, 1993, 1994a,d 1998).
$^b$ Unit of permeability is in $fl\,m\,m^{-2}\,s^{-1}\,Pa^{-1}$; f is an abbreviation for femto ($10^{-15}$).
$^c$ Unit of permeability is $ng\,m\,m^{-2}\,s^{-1}\,Pa^{-1}$; n is an abbreviation for nano ($10^{-9}$).

lipid (Myvacet 7-00$^{TM}$) into HPC film decreased the $CO_2$ permeability by 43.2%. $CO_2/O_2$ permeability ratios of edible films were higher than those of plastic films (Kader *et al.*, 1989).

SPE coatings provide very high water vapor barriers compared with other edible coatings, as shown in Table 6.1. WVPs of SPE coatings were lower than that of polyethylene film and more than 100 times lower than the values for cellulose and protein films. These high oxygen and water vapor barrier properties will make SPE coatings desirable for fresh produce as a replacement for wax (Risse *et al.* 1987; Segall *et al.* 1974). The WVPs of other edible coating films were much higher than those of plastic films. The WVP of wheat protein film was $0.603-0.630\,ng\,msPa^{-1}$, the highest of all edible films tested. Wheat protein film exhibited high permeability to water vapor probably because wheat protein was dispersed by addition of ammonium hydroxide (6N) as part of the formulation, and also contained a higher concentration of plasticizer, 40% (wt. plasticizer/wt. protein). The addition of lipid (Myvacet 7-00$^{TM}$) into HPC film decreased the water vapor permeability by 24.7%. Plastic is the most widely used food wrap, but water vapor commonly condenses on the inner surface of plastic packaging materials thus creating a potential source of microbial contamination in fresh produce (Ben-Yehoshua, 1985). Thus, a film with greater water vapor permeability is desirable, although a film with extremely high water vapor permeability is also not desirable as it can result in excessive moisture loss from fruits during storage.

## 6.5    Wettability and coating effectiveness

The effectiveness of edible coatings on fruits and vegetables depends primarily on controlling the wettability of the coating solutions, which affects the coating thickness of the film (Park, 1999). Edible coating formulations must wet and spread on the fruit's surface uniformly and upon drying form a coating that has adequate adhesion, cohesion and durability to function properly (Krochta and Mulder-Johnston 1997). Hershko and Nussinovitch (1998) indicated that suitable hydrocolloid coatings could only be achieved by exploring the wettability of the coating solution further. Coatings on fruits and vegetables that exceed a critical thickness can cause detrimental effects from reduced internal $O_2$ concentration and increasing $CO_2$ concentration associated with anaerobic fermentation. Tomatoes coated with 66.04 $\mu$m zein film produced alcohol and off-flavors internally (Park et al., 1994c).

Choi et al. (2001) reported that the contact angle of a chitosan coating solution on the apple skin was 89.0°. The wettabilities of edible coatings can be calculated as shown in Box 2.

Because the coating angle is close to 90°, it implies that chitosan coating solution does not easily coat apple skin that has a wax barrier. The measured

---

## Box 2    Wettability

The wettability of a solid by a liquid is determined by the balance between adhesive forces (work of adhesion, $W_a$) of the liquid on the solid and cohesive forces (work of cohesion, $W_c$) of the liquid. Adhesive forces cause the liquid to spread over the solid surface while cohesive forces cause it to shrink:

$$W_a = \gamma_{LV} + \gamma_{SV} - \gamma_{SL} - W_c = 2\gamma_{LV} \qquad 6.5$$

The contact angle of a liquid drop on a solid surface is defined by the mechanical equilibrium of the drop under the action of three interfacial tensions: solid–vapor ($\gamma_{SV}$), solid–liquid ($\gamma_{SL}$) and liquid–vapor ($\gamma_{LV}$). This equilibrium relation is known as Young's equation (Rulon and Robert, 1993):

$$\cos\theta = (\gamma_{SV} - \gamma_{SL})/\gamma_{LV} \qquad 6.6$$

When a solid comes into contact with a liquid in the presence of vapor, the liquid will adhere well on the solid surface if the total free energy required for the creation of the new interface decreases. The physical significance of this energy change is the work needed to separate the solid and liquid from the solid/liquid interface. The equilibrium spreading coefficient (Ws) is defined by equation [6.7] (Rulon and Robert, 1993) and it can only be negative or zero:

$$W_s = W_a - W_c = \gamma_{SV} - \gamma_{LV} - \gamma_{SL} \qquad 6.7$$

contact angles on watermelon, melon, tomato and mandarin were also from 87.5° to 90.0° (Table 6.2). The critical surface tension ($\gamma_C$) of apple skin was 18.7 dyne cm$^{-1}$ ($R^2 = 0.99$). Hershko and Nussinovitch (1998) observed that the critical surface tension of garlic skin was 18.3 dyne cm$^{-1}$. Hagenmaier and Baker (1993) found that the critical surface tension was about 23 dyne$^{-1}$ for grapefruit (Table 6.2). These results indicate that the skin of most fruit covered with a layer of wax has a low surface energy. The layer with low surface energy interacts with liquids primarily through dispersion (van der Waals) forces (Rulon and Robert, 1993). The contact angle of the chitosan coating solution on the pear skin was 8.5° (Table 6.2), an unusually low value. It may have been caused by the surface characteristics of pears which have a coarser surface than

**Table 6.2**    Surface tension, contact angle and critical surface tension of fruits and vegetables

| Coating emulsion | Surface tension (dyne cm$^{-1}$) | Fruits | Critical surface tension (dyne cm$^{-1}$) | Contact angle (degrees) | Spreading coefficient G (dyne cm$^{-1}$) |
|---|---|---|---|---|---|
| Chitosan emulsion | | | | | |
| Chitosan[a] Without emulsifier[a] | 61.5 | Apple | 18.7 | 88.9 | −66.8 |
| | | Tomato | − | 90.0 | − |
| | | Melon | − | 88.0 | − |
| | | Tangerine | − | 87.5 | − |
| | | Pear | − | 8.5 | − |
| Other emulsions | | | | | |
| Alginate (2.0%)[b], without emulsifier | 51.5 | Garlic[a] | 18.3 | 81 | −43.0 |
| Alginate (2.0%)[b], added β-sitosterol (2000 ppm) | 31.1 | Garlic[a] | 18.3 | 51 | −11.2 |
| Shellac[c] | 33.4 | Grapefruit[b] | 23.0 | 53 | |
| Polyethylene wax[c] | 33.4 | Grapefruit[b] | 23.0 | 56 | |
| Carnauba wax[c] | 28.8 | Orange[b] | 20.0 | 46 | |
| Resin[c] | 35.6 | Orange[b] | 20.0 | 46 | |

[a]  Choi *et al.* (2001).
[b]  Hershko and Nussinovitch (1998).
[c]  Hagenmaier and Baker (1993).

that of other fruits. Park and others (1996) reported that pear surface was more evenly coated by corn-zein and Semperfresh[TM] solutions.

## 6.6    Determining diffusivities of fruits

Knowledge of the diffusivities of gases in bulky plant organs is essential in understanding physiological changes, gas exchanges and internal gas composition. The internal gas composition of fruits is determined by the diffusivities of skin, flesh and stem (Burg and Burg, 1965; Cameron and Yang, 1982). Burg and Burg (1965) designed a system to determine gas resistance factors which can be used to estimate gas diffusivities in bulky plant organs using the ratio of internal concentration to the ratio of the production of carbon dioxide and ethylene in the steady state. The diffusivities of gases in bulky plant tissue can be calculated as shown in Box 3.

There have been several reports on determining the diffusivities of bulky plant organs. Burg and Burg (1965) defined a resistance factor ($R$) which could be estimated for bulky plant organs, in banana and tomato, as the ratio of internal concentration to the ratio of production of carbon dioxide and ethylene in the steady state. They estimated that more than 60% of gas exchange takes place through the stem scar in tomatoes. But this resistant factor is only an empirical value without conventional dimensions and is not constant with changes in the surface to volume ratio. Cameron and Yang (1982) measured the efflux of a metabolic inert gas, ethane, which is neither produced nor metabolized to a significant degree by the tissue. It was shown that over 97% of gas exchange in tomato fruits occurs through the stem scar. However, the measurement of ethane efflux introduces several uncertainties because they did not measure the diffusivities of exocarp, pericarp and stem scar separately.

Solomos (1987), in a review of the principles of gas exchange in bulky plant organs, considered stationary states for $CO_2$ diffusion through spherical- and cylindrical-shaped plant organs and determined the diffusivities of flesh and skin of apple in the peeled and intact fruit. The effect of the stem in gas transfer was not considered in determining the apparent diffusivities of apple.

Wax undoubtedly serves as a gas barrier to oxygen, carbon dioxide and water vapor and other metabolic gases and also provides protective functions (for example, mechanical damage, fungal and insect attack). Therefore, it can be assumed that the primary factor which regulates the internal concentration of gases is the skin in bulky plant organs. In apple the resistance of apple skin to gas diffusion was 10- to 20-fold greater than that of the flesh, depending on the cultivar (Solomos, 1987). Chinnan and Park (1995) built such a system from Plexiglass (diffusion cell, Fig. 6.1) and used it to determine the gas diffusivities of skin, pericarp and stem scar of tomatoes (see Fig. 6.2).

The gas diffusivities of exocarp plus pericarp, pericarp and stem scar increased as the tomatoes developed from the green stage to the red stage. The oxygen and carbon dioxide diffusivities of the stem scar increased 1.2–1.3 times

## Box 3   Diffusivity

Gas exchange in bulky plant tissue can be approximated by Fick's first law. The flux of a gas in Fick's law is dependent on the gradient of concentration and diffusivities of plant organs. However, to determine the gradient of gases, Fick's second law can be employed (Chang, 1981; Gerard, 1931; Hill, 1928; Ricciardi, 1977; Solomos, 1987, 1989). If diffusion is one-dimensional and the diffusion coefficient is constant, the rate of transfer through unit area becomes:

$$\partial C / \partial t = D \partial C / \partial X \qquad 6.8$$

In the non-steady state, all the solutions can be obtained either by the method of separation of variables and Fourier series or by the Laplace transformation (Carslaw and Jaeger, 1959; Crank, 1975; Doty, 1946; Edwards and Penny, 1985; Jost, 1960; Tuwiner, 1962).

If surface concentrations are constant, the following boundary and initial conditions may apply:

$$C = C_1, x = 0, t \geq 0$$
$$C = 0, x = L, t \geq 0$$
$$C = 0, 0 < x < L, t = 0$$

The solution in the form of a trigonometrical series is:

$$C(x,t) = C_1(1 - x/L) - 2/\pi \sum_{n=1}^{\infty} C_1/n \, \sin(nx/L) \exp(-Dn^2 \pi^2 t / L^2) \qquad 6.9$$

As $t$ approaches infinity the terms involving the exponential vanish and we simply have the linear concentration distribution. The rate at which the gas emerges from unit area of the surface $x = L$ of the test sample is given by $-D(\partial C / \partial X)_{x=1}$, which is easily deduced from equation [6.9]. By integrating with respect to $t$, we obtain the total amount of diffusing substance $Q_t$ which has passed through the membrane in time $t$ as follows:

$$Q_t / L C_1 = Dt / L^2 - 1/6 - 2\pi \sum_{n=1}^{\infty} (-1) \exp(-Dn^2 \pi^2 t / L^2) \qquad 6.10$$

As $t$ approaches infinity, equation [6.10] approaches the line:

$$Q_t = DC_1 / L(t - L^2 / 6D) \qquad 6.11$$

This has an intercept $L$ on the $t$-axis given by:

$$L_t = L^2 / 6D \qquad 6.12$$

The intercept $L_t$ is referred to as the 'time lag'. Thus, the measured values of concentration of the diffusion constant can be determined from the linear portion of the plot (Floros and Chinnan, 1989).

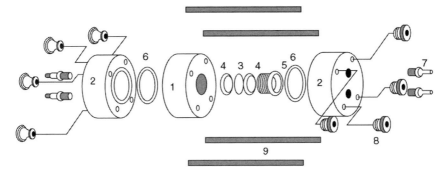

**Fig. 6.1**   Diffusion cell is constructed from Plexiglass™ to determine diffusivities. The cell is composed of three main parts: the sample holder, the supplying chamber and the sampling chamber. The face of each part is tooled for an O-ring which provides a tight connection. Chinnan and Park (1995) modified and reconstructed the apparatus for this gas diffusion study. (1) Sample holder, (2) gas chamber, (3) sample, (4) sample retainers, (5) threaded bush, (6) sealing O-ring, (7) tubing adapters, (8) thumb nuts, (9) thread rods.

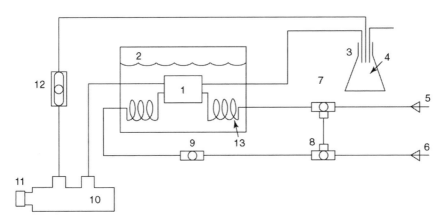

**Fig. 6.2**   Diffusivity can be measured by the following procedures (Chinnan and Park, 1995). Each of the cored and sliced samples prepared for the study is placed in the diffusion cell and a premixed gas (9.9% $O_2$, 10.1% $CO_2$, 80.0% $N_2$) is introduced to the supplying chamber. The amount of $CO_2$ and $O_2$ diffusing through the sample in time $t$ into the sampling chamber can be measured by gas chromatography. The sampling interval is 5 min, and the total sampling period is 2 h. The diffusion cell is immersed in a water bath maintained at 21°C. All equipment for determining gas diffusivities is placed in a heat insulated chamber and the temperatures at several places inside the chamber are monitored. (1) Diffusion cell, (2) water bath, (3) flask, (4) mineral oil, (5) test gas inlet, (6) nitrogen inlet, (7) three-way valve, (8) three-way connector, (9) two-way valve, (10) sampling chamber, (11) silicone septum, (12) gas flowmeter, (13) brass tubing.

as the tomatoes developed from green to red. The extent of increase in gas diffusivities for exocarp plus pericarp and pericarp were greater than that of the stem scar during the ripening process. Progressive loss of firmness during the ripening process is the result of a gradual transformation of protopectin into pectin which is degraded by the enzyme polygalacturonase in the cell wall (Hobson and Davies, 1971). This enzymatic degradation of pectin can probably be attributed to greater diffusion of gases in the bulky organs of tomato.

## 6.7   Measuring internal gas composition of fruits

A cylindrical plug of tissue was removed from individual fruits (oranges, apples, tomato, cantaloupe, water melon and pineapple) using a rubber stopper corer. A glass tube was sealed around the hole to the surface of the produce sample. In order to measure internal gas composition, gas in the glass tube was allowed to equilibrate with internal gases (Banks and Kays, 1988; Park *et al.*, 1994c). Then a gas sample was taken from the glass tube with a syringe injected through the sealing stopper. By immersing both produce sample and attached glass tube in water atmospheric contamination at the point of syringe insertion can be prevented. Gas samples will be analyzed by gas chromatography. Required equilibrium times (when gas composition of the inside of the glass tube is constant) need to be determined by periodically monitoring gas changes inside the glass tube. Equilibrium time can be expected to vary with variety, ripeness, temperature and harvesting season for various fruits but two hours is usually enough time.

## 6.8   Future trends

Using gas permeation data on edible coatings, diffusivity data for the skin and flesh of fruits and mathematical models, the internal gas composition can be predicted for selected fruits. Predictions of internal gas compositions with and without coatings will enable better matches to be made between individual fruits and individual edible coatings. The mathematical model could be verified by comparing predicted and measured internal gas composition for various coating materials and thicknesses on selected fruits. Also optimum edible coating thickness can be calculated for each produce–coating combination.

### 6.8.1   Predicting internal gas composition

Gas diffusion models will be determined according to physical shape and composition of individual fruits. For example, if one-dimensional steady state diffusion with a constant diffusion coefficient is assumed, the gas diffusion model for a hollow sphere can be used to predict the internal oxygen composition of some fruits such as apples and cantaloupes as follows. In one-dimensional diffusion with a constant diffusion coefficient, the rate of gas

---

## Box 4   Optimal edible coating thickness

The hollow sphere model can also be used to determine the optimal edible coating thickness in some fruits such as apple and cantaloupe melons. In edible film-coated apple and cantaloupe, the flux of oxygen passing through the spherical fruit wall from the center to the interface between the film coating and the fruit surface should equal the flux of oxygen passing through the edible coating from the interface between the film coating and the fruit surface to the atmosphere, and should equal the rate of oxygen consumption of the edible film-coated apple and cantaloupe in the steady state (Carslaw and Jaeger, 1959; Chang, 1981; Crank, 1975; Doty, 1946; Jost, 1960; Solomos, 1987):

$$Q_t = 4\pi D_{app}ab(C_2 - C_1)/(b - a)$$
$$= 4\pi D_{cz}((C_2 - C_x)/X)b^2 = R_c(O_2)W \qquad 6.17$$

where $R_c(O_2)$ is the oxygen consumption rate of coated fruits, $D_{cz}$ is the diffusivity of edible coatings and $X$ is the thickness of the edible coating. $C_x$ is oxygen concentration at the surface between the edible coating and the surface of fruits.

The optimal coating thickness which will create a desirable range of internal oxygen concentrations ($C_1$) in apples, (i.e., 2–3%) and cantaloupe melons (3–5%) can be calculated from equation 6.18]:

$$X = 4\pi D_{cz}(C_2 - C_x)b^2/R_c(O_2)W) \qquad 6.18$$

where $b + X$ becomes $b$ when $X$ is very small. $C_x$ is determined from equation [6.17] with $C_2 = C_x$.

---

transfer in the sphere is (Carslaw and Jaeger, 1959; Chang, 1981; Crank, 1975; Doty, 1946; Jost, 1960; Solomos, 1987):

$$\partial C/\partial t = D(\partial^2 C/\partial r^2 + (2/r)(\partial C/\partial r)) \qquad 6.13$$

on substituting $u = Cr$ in the equation [6.13], we have: $\partial u/\partial t = D\,(\partial^2 C/\partial r^2)$. In the steady state, the differential equation for this case is:

$$d(r^2\,dC/dr)/dr = 0 \qquad 6.14$$

In a hollow sphere where $a \leq r \leq b$, if gas concentrations are kept constant at the surfaces so that they are equivalent to $C_1$ at $r = a$ and $C_2$ at $r = b$, then $C = [aC_1(b - r) + bC_2(r - a)]/r(b - a)$. By integrating with respect to time $t$ over the surface area, the total amount of diffusing gas $Q_t$ passing through the wall can be determined by (Carslaw and Jaeger, 1959; Crank, 1975; Solomos, 1987):

$$Q_t = 4\pi D_{app}ab(C_2 - C_1)/(b - a) \qquad 6.15$$

where $D_{app}$ is apparent diffusivity of the hollow sphere and $a$ and $b$ are constants for individual fruits.

However, in the steady state the flux of oxygen passing through the spherical fruit wall should equal the rate of gas consumption, thus:

$$Q_t = 4\pi D_{app} ab(C_2 - C_1)/(b - a) = R(O_2)W \qquad 6.16$$

where $R(O_2)$ is respiration rate of oxygen per fruit and $W$ is weight of the fruit.

The internal oxygen composition, $C_1$, can be predicted using equation [6.16]. The correlation factors can be calculated from actual measurement of internal gas composition. Also, the predicted internal gas composition of edible film-coated fruits and vegetables can be verified by measuring internal gas composition. Optimum edible coating thickness can be calculated for each produce–coating combination as shown in Box 4.

### 6.8.2   Measurement of quality and shelf-life change

Quality criteria for edible film-coated fruits must be determined carefully and the quality parameters must be monitored throughout the storage period. For example, the color change and firmness are very important quality parameters in some fruits. The color change, loss of firmness, ethanol fermentation, decay ratio and weight loss of edible film-coated fruits need to be monitored (Shewfelt *et al.*, 1987). The color change is monitored by the change in hue angle. An Instron universal test machine can be used to measure firmness by a non-destructive method (Bourne, 1982). Sensory evaluation and consumer acceptability tests need to be examined during storage.

## 6.9   References

ASTM (1987) *Annual Book of ASTM Standards*, Philadelphia, American Society for Testing and Materials.

AYDT T P, WELLER C L and TESTIN R F (1991) 'Mechanical and barrier properties of edible corn and wheat protein films', *Trans ASAE*, **34** (1) 207.

BANKS N H (1984) 'Some effects of TAL Pro-long coating on ripening bananas', *J Exp Bot* **35** 127.

BANKS N H and KAYS S J (1988) 'Measuring internal gases and lenticel resistance to gas diffusion in potato tubers', *J Am Hortic Sci*, **113** (4) 577.

BEN-YEHOSHUA S (1969) 'Gas exchange, transportation, and the commercial deterioration in storage of orange fruit', *J Am Soc Hortic Sci*, **94** 524–8.

BEN-YEHOSHUA S (1985) 'Individual seal-packaging of fruit and vegetables in plastic film – a new postharvest technique', *J Am Soc Hort Sci*, **20** 32–7.

BOURNE M (ED) (1982) *Food Texture and Viscosity: Concept and Measurement*, New York, Academic Press.

BURG S P and BURG E A (1965) 'Gas exchange in fruits', *Physiological Plantarum*, **18** 870–84.

CAMERON A C and YANG S F (1982) 'A simple method for the determination of resistance to gas diffusion in plant organs', *Plant Physiol*, **70** (1) 21–3.

CARSLAW H and JAEGER J (1959) *Conduction of Heat in Solids*, Oxford, Clarendon Press.

CHANG R (1981) *Physical Chemistry with Applications to Biological Systems*, New York, Macmillan.

CHINNAN M S and PARK H J (1995a) 'Effect of plasticizer level and temperature on water vapor transmission of cellulose-based edible films', *J Food Process Eng*, **18** 417–29.

CHINNAN M S and PARK H J (1995b) 'Determining oxygen and carbon dioxide diffusivities of exocarp, pericarp and stem scar in tomatoes', *J Appl Eng Agric*, **11** (3) 393–6.

CHOI W Y, PARK H J, AHN D J, LEE J S and LEE C Y (2001) 'Wettability of chitosan coating solution on ''Fuji'' apple skin', J Food Sci, in press.

CHU C L (1986) 'Poststorage application of TAL Pro-long on apples from controlled atmosphere storage'. *HortScience*, **21** (2) 267–8.

CRANK J (ed) (1975) *The Mathematics of Diffusion*, London, Oxford University Press.

DOTY P (1946) 'On the diffusion on vapors through polymers', *J Chem Phys*, **14** (4) 244–52.

EDWARDS C and PENNY D (1985) *Elementary Differential Equations with Applications*, Englewood Cliffs, NJ, Prentice Hall.

ERBIL H Y and MUFTUGIL N (1986) 'Lengthening the postharvest life of peaches by coating with hydrophobic emulsions', *J Food Proc Pres*, **10** 269–79.

FLOROS J D and CHINNAN M S (1989) 'Determining the diffusivities of sodium hydroxide through tomato and capsicum skins', *J Food Eng*, **9** (2) 129–41.

GERARD R W (1931) 'Oxygen diffusion in cells', *Biol Bull*, **60** (3) 245–68.

GILBERT S G and PEGAZ D (1969) 'Finding a new way to measure gas permeability', *Package Eng*, **14** (1) 66–9.

GIST-BROCADES N V (1981) British Patent 1 593 856.

HAGENMAIER R D and BAKER R A (1993) 'Reduction in gas exchange of citrus fruit by wax coatings', *J Agric Food Chem*, **41** 283–7.

HARDENBURG R E (1967) *Wax and Related Coatings for Horticultural Products. A Bibliography*, Agricultural Research Service Bulletin 51–55, United States Department of Agriculture, Washington, DC.

HERSHKO V and NUSSINOVITCH A (1998) 'The behavior of hydrocolloid coatings on vegetative materials', *Biotechnol Prog*, **14** 756–65.

HILL A V (1928) 'Diffusion of oxygen and lactic acid through tissue', *Proc R Soc Biol Ser B*, **104** (728) 39–96.

HOBSON G and DAVIES J (1971) *The tomato, in The Biochemistry of Fruits and their Products*, London and New York, Academic Press, 437–82.

JOST W (1960) *Diffusion in Solids, Liquids, Gases*, New York, Academic Press.

KADER A A, ZAGORY D and KERBEL Z L (1989) 'Modified atmosphere packaging of fruits and vegetables', *Crit Rev Food Sci Nutr*, **28** (1) 1.

KAMPER S L and FENNEMA O (1984) 'Water vapor permeability of edible bilayer films', *J Food Sci*, **49** 1478.

KROCHTA J M and DE MULDER-JOHNSTON C (1997) 'Edible and biodegradable polymer films challenges and opportunities', *Food Technol*, **51** (2) 61–74.

LANDROCK A H and PROCTOR B E (1952) 'Gas permeability of films', *Modern Packaging*, 6 131–201.

LOWINGS P H and CUTTS D F (1982) 'The preservation of fresh fruits and vegetables', *Proc Inst Food Sci Technol*, **15** 52–4.

NISPEROS-CARRIEDO M O, SHAW P E and BALDWIN E A (1990) 'Changes in volatile flavor components of pineapple orange juice as influenced by the application of lipid and composite films', *J Agric Food Chem*, **38** (6) 1382.

PARK H J (1999) 'Development of advanced edible coatings for fruits', *Trends Food Sci Technol*, **10** 254–60.

PARK H J, WELLER C L, VERGANO P J and TESTIN R F (1993) 'Permeability and mechanical properties of cellulose-based edible films'. *J Food Sci*, **58** (6) 1361–4, 1370.

PARK H J and CHINNAN M S (1995a) 'Gas and water vapor barrier properties of edible films from proteins and cellulosic materials', *J Food Eng*, **25** 497–507.

PARK H J, BUNN J M, VERGANO P J and TESTIN R F (1994a) 'Gas permeation and thickness of the sucrose polyesters, Semperfresh™, coatings on apples', *J Food Proc Pres*, **18** 349–58.

PARK H J, CHINNAN M S and SHEWFELT R L (1994b) 'Edible coating effects on storage life and quality of tomatoes', *J Food Sci*, **59** (3) 568–70.

PARK H J, CHINNAN M S and SHEWFELT R L (1994c) 'Edible corn-zein film coatings to extend storage life of tomatoes', *J Food Proc Pres*, **18** 317–31.

PARK H J, BUNN J M, VERGANO P J and TESTIN R F (1994d) 'Water vapor permeability and mechanical properties of grain protein-based films as affected by mixtures of poly-ethylene glycol and glycerin plasticizers', *Trans ASAE*, **37** (4) 1281–5.

PARK H J, RHIM J W and LEE H Y (1996) 'Edible coating effects on respiration rate and storage life of "Fuji" apples and "Shingo" pears', *Food Biotechnol*, 5 59–63.

PARK H J, JUNG S T, SONG J J, KANG S G, VERGANO P J and TESTIN R F (1998) 'Mechanical and barrier properties of chitosan-based biopolymer film', *Chitin Chitosan Res*, **5** 16–29.

RICCIARDI L (1977) *Diffusion Processes and Related Topics in Biology*, Beltz Offsetdruck, Springer-Verlag.

RISSE L A, CHUN D, MCDONALD R E and MILLER W R (1987) 'Volatile production and decay during storage of cucumbers waxed, imazalil-treated, and film-wrapped', *HortScience*, **22** (2) 274–6.

RULON J and ROBERT H (1993) *Wetting of Low-energy Surfaces*, ed. John C, Wettability, Seattle, Marcel Dekker Inc.

SANTERRE C R, LEACH T F and CASH J N (1989) 'The influence of the sucrose polyester, Semperfresh™, on the storage of Michigan grown "McIntosh" and "Golden Delicious" apples', *J Food Proc Pres*, **13** 293–305.

SEGALL R H, DOW A and DAVIS P L (1974) 'Effect of waxing of decay, weight loss, and volatile pattern of cucumbers', *Proc Florida State Hortic Soc*, **37** 250–1.

SHEWFELT R L, PRUSSIA S E, RESURRECCION A V A, HURST W C and CAMPBELL D T (1987) 'Quality changes of vine-ripened tomatoes within the postharvest handling system', *J Food Sci*, **52** (3) 661–72.

SMITH S M and STOW J R (1984) 'The potential of a sucrose ester coating material for improving the storage and shelf-life qualities of Cox's Orange Pippin apples', *Annu Appl Biol*, **104** 383–91.

SMITH S, GEESON J and STOW J (1987) 'Production of modified atmospheres in deciduous fruits by the use of films and coatings', *HortScience*, **22** (5) 772–6.

SMOCK R M (1935) 'Certain effects of wax treatments on various varieties of apples and pears', *Am Soc Hortic Sci*, **33** 284–9.

SMOCK R M (1940) 'Some additional effects of waxing apples', *Am Soc Hortic Sci*, **37** 448–52.

SOLOMOS T (1987) 'Principles of gas exchange in bulky plant tissues', *HortScience*, **22** (5) 766–71.

SOLOMOS T (1989) 'A simple method for determining the diffusivity of ethylene in "McIntosh" apples', *Sci Hortic*, **39** (4) 311–18.

SPARKS W (1976) 'Losses in potatoes and lesser fruits and vegetables', in *Proceedings of National Food Loss Conference*, eds Zaehringer M and Early J, College of Agriculture, University of Idaho, Moscow.

SPURGEON D (ed) (1976) *Hidden Harvest*, International Development Research Center, Ottawa, Canada.

TUWINER S (1962) *Diffusion and Membrane Technology*, American Chemical Society Monograph Series, New York, Reinold.

ZHANG D L and QUANTICK P C (1997) 'Effects of chitosan coating on enzymatic browning and decay during postharvest storage of litchi fruit', *Postharvest Biol Technol*, **12** 195–202.

# Part II

# Traditional preservation technologies

# 7

# The control of pH

**F.-K. Lücke, University of Applied Sciences (Fulda), Germany**

## 7.1  Introduction

The pH is the negative logarithm of the hydrogen ion activity (where activity approximates concentration if the solution becomes more dilute). It is evident that pH is an important factor affecting growth of micro-organisms in food because it affects (i) microbial energy metabolism involving the build-up of gradients of hydrogen ions across membranes, and (ii) microbial enzyme activity and stability of cellular macromolecules. Moreover, pH also affects the sensory properties of many foodstuffs. This applies not only to taste, but also to consistency of food. For example, lowering the pH causes coagulation of milk casein and meat proteins, changes the solubility of pectins, and inactivates amylases in rye dough.

The pH of a food is mainly determined by free carboxyl and amino groups in low molecular weight compounds – and to a lesser extent – in the cellular macromolecules (proteins, nucleic acids, polysaccharides). It can be controlled by the choice of raw material (e.g., plant varieties, animal tissues) and by the addition or *in situ* formation of acidic or alkaline low molecular weight compounds. Growth of micro-organisms may be inhibited by either low or high pH. However, only few food commodities (e.g., eggs; see Leistner and Gould, 2002) are still edible at pH above 9.0, the maximum pH still permitting growth of a wide range of micro-organisms. Hence, organic acids are most important in food preservation.

As will be shown in detail in section 7.2, the effect of organic acids on micro-organisms in foods depends on their dissociation constant and from the ability of their undissociated form to penetrate the cytoplasmic membrane. Some organic acids act virtually only by the latter mechanism, and are, accordingly, classified as 'preservatives' in food legislation. This applies to sorbic, benzoic and propionic acids. Use of these acids is also treated in this paper, even though its emphasis is on acidulants that are naturally present in many foodstuffs or that have been used for food preservation before the advent of synthetic chemicals.

## 7.2   The effect of pH on cellular processes

Micro-organisms can survive and grow only in low-pH environments if they are able to maintain their cytoplasmic pH fairly constant at near-neutral levels, i.e., to maintain a 'pH homeostasis'. 'Passive pH homeostasis' means that micro-organisms either prevent external protons from entering the cell or increase the buffering capacity of their cytoplasm by synthesis of glutamate and/or citrate. A major factor for passive pH homeostasis is the very low permeability of the cell membrane to protons and other ions. To pass through the membranes, these protons require special protein 'pumps' such as the proton-translocating ATPase synthesizing ATP. Protons also enter the cell if their concentration is high enough to damage the membrane (or structures stabilizing it), or if processes injuring the cells (e.g., sublethal heat treatment) permeabilize the cytoplasmic membrane and/or the outer membrane of Gram-negative bacteria. However, the membrane barrier is overcome if organic acids penetrate the cell membrane and dissociate at the pH of the cytoplasm, thus liberating protons. This is the 'classic' (Freese *et al.*, 1973) explanation of the antimicrobial effect of undissociated lipid-soluble weak organic acids. 'Active pH homeostasis' means that the cells maintain their cytoplasmic pH through metabolic activity. A classic example for this is the pH-dependent shift from acid to neutral fermentation products observed with certain *Enterobacteriaceae* and clostridia. However, a more general reaction is the excretion of protons or proton donors by active transport systems. The most important mechanism is the energy-dependent exchange of protons by potassium ions (cf. Hill *et al.*, 1995; Booth, 1999). In addition, some acid-resistant micro-organisms have transport systems to excrete organic acids. Active excretion of lactate has been demonstrated in *Lactobacillus helveticus* (Gätje *et al.*, 1991), and there is evidence that preservative-resistant yeasts such as *Zygosaccharomyces baillii* have inducible transport systems to excrete acetate (Sousa *et al.*, 1996), sorbate and benzoate (Warth, 1977).

Growth ceases once the energy expenditure for active pH homeostasis adds so much to the maintenance energy that the rate of energy supply by catabolism is exceeded (Bracey *et al.*, 1998). From these considerations, it is evident that the minimum pH for growth, as well as the rate of inactivation of micro-organisms by acid is affected by (i) the nature of the acidulant; (ii) the presence of other inhibitory factors (e.g., low water activity, preservatives, low temperature) that may interfere with energy metabolism or increase the need for maintenance energy; (iii) the ability of the micro-organism to react to acid stress and to maintain passive and active pH homeostasis.

### 7.2.1  Effect of acidulants

Acids are characterized by their dissociation constant or its negative logarithm, the $pK_a$ value. Table 7.1 ranks the organic acids discussed in this chapter by their $pK_a$ values and the lipophilicity of their undissociated forms. The $pK_a$ values are in the range of the pH values of many foods. This means that at the pH of most foods, 3–7, significant amounts of these acids are undissociated. If the undissociated acid is not soluble in lipids, it is unlikely to have any inhibitory effect on micro-organisms because the cell membrane is impermeable to protons and to polar compounds such as citric and malic acids, unless it contains specific carrier proteins. On the other hand, lipophilic undissociated acids will penetrate the cell membrane and acidify the cytoplasm. This is the main mechanism by which these acids inhibit micro-organisms, with little if any effect on the pH of the food, however, other mechanisms may be involved, too. Stratford and Anslow (1998) provided evidence that sorbate also acts on yeasts by damaging their cell membrane, and McWilliam Leitch and Stewart (2002) reported different effects of L- and D-lactate on growth of *Escherichia coli* O157, indicating the involvement of enzymes and/or stereo-specific carrier proteins.

Propionic, sorbic and benzoic acids are classified by food legislators as 'preservatives' rather than 'acidulants', e.g., in Annex III to EU Directive 95/2. In foods manufactured with the addition of vinegar, acetic acid acts both as a source of external hydrogen ions and as a proton carrier though the membranes. However, because acetic acid is a natural metabolite in human metabolism and because it has been used in food preservation for thousands of years (see Adams, 1998), it is not classified as a food preservative in EU Directive 95/2.

There are strict limitations on the use of weak lipophilic organic acids in food preservation. In many foods, only low levels of acetic acid are tolerated sensorially. Limits on the use of propionate, sorbate and benzoate are set by sensory criteria, by legislation and by the poor acceptance of 'chemically' preserved food by consumers.

**Table 7.1**  $pK_a$ values for various food-grade organic acids

| Acid | Lipophilicity of undissociated acid | pK$_a$ at 25°C for | | |
|---|---|---|---|---|
|  |  | First H$^+$ | Second H$^+$ | Third H$^+$ |
| Citric | – | 3.13 | 4.76 | 6.40 |
| Malic | – | 3.40 | 5.11 | |
| Tartaric | – | 2.98 | 4.34 | |
| Gluconic | – | 3.6 | | |
| Lactic | ± | 3.86 | | |
| Acetic | + | 4.75 | | |
| Propionic | ++ | 4.86 | | |
| Sorbic | +++ | 4.76 | | |
| Benzoic | ++++ | 4.19 | | |

Modified from Lund and Eklund, 2000.

## 7.3    Combining pH control with other preservation techniques

The stability and safety of 'real foods' are affected by more than one factor (henceforth termed 'hurdle'; Leistner and Gould, 2002). In particular, foods are inedible if their pH is outside the range in which microbial growth is possible. One important strategy is to combine pH values between 3 and 5 with a pasteurization process inactivating acid-tolerant micro-organisms, or with preservatives inhibiting yeasts and moulds. Other foods are stabilized by appropriate combinations of low pH and low water activity.

### 7.3.1    Water activity ($a_w$)

To cope with osmotic stress (low $a_w$), cells synthesize compatible solutes such as betaine, ectoine, trehalose and proline (Booth, 1999). This requires additional energy, and it is not surprising that the minimum pH for growth increases at low water activities. However, Krist et al. (1998) provided data indicating that this additional energy burden should not be overestimated.

### 7.3.2    Preservatives

Most preservatives are weak acids active in their undissociated forms. As pH is lowered, the percentage of this form and thus the antimicrobial activity increases. In the pH range of most cured meats, relevant equilibrium levels of nitrous acid ($pK_a = 3.36$) are formed from nitrite. Unlike weak organic acids, nitrous acid perturbs energy-yielding reactions directly by reacting with iron involved in electron transport systems (heme iron in the respiratory chain, non-heme iron in ferredoxin and in pyruvate ferredoxin oxidoreductase, factors essential for clostridial energy metabolism; Cammack et al., 1999).

### 7.3.3    Low temperature

Cells tend to become more susceptible to low pH at temperatures close to their growth minima. This has been shown, for example, for non-proteolytic strains of Clostridium botulinum (Graham et al., 1997) and for Listeria monocytogenes (Tienungoon et al., 2000). However, there seems to be little synergy between pH and low temperature, indicating that there is little additional energy burden imposed on the cells by low temperature, and that temperature coefficients for growth and for the effect of the acids are comparable (Krist et al., 1998).

### 7.3.4    Oxygen availability

In facultative anaerobes such as Enterobacteriaceae or Listeria spp., the rate of ATP regeneration by aerobic respiration is markedly higher than by fermentation under anaerobic conditions. Accordingly, anaerobic growth of these organisms ceases at higher pH values than does aerobic growth. This is of particular relevance to the storage of vacuum-packaged meats (Grau, 1981).

### 7.3.5   Acid inactivation and acid adaptation

There is an increasing interest in predicting the rates of non-thermal inactivation of micro-organisms, in particular of pathogens with a low infective dose such as enterohemorrhagic strains of *Escherichia coli* (type O157:H7 and related strains). The prediction of survival of micro-organisms in acid environments is complicated by the phenomenon of acid adaptation in which micro-organisms exposed to suboptimal pH values acquire the ability to survive pH values that would otherwise rapidly kill them. Acid adaptation has been shown in various pathogens, including salmonellae (Leyer and Johnson, 1993), *Listeria monocytogenes* (Davis *et al.*, 1996) and, in particular, *Escherichia coli* O157:H7 (Leyer *et al.*, 1995). The occurrence and the mechanism of acid adaptation (acid tolerance response) has been reviewed by Hill *et al.* (1995), and, more recently, by Brul *et al.* (2002). It is dependent on protein synthesis. In the so-called 'global response', different types of stress (including acid stress) induce the synthesis of a sigma factor (RpoS) that modifies the DNA binding properties of RNA polymerase. Consequently, genes are transcribed that encode for different proteins that increase, by various means, the stress resistance of the cell. For example, chaperons may be formed which, by definition, stabilize the correct conformation of essential proteins.

Under conditions below (but close to) the threshold for growth, micro-organisms usually lose viability more rapidly at ambient than at chill temperatures. This phenomenon was termed 'metabolic exhaustion' (Leistner and Gould, 2002) and was also observed at acid pH, for example in fermented sausages (Nissen and Holck, 1998) and apple juice (Uljas and Ingham, 1999).

## 7.4   The effect of pH on the growth and survival of foodborne pathogens

With respect to their capabilities to grow at acid pH, micro-organisms of relevance to foods may be subdivided into five groups:

- Group 1 comprises virtually all species of yeasts and moulds. The minimum pH for their growth is outside the range of the pH of foods as acid as lemon juice. Hence, pH as a single hurdle will not be able to preserve a food from spoilage by these organisms.
- Group 2 comprises bacteria that are still able to grow in acid foods with pH values between 3 and 4. These bacteria include the acetic acid bacteria, *Alicyclobacillus,* and some species of lactic acid bacteria (*Oenococcus* and various *Lactobacillus* species).
- Group 3 comprises most of the strains of lactic acid bacteria capable of growth at rather high levels of lactic and acetic acids, but growing poorly or not at all at pH values below 4.0. This applies, for example, to the lactococci.
- Group 4 comprises most bacterial agents of food spoilage or foodborne diseases, and certain bacteria relevant for some food fermentations. Important

bacterial groups in this category are *Enterobacteriaceae, Staphylococcus, Pseudomonas,* as well as most genera forming heat-resistant spores (*Bacillus, Paenibacillus, Clostridium*). If the pH is adjusted with hydrochloric acid or citric acid, these organisms, under otherwise optimal conditions, may be able to grow at pH values down to 4.0 or slightly below. In the presence of about 50 mM titratable lactic acid and otherwise optimal conditions, the minimum pH for growth is of the order of 4.5, as shown, for example, for *Escherichia coli* (Presser *et al.*, 1998). It is therefore logical that the 'official' borderline between 'low-acid' and 'acid' food is set at pH 4.5 (see, for example, ICMSF, 1980). Growth of group 4 organisms in foods preserved by acetic acid (e.g., delicatessen salads) usually ceases at pH values below 5.0.

- Group 5 consists of some species very sensitive to pH, many of them from marine habitats. A typical representative of this group is *Shewanella putrefaciens*, a major psychrotrophic spoilage organism of fish. This bacterium is unable to grow at pH below 6.0 (Gill and Newton, 1979).

For details of the pH ranges for growth of micro-organisms important in relation to food, the reader is referred to textbooks or recent reviews (e.g., by Lund and Eklund, 2000). Various models predicting growth rates and growth/no growth interfaces have been published, in particular for *Salmonella, Escherichia coli, Clostridium botulinum, Listeria monocytogenes* and other bacterial pathogens (cf. McMeekin *et al.*, 2000), but also for specific spoilage organisms such as *Penicillium brevicompactum* (Membré *et al.*, 2001), *Zygosaccharomyces baillii* (Jenkins *et al.*, 2002), and *Lactobacillus curvatus* (Wijtzes *et al.*, 2001). Software packages available include Food MicroModel$^{TM}$ (McClure *et al.*, 1994) and Pathogen Modeling Program (Buchanan, 1993).

## 7.5    The use of pH control to preserve dairy, meat and fish products

This part of the chapter summarizes information on the critical limits for pH of those foods in which pH is a major hurdle. These limits may be used in setting up HACCP plans and sampling plans for these products. However, the critical pH values depend on other factors (hurdles) affecting microbial growth, in particular, the $a_w$ or the expected storage temperature. It should also be noted that it often takes time for the acid to be formed (by fermentation) or to penetrate into the food to be preserved. Therefore, HACCP plans for such products must also specify times and temperature for these processes.

### 7.5.1    Dairy products

The stability and safety of many dairy products are completely or partially due to lactic acid formed by lactose-fermenting lactic acid bacteria. The maximum levels of lactic acid and the final pH in fermented milk products depends on the acid tolerance of the starter culture and their proteolytic activity which they require to utilize milk proteins. Of the thermophilic (i.e., with optimal growth at about 40–45°C) homofermentative lactobacilli, strains of the species *Lactobacillus delbrueckii (ssp. bulgaricus, helveticus, lactis)* may accumulate up to 250 mM lactic acid and lower the pH to about 3.7 while most commercial starter cultures belonging to the *Lactobacillus acidophilus* group stop fermenting lactose at pH values of 4.0–4.3. When growing in axenic culture, *Streptococcus thermophilus* lowers the pH to about 4.3–4.6. The final pH of milk soured by mesophilic *Lactococcus* species is about 4.5.

Table 7.2 lists the target pH values of representative fermented dairy products. For sensory purposes, fermentation is usually stopped before the minimum possible pH is reached. In sourmilks, this can be done by chilling; for example, fermenting yoghurts are usually chilled once a pH of about 4.5 is reached, giving a target pH of about 4.2 in the final product. For the manufacture of cottage cheese, the curd is cut into pieces after fermentation, and a significant amount of the lactic acid formed is removed by washing the pieces. In most ripened cheeses coagulated by means of rennet, fermentation is also slowed down by salting, and for hard cheese manufacture, most of the lactose is removed by pressing and scalding the curd prior to fermentation.

In cheeses with pH values above 5.0, safety and sufficient stability must be assured by other hurdles, in particular, low $a_w$. In Emmental-type cheeses, propionic and acetic acids formed from lactate by propionibacteria to levels up to 100 and 40 mmoles/kg cheese, respectively (Teuber, 2000) help to inhibit undesired micro-organisms such as moulds. On surface-ripened soft cheeses, a microflora of moulds, yeasts and coryneform bacteria develops. The micro-organisms degrade lactic acids and liberate ammonia from amino acids, thus raising the pH to levels permitting growth of bacterial pathogens. Hence, it is essential to avoid contamination of such cheeses by pathogens such as *Listeria monocytogenes* or pathogenic *Escherichia coli* strains. Processed cheese with

**Table 7.2**    Target pH values of some fermented dairy products

| Product | Target pH in final products |
| --- | --- |
| Yoghurt (mild) | 4.1–4.4 |
| Kefir | 4.4–4.6 |
| Scandinavian-type sourmilks, buttermilk | 4.6 |
| Fresh cheeses: Quark | 4.6–4.7 |
| Fresh cheeses: Cottage cheese | 5.0 |
| Fresh cheeses: Mozzarella | 5.0–5.2 |
| Ripened cheeses without surface flora (most hard and semi-hard cheeses) | 5.2–5.8 |
| Ripened cheeses with surface flora (e.g., Camembert) | >5.8 |

Based on data compiled by Teuber, 2000.

$a_w$/pH combinations still allowing the growth of clostridia may be stabilized by the addition of sorbate at levels up to 0.2% (Sofos, 1989).

### 7.5.2   Muscle foods (meat, poultry and fish products)

The pH of muscle food depends mainly on the levels of glycogen in the muscles, and the activity of tissue enzymes converting glycogen into lactate and proteins into basic compounds such as ammonia and amines. In most lean skeletal muscles derived from pigs, cattle and sheep, about 100 mmoles of L-lactate per kg are accumulated during post-mortem glycolysis (Lawrie, 1991). Because of the high buffering capacity of muscle tissue, this level corresponds to a pH of about 5.6–5.8 and to a level of undissociated lactic acid of about one mM. Under these conditions, growth of many acid-sensitive bacteria is delayed. In contrast, the pH of liver, chicken legs and fish flesh does not drop below 6.2. Moreover, in fish tissue there is a large pool of readily degradable non-protein nitrogen compounds, causing the pH to rise significantly during storage (Gram and Huss, 2000). These data explain why most red meats keep better than edible offal, poultry and fish.

Rinsing fluids containing 1–3% lactic and/or acetic acids have been shown to reduce the bacterial counts on carcasses by about 1.5 log cycles (see Smulders and Greer, 1998). However, effects of such treatments on pathogens such as *Escherichia coli* O157:H7 should not be overestimated (Uyttendaele *et al.*, 2001). Due to the buffering capacity of the meat and the diffusion of the acids into the tissue, there is little if any lasting effect on pH and hardly any inhibitory effect on surviving micro-organisms. In addition, acid washes may lead to undesirable changes in appearance. Such treatment is mainly suited for cuts to be used for the production of hamburger meat or raw sausages. Treatments of carcasses and primal cuts with acid rinses are permitted in the United States but not in the European Union where it is maintained that strictly controlled processing hygiene is sufficient to ensure the safety of the product.

During meat processing, the pH may be lowered by the addition of organic acids or by microbial fermentation. The latter method, however, necessitates the addition of fermentable sugar since the tissue levels of glucose and glucose-6-phosphate in post-mortem lean meat do not exceed eight and five mmoles/kg, respectively (Lawrie, 1991), and even if one assumes that some ribose is also fermented, the additional lactic acid formed by fermentation is unlikely to exceed 25 mmoles/kg. Hence, at least 0.3% (15–20 mmoles/kg) of fermentable sugar is added to meat batters to be processed into fermented sausages.

The critical pH to be reached during dry sausage manufacture depends on additional inhibitory factors (hurdles) including $a_w$, nitrite and ripening temperature (Lücke, 2000). If the initial $a_w$ is about 0.96 – as in most dry sausage batters – it is sufficient to lower the pH to 5.3. As an alternative to microbial fermentation, glucono-$\delta$-lactone (GdL) is sometimes used, a compound that slowly hydrolyses to gluconic acid during the first hours after stuffing. However, gluconic acid is further degraded by many meat lactobacilli to lactic and acetic acids. This reaction interferes with the development of sensory characteristics typical for dry sausages. Therefore, GdL is seldom used for the manufacture of long-ripened dry sausages.

Survival of enterohemorrhagic strains of *Escherichia coli* in dry sausages has been studied by various authors in the context of the United States Department of Agriculture Food Safety and Inspection Service (USDA-FSIS) demand for a reduction of this organism by five log cycles (see Pond *et al.*, 2001, for review). The overall picture from these and German investigations (Stiebing *et al.*, 1998; Kofoth *et al.*, 1998) is that inactivation was most rapid at low pH and low $a_w$. When the finished sausages were stored at ambient temperature, the bacteria died faster than during chilled storage (see, for example, Nissen and Holck, 1998). However, with current industrial manufacturing conditions, it was hardly possible to achieve a reliable 5-D reduction of *Escherichia coli*.

A few cooked meat products (e.g., 'brawns') are preserved by acetic acid in combination with pasteurization. In the manufacture of such products, pieces of meat, sausage or ham are placed in a brine containing vinegar, gelatin, other solidifying agents (such as agar), salt, sugar and spices. The product is then heated to a core temperature between 72°C and 80°C. It contains about 60% of meat and 40% of solidified brine, has a pH of about 5.2 and is stable at ambient temperatures for about one week (Leistner and Gould, 2002). Use of organic acids to stabilize the more common cooked meats such as frankfurters and cooked hams is limited because water binding capacity is decreased, resulting in jelly separation, low yields and unsatisfactory eating quality. An example of a meat product in which the pH hurdle is successfully used to stabilize it is 'Gelderse Rookwurst'. To prepare this sausage, glucono-$\delta$-lactone is added to lower the pH to 5.4–5.6 after stuffing, jelly separation is minimized by adding pork rinds and diphosphate to the mix, and by heating it to 80°C core temperature only. Recontaminants are inactivated by reheating the packaged product, and the sausage is stable at ambient temperatures for several weeks (Leistner and Gould, 2002).

Another promising approach is the addition of mixtures of lactate and acetate (as 'diacetate') to these products. In the last few years, several papers have been published on the effect of lactic and acetic acid alone (Qvist *et al.*, 1994; Schmidt, 1995) and in mixtures on the microbiological safety and stability of meat products, in particular, bologna-type sausages, wieners, frankfurters and cooked hams. Unfortunately, many of these papers did not report on the sensory acceptability of the treated products, but the overall picture is that, at analytical levels of about 2% lactate and 0.16% acetate at pH 6.2 (corresponding to approximately one mmole each of undissociated lactic and acetic acid per kg), a significant extension of shelf life and, more importantly, suppression of *Listeria monocytogenes* in bologna-type sausages during storage at 7°C or below can be achieved while sensory deviations were still tolerable (Blom *et al.*, 1997; Stekelenburg, 2003).

In the manufacture of marinated fish, the raw material (e.g., herring fillets) is placed into a brine containing salt and vinegar and ripened for 35 days to obtain fish tissue containing at least 2.4% acetic acid and 6% sodium chloride in its water phase. This corresponds to pH values of 4.0–4.2 and $a_w$ values between 0.955 and 0.960. These conditions also assure the inactivation of nematode larvae and are stipulated in official regulations such as Annex 1 to the German 'Fischhygiene-Verordnung'. The marinated tissue is then placed in a brine containing spices. According to the German Code of Practice ('Leitsätze'), the pH of the final product must be 4.8 or below, corresponding to a concentration of acetic acid of at least 1.8% in its water phase. For the production of Scandinavian-type anchovies, the brine contains sugars, acidulants (sometimes also lactic acid bacteria) moderate levels of salts, and occasionally nitrate, and the fish is 'fermented' for 1–2 days at ambient temperature prior to ripening at chill temperatures. The pH does not normally drop to 5.5 or below, and the products are stabilized mainly by salt and by added preservatives. Benzoic and sorbic acids are frequently used to inhibit yeasts and moulds (levels of up to 0.2% – based on the sum of the content of the undissociated form of these acids – are permitted in Annex III to the EU Directive 95/2 on Food Additives).

## 7.6   The use of pH control to preserve vegetables, fruits, sauces and cereal products

Vegetables (including fruits such as cucumbers, melons and olives) have pH values above 5.2, and the undissociated forms of the responsible acids (predominantly malic and citric acids) are present only at very low concentrations and have little if any inhibitory effect *per se*. These products may be preserved by low pH obtained by lactic fermentation or addition of vinegar. In the latter method, boiled vinegar is added to the blanched raw materials (e.g., cucumbers) to give a concentration of acetic acid of at least 0.5% (according to the German Code of Practice 'Leitsätze') and a pH of about 3.7 (corresponding to about 90 mmoles of undissociated acetic acid per kg). This level of acetic acid is tolerated sensorially if sugar or sweeteners are added to the brine. For long shelf life at ambient temperatures, the products are usually pasteurized in order to inactivate some strains of yeasts, lactic acid bacteria or acetic acid bacteria that may slowly proliferate in the presence of high levels of acetic acid.

Reviews on the fermentation of vegetables have been published by Buckenhüskes *et al.* (1990) and Nout and Rombouts (2000). Fermented olives, cucumbers and cabbage have a significant market share while other vegetables are fermented on a small or domestic scale and sold though health stores or are used only for family supply, respectively.

Because plant tissues contain more than 1% of fermentable sugar and have limited buffering capacities, prolonged lactic fermentation leads to products with 2% or more titratable acid. Such products are not readily accepted by the consumer. Hence, the market share for unpasteurized products is low (e.g., about 17% in Germany for sauerkraut), and fermentation is often stopped by pasteurization of the product. A survey of pasteurized sauerkraut in Germany revealed pH values between 3.7 and 4.2, corresponding to about 100 mmoles of lactic and 50 mmoles of acetic acid per kg, respectively (cf. Buckenhüskes *et al.*, 1990). To achieve sufficient microbial stability and safety, a final pH of 4.2 should not be exceeded (Holzapfel, 1996). This is also true for Spanish-style fermented green table olives (target pH 3.8–4.2, corresponding to about 100 mmoles of lactic acid/kg) and fermented cucumbers. These products contain less acetic acid than does sauerkraut because fermentation takes place at higher salt concentrations and for longer periods. Under such conditions, homofermentative lactobacilli easily outgrow the heterofermentative leunocostocs (Nout and Rombouts, 2000). Untreated ripe (black) olives are fermented for shorter periods at higher salt concentrations, and lactic acid accumulates only to levels of 0.3–0.5% titratable acid, corresponding to a pH of around 4.5 (Garrido-Fernández *et al.*, 1995). Fermented vegetable juices are produced by adding homofermentative lactic acid bacteria that lower the pH to 3.8–4.0 (cf. Buckenhüskes *et al.*, 1990).

In contrast, most ripe fleshy fruits formed by multiannual plants (pome, stone, citrus, tropical fruits; berries), as well as tomatoes have pH values below 4.7, and growth potential for bacterial pathogens is low. The pH is mainly determined by the content of citric and malic acids in the fruits, and growth of fungi is possible throughout the whole pH range down to pH 2.2 (on lemons). However, the pH determines the requirements for heat treatment of fruit products such as canned fruits, jams and fruit juices. In the range of pH 4.0–4.5, 'butyric' anaerobic spore-forming bacteria (*Clostridium butyricum*, *Clostridium pasteurianum*), and, at storage temperatures above 25°C, *Bacillus coagulans* may still grow. This necessitates a more severe heat treatment (equivalent to an exposure to 100°C for 1–2 minutes).

Acidulants such as citric acid may be added to fruits with pH values in this range or even above, e.g., tomatoes and pears. At pH values below 4.0, a pasteurization treatment equivalent to an exposure to 80°C for about ten minutes (or to 92–99°C for 10–60 seconds) is usually applied. This treatment, however, is not sufficient to inactivate spores of *Alicyclobacillus spp.* (capable of developing at low pH and temperatures above 25–30°C), and not always sufficient to inactivate heat-resistant ascospores of *Byssochlamys spp.* and some other fungal species. These moulds may be inhibited by low $a_w$ (as prevailing in many jams) and/or sorbic and benzoic acids. The latter preservatives are, at levels below 0.1%, permitted by EU Directive 95/2 for the preservation of certain low-sugar jams and soft drinks. Acidulants are often added to fruit products for purposes other than microbial stability. Citric acid delays enzymatic browning and modifies the gelling properties of pectins, thus affecting the viscosity of jams and similar products.

'Drop' apples may become contaminated with animal faeces, and unpasteurized apple juice ('cider') was identified as a vector for foodborne infections. Hence, the United States Food and Drug Administration demands a warning on the label unless a reduction of *Escherichia coli* O157:H7 by five log cycles is ascertained. Non-thermal processes by which this reduction is achieved were designed (Uljas and Ingham, 1999; Comes and Beelman, 2002). These authors found that inactivation rates of salmonellae and *Escherichia coli* were higher in juices of low pH, higher storage temperatures (25–35°C), and in the presence of preservatives such as benzoic acid.

### 7.6.1   Mayonnaise, salad dressings, ketchups, and delicatessen salads

Mayonnaise, salad dressings, ketchups and comparable products are preserved by a combination of low pH (adjusted by acetic and citric acid), low $a_w$ (mainly depending on the relative levels of oil, water and salt in the formulation), and – sometimes – preservatives such as sorbic and benzoic acids. The target pH value depends on the level of other inhibitory factors such as $a_w$ and the presence of preservatives, but is generally about 4.0 (see Table 7.3). In contrast to ketchups, emulsion-type products cannot be pasteurized after mixing. When designing the formulation of the latter products, one must take into account the partition coefficient of the preservative agents between the water and the oil phase.

When sauces are used for the preparation of delicatessen salads, the acid is diluted and the relative proportions of sauces and solids should be adjusted so that the final salad has a pH value of 5.0 or below, and a concentration of undissociated acetic acid in the water phase is at least 0.1% or 16 mM. It should also be noted that considerable time is needed for the acid to penetrate through the solids. During this time there is a risk of growth of acid-sensitive bacteria in the solids (Baumgart, 1996).

Delicatessen salads may be spoiled by yeasts, moulds and/or lactic acid bacteria tolerating acetic acid. Growth of yeast and moulds is inhibited by sorbate. This preservative, however, has little if any effect on lactic acid bacteria, and some yeasts (especially *Zygosaccharomyces baillii*) are rather resistant to it. Hence, sorbate is mostly used in combination with benzoate. EU Directive 95/2 permits levels up to 0.15% (calculated as the sum of the undissociated forms) of these acids.

**Table 7.3**   Some critical limits for pH and acidity in mayonnaises, dressings and ketchups

| Product | Fat content % | $a_w$ | pH | Acetic acid in aqueous phase | |
|---|---|---|---|---|---|
| | | | | % | mmoles of undissociated acid/kg |
| Mayonnaise | 80 (emulsified) | *ca.* 0.93 | $\leq$ 4.1 | 2% | 270 mM |
| Emulsified salad dressings | 50 (emulsified) | *ca.* 0.95 | $\leq$ 4.2 | 1% | 130 mM |
| Tomato ketchup | <1 | *ca.* 0.94 | 3.8–4.0 | 0.9 % | 130 mM |

Based on data provided by Baumgart (1996) and Michels and Koning (2000).

### 7.6.2   Cereal products

The baking process destroys vegetative micro-organisms and mould spores, but not bacterial spores. In some wheat breads prepared without dough acidification, the combination of the hurdles pH (5.4–6.0) and $a_w$ (0.94–0.97) may still permit growth of some *Bacillus* strains. To prevent this, acetate is sometimes added to the flour to give a level of about 1–2 mmoles of undissociated acetic acid in the bread. Sourdoughs have pH values around 4.0, brought about by fermentation of maltose and glucose to lactic and acetic acids by homofermentative and heterofermentative lactic acid bacteria. The titratable acidity of the final dough ranges from 30 to 120 meq/kg, with a molar ratio between lactic and acetic acid of about 5. However, preservation is not the main purpose of sourdough use. Rather, the acid improves water uptake by the pentosans and inhibits amylases in rye flour. This is essential for breadmaking if the dough contains more than about 20% of rye flour.

Sorbate or propionate may be added to the dough in order to delay mould spoilage of baked goods. However, EU Directive 95/2 restricts the use of these preservatives to baked goods more prone to spoilage by moulds, namely, sliced and some other prepackaged products. The Directive also limits the levels to 0.1–0.3%, depending on the product.

## 7.7   Future trends

As stated by Leistner and Gould (2002), the future of food preservation techniques will be a skilled combination of hurdles to ascertain microbiological safety and stability while keeping sensory quality at a maximum. This approach could help to solve the dilemma caused by consumers' conflicting demands for freshness, convenience and low price. With respect to the hurdles 'pH' and 'weak acid preservatives', it is important to note the following:

- If adjusted with weak organic acids (lactate, acetate, weak-acid preservatives), pH inhibits micro-organisms by forcing them to use their metabolic energy to export protons and – in some cases – undissociated acids from the cell. Hence, a hurdle perturbing energy metabolism by, for example, damaging the cytoplasmic membrane of bacteria could potentiate the effect of low pH ('multitarget preservation'; Leistner and Gould, 2002).
- The 'pH hurdle' alone will not ascertain sufficient safety and stability of a food. Hence, predictive models that take the effect of other hurdles into account are valuable. Current models are based on a limited number of 'classic hurdles' such as $a_w$, pH, temperature, undissociated acids, preservatives. Several other factors may also affect the stability and safety of a food, for example, structural barriers or natural antimicrobial constituents in plant food. Hence, current predictive models usually predict less stability and safety than a food actually has. Therefore, they must be used with caution, and their output compared with the experience of food

processors and epidemiologists. Otherwise, unjustified public health concerns may cause loss of high-quality food from our markets. To predict growth and survival of micro-organisms in food more precisely, models should become less descriptive and more based on the biological processes involved. This is especially true for models trying to predict inactivation rates of micro-organisms.

- Studies on the effect of acids – including weak-acid preservatives – on micro-organisms in food are of limited value to industrial practice unless combined with a proper sensory evaluation of the product.
- When developing new methods of food preservation, adaptation and resistance development of target micro-organisms must be taken into account, bearing in mind that the resistance of individual cells within a population is heterogeneously distributed (Booth, 2002). This could become a problem with minimally processed foods where conditions are only slightly below the threshold permitting growth of target organisms.

## 7.8    References

ADAMS MR (1998), 'Vinegar', in Wood BJB, *Microbiology of fermented foods*, 2nd edn, Glasgow, Blackie, 1–44.

BAUMGART J (1996), 'Feinkosterzeugnisse', in Sinell HJ, Meyer H, *HACCP in der Praxis*, Hamburg, Behr's, 345–382.

BLOM H, NERBRINK E, DAINTY R, HAGTVEDT T, BORCH E, NISSEN H, NESBAKKEN T (1997), 'Addition of 2.5% lactate and 0.25% acetate controls growth of *Listeria monocytogenes* in vacuum-packed, sensory-acceptable servelat sausage and cooked ham stored at 4 degrees C', *Int J Food Microbiol* 38, 71–76.

BOOTH IR (1999), 'Adaptation to extreme environments', in Lengeler JW, Drews G, Schlegel HG, *Biology of the prokaryotes*, Stuttgart, Thieme, 652–671.

BOOTH IR (2002), 'Stress and the single cell: intrapopulation diversity is a mechanism to ensure survival upon exposure to stress', *Int J Food Microbiol* 78, 19–30.

BRACEY D, HOLYOAK CD, COOTE PJ (1998), 'Comparison of the inhibitory effect of sorbic acid and amphotericin B on *Saccharomyces cerevisiae*: is growth inhibition dependent on reduced intracellular pH?' *J Appl Microbiol* 85, 1056–1066.

BRUL S, COOTE P, OOMES S, MENSONIDES F, HELLINGWERF K, KLIS F (2002), 'Physiological action of preservative agents: prospective of use of modern microbiological techniques in assessing microbial behaviour in food preservation', *Int J Food Microbiol*, 79, 55–64.

BUCHANAN RC (1993), 'Developing and distributing user friendly application software', *J Ind Microbiol* 12, 251–255.

BUCKENHÜSKES H, JENSEN HA, ANDERSSON R, GARRIDO FERNÁNDEZ A, RODRIGO M (1990), 'Fermented vegetables', in Zeuthen P, Cheftel JC, Eriksson C, Gormley TR, Linko P, Paulus K., *Processing and Quality of Foods Vol 2: Food Biotechnology: Avenues to Healthy and Nutritious Products*, London, Elsevier Applied Science, pp. 2-162-2.187.

CAMMACK R, JOANNOU CL, CUI XY, TORRES MARTINEZ C, MARAJ SR, HUGHES MN (1999), 'Nitrite and nitrosyl compounds in food preservation', *Biochim Biophys Acta* 1411,

475–488.

COMES JE, BEELMAN RB (2002), 'Addition of fumaric acid and sodium benzoate as an alternative method to achieve a 5-log reduction of Escherichia coli O157:H7 populations in apple cider'. *J Food Protect* 65, 476–483.

DAVIS MJ, COOTE PJ, O'BYRNE CP (1996), 'Acid tolerance in *Listeria monocytogenes*: the adaptive acid tolerance response (ATR) and growth-phase-dependent acid resistance', *Microbiology* 142, 2975–2985.

FREESE E, SHEU, CW, GALLIERS E (1973), 'Function of lipophilic acids as antimicrobial food additives', *Nature* 214, 321–325.

GARRIDO FERNÁNDEZ A, GARCIA PG, BALBUENA MB (1995), 'Olive fermentations', in Rehm HJ, Reed G, Pühler A, Stadler P, *Biotechnology Vol. 9, Enzymes Biomass, Food and Feed*. Weinheim, VCH, 593–627.

GÄTJE G, MÜLLER V, GOTTSCHALK G (1991), 'Lactic acid excretion via carrier-mediated facilitated diffusion in *Lactobacillus helveticus*', *Appl Microbiol Biotech* 34 (6) 778–782.

GILL CO, NEWTON KG (1979), 'Spoilage of vacuum-packaged dark, firm, dry meat at chill temperatures', *Appl Environ Microbiol* 37, 362–364.

GRAHAM AF, MASSON DM, MAXWELL FJ, PECK MW (1997), 'Effect of pH and NaCl on growth from spores of non-proteolytic *Clostridium botulinum* at chill temperatures', *Lett Appl Microbiol* 42, 95–100.

GRAM L, HUSS HH (2000), 'Fresh and processed fish and shellfish', in Lund BM, Baird-Parker AC, Gould GW, *The microbiological safety and quality of food*, Gaithersburg (Md), Aspen, Vol. I, 472–506.

GRAU FH (1981), 'Role of pH, lactate, and anaerobiosis in controlling the growth of some fermentative Gram-negative bacteria on beef', *Appl Environ Microbiol* 42, 1043–1050.

HILL C, O'DRISCOLL B, BOOTH IR (1995), 'Acid adaptation and food poisoning microorganisms', *Int J Food Microbiol,* 28, 245–254.

HOLZAPFEL WH (1996), 'Haltbarmachung durch Säuren', in Sinell HJ, Meyer H, *HACCP in der Praxis*, Hamburg, Behr's, 111–132.

INTERNATIONAL COMMISSION ON MICROBIOLOGICAL SPECIFICATIONS FOR FOODS (ICMSF) (1980), *Microbial ecology of foods, Vol I: Factors affecting life and death of microorganisms*, New York, Academic Press.

JENKINS P, POULOS PG, COLE MB, VANDEVEN MH, LEGAN JD (2000), 'The boundary for growth of *Zygosaccharomyces bailii* in acidified products described by models for time to growth and probability of growth', *J Food Prot* 63, 222–230.

KOFOTH C, RÖDEL W, GAREIS M (1998), 'Beeinflussung des Überlebens von enterohämorrhagischen *E. coli* (EHEC) in Rohwurstprodukten', *Mitteilungsblatt der Bundesanstalt für Fleischforschung Kulmbach* 37, 153–159.

KRIST KA, ROSS T, MCMEEKIN TA (1998), 'Final optical density and growth rate; effects of temperature and NaCl differ from acidity', *Int J Food Microbiol* 43, 195–203.

LAWRIE RA (1991), *Meat Science*, 5th edition, Oxford, Pergamon.

LEISTNER L, GOULD GW (2002), *Hurdle technologies – Combination treatments for food stability, safety and quality*. New York, Kluwer.

LEYER GL, JOHNSON EA (1993), 'Acid adaptation induces cross-protection against environmental stresses in *Salmonella typhimurium*', *Appl Environ Microbiol* 59, 1842–1847.

LEYER GL, WANG LL, JOHNSON EA (1995), 'Acid adaptation of *Escherichia coli* increases survival in acid foods', *Appl Environ Microbiol* 61, 3752–3755.

LÜCKE FK (2000), 'Fermented meats', in Lund BM, Baird-Parker AC, Gould GW, *The microbiological safety and quality of food*, Gaithersburg (Md), Aspen, Vol. I, 420–444.

LUND BM, EKLUND T (2000), 'Control of pH and use of organic acids', in Lund BM, Baird-Parker AC, Gould GW, *The microbiological safety and quality of food*, Gaithersburg (Md), Aspen, Vol. I, 175–199.

MCCLURE PJ, BLACKBURN CDEW, COLE MB, CURTIS PS, JONES JE, LEGAN JD, OGDEN ID, PECK MW, ROBERTS TA, SUTHERLAND JP, WALKER SJ (1994), 'Modelling the growth, survival and death of microorganisms in foods: The UK Micromodel approach', *Int J Food Microbiol* 23, 265–275.

MCMEEKIN TA, PRESSER K, RATKOWSKY D, ROSS T, SALTER M, TIENUNGOON S (2000), 'Quantifying the hurdle concept by modelling the bacterial growth/no growth interface', *Int J Food Microbiol* 55, 93–98.

MCWILLIAM LEITCH EC, STEWART CS (2002), '*Escherichia coli* O157 and non-O157 isolates are more susceptible to L-lactate than to D-lactate', *Appl Environ Microbiol* 68, 4676–4678.

MEMBRÉ JM, KUBACZKA M, CHÈNÉ C (2001), 'Growth rate and growth-no-growth interface of *Penicillium brevicompactum* as functions of pH and preservative acids', *Food Microbiol* 18, 531–538.

MICHELS MJM, KONING W (2000), 'Mayonnaise, dressings, mustard, mayonnaise-based salads, and acid sauces', in Lund BM, Baird-Parker AC, Gould GW, *The microbiological safety and quality of food*, Gaithersburg (Md), Aspen, Vol. I, 807–835.

NISSEN H, HOLCK A (1998), 'Survival of *Escherichia coli* O157:H7, *Listeria monocytogenes* and *Salmonella kentucky* in Norwegian fermented, dry sausage', *Food Microbiol* 15, 273–279.

NOUT MJR, ROMBOUTS FM (2000), 'Fermented and acidified plant foods', in Lund BM, Baird-Parker AC, Gould GW, *The microbiological safety and quality of food*, Gaithersburg (Md), Aspen, Vol. I, 685–737.

POND TJ, WOOD DS, MUMIN IM, BARBUT S, GRIFFITHS MW (2001), 'Modelling the survival of *Escherichia coli* O157:H7 in uncooked, semidry, fermented sausage', *J Food Protect* 64, 759–766.

PRESSER KA, ROSS T, RATKOWSKY DA (1998), 'Modelling the growth limits (growth/no growth interface) of *Escherichia coli* as a function of temperature, pH, lactic acid concentration, and water activity', *Appl Environ Microbiol* 64, 1773–1779.

QVIST S, SEHESTED K, ZEUTHEN P (1994), 'Growth suppression of *Listeria monocytogenes* in a meat product', *Int J Food Microbiol* 24, 283–293.

SCHMIDT U (1995), 'Vakuumverpackter Brühwurstaufschnitt – Hemmung des Listerienwachstums durch technologische Maßnahmen', *Fleischwirtschaft* **75**, 24–27.

SMULDERS FJM, GREER GG (1998), 'Integrating microbial decontamination with organic acids in HACCP programmes for muscle foods: prospects and controversies', *Int J Food Microbiol* 44, 149–169.

SOFOS J (1989), *Sorbate food preservatives*, Boca Raton, CRC Press.

SOUSA MJ, MIRANDA L, CÔRTE-REAL M, LEÃO C (1996), 'Transport of acetic acid in *Zygosaccharomyces baillii:* Effects of ethanol and their implications on the resistance of the yeast to acidic environments', *Appl Environ Microbiol* 62, 3152–3157.

STEKELENBURG FK (2003), 'Enhanced inhibition of *Listeria monocytogenes* in Frankfurter sausage by the addition of potassium lactate and sodium diacetate mixtures', *Food Microbiol* 20, 133–137.

STIEBING A, BAUMGART J, VOGT N (1998), 'EHEC – Überlebensfähigkeit in schnittfester und streichfähiger Rohwurst', *Mitteilungsblatt der Bundesanstalt für Fleischforschung Kulmbach* 37, 160–167.

STRATFORD M, ANSLOW PA (1998), 'Evidence that sorbic acid does not inhibit yeast as a classic weak acid preservative', *Lett Appl Microbiol* 27, 203–206.

TEUBER M (2000), 'Fermented milk products', in Lund BM, Baird-Parker AC, Gould GW, *The microbiological safety and quality of food*, Gaithersburg (Md), Aspen, Vol. I, 535–589.

TIENUNGOON S, RATKOWSKY DA, MCMEEKIN TA, ROSS T (2000), 'Growth limits of *Listeria monocytogenes* as a function of temperature, pH, NaCl, and lactic acid', *Appl Environ Microbiol* 66, 4979–4987.

ULJAS HE, INGHAM SC (1999), 'Combinations of intervention treatments resulting in 5 $\log_{10}$-unit reductions in numbers of *Escherichia coli* O157:H7 and *Salmonella typhimurium* DT104 organisms in apple cider', *Appl Environ Microbiol* 65, 1924–1929.

UYTTENDAELE M, JOZWIK E, TUTENEL A, DE ZUTTER L, URADZINSKI J, PIERARD D, DEBEVERE, J (2001), 'Effect of acid resistance of *Escherichia coli* O157:H7 on efficacy of buffered lactic acid to decontaminate chilled beef tissue and effect of modified atmosphere packaging on survival of *Escherichia coli* O157:H7 on red meat', *J Food Protect* 64, 1661–1666.

WARTH AD (1977), 'Mechanism of resistance of *S. baillii* to benzoic, sorbic and other weak acids used as food preservatives', *J Appl. Bacteriol* 43, 215–230.

WIJTZES T, ROMBOUTS FM, KANT-MUERMANS ML, VAN RIET K, ZWIETERING MH (2001), 'Development and validation of a combined temperature, water activity, pH model for bacterial growth rate of *Lactobacillus curvatus*', *Int J Food Microbiol* 63, 57–64.

# 8

# The control of water activity

S. M. Alzamora, Universidad de Buenos Aires, Argentina,
M. S. Tapia, Universidad Central de Venezuela, A. López-Malo and
Jorge Welti-Chanes, Universidad de las Américas, México

## 8.1 Introduction

The influence of food water content on perishability has been known since ancient times. Between 15,000 and 10,000 BC our ancestors began to preserve excess fish, meat and fruit by drying in the wind and sun (Ray, 1992). Around 8,000 BC, many innovations in preservation techniques were introduced. To ensure a steady supply of food, grains and fruits were stabilized by natural drying and excess meat and fish preserved by smoking and dry salting. In 1795, Masson and Challet applied artificial drying to vegetables in a hot air room. In the 20th century, innovations have included artificial drying of liquids by drum or spray drying, and freeze drying.

These methods of preservation of food by drying and salting, developed over several millennia, were empirical and were more of an art than a science. Considerable interest in the influence of water activity ($a_w$) on food product quality and stability began in the early 1950s (Scott, 1953 and 1957). It was promoted by empirical and inconsistent observations between total moisture content and product stability. On the contrary, measured value of $a_w$ generally correlates well with the potential for growth and metabolic activity and so it has been assumed as a good indicator of water availability for microbial activity (Christian, 2000; Chirife, 1995; Lenovich, 1987). As a result, over the past several years, the $a_w$ control has been included into various government regulations, considering that $a_w$ rather than total moisture content, determines growth, death, survival, sporulation and toxin production by diverse microorganisms and setting $a_w$ limits on food products. Of all the factors affecting microbial growth, death and survival in food, the influence of $a_w$ on vegetative microorganisms and spores has been one of those most intensively studied by food microbiologists.

## 8.2    The concept of water activity

A review of basic and applied thermodynamics is required to understand the $a_w$ concept (Robinson and Stokes, 1965, Welti and Vergara, 1997). The concept of 'activity', assuming thermodynamic equilibrium, states that $a_w$ is equal to $f/f_o$, where $f$ is the fugacity of water in the system (i.e., the escaping tendency of water from solution) and $f_o$ is the fugacity of pure water at the same temperature. For an ideal gas in a mixture, the fugacity is coincident with its partial pressure. For a real gas, the fugacity is a function of pressure; as total pressure is reduced, the fugacity approximates the vapour pressure value (since all gases present ideal behaviour when pressure tends to zero). Then, for ideal gases or real gases at low pressures, the fugacities ratio can be replaced by the pressures ratio:

$$a_w = p_w/p_{w^o} = ERH/100 \qquad\qquad 8.1$$

where $p_w$ is the vapour pressure of water in equilibrium with the food, and $p_{w^o}$ is the vapour pressure of pure water at the same temperature. The vapour pressure of water in equilibrium with the food can be measured or related with the relative humidity of the atmosphere in equilibrium (ERH) with the food or the solution.

Water activity depends on water concentration as shown by equation:

$$a_w = x_w . \gamma_w \qquad\qquad 8.2$$

where $x_w$ is the mole fraction and $\gamma_w$ is the activity coefficient of the water. So, the chemical potential of the water, $\mu_w$, can be expressed as:

$$\mu_w = \mu_{wo} + R\,T \ln a_w = \mu_{wo} + R\,T \ln x_w + R\,T \ln \gamma_w \qquad\qquad 8.3$$

where $\mu_{wo}$ is the chemical potential of the pure water at the same temperature and pressure. The activity coefficient (equal to one for ideal solutions) indicates a departure from the so-called ideal behaviour and depends on relative solute size, polarity, solute-solute interactions and cooperative solvation. Many other alternative expressions (i.e., activity coefficient, water potential, practical osmotic coefficient and rational osmotic coefficient), easily transposed into $a_w$, are also used for practical convenience (Lilley, 1994).

In recent years, however, questions related to the meaningfulness of the $a_w$ concept have been asked by many researchers. First of all, water activity is defined only for a system that presents a thermodynamic equilibrium, which is, the measured partial vapour pressure above the food is presumed to be the same as that of water within the food, and also is defined at a specific temperature and total pressure. The equilibrium assumption is valid for infinite dilute systems, where diffusion rates of water molecules are high compared to the time scale of the measurement. But most intermediate moisture foods and dried foods are usually non-equilibrium systems. For example, the existence of two different paths between the adsorption and desorption isotherms (i.e., moisture sorption hysteresis) indicates, according to Franks (1991), the presence of non-equilibrium. The food material may be in a state of thermodynamic instability ('pseudo' stability) and frequently this unstable state lasts longer than the product's shelf-life (Wolf *et al.*, 1985, van der Berg and Bruin, 1981). Furthermore, the moisture contents of a food 'in equilibrium' with certain ERH can be subjected to changes during measuring periods. Also, many multicomponent food systems constituted by two or more phases (solid, liquid, aqueous and oil) may not present equilibrium from one phase to the other because of kinetic constraints. Or there may be a difference in water content near the surface of the packaging film and the bulb of the package.

These non-equilibrium situations may have important, negative or positive, implications in chemical and microbiological stability. In foods presenting hysteresis, for the same moisture content, the $a_w$ would be lower in foods prepared by desorption than by adsorption. A small water gain by a dried food may lead to unstable $a_w$ values. On the contrary, a much delayed crystallization of amorphous sugars in dried foods (that would significantly increase the $a_w$ value) would maintain the product in a state of 'pseudo-stability' during the normal lifetime. Another negative non-equilibrium situation is presented when moisture distribution in dried foods is non-homogeneous; the product may cake or show mould growth on the surface while the interior of the package remains intact.

A second problem arising from the $a_w$ consideration is the temperature dependence of the sorption isotherm. A change in temperature results in a change in $a_w$ at each moisture level. This change will be small for most saturated salt solutions but can be significant for dried products, whose structure may be modified affecting its entropy and thus its water sorption behaviour.

A third problem with the $a_w$ concept is that it does not take into account the effect *per se* of solute-solute and solute-water interactions, which have a profound influence on the kinetics of food deterioration reactions. The introduction of a solute perturbs the water structure, altering the nature and extent of hydrogen bonding (Le Maguer, 1987) and affecting the rate of physicochemical and microbiological phenomena. The effect of water activity cannot be separated from the nature of the compounds used for adjusting $a_w$. Many foods having the same $a_w$ (adjusted with different solutes) significantly differ in deterioration time.

From another perspective, Levine and Slade introduced in the late 1980s the polymer science approach to food science, in which molecular mobility is considered key to product stability. A material stored below the glass transition temperature, $T_g$ (i.e., in a solid glassy state), would be physically, chemically and biologically stable, while at temperatures above $T_g$ (i.e., in a viscous liquid or rubbery state) would not. In a glassy state, due to the high viscosity, the small molecules lose their translational mobility and the molecular motions are restricted to vibrations and short-range rotational motions, behaving in the material practically like solid liquids. In the rubbery state, on the contrary, there is a dramatic increase in molecular mobility due to the drop in viscosity. So, this approach addresses the importance of maintaining solid foods in kinetically metastable, dynamically constrained glassy states.

Based on the above, it is now accepted that food stability must be predicted by both thermodynamic and mobility concepts. The concept of $a_w$ (with all the limitations previously mentioned such as specific solute effects and non-equilibrium situations) enables the prediction of microbial activity and of chemical reactions controlled by chemical reactivity. On the other hand, the concept of molecular mobility is useful for predicting virtually all physical properties and also chemical reactions limited by diffusion.

## 8.3    Water activity, microbial growth, death and survival

The optimum $a_w$ for growth of the majority of microorganisms is in the range 0.99–0.98. Every microorganism has limiting $a_w$ values below which it will not grow, form spores, or produce toxic metabolites (Beuchat, 1987). Considering $a_w$ in relation to microbial stability, the minimum $a_w$ values that permit microbial growth for different types of microorganisms are of great concern. Table 8.1 presents the $a_w$ values of various foods and their associated microbial spoilage, showing also the classification of microorganisms into osmosensitive and osmotolerant. Extensive tables with minimum $a_w$ values for growth and toxin production of several pathogenic and spoilage microorganisms have been reported by many authors (Corry, 1973, Beuchat, 1983, 1987, and Gould, 1989). Table 8.2 shows the minimal $a_w$ for growth of selected microorganisms at their optimal conditions of pH, nutrient availability and temperature. Several findings obtained from literature data and Table 8.2 can be summarized as follows:

- $a_w$ limits for growth differ between microorganisms. In general, common spoilage bacteria are inhibited at an $a_w$ about 0.97; clostridial pathogen at $a_w$ 0.94; and most *Bacillus* species at $a_w$ 0.93. *Staphylococcus aureus* is the most $a_w$-tolerant pathogen, and can grow in aerobiosis at $a_w$ 0.86 and in anaerobiosis at $a_w$ 0.91. Many yeasts and moulds are able to proliferate at an $a_w$ below 0.86, while some osmophilic yeasts and xerophilic moulds are capable of slow growth just above 0.6. So, to preserve a food by using only a reduction in $a_w$ as stress factor, its $a_w$ should be at least lowered to 0.6. Fully dehydrated foods, for instance, have $a_w$ about 0.3 in order to control not only microbial growth but other physico-chemical and biochemical reactions deleterious to colour, texture, flavour and nutritive value of foods.
- Minimum $a_w$ for growth is always equal or lower than minimum $a_w$ for toxin production.
- Minimum $a_w$ for growth depends on the solute used to control $a_w$. Gould (1989) recognized that in some instances solute effects may depend on the ability of the solute to permeate the cell membrane, as in the case of glycerol, which readily permeates the membrane of many bacteria and therefore has a lower inhibitory water activity. Chirife (1994) discussed in detail the 'specific solute effect' for *S. aureus*. He concluded that the inhibitory effects of solutes most often present in low $a_w$ preserved foods, such as NaCl and sucrose, are

**Table 8.1**  Water activity values of selected foods and associated microbial spoilage

| Range of $a_w$ | Microorganisms inhibited | Examples of foods |
|---|---|---|
| 1.00–0.95 | Some yeasts, Gram-negative rods, bacterial spores | Fresh foods; foods containing 40% sucrose or 7% salt (canned foods, processed cheese, several sausages, bread, etc.) |
| 0.95–0.91 | Most cocci, lactobacilli, vegetative cells of bacilli, some moulds | Foods containing 50% sucrose or 12% salt (mayonnaise, bacon, some hard cheeses, raw ham, low-calorie jams, etc.) |
| **0.94** | **Growth and toxin production by all types of *Clostridium botulinum*** | |
| 0.91–0.86 | Most yeasts | Foods containing 65% sucrose or 15% salt (dry ham, fruit jams, fruit juice concentrates, some hard cheeses, etc.) |
| **0.86** | **Aerobic growth *of Staphylococcus aureus*** | |
| 0.86–0.80 | Most moulds | Foods containing 15–20% water (fruit cake, high moisture prunes, sweetened condensed milk, etc.) |
| 0.80–0.75 | Most halophilic bacteria | Foods with 26% salt or very high sugar content (salted fish, molasses, prunes, fondants, etc.) |
| **0.80** | **Production of micotoxins** | |
| 0.75–0.65 | Xerophilic moulds | Foods containing less than 10% water (dates, figs, nuts, rolled oats, etc.) |
| 0.68 | Practical limit for fungi | |
| **0.65–0.60** | **Osmophilic yeasts** | Confectionery products, dried fruits containing 15–20% water, honey |
| **Below 0.60** | **No microbial growth** | Dried milk, instant coffee, dried egg, spices, crackers, flour, cereals, etc. |

Adapted from Troller (1978).

primarily related to their $a_w$ lowering capacity. But for other solutes such as ethanol, propylene glycol, butylene glycol and various polyethylene glycols, antibacterial effects (attributed mainly to the effects of these molecules on membrane enzymes responsible for peptidoglycan synthesis) are important.

When a microorganism is transferred to a new environment, there are two possible outcomes, survival or death. Microbial survival or death will be based on the ability of the microorganism to adapt in the new environment. The basis

**Table 8.2**  Minimal water activity for growth of foodborne bacterial pathogens under optimum pH and temperature conditions

| | $a_w$ |
|---|---|
| Infectious pathogens | |
| *Campylobacter jejuni* | 0.99 |
| *Aeromonas hydrophila* | 0.97 |
| *Shigella* spp | 0.96 |
| *Salmonella* spp | 0.94 |
| *Yersinia enterocolitica* | 0.95 |
| *Escherichia coli* | 0.93–0.95 |
| *Listeria monocytogenes* | 0.90–0.92 |
| *Vibrio parahaemolyticus* | 0.94 (glycerol) |
| | 0.95 (NaCl) |
| | 0.96 (sucrose) |
| | |
| Toxinogenic spore-forming pathogens | |
| *Clostridium perfringens* | 0.93–0.95 |
| *Clostridium botulinum* A & proteolytic *B* strains | 0.94 |
| *Clostridium botulinum* E & non-proteolytic strains B and F | 0.96 |
| *Clostridium botulinum* G | 0.96 |
| *Bacillus cereus* | 0.90 (glycerol) |
| | 0.94 (NaCl) |
| | |
| Toxinogenic pathogens | |
| *Staphylococcus aureus* (anaerobic) | 0.91 |
| *Staphylococcus aureus* (aerobic) | 0.86 |
| *Staphylococcus aureus* (aerobic) | 0.93 (xylitol) |
| *Staphylococcus aureus* (aerobic) | 0.95 (erythritol) |
| *Staphylococcus aureus* (aerobic) | 0.89 (glycerol) |
| | |
| Moulds and yeasts | |
| *Aspergillus flavus* | 0.80 (TP: 0.83–0.87) |
| *Aspergillus parasiticus* | 0.82 (TP: 0.87) |
| *Botrytis cinerea* | 0.93 |
| *Byssoclamys nivea* | 0.84 |
| *Aspergillus ochraceus* | 0.77 (TP: 0.80–0.88) |
| *Penicillium citrinum* | 0.80 |
| *Penicillium cyclopium* | 0.81 |
| *Penicillium patulum* | 0.81 (TP: 0.85–0.95) |
| *Eurotium* spp | 0.66–0.73 |
| *Monascus bisporus* | 0.61 |
| *Saccharomyces cerevisiae* | 0.89 (glucose) |
| | 0.90 (sucrose) |
| | 0.92 (NaCl) |
| *Zygosaccharomyces bisporus* | 0.70 |
| *Zygosaccharomyces rouxii* | 0.65 |
| *Torulopsis candida* | 0.65 |

TP: toxin production.

for survival and death of microorganisms as influenced by $a_w$ is complex. Several intrinsic and extrinsic factors may affect this relation but differ within food types and processes and among types of microorganisms involved. Temperature, oxygen, chemical and other physical treatments are some extrinsic factors that influence microbial spoilage of foods and also the $a_w$-microorganism response.

The effects of temperature on survival of microorganisms are widely documented, the heat resistance of vegetative cells and spores as influenced by $a_w$ probably being the most extensively studied area in terms of microbial inactivation (Lenovich, 1987). In general, vegetative cells and spores are more resistant as $a_w$ of the heating menstrum is reduced. But the type of solute used to adjust $a_w$ to the same value may result in significant differences in the heat resistance of a given microorganism. Ionic solutes may decrease heat resistance at low levels but afford considerable protection at a high concentration. Non-ionic solutes have a variable effect. Larger molecular weight solutes, such as sucrose, exert a protective effect against heat inactivation, while glycerol causes only a little increase in heat resistance. For instance, *S. aureus* heated in skim milk has a $D_{60^\circ C}$ value of 5.3min while in skim milk plus 57% sugar the $D_{60^\circ C}$ value is of about 22min. For bacterial and fungal spores, the resistance to the lethal effects of heat may increase a thousand times or more at a low $a_w$, usually showing a maximum in the $a_w$ range 0.2–0.5 (Mossel *et al.*, 1991).

### 8.3.1    Osmotic stress and osmoregulation in microorganisms

From the microbiological point of view, food preservation implies exposing the microorganisms to a hostile environment (i.e., to one or more adverse factors) to prevent or delay their growth, shorten their survival or cause their death. Unfortunately, microorganisms have evolved different mechanisms to resist the effects of these environmental stress factors. Internal media stability (composition and volume of fluids) is vital for survival and growth. This stability or homeostasis is maintained through feedback mechanisms that act in response to relatively minor changes in physiological variables, leading to a series of events that will in turn restore the altered variable to its original value (Gould, 1996). These mechanisms, called 'homeostatic mechanisms', act to ensure that key physiological activities and parameters in the microorganisms remain relatively unchanged, even when the environment around the cell is different and greatly perturbed (Leistner and Gould, 2002). In the case of vegetative microorganisms, the homeostatic mechanisms are energy-dependent because the cell must expend energy to resist the stress factors, e.g., to repair damaged components, to synthesize new cell components, etc. In the case of spores, the homeostatic mechanisms do not consume energy but they are built in to the cell prior to being exposed to an environmental stress (Leistner and Gould, 2002). So, to be effective, the preservation factors must overcome the microbial homeostatic resistance.

Gould (2000) revised the induced tolerance of microorganisms to stress factors, reaffirming that the response of microorganisms to lowered water activity is essentially a response to osmotic stress, and is therefore often referred to as 'osmoregulation' or 'osmoadaptation'. This reaction is most developed in microorganisms, particularly in the most osmotolerant of the yeasts and moulds, but is also widespread in animals and plants. Microbial cells have an internal osmotic pressure that is higher than that of the surrounding medium (Gutierrez *et al.*, 1995). When a microorganism is put in a concentrated aqueous solute solution of reduced $a_w$, water is extracted from the cytoplasm of the cell and membrane turgor is lost. The homeostasis (or internal equilibrium) is disturbed and the organism will not multiply but will remain in the lag-phase until the equilibrium is re-established. One of the main reactions of cells to reduced $a_w$ is the accumulation of low molecular weight solutes in their cytoplasm at concentrations sufficient to just exceed the osmolality of the external medium. In this way the cells regain, or avoid loss of, water by osmosis and maintain the turgor in the cell membrane that is essential for its proper functioning. The general reaction therefore appeared to be a homeostatic mechanism with respect to cell water content (Gould, 1989). Compatible solutes (so called because, even at very high relative concentrations, they do not appreciably interfere with the metabolic and reproductive functions of the cell) attract water and thereby restore or partially restore isoosmotic conditions across the cell membranes, thus maintaining essential metabolic reactions. While amino acids (proline, $\alpha$-keto glutarate, $\gamma$-amino butyric acid, glutamic acid) appear to be the most common compatible solutes in bacteria, polyols of various types (mannitol, cyclohexanetetrol, arabitol, sorbitol, glycerol, erythritol, etc.) are the predominant protoplasmic solutes in many fungi (Troller, 1987). These compatible solutes have the following common properties (Gutierrez *et al.*, 1995):

- they are soluble to high concentrations and can be accumulated to very high levels in the cytoplasm of the cells;
- they do not modify enzyme activity and can even protect enzymes for denaturation by salts;
- they are small and usually neutral or zwitterionic molecules;
- the cell membrane exhibits controlled permeability to them.

Compatible solutes can either be transported from the environment or synthesized *de novo* in the cytoplasm. Many foods contain a wide range of substances that will act as compatible solutes (among them betaine, proline and choline) and thereby facilitate growth at lowered $a_w$.

Another major microbial response to a change in $a_w$ is the adaptation of the membrane composition (Russell *et al.*, 1995). For a wide range of bacteria, the commonest alteration is the increase in the membrane proportion of anionic phospholipids and/or glycolipid as a means to preserve the proper bilayer phase and maintain its vital functions.

Because of their central role, research has concentrated on the compatible solutes and much of the genetic basis of osmoregulation has been elucidated (Gould, 2000). Adaptive strategies involve the osmotic regulation of the expression of a number of genes to optimize growth under the stress condition (e.g., genes linked to the synthesis or uptake of compatible solutes in *E. coli* and *S. typhimurium*). It is accepted now that there is a general response mechanism (the so-called 'global response') underlying many of the apparent distinct responses of microorganisms to different stresses imposed on them in foods (e.g., low $a_w$, low pH, low or high temperature, etc.). This global response is mediated by the stationary-phase regulator RpoS, that regulates the expression of many important stationary-phase stress resistance genes linked to survival or starvation and to survival in the stationary-phase. As Gould (2000) stated, this fact would explain the cross-resistances to different stresses that have usually been found to occur in response to a single stress.

## 8.4    Combining control of water activity with other preservation techniques

The most important techniques commonly used in food preservation act by inhibiting the growth of microorganisms rather than by inactivating them (Gould, 1995). Among the inhibitory techniques are:

- water activity reduction (curing, conserving, drying, evaporation)
- temperature (high or low)
- acidity or pH reduction by addition of inorganic and organic acids
- redox potential (Eh), preservatives (e.g., nitrite, sorbate, sulphites)
- competitive microorganisms (e.g., lactic acid bacteria)
- modified atmosphere packaging (vacuum, nitrogen, carbon dioxide, oxygen).

On the other hand, few techniques act primarily by inactivating microorganisms in foods. Heat is by far the most employed inactivation technique (thermization, pasteurization, sterilization), with increasing use of alternatives like ionizing radiation and the new and 'emerging' technologies such as high hydrostatic pressure, high voltage electric discharge, ultrasound, ultraviolet light and high-intensity light pulses (Gould, 2000; Leistner, 2000).

As stated by Leistner (1978, 1987) it soon became apparent that in most foods for which $a_w$ is important for quality and stability, other factors, referred to by Leistner as 'hurdles', contribute to the desired product, and the interest taken initially in $a_w$ for food manufacturers was extended to other factors (e.g., Eh, pH, temperature, incorporation of additives, etc.). The goal was to obtain stable products based on an intelligent combination of factors by combination preservation technology or hurdle technology. More than 60 potential hurdles for foods of animal or plant origin, which improve the stability and/or quality of these products, have been already described, and the list of possible hurdles for food preservation is by no means complete (Leistner, 2000).

Combined preservation techniques interfere with the active homeostatic mechanisms that operate in the vegetative microbial cell and the passive refractory homeostatic mechanisms that operate in microbial spores at a number of sites or in a cooperative manner (Gould, 1996). According to Leistner (1999, 2000), in foods preserved by hurdle technology, the possibility exists that different hurdles in a food will not just have an additive effect on stability, but could act synergistically. A synergistic effect could be obtained if the hurdle in a food hits different targets (e.g., cell membrane, DNA, enzyme systems, pH, $a_w$, Eh) within the microbial cell, and thus disturbs the homeostasis of the microorganisms present in several ways. Therefore, employing different hurdles in the preservation of a particular food should be an advantage, because microbial stability could be achieved with a combination of gentle hurdles. In practical terms, this could mean that it is more effective to use different preservative factors at low levels in a food than only one preservative factor at a high level, because different preservative factors might hit different targets within the bacterial cell, and thus act synergistically.

The slight reduction in $a_w$ resulting from the addition of sugars or other solutes to foods such as minimally preserved fruits and vegetables, means that microorganisms surviving processing in such foods, or contaminating the food after processing, will be osmoregulating at some level or other. However, if osmoregulation diverts resources away from normal cell biosynthetic processes, then it is clear that the stressed cells may be more vulnerable to other stresses in combination preservation systems, particularly when the other stresses also divert away from the synthesis of new cell material. Since homeostatic responses often require the expenditure of energy by the stressed cells, restriction of the availability of energy is then a sensible target to pursue. According to Gould (2000), this probably forms the basis of many of the successful, empirically derived, mild combination preservation procedures, exemplified by the 'hurdle technology' and 'multitarget preservation' preservation approaches of Leistner.

Microbial stability and sensory quality of most foods are nowadays based on a combination of hurdles. Hurdle technology has proved useful in the optimization of traditional foods as well as in the development of novel products. However $a_w$ continues to be one of the main hurdles to be manipulated and the use of combinations of extrinsic and intrinsic factors together with lowered $a_w$ levels are common in the food industry. Generally, as the minimal $a_w$ for growth of a microorganism is approached, changes of other environmental factors will have a greater impact on death or survival.

## 8.5   Applications: fully dehydrated, intermediate and high moisture foods

Improved knowledge of the relation of water in foods led to the rediscovery and optimization of old preservation techniques and to a renewed interest in foods that are shelf-stable by control of water activity. This applies for fully dehydrated, intermediate and high moisture traditional foods with inherent empiric hurdles, and also for novel products, especially high water activity foods, for which the hurdles are intelligently selected and intentionally applied. Traditional fully dehydrated and intermediate moisture foods (IMF) can be regarded as some of the oldest foods preserved by man. However, in the quest for quality, the importance of considering the combined action of decreased $a_w$ with other preservation factors as a way to develop new improved foodstuffs moved along almost simultaneously with modern food processing to the point that, currently, consumers are searching for fresh-like characteristics in many processed products. The food industry has responded to these demands with the so-called minimally processed foods, which have become a widespread industry that is receiving a lot of attention lately.

Therefore, the control of $a_w$ for food design is being used in many ways according to needs:

- At various stages of the food distribution chain, it is used during storage, processing, and/or packaging as a 'back-up' hurdle in existing minimally processed products with short shelf-life to diminish microbial pathogenic risk and/or increase their shelf-life (i.e., a slight reduction in $a_w$ in addition to refrigeration).
- Traditionally, it is used for obtaining long shelf-life products (fully dehydrated and intermediate moisture ones). Actual trends in these applications are to obtain very high sensory quality products by using the advances in the knowledge of water sorption phenomena, $a_w$ prediction, deleterious physico-chemical reactions and polymer science, as well as more controlled and/or sophisticated drying techniques.
- As one of the preservative factors (together with other emerging and/or traditional preservative factors), it is used to obtain high moisture novel foods by hurdle techniques.

In industrialized countries, with ready availability of energy and infrastructure and wide use of refrigeration, the control of $a_w$ has been mainly applied to develop a great variety of mild thermally processed, chill- and frozen-distributed foods. Topical applications include fermented meats (fermented sausages, raw hams) and shelf-stable mild heated meats (ready-to-eat fresh-like meats); *sous vide* and cook-chill dishes, health foods (low-fat and/or low-salt and functional foods); and foods processed by emerging techniques (e.g., hydrostatic high pressure) (Leistner and Gould, 2002).

On the contrary, in many developing countries, refrigeration is expensive and not always available. Thus, the emphasis of the $a_w$ lowering approach has been on the development of ambient-stable foods, which have minimal energy, machinery and infrastructure requirements for processing, storage and distribution (Leistner and Gould, 2002). Common applications entail foods with reduced $a_w$ (achieved by partial drying or addition of salt or sugar), usually combined with acidification (i.e., a reduction of pH) and addition of preservatives; fermented foods, and fully dehydrated foods.

Most of the traditional foods that remain stable, safe and tasty during long-term storage without refrigeration in the developing countries of Africa, Asia and Latin America are intermediate moisture foods, in which lowering of $a_w$ is one of the main preservative factors or hurdles (Leistner and Gould, 2002). Many of the manufacturing processes for IMF were empirically developed, but now the hurdles and their specific roles are better understood and can be rationally selected to design or to optimize the preservation system. There are actually two categories of foods with reduced $a_w$ whose stability is based on a combination of factors: intermediate moisture (IM) foods and high moisture (HM) foods.

IM foods range generally from 0.60 to 0.90 $a_w$ and 10–50% water by weight (Jayaraman, 1995). Additional hurdles provide the margin of safety against spoilage by microorganisms resistant to $a_w$ (mainly moulds and yeasts, which can grow at $a_w$ as low as 0.60), and also against some bacterial species that are likely to grow when the $a_w$ value of the IM food is near the upper limit of water activities (i.e., $a_w$ 0.90). With these targets, the lowering in $a_w$ is often combined with chemical preservatives (i.e., nitrites, sorbates, sulphites, benzoates, antimicrobials of natural origin, smoke components) and a reduction of pH (that usually inhibits or decreases bacterial growth, accentuates the action of preservatives and increases the minimum $a_w$ values for bacterial growth), and sometimes with competitive microorganisms. Other IM products receive a thermal treatment during manufacturing process that inactivates heat-sensitive microorganisms, while the subsequent hot filling in sealed containers further improves microbial stability (Leistner and Gould, 2002).

Most of IM foods are designed to be storable for several months at ambient temperature even in tropical climates and to be eaten 'as is' without rehydration. They are moist enough to be ready to eat without giving rise to a sensation of dryness but dried enough to be ambient-stable (Karel, 1973, 1976; Jayaraman, 1995). Many IM products, due to the addition of very high amounts of solutes (such as sugar or salt) to reduce $a_w$ to the desired level, are too sweet or too salty, becoming undesirable from the nutritional and sensory point of view. Therefore, this category of products has been subjected in the last decade to continuous revision and discussion.

On the other hand, high-moisture foods have an $a_w$ value well above 0.90. Thus, in this category, the reduction of $a_w$ is a hurdle of less relative significance because most of the microorganisms are able to proliferate (Leistner and Gould, 2002). Stability at ambient temperature is reached by applying intentional and carefully designed hurdle technology. HM fresh-like fruits and cooked meat products, preserved by the interaction of $a_w$ – mild heat treatment – pH – preservatives and storable without refrigeration, represent a rational application of the combined approach (Alzamora et al., 1995, 2000, Leistner and Gould, 2002).

In 1994, within the Science and Technology for Development (CYTED) Program, Project 'Development of intermediate moisture foods (IMF) from Iberoamerica', a survey was conducted in eleven countries, collecting information on 260 traditional IM and HM foods. Table 8.3 shows the main factors used in Spain and Latin America for the preservation of the traditional

**Table 8.3** Main factors used in Iberoamerican countries for the preservation of traditional food by the combined methods technology

| Product category | Preservation factors | | | | | | |
| --- | --- | --- | --- | --- | --- | --- | --- |
| | $a_w$ | pH | F | t | Smoke | Preser. | C.F. |
| Fruits & vegetables | X | X | X | – | – | X | X |
| Meat | X | X | X | – | X | X | X |
| Fish | X | X | X | X | X | – | – |
| Dairy | X | X | X | X | – | X | X |
| Bakery | X | – | X | – | – | X | – |
| Miscellaneous | X | X | X | – | – | X | – |

F = mild heat treatment; t = mild refrigeration; Preser. = preservatives; C.F. = competitive flora.

foods evaluated (Welti *et al.*, 1994; Tapia *et al.*, 1994). Many of these products, which are also common in different parts of the world, are safe and storable without refrigeration and require inexpensive packaging. Selected representative products of each category, the process parameters involved and their contribution as microbial stability factors (hurdles) are shown in Table 8.4. Most shelf-stable foods do not rely solely on $a_w$ for microbial control but on other preservation factors. The binary combination of $a_w$ and pH acts as a relevant hurdle in many of these products preventing proliferation of pathogenic microorganisms, while the rest (antimicrobials, thermal treatment, etc.) play a secondary role, mainly against spoilage flora (Tapia *et al.*, 1994).

Different approaches have been explored for obtaining shelf-stability and freshness in fruit products. Commercial, minimally processed fruits are fresh (with high moisture), and are prepared for convenient consumption and distribution to the consumer in a fresh state. Minimum processing includes minimum preparation procedures like washing, peeling and/or cutting, packing, etc., after which the fruit product is usually placed in refrigerated storage where its stability varies depending on the type of product, processing, and storage conditions. However, product stability without refrigeration is an important issue not only in developing countries but in industrialized countries as well. The principle used by Leistner for shelf-stable high moisture meats ($a_w > 0.90$), where only mild heat treatment is used and the product still exhibits a long shelf life without refrigeration, can be applied to other foodstuffs. Fruits would be a good choice. Leistner states that for industrialized countries, production of shelf-stable products (SSP) is more attractive than IM foods because the required $a_w$ for SSP is not as low and less humectants and/or less drying of the product is necessary (Leistner, 2000).

If fresh-like fruit is the goal, dehydration should not be used in processing. Reduction of $a_w$ by addition of humectants should be employed at a minimum level to maintain the product in a high moisture state. To compensate for the

**Table 8.4** Preserving factors in selected food products of reduced $a_w$ (adapted from Tapia et al., 1994)

| Product | PRESERVING FACTORS | | | | | | LEVEL OF HURDLE RELEVANCE | |
| --- | --- | --- | --- | --- | --- | --- | --- | --- |
| | $a_w$ | pH | Antimicrobial | Thermal treatment | Refrigeration requirement | Competitive flora | Most relevant | Secondary |
| *Meat products* | | | | | | | | |
| Sausage | 0.92 | 5.6 | Sodium nitrite | No | No | Yes | $a_w$ | A, CF |
| Sausage | 0.74 | 4.5 | Sodium nitrite | No | No | Yes | $a_w$, pH | A, CF |
| Spanish ham | 0.85 | 6.2 | Sodium nitrite | No | No | No | $a_w$ | A |
| Beef foie grass | 0.87 | 6.3 | Sodium nitrite | Yes | Yes | No | $a_w$, R | T |
| *Vegetable products* | | | | | | | | |
| Ketchup | 0.94 | 3.8 | Potassium sorbate | Yes | No | No | pH, $a_w$ | A, T |
| Garlic cream | 0.84 | 4.0 | Essential oils of natural occurrence | No | No | No | $a_w$, pH | A |
| Garlic sauce | 0.96 | 3.7 | Essential oils of natural occurrence | Yes | No | No | pH, $a_w$ | T |
| Chili cream | 0.84 | 4.2 | Essential oils of natural occurrence | Yes | No | No | $a_w$, pH | A, T |
| *Fruit products* | | | | | | | | |
| Candied papaya | 0.70 | 4.6 | No | Yes | No | No | $a_w$ | pH, T |
| Candied pineapple | 0.80–0.87 | 4.5–5.6 | No | Yes | No | No | $a_w$ | pH, T |
| Dehydrated plum | 0.77 | 3.9 | No | No | No | No | $a_w$ | pH |
| Dehydrated banana | 0.62 | 5.1 | No | No | No | No | $a_w$ | No |
| Peach jam | 0.83 | 3.1 | No | Yes | No | No | $a_w$, pH | T |
| Mango jam | 0.81 | 5.0 | Sodium benzoate | Yes | No | No | $a_w$, pH | T, A |
| Guava paste | 0.78–0.88 | 3.5 | Sulphite | Yes | No | No | $a_w$, pH | A, T |
| Sweet potato paste | 0.84 | 3.4 | Sodium benzoate | Yes | No | No | $a_w$, pH | A, T |

**Table 8.4** continued

| Product | $a_w$ | pH | Antimicrobial | Thermal treatment | Refrigeration requirement | Competitive flora | Most relevant | Secondary |
|---|---|---|---|---|---|---|---|---|
| | | | PRESERVING FACTORS | | | | LEVEL OF HURDLE RELEVANCE | |
| *Fishery products* | | | | | | | | |
| Brined anchovies | 0.75 | 6.2 | No | No | No | No | $a_w$ | |
| Dry-salted anchovies | 0.71– 0.74 | 5.6– 5.8 | No | No | Yes | No | $a_w$ | R |
| Cod-type dry fish | 0.74– 0.75 | 7.5– 8.6 | No | No | No | No | $a_w$ | |
| Anchovies in oil | 0.76– 0.80 | 6.1– 6.2 | No | No | Yes | No | $a_w$ | R |
| Smoked trout | 0.96 | 5.4 | Smoke | No | Yes | No | $a_w$ | R, S |
| Smoked salmon | 0.96– 0.98 | 5.7– 6.2 | Smoke | No | Yes | No | Refrigeration | S |
| *Dairy products* | | | | | | | | |
| Sweet condensed milk | 0.84 | 6.6 | No | Yes | No | No | $a_w$, T | |
| Melted cheese | 0.97– 0.98 | 5.7– 6.0 | No | Yes | Yes | No | T, refrigeration | |
| Milk jam | 0.81– 0.85 | 5.6– 6.0 | No | Yes | No | No | $a_w$ | Maillard products? |
| Goat cheese | 0.91 | 5.6 | No | Yes | Yes | No | $a_w$ | T, pH, R |
| Reggianito cheese | 0.86 | 5.5 | No | Yes | No | No | $a_w$ | T, pH |
| *Miscellaneous products* | | | | | | | | |
| Mayonnaise | 0.93– 0.94 | 3.8– 3.9 | Potassium sorbate | Yes | No | No | pH, $a_w$ | A |
| Honey | 0.62– 0.69 | 3.1– 3.3 | No | No | No | No | $a_w$, pH | |
| Soy sauce | 0.79 | 4.7 | No | Yes | No | No | $a_w$, pH | T |
| Soy sauce | 0.79 | 4.8 | Sodium benzoate | Yes | No | No | $a_w$, pH | A, T |

A: Antimicrobial; CF: Competitive flora; R: Refrigeration; S: Smoke; T: Thermal treatment.

high moisture left in the product (in terms of stability), a controlled blanching can be applied without affecting the sensory and nutritional properties; pH reductions can be made that will not impair flavour; and preservatives can be added to alleviate the risk of potential spoilage microflora. In conjunction with the above-mentioned factors, a slight thermal treatment, pH reduction, slight $a_w$ reduction and the addition of antimicrobials (sorbic or benzoic acid, sulfite), all placed in context with the hurdle technology principles applied to fruits, make up an interesting alternative to IM preservation of fruits, as well as to commercial minimally processed refrigerated fruits. Considerable research effort has been made within the CYTED Program and the Multinational Project on Biotechnology and Food of the Organization of American States (OAS) in the area of combined methods, geared to the development of shelf-stable high-moisture fruit products. Over the last two decades, use of this approach led to important developments of innovative technologies for obtaining shelf-stable 'high-moisture fruit products' storable for 3–8 months without refrigeration. These new technologies are based on a combination of inhibiting factors to combat the deleterious effects of microorganisms in fruits, including additional factors to diminish major quality loss. Slight reduction of water activity ($a_w$ 0.94–0.98), control of pH (pH 3.0–4.1), mild heat treatment, addition of preservatives (concentrations $\leq 1,500$ ppm), and antibrowning additives were the factors selected to formulate the preservation procedure (Alzamora *et al.*, 1989, 1993, 1995; Guerrero *et al.*, 1994; Cerrutti *et al.*, 1997).

Novel (in their application) and refined impregnation techniques exist for developing minimal processes. Pulsed vacuum osmotic dehydration, a new method of osmotic dehydration that takes advantage of the porous microstructure of vegetable tissues, is a technique that uses vacuum impregnation (VI) to reduce process time and improve additives incorporation. During VI of porous materials, important modifications in structure and composition occur as a consequence of external pressure changes. VI shows faster water loss kinetics in short-time treatments as compared with time-consuming atmospheric 'pseudo-diffusional' processes, due to the occurrence of a specific mass transfer phenomenon, the hydrodynamic mechanism (HDM), and the result produced in the solid-liquid interface area. Many fruits and vegetables have a great number of pores and offer the possibility of being impregnated by a predetermined solution of solute and additives. Thus, product composition as well as its physical and chemical properties may be changed to improve its stability. An important advantage of using low pressures (approx. 50 mbar) in the minimal preservation of fruit is that equilibration times are shorter than at atmospheric pressure (e.g., 15 minutes under vacuum versus a few hours in forced convection at atmospheric conditions, or a few days in media without agitation for reducing $a_w$ to 0.97) (Alzamora *et al.*, 2000). This process could be appropriate in the development of new minimally processed fruit products or in the development of improved pretreatments for such traditional preservation methods as canning, salting, freezing or drying, and also in high-quality jam processes (Alzamora *et al.*, 2000).

At present, especially physical, non-thermal processes (high hydrostatic pressure, mano-thermo-sonication, oscillating magnetic fields, pulsed electric fields, light pulses, etc.), receive considerable attention, since in combination with other conventional hurdles they are of potential use for the microbial stabilization of fresh-like food products with little degradation of nutritional and sensory properties. With these novel processes often not a sterile product but only a reduction of the microbial load is intended, and growth of the residual microorganisms is inhibited by additional, conventional hurdles. Interesting results have been reported by the research group of the Universidad de las Américas (Mexico) for obtaining minimally processed avocado sauce, avocado purée and banana purée. These fruit products were preserved by the interaction of blanching, high-pressure, reduction of pH and $a_w$ and preservatives, and the combination of heat treatment and high pressure significantly decreased browning reactions (Alzamora *et al.*, 2000). Another group of hurdles which is at present of special interest in industrialized as well as in developing countries are 'natural preservatives' (spices and their extracts, hop extracts, lysozyme, chitosan, pectine hydrolysate, etc.) (Leistner, 2000). As an example, high-moisture strawberry can be preserved for at least three months by combining mild heat treatment, 3,000 ppm vanillin (instead of synthetic antimicrobials), 500 ppm ascorbic acid, and adjustment of $a_w$ to 0.95 and pH to 3.0 (Cerrutti *et al.*, 1997).

Lastly must be mentioned the excellent recopilation of traditional and artisanal combined methods employed around the world (many of them involving the control of $a_w$) by the world's two leading authorities on hurdle technology: Professor Lothar Leistner and Dr Grahame Gould (Leistner and Gould, 2002). This overview covers hurdle techniques applied in developed countries and also in Latin America, India, China and Africa. Basic principles underlying preservation procedures are critically discussed for many popular products. Among them, it is interesting to cite the following:

- Paneer, a cottage cheese-type Indian product (hurdles: $a_w$ 0.97; pH 5, Fo value 0.8), stable for several weeks without refrigeration.
- Dudh churpi, an Indian dairy product (preparation: heating, acid coagulation, addition of sugar and potassium sorbate, smoking, drying).
- Meat (preparation: marination in salt, glycerol, nitrite, acidulants and ascorbate, cooking and packaging; $a_w$ 0.70 or 0.85, pH 4.6) storable at room temperature for one month or at 5°C for more than four months.
- Rabbit meats, quite popular in China, marinated and cooked; fried; brined and cooked; or smoked (hurdles: $a_w$ 0.92–0.98, refrigeration).

## 8.6    Measurement and prediction of water activity in foods

### 8.6.1    Measurement of water activity

Fast, convenient and reliable laboratory analytical methods of measuring $a_w$ are demanded in the food industry and in research laboratories for quality assurance, process design, food formulation and selection of storage conditions. This is particularly true for those foods in which control of $a_w$ is critical for determining microbiological activity and safety. Diverse reviews and collaborative studies about the methods used to measure $a_w$ in foods have been published (Stoloff, 1978; Labuza *et al.*, 1976; Troller, 1983; Schurer, 1985; Johnston and Ling, 1987; Christian, 2000), showing the different available techniques, their accuracy and precision. Some of the instruments for $a_w$ determination in common use are described below.

*Vapour pressure manometers*
Based on the $a_w$ definition, the food is placed under vacuum conditions allowing it to reach equilibrium (at controlled temperature) with the surrounding atmosphere and then the vapour pressure of the atmosphere in equilibrium with the sample is measured with a manometer or a pressure transduce. Since the time needed to reach equilibrium is long, this method is not adequate for quick routine analysis. Methods based on this principle are considered as a reference (since the vapour pressure of the food is a direct measure of $a_w$) with which other methods and devices are compared. This technique cannot be used with respiring or fermenting materials and requires a sensitivity of 0.01 mm Hg in pressure measurement. The precision is $\pm 0.005$ $a_w$ below 0.85 $a_w$ but above this value the accuracy is 0.02 $a_w$ because of problems of condensation and control of temperature.

*Dew point hygrometer (instruments available: Decagon, EG&G, General Eastern)*
This method is based on the condensation of water vapour on the surface of a mirror that is cooled down to the dew temperature of the atmosphere generated by the studied sample. The dewpoint is photoelectrically detected and related to $a_w$ using psychrometric charts. This device is used to determine $a_w$ to a wide range (precision: $\pm 0.005$ $a_w$) and also allows measurements at different temperatures. The measurement is very fast (approximately two minutes) but can be affected by condensibles with lower critical temperatures than water and by an unclean mirror surface.

*Freezing point depression methods (instrument available: Advanced Instrument Milk Cryoscope)*
The depression of the freezing point, as well as the changes in other colligative properties, can be quantitatively related to $a_w$ (Robinson and Stokes, 1965). This method is adequate to measure mainly the $a_w$ of liquid foods with $a_w > 0.97$ (precision $\pm 0.0004$ $a_w$), although it has been recommended for values as low as 0.80 and also for aqueous extracts and homogenates of solid foods (Ferro Fontán and Chirife, 1981a). The $a_w$ values calculated from freezing point measurements are not very different from values measured at 25°C (differences are $< 0.01$ $a_w$) and may be considered as having an acceptable level of accuracy in most food-related applications.

*Electric hygrometers*
These instruments are based on three types of hygrosensors (Johnston and Ling, 1987):

1.  Sensors formed by an electrical wire covered by a high hygroscopic salt, usually lithium chloride, whose electrical conductance or resistance depends on the degree of hydration and hence on the relative humidity of the head space of the sample (in equilibrium with the sensor) (instruments available: Beckman, Novasina, Rotronic, American Instrument)
2.  Sensors constituted by a liquid hygroscopic substance, which absorbs or desorbs moisture and whose electrical impedance varies with the moisture content
3.  Sensors constituted by a thin polymer film capacitor, whose capacitance changes proportionally to the relative humidity (instruments available: Vaisala, General Eastern, WeatherMeasure).

For the three types of measurements systems, confidence interval is in the range of $\pm 0.005$ $a_w$. Sensor contamination with non-aqueous food volatiles is a major problem. Some manufacturers provide filters to protect the sensor but they notoriously increase the equilibration time before $a_w$ readings (Chirife, 1995). Other problems noted in general are the need for frequent calibration and their dependence on temperature, the inaccuracy at certain levels of $a_w$, sensor ageing and hysteresis effects at high $a_w$ levels (Stamp et al., 1984). However, the performance of these hygrometers varies between the different commercially available instruments. Kitic et al., (1986), when testing one particular device, the Novasina Thermoconstanter Humidity Meter, reported as relevant charac-teristics a very high level of precision in the $a_w$ range studied (0.50–0.97), the stability of calibration curve, a reasonably short time for measurement of $a_w$ in various materials (from 10 to 30 minutes according to $a_w$ level), absence of hysteresis and a built-in temperature-controlled device for measurements over the range 0°C–50°C.

*Fibre hygrometer (instruments available: Abbeon, Lufft)*
This instrument employs as sensor a synthetic polyamide thread that shrinks when it is exposed to high relative humidity. The longitudinal change is recorded and related to sample $a_w$. Equilibration times between the food and the fibre are approximately three hours with a precision of $\pm 0.01$ $a_w$. The sensor response is affected in an important way by temperature changes and by the presence of volatiles. Other problems are hysteresis (Gerschenson et al., 1984) and sensor ageing. In spite of its low sensitivity, as it is relative inexpensive, the fibre hygrometer is widely used for routine examinations in the food industry.

Direct measurement of vapour pressure is extremely difficult and indirect methods are usually employed for $a_w$ determination (Schurer, 1985). The accuracy obtained with indirect methods (electric, fibre, and dewpoint hygrometers; gravimetric methods) depends on obtaining a calibration curve with reference standard sources in the $a_w$ range of interest (Favetto et al., 1983).

Five different sources have been suggested as a convenient number of points to construct a calibration curve (Stoloff, 1978). It must be noted that poor results have been reported when the meters are calibrated according to manufacturer's instructions (adjusting the sensor with only one standard saturated solution). Saturated salt solutions (salt slurries) have been recommended by numerous workers as a convenient, easy and accurate way to provide solutions of known $a_w$. They are reproducible reference standards because no measurement of concentration is needed and if the salts are properly chosen no interfering vapours are present. However, most reports in the literature do not agree on the exact $a_w$ of each saturated salt solution (Greenspan, 1977; Labuza et al., 1976).

Resnik et al. (1984) performed a world survey of $a_w$ of selected saturated salt solutions used as standards by researchers of 38 laboratories for food related applications in the range of microbiological growth (0.57–0.97) at 25°C. The results indicated that there was a good agreement on the exact value to be assigned to NaBr, NaCl, KCl, and $BaCl_2.2H_2O$, and to a lesser extent, to $K_2SO_4$, but a significant discrepancy was found on the value assigned to $(NH_4)_2SO_4$ and $KNO_3$. It is noteworthy that the most accepted values agree within 0.002–0.003 with those calculated using theoretical models for thermodynamics properties of strong electrolytic aqueous solutions (Chirife et al., 1983). Table 8.5 shows a compilation of data of $a_w$ values of saturated solutions for various salts used to calibrate hygrometers. The most accepted values reported in the survey have been included.

Although for electrical hygrometers precision is in the range of $\pm0.005$ $a_w$, the data for foods obtained in collaborative studies varied by $\pm0.02$ $a_w$ units. Many sources of error in the measurement of $a_w$ have been pointed out by Labuza et al. (1976) and question the validity of literature values reported to three decimal places or the absolute values for limits on microbial growth. For cases where there is no general agreement on the value to be assigned to certain saturated salt solutions, or where there is lack of saturated salt solutions of known $a_w$ that cover the necessary $a_w$ range, the use of unsaturated NaCl solutions has been proposed for the calibration of $a_w$-measuring devices for $a_w$ values above 0.76 (Chirife and Resnik, 1984).

## 8.6.2   Prediction of water activity in practical applications

$a_w$ can be influenced in at least three ways during the preparation of dried, intermediate and high moisture foods:

1.   Water can be removed by a dehydration, evaporation or concentration process.
2.   Additional solute can be added. The impregnation of solute can be performed by moist infusion or by dry infusion. Moist infusion consists in soaking the food pieces in a water-solute solution of lower $a_w$ while dry infusion involves direct mixing of food pieces and solutes in required proportions. When water-rich solid products, such as fruit and vegetables, are subjected to moist or dry infusion, three flows arise:

**Table 8.5**   Water activity of selected saturated salt solutions used as standards

| SALT | 10°C | 15°C | 20°C | 25°C | 30°C |
|---|---|---|---|---|---|
| Lithium bromide | 7.1 | 6.9 | 6.6 | 6.4 | 6.2 |
| Sodium hydroxide | – | 9.6 | 8.9 | 8.2 | 7.6 |
| Lithium chloride | 11.3 | 11.3 | 11.3 | 11.3 | 11.3 |
| Potassium acetate | 23.5 | 23.5 | 23.0 | 22.5 | 22.0 |
| Magnesium chloride | 33.5 | 33.0 | 33.0 | 33.0 | 32.5 |
| Potassium carbonate | 44.0 | 43.5 | 43.0 | 43.0 | 43.0 |
| Sodium bromide | 60.0 | 59.0 | 58.0 | 57.7* | 56.5 |
| Copper chloride | 68.0 | 68.0 | 68.0 | 67.5 | 67.0 |
| Potassium iodide | 72.0 | 71.0 | 70.0 | 69.0 | 68.0 |
| Sodium chloride | 76.0 | 75.5 | 75.5 | 75.3* | 75.0 |
| Ammonia sulfate | 81.0 | 80.5 | 80.5 | 80.1* | 80.0 |
| Potassium chloride | 87.0 | 86.0 | 85.0 | 84.3* | 84.0 |
| Sodium benzoate | 88.0 | 88.0 | 88.0 | 88.0 | 88.0 |
| Barium chloride | | 91.0 | 90.6 | 90.2* | 89.9 |
| Potassium nitrate | 95.5 | 95.0 | 94.0 | 92.5* | 92.0 |
| Potassium sulfate | 98.0 | 98.0 | 97.5 | 97.2* | 97.0 |

Adapted from Labuza *et al.*, 1976; Stamp *et al.*, 1984; Stoloff, 1978; Greenspan, 1977.

* Survey (Resnik *et al.*, 1984).

- a water outflow, from product to the environment;
- a solute flow, from the environment to product, and
- an outflow of the product's own solutes.

This process is called 'osmotic dehydration' and allows the infusion of not only the solute used to control $a_w$ but also the desired quantities of antimicrobial and antibrowning agents or any solute for improving sensory and nutritional quality. By controlling these above complex exchanges it is possible to conceive different combinations of water loss and solid gain, from a simple dewatering process (with substantial water removal and only marginal sugar pickup) to a candying or salting process (in which solute penetration is favoured and water removal limited) (Torregiani and Bertolo, 2002). For porous foods, moist infusion can be also performed under vacuum, as previously mentioned. The internal gas or liquid occluded in the open pores is exchanged for an external liquid phase (of controlled composition) due to pressure changes.

3. Combining 1. and 2. when the food pieces are infused with the solutes and additives and then partially dried. The advantages obtained with this combination as compared to only drying are an increase in the stability of the pigments responsible for the colour, an enhancement of the natural flavour, a better texture and a greater loading of the dryer.

Whatever the procedure used to reduce $a_w$, it is necessary to know the water activity-moisture content relationship in the food. Important contributions have been made in the field of $a_w$ prediction over the past 50 years and

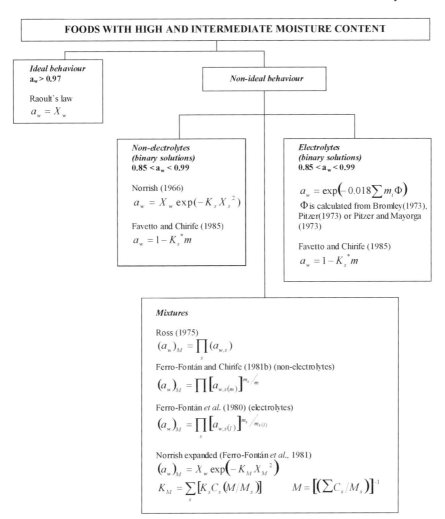

$X_w$: molar fraction of water; $X_s$: molar fraction of solute; $K_s$: Norrish' content for a non-electrolyte s; $K_s^*$: constant for each solute (electrolyte or non-electrolyte); $m$: molality; $m_i = vm$, where $v$ is the number of ionic species per mol of the solute $i$: $\Phi$: osmotic coefficient; $(a_w)_M$: water activity of a complex solution; $(a_{w,s})$: water activity of each s component when measured at the same molality as in the complex solution; $m_s$: molality of the s component in the mixture; $m_{s(I)}$: total molality (dissociated) of the solute that would produce an ionic force equal to the one of the mixture, $a_{w,s(I)}$: water activity of the solute s in a binary solution at a molality $m_{s(I)}$; $C_s$: weight of solute s/ weight of total solids; $M_s$: molecular weight of solute s.

**Fig. 8.1**   Scheme and selected models for practical prediction of water activity in moist and semi-moist foods.

comprehensive analysis of the procedures traditionally employed to calculate $a_w$ have been performed by van der Berg and Bruin (1981), Chirife (1995) and Welti and Vergara (1997). In each case, the applicability of various theoretical and empirical equations was analyzed, presenting some descriptive examples.

There is no model with a simple mathematical structure capable of representing the sorption or $a_w$ lowering characteristics of foods or their components in the whole range of water activities, since the depression of $a_w$ in foods is due to a combination of mechanisms each of which may be predominant in a given range of water activity. In high and intermediate moisture foods, $a_w$ is mainly determined by the nature and concentration of soluble substances (i.e., sugars, NaCl, polyols, aminoacids, organic molecules, other salts) in the aqueous phase of the food (Chirife, 1995). A number of equations, based on the thermodynamic properties of binary and multicomponent electrolyte and non-electrolyte solutions, have been studied theoretically and experimentally for calculating or predicting the $a_w$ of these foods. Figure 8.1 summarizes several of theoretical and empirical models suggested for the calculation of $a_w$ in semi-moist and moist foods (van der Berg and Bruin, 1981; Chirife, 1995).

In low-moisture foods, adsorption of water in surfaces is responsible for $a_w$ reduction (Chirife and Iglesias, 1978). Although the physical chemistry of surfaces has provided the food scientists with a large number of theoretical equations, the relationship of water sorption-$a_w$ cannot be predicted but must be experimentally determined due to many reasons. As food sorbs water, it can undergo changes of constitution, dimensions and other properties and sugars contained in the food may experience phase transformations. The moisture sorption isotherm integrates the hygroscopic properties of numerous constituents whose sorption properties may change due to physical/chemical interactions induced by heating and other pre-treatments. Critical compilations of empirical and theoretical adsorption models for fitting experimental water sorption isotherms of food and food products have been made by Chirife and Iglesias (1978); Iglesias and Chirife (1982), Boquet et al., (1978) and Weisser (1985).

The Brunauer, Emmett and Teller (BET) formula (application range $0.05 < a_w < 0.45$) is one of the most widely used models to characterize the monolayer water. The theory supposes, among other things, that the binding energy of the monolayer is the same for all the water molecules and on the other layers is equal to that of pure water. Although the theoretical assumptions are incorrect for heterogeneous food surface interactions, for practical purposes this equation has been found very useful in determining the optimum moisture content (i.e., that corresponding to the monolayer water) for storage chemical stability of dehydrated foods (Rahman and Labuza, 1999). The Guggenheim, Anderson and de Boer (GAB) equation (applicability range $0 < a_w < 0.9$), now recognized as the most versatile sorption model and recommended as such by the European COST 90 Project, modifies the BET model to take into account the energies of interaction between the first and distant sorbed molecules at the individual sorption sites. It also allows calculation of the monolayer water (Maroulis et al., 1988).

## 8.7   Future trends

The food scientist involved in product development, process design or production, no matter if the preservation technology is novel or traditional, continues to be confronted daily with the desirable or undesirable effect of water on the food material and its role in mass transfer, chemical and microbial reactions and in determining its shape, structure, physical and chemical properties. There have been significant advances in the understanding of microbial homeostatic responses to reduced $a_w$ in the past thirty years and also in the development of predictive models. This quantitative approach has been mainly orientated towards the growth of pathogens in foods preserved by the interaction of $a_w$, pH, temperature and traditional antimicrobials. Future major advances in the control of $a_w$ as a means of food preservation will be contingent upon the following points:

- the improvement of food sensory aspects resulting from a lowering of $a_w$ and the refinement of techniques controlling $a_w$
- the use of predictive microbiology to select and combine on a scientific basis other less conventional hurdles (traditional and emerging) with the control of $a_w$, in such a way that microbial stability and safety can be assured while retaining sensory acceptance and nutritional characteristics. Quantitative data allow the prediction of adequate and necessary levels of each hurdle, keeping their levels at a minimum.

## 8.8   Sources of further information and advice

For readers interested in pursuing the concepts further, a number of reviews and books treat various aspects of preserving food through $a_w$ control. Particularly recommended are books by Troller and Christian (1978); Rockland and Stewart (1981); Rockland and Beuchat (1987); and Simatos and Multon (1985); and the ISOPOW symposium conferences published by Fito *et al.*, 1994; Welti-Chanes and Barbosa-Cánovas, 1995; and Roos *et al.*, 1999.

## 8.9   References

ALZAMORA S M, GERSCHENSON L N, CERRUTTI P, ROJAS A M (1989), 'Shelf stable pineapple for long-term non refrigerated storage', *Lebensm Wiss u Technol* 22, 233–236.

ALZAMORA S M, TAPIA M S, ARGAIZ A, WELTI J (1993), 'Application of combined methods technology in minimally processed fruits', *Food Res Intern* 26, 125–130.

ALZAMORA S M, CERRUTTI P, GUERRERO S, LÓPEZ-MALO A (1995), 'Minimally processed fruits by combined methods', in Welti-Chanes J, Barbosa-Cánovas G, *Food Preservation by Moisture Control – Fundamentals and Applications*, Lancaster, Technomic Pub. Co., 463–492.

ALZAMORA S M, FITO P, LÓPEZ-MALO A, TAPIA M S, PARADA-ARIAS E (2000), 'Minimally processed fruit using vacuum impregnation, natural antimicrobial addition and/or

high hydrostatic pressure techniques', in Alzamora S M, Tapia M S, López Malo
A, *Minimally Processed Fruits and Vegetables. Fundamental Aspects and Applications*, Gaithersburg, Aspen Publishers, Inc., 293–315.

BEUCHAT L R (1983), 'Influence of water activity on growth, metabolic activities and survival of yeasts and molds', *J. Food Protect*, 46, 135–140.

BEUCHAT L R (1987), 'Influence of water activity on sporulation, germination, outgrowth, and toxin production' in Rockland L B and Beuchat L R, '*Water Activity: Theory and Applications to Food,*' New York, Marcel Dekker, Inc., 137–151.

BOQUET R, CHIRIFE J, IGLESIAS H A (1978), 'Equations for fitting water sorption isotherms of foods II. Evaluation of various two parameters models', *J Food Technol*, 13, 319–327.

BROMLEY L A (1973), 'Thermodynamic properties of strong electrolytes in aqueous solutions', *AICHEJ*, 19, 313–320.

CERRUTTI P, ALZAMORA S M, VIDALES S L (1997), 'Vanillin as antimicrobial for producing shelf-stable strawberry purée'. *J Food Sci* 62, 608–610.

CORRY J E L (1973), 'The water relations and heat resistance of microorganisms', *Prog. Ind. Microbiol*. 12, 73–80.

CHIRIFE J (1994), 'Specific solute effects with special reference to *Staphylococcus aureus*', in Fito P, Mulet A, McKenna B, *Water in Foods. Fundamental Aspects and their Significance in Relation to Processing of Foods*, Great Britain, Elsevier Applied Science, 409–419.

CHIRIFE J (1995), 'An update on water activity measurements and prediction in intermediate and high moisture foods: the role of some non-equilibrium situations', in Barbosa-Cànovas G and Welti-Chanes J, *Food Preservation by Moisture Control. Fundamentals and Applications,* Lancaster, Pennsylvania, Technomic Publishing Company, 169–189.

CHIRIFE J, IGLESIAS H A (1978), 'Equations for fitting water sorption isotherms of foods: Part 1 a review', *J Food Technol*, 13, 159–174.

CHIRIFE J, RESNIK S L (1984), 'Unsaturated solutions of sodium chloride as reference sources of water activity at various temperatures', *J Food Sci*, 49, 1486–1488.

CHIRIFE J, FAVETTO G, FERRO FONTÁN C, RESNIK S L (1983), 'The water activity of standard saturated salt solutions in the range of IM foods', *Lebensm Wiss u Technol*, 16, 36–38.

CHRISTIAN J H B (2000), 'Drying and reduction of water activity', in Lund B M, Baird-Parker T C and Gould G W, *The Microbiological Safety and Quality of Foods*, Maryland, Aspen Pub., 146–174.

FAVETTO G J, CHIRIFE J (1985), 'Simplified method for the prediction of water activity in binary solutions', *J Food Technol*, 20, 631–636.

FAVETTO G J, RESNIK S L, CHIRIFE J, FERRO FONTÁN C (1983), 'Statistical evaluation of water activity measurements obtained with the Vaisala Humicap humidity meter', *J Food Sci*, 48, 534–538.

FERRO FONTÁN C, CHIRIFE J (1981a), 'The evaluation of water activity in aqueous solutions from freezing point depression', *J Food Technol*, 16, 21–30.

FERRO FONTÁN C, CHIRIFE J (1981b), 'Technical note: a refinement of Ross' equation for predicting the water activity of non-electrolyte mixtures', *J Food Technol* 16, 219–221.

FERRO FONTÁN C, BENMERGUI E A, CHIRIFE J (1980), 'The prediction of water activity in aqueuos solutions in connection with intermediate moisture foods. III. Prediction in multicomponent strong electrolyte aqueous solutions', *J Food Technol*, 15, 47–52.

FERRO FONTÁN C, CHIRIFE J, BOQUET R (1981), 'Water activity in multicomponent non-electrolyte solutions', *J Food Technol*, 16, 219–225.

FITO P, MULET A, MCKENNA B (1994), *Water in Foods. Fundamentals Aspects and their Significance in Relation to Processing of Foods*, Oxford, Elsevier Science Limited.

FRANKS F (1991), 'Water activity: a credible measure of food safety and quality?', *Trends Food Sci*, March, 68–72

GERSCHENSON L N, FAVETTO G, CHIRIFE J (1984), 'Influence of organic volatiles during water activity measurement with a fiber-dimensional hygrometer', *Lebensm Wiss u Technol*, 17, 342–344.

GOULD G W (1989), 'Drying, raised osmotic pressure and low water activity', in Gould G W, *Mechanisms of Action of Food Preservation Procedures*, New York, Elsevier Applied Science.

GOULD G.W (1995), 'Overview', in Gould G W, *New Methods of Food Preservation*, London, Blackie Academic and Professional.

GOULD G W (1996), 'Methods for preservation and extension of shelf life', *Int Food Microbiol* 33, 51–64.

GOULD G W (2000), 'Induced tolerance of microorganisms to stress factors', in Alzamora S M, Tapia M S, Lopez-Malo A, *Minimally Processed Fruits and Vegetables. Fundamental Aspects and Applications*, Gaithersburg, Maryland, Aspen Publishers Inc., 29–37.

GREENSPAN L (1977), 'Humidity fixed points of binary saturated aqueous solutions', *J Res Nat Bur Stan – A Phys & Chem*, 81A, 89–96.

GUERRERO S, ALZAMORA S M, GERSCHENSON L N (1994), 'Development of a shelf-stable banana purée by combined factors: microbial stability', *J Food Protec* 57, 902–907.

GUTIERREZ C, ABEE T, BOOTH I R (1995), 'Physiology of the osmotic stress response in microorganisms', *Int J Food Microb*, 28, 233–244.

IGLESIAS H A, CHIRIFE J (1982), *Handbook of Food Isotherms: Water Sorption Parameters for Food and Food Components*, New York, Academic Press.

JAYARAMAN K S (1995), 'Critical review on intermediate moisture fruits and vegetables', in Welti-Chanes J, Barbosa-Cánovas G, *Food Preservation by Moisture Control – Fundamentals and Applications*, Lancaster, Technomic Pub. Co., 411–442.

JOHNSTON M R, LING R C (1987), 'FDA views on the importance of $a_w$ in good manufacturing practices', in Rockland L B and Beuchat L, *Water Activity: Theory and Applications to Food*, New York, Marcel Dekker, Inc., 287–294.

KAREL M (1973), 'Recent research and development in the field of low moisture and intermediate moisture foods', *CRC Crit Rev Food Technol*, 3, 329–373.

KAREL, M (1976), 'Technology and application of new intermediate moisture foods', in Davies R., Birch G G, Parker K J, *Intermediate Moisture Foods*, London, Applied Science Publishers Ltd., 4–31.

KITIC D, FAVETTO G J, CHIRIFE J, RESNIK S L (1986), 'Measurement of water activity in the intermediate moisture range with the Novasina thermoconstanter humidity meter', *Lebensm Wiss u Technol*, 19, 297–301.

LABUZA T P, ACCOT K, TATINI S R, LEE R Y (1976), 'Water activity determination: a collaborative study of different methods', *J Food Sci*, 41, 910–917.

LEITSNER L (1978), 'Hurdle effect and energy saving', in Downey W K, *Food Quality and Nutrition*, London, Applied Science Publishers, 553–557.

LEISTNER L (1987), 'Shelf-stable products and intermediate foods based on meat', in Rockland L B and Beuchat L, *Water Activity: Theory and Applications to Food*,

New York, Marcel Dekker, Inc., 295–327.

LEISTNER L (1999), 'Combined methods for food preservation', in: Shafiur Rahman M, *Food Preservation Handbook*, New York, Marcel Dekker, Inc.; 457–485.

LEISTNER L (2000), 'Hurdle technology in the design of minimally processed foods', in Alzamora S M, Tapia M S, Lopez-Malo A, *Minimally Processed Fruits and Vegetables. Fundamental Aspects and Applications*, Gaithersburg, Maryland, Aspen Publishers Inc., 13–27.

LEISTNER L, GOULD G W (2002), *Hurdle Technologies. Combination Treatments for Food Stability, Safety and Quality*, New York, Kluwer Academic/Plenum Publishers.

LE MAGUER M (1987), 'Mechanisms and influence of water binding on water activity', in Rockland L B and Beuchat L, *Water Activity: Theory and Applications to Food*, New York, Marcel Dekker, Inc., 1–26.

LENOVICH. L M (1987), 'Survival and death of microorganisms as influenced by water activity', in Rockland L B and Beuchat L, *Water Activity: Theory and Applications to Food*, New York, Marcel Dekker, Inc., 119–136.

LILLEY T H (1994), 'Basic physical chemistry and links between hydration and solute interactions', in Fito P, Mulet A, McKenna B, *Water in Foods. Fundamental Aspects and their Significance in Relation to Processing of Foods*, Oxford, Elsevier Science Limited, 13–26.

MAROULIS Z B, TSAMI E, MARINOS-KOURI D, SARAVACOS G D (1988), 'Application of the GAB model to sorption isotherms of fruits', *J Food Eng*, 7, 63–78.

MOSSEL D A A, CORRY J E L, STRUIJK C B, BAIRD R M (1991), *Essentials of the Microbiology of Foods. A Text for Advanced Studies*, Chichester, John Wiley and Sons Ltd., 91–93.

NORRISH R S (1966) 'An equation for the activity coefficients and equilibrium relative humidities of water confectionery syrups', *J Food Technol*, 1, 25–32.

PITZER K S (1973), 'Thermodynamics of electrolytes. I. Theoretical basis and general equations'. *J Phys Chem*, 77, 268–277.

PITZER K S, MAYORGA G (1973), 'Thermodynamics of electrolytes. II. Activity and osmotic coefficients for strong electrolytes with one or both ions univalent', *J Phys Chem*, 77, 2300–2308.

RAHMAN M S, LABUZA T P (1999), 'Water activity and food preservation', in Rahman M S, *Handbook of Food Preservation*, New York, Marcel Dekker, Inc, 339–82.

RAY B (1992), 'The need for food biopreservation', in Ray B and Daeschel M, *Food Biopreservatives of Microbial Origin*, Florida, CRC Press, 1–24.

RESNIK S L, FAVETTO G, CHIRIFE J, FERRO FONTÁN C (1984), 'A world survey of water activity of selected saturated salt solutions used as standards at 25°C', *J Food Sci*, 49, 510–513.

ROBINSON R A, STOKES R M (1965), *Electrolyte Solutions*, 2nd edn., London, Butterworths Scientific Pub.

ROCKLAND L B AND BEUCHAT L R (1987), *Water Activity: Theory and Applications to Food*, New York, Marcel Dekker, Inc.

ROCKLAND L B, STEWART G F (1981), *Water Activity: Influences on Food Quality*, New York, Academic Press.

ROOS Y H, LESLIE R B, LILLFORD P J (1999), *Water Management in the Design and Distribution of Quality Foods*, Lancaster, Technomic Publ. Co.

ROSS K D (1975), 'Estimation of water activity in intermediate moisture foods', *Food Technol*, 29, 26–30.

RUSSELL N J, EVANS R I, TER STEEG P F, HELLEMONS J, VERHEUL A, ABEE T (1995),

'Membranes as a target for stress adaptation', *Int J Food Microbiol*, 28, 255–261.

SCOTT W J (1953), 'Water relations of *Staphylococcus aureus* at 30°C', *Aust J Biol Sci*, 6, 549–564.

SCOTT W J (1957), 'Water relations of food spoilage microorganisms', *Adv in Food Res*, 7, 83–127.

SCHURER K (1985), 'Comparison of sensors for measurement of air humidity', in Simatos D and Multon J L, *Properties of Water in Foods in Relation to Quality and Stability*, Dordrecht, Martinus Nijhoff Pub., 647–660.

SIMATOS D AND MULTON J L (1985), *Properties of Water in Foods in Relation to Quality and Stability*, Dordrecht, Martinus Nijhoff Pub.

STAMP J A, LINSCOTT S, LOMAURO C, LABUZA T P (1984), 'Measurement of water activity of salt solutions and foods by several electronic methods as compared to direct vapour pressure measurement', *J Food Sci*, 49, 1139–1142.

STOLOFF L (1978), 'Calibration of water activity measuring instruments and devices: collaborative study', *J Assoc Off Anal Chem*, 61, 1166–1178.

TAPIA M S, AGUILERA J M, CHIRIFE J, PARADA E, WELTI J (1994), 'Identification of microbial stability factors in traditional foods from Iberoamerica', *Rev Española Ciencia Tecnol Alim*, 34, 145–163.

TORREGIANI D, BERTOLO G (2002), 'The role of an osmotic step: combined processes to improve quality and control functional properties in fruit and vegetables', in Welti-Chanes J, Barbosa Cánovas G V, Aguilera J M, *Engineering and Food for the 21st Century*, Boca Raton, CRA Press, 651–670.

TROLLER J A (1983), 'Methods to measure water activity', *J Food Protec*, 46, 129–134.

TROLLER J A (1987), 'Adaptation and growth of microorganism in environments with reduced water activity', in Rockland L B and Beuchat L, *Water Activity: Theory and Applications to Food*, New York, Marcel Dekker, Inc., 111–117.

TROLLER J A, CHRISTIAN J H B (1978), *Water Activity and Food*, New York, Academic Press.

VAN DEN BERG C, BRUIN S (1981), 'Water activity and its estimation in food systems: theoretical aspects', in Rockland L B, Stewart G F, *Water Activity: Influences on Food Quality*, New York, Academic Press, 1–61.

WELTI-CHANES J, BARBOSA-CÁNOVAS (1995), *Food Preservation by Moisture Control – Fundamentals and Applications*, Lancaster, Technomic Pub. Co.

WELTI J, VERGARA F T (1997), 'Actividad de agua: concepto y aplicación en alimentos con alto contenido de humedad', in Aguilera J M, *Temas en Tecnología de Alimentos*, México, CYTED- Instituto Politécnico Nacional, 11–43.

WELTI J, TAPIA M S, AGUILERA J, CHIRIFE J, PARADA E, LÓPEZ-MALO A, LÓPEZ L C, CORTE P (1994), 'Classification of intermediate moisture foods consumed in Ibero-America', *Rev Española Ciencia Tecnol Alim*, 34, 53–63.

WEISSER H (1985), 'Influence of temperature on sorption equilibrium', in Simatos D and Multon J L, *Properties of Water in Foods in Relation to Quality and Stability*, Dordrecht, Martinus Nijhoff Pub., 95–118.

WOLF W, SPIESS W E L, JUNG J (1985), 'Standardization of isotherms measurements (COST Project 90 and 90 bis)', in Simatos D and Multon J L, *Properties of Water in Foods in Relation to Quality and Stability*, Dordrecht, Martinus Nijhoff Pub., 661–679.

# 9

# Developments in conventional heat treatment

**G. Bown, Alcan Packaging, UK**

## 9.1 Introduction

The delivery of an adequately lethal thermal process is central in the preservation of food by the application of heat, both to prevent a risk to public health and to achieve a commercially reliable shelf life for the food. Conventional heat treatment systems must reliably deliver the required thermal process and at the same time accommodate many product, process and package variables and their interactions with each other and the thermal process. By its very nature, thermal processing has a detrimental effect on some food quality attributes and the food processor must design the thermal process to balance the unavoidable needs of commercial sterility with the commercial desire to present a high-quality product.

This chapter offers a short review of conventional heat treatment systems for delivering sufficiently lethal thermal processes, concentrating on retorts for sterilising and pasteurising batches of sealed containers (cans, semi-rigid heat sealed containers and flexible pouches). References are included to indicate sources of more detailed information. In addition, commonly encountered process variations and the interactions between product, process and packaging is discussed with particular reference to semi-rigid and flexible plastic packaging, to provide the processor with some insight into the influence they may have on commercial thermal processes.

## 9.2 Thermal technologies: cookers

The preservation of food by the application of heat is achieved by the large-scale inactivation of viable micro-organisms. *Clostridium botulinum* is generally considered to be the most heat resistant food poisoning organism and so the organism most likely to survive a thermal process. Surviving spores of this organism can germinate in the container and produce toxins in the consumer, which often prove fatal. The thermal process is required to achieve commercial sterility, that is 'to render the food free from viable micro-organisms, including those of known public health significance, capable of growing in the food at temperatures at which the food is likely to be held during distribution and storage' (DHSS 1994).

The severity of the thermal process selected to deliver sufficient lethality to ensure that processed foodstuffs achieve commercial sterility, the required shelf life and do not pose a risk to public health, is a function of the probability of survival of target organisms. A wide range of variables including the level of water activity within the product and the pH of the product, influence the probability of survival of target organisms in a given food product. These too need to be considered when defining the boundary conditions of a thermal process.

In general, pathogens are more heat resistant than non-pathogens and so populations of pathogens need to be exposed to higher temperatures, often for longer times than populations of non-pathogens, to achieve a state of commercial sterility. There are exceptions to this generalisation and so the food processor must ensure he has a full knowledge of his products and processes. If necessary, advice can be obtained from industry experts, for instance the Campden and Chorleywood Food Research Association (CCFRA) (contact details are given in 9.8.2.).

The temperature of target organisms enclosed within sealed containers of foods, when subjected to a thermal process delivered by a retort, is increased by the application of heat to the outside of the container, delivered via a heating fluid (steam, steam/air mixture or water (immersion or spray systems)) and subsequent heat transfer from the inner surface of the container, via the foodstuff and its covering fluids. In the context of commercial sterility, it is usual to define the location of the target organism as that where the probability of survival is the highest, usually at a point that heats slowest.

Given that a satisfactory thermal process achieves commercial sterility within a container of food, the food processor must take care, as far as possible, to maintain this state to the point of sale and beyond. Food containers are designed to be robust and to survive the handling anticipated during factory production processes, packing, storage, distribution, retailing and eventually domestic carriage and storage. The food processor must ensure that the production process does not reduce the durability of the container and its seals and that handling systems do not present new microbial challenges to the finished product (for instance handling when wet with the attendant risk of post-process spoilage).

Conventional cookers under consideration here are those that deliver a thermal process to foodstuffs sealed inside an appropriate container (e.g., can, semi-rigid plastic container with heat sealed lid, heat sealed flexible pouch) by the application of wet heat (steam, steam/air mixture and or hot water (immersion or water sprays)). Other systems exist that deliver pasteurising and sterilising processes to foodstuffs in other situations, for instance, aseptic systems bring food products directly into contact with heated surfaces or systems that generate heat by the direct application of electrical energy (Ohmic heating), before they are sealed inside a container or systems where ultra-high pressures are applied to denature the physiology of target micro-organisms (high pressure treatment). Discussion of these systems is not specifically included, however some aspects of these discussions will be applicable.

Food industry cookers of the type considered in this chapter, use steam as the primary source of heat applied to the container, given its practical ability to be efficiently generated, managed and moved around a factory area and its high capacity to deliver large quantities of heat to cooler surfaces as it condenses and gives up its latent energy. These cookers fall into two basic categories, continuous and batch according to the flow of packaged products.

- Continuous cookers apply a thermal process to a moving procession of containers. The thermal process is divided into stages that are performed in certain sections of the cooker. The 'ends' of the cooker allow unprocessed containers into the cooker and processed containers out.
- Batch cookers are completely closed before a thermal process starts and remain closed until the thermal process cycle is complete.

In general, continuous pasteurisation is achieved in open-ended tunnels at atmospheric pressure, where (usually hot filled) containers move on belts through high velocity water sprays arranged in zones at different temperatures (pre-heat, cook and cool). These systems have traditionally been used to pasteurise products in cans and glass jars but more recently, have been used to process products in semi-rigid and flexible plastic packaging. However care is required to maintain seal/container integrity and to ensure adequate lethality is delivered to achieve 'commercial sterility' relative to the target organism, particularly given a maximum cook temperature of about 98°C in atmospheric pressure conditions.

Traditionally, sterilising is achieved in pressurised systems since much higher temperatures are required and a pressure is required to permit these temperatures to be achieved using steam (typically 121°C requires an atmosphere of about 1bar above atmospheric pressure (1bg)) and so sterilisers need to be closed to maintain an internal pressure.

A continuous hydrostatic cooker collects cans (and sometimes bottles) end-to-end to form a 'stick' in a carrier system slung between two chains. The chains move the procession of carrier bars and containers through two open-ended water columns, one each side of a steam chamber (pre-heat and pre-cool water columns). The height of water balances the pressure within the steam chamber (and so the cooker is in the form of a tower perhaps 25 m high) and effectively closes the pressurised sections of the cooker. The chains also take the containers past columns of cooling water sprays en route to the discharge point. These very large cookers can operate at speeds in the order of 1,000 containers per minute.

A smaller and slower continuous cooker type, that has found more applications throughout the food industry, uses entry and exit valves to permit round containers into and out of process chambers, some of which are under pressure (cooking chamber) and others at atmospheric pressure (pre-heating and cooling chambers). The valves connect the chambers and permit the transfer of containers without disturbing the environment within the chamber. The cans move along a rotating reel and are guided by a static spiral track welded to the inside of the process chamber. The containers are able to spin as they roll along the lower (third) of the chamber, imparting a significant amount of agitation to the enclosed products, increasing heat transfer rate significantly. This style of continuous cooker achieves speeds in the order of 300 containers per minute and is generally designed to suit specific product and container applications. The non-cylindrical non-rigid nature of semi-rigid and flexible containers makes them unsuitable for this type of cooker.

Batch cookers have been in use from the very beginnings of heat processed foods. In their simplest form, they are pressure vessels with bolt-down lids and are connections to steam and cooling water supplies and to vent and drain lines. These simple cookers are often controlled manually and provide a thermal process adequate for traditional rigid cans. Modern batch cookers have added sophistication to allow independent temperature and pressure control, to agitate foods by rotation and to perform thermal process cycles totally automatically.

A growing number of food processors deliver sterilising processes to semi-rigid and flexible packaging using overpressure batch cookers that allow the processor to control chamber pressure independently of temperature, and so develop pressures higher than those usually associated with pure steam to maintain container geometry and integrity. It is possible to manage and synchronise the cycles of a series of batch cookers so that unprocessed containers flow continuously towards them and processed containers flow continuously away so that the system provides continuous cooking. However, at the point of thermal process delivery, the individual cooker performs a batch process.

Retort systems are also becoming more fully integrated with energy saving and energy recovery systems to minimise costs and reduce their impact on the environment and energy consumption. The canning industry has used batch and continuous cookers for very many years and a great deal has been written by very many to describe their operation including May (2001), CCFRA (1997a), NFPA (1982) and of course, cooker manufacturers some of whom are listed in section 9.8.1. This chapter will deal principally with batch sterilisers and will consider in particular their interaction with semi-rigid and flexible containers.

## 9.3   Thermal technologies: retorts

A wide range of batch sterilisers (usually called retorts) are available, ranging from simple pressure shells enclosing sealed food containers which allow live steam to condense and give up its energy directly to the surface of the food containers, to complex thermally efficient systems that use highly agitated but re-circulated water or steam/air mixtures to transfer heat from indirect steam heated heat exchanger surfaces or by direct steam injection, to sealed food containers. Some retorts increase the rate of heat transfer from the container surface to the food by agitating the foodstuff inside the container. These retorts induce movement within the container by rotating the containers about their vertical or horizontal axis and either cause the food to move under the influence of gravity or move a gaseous headspace through the foodstuff, using its natural inclination to rise to the (current) top of the container. Not all foods are appropriate for this treatment, for instance, delicate noodle soups may incur mechanical damage or solid pack meats simply may not move at all. For those appropriate food products, rotation may also help minimise the degree of over-cook delivered to perhaps heat sensitive products.

Most recent retort styles have horizontal pressure shells, sometimes two shells are employed within a single system, arranged one above the other. The upper pressure shell may be used to store cooling water during the cooking phase or pre-heated water during the cooling phase or may in fact be used as an 'extension' to the process chamber below to allow careful over-pressure control. Whatever the design style, all retorts share two common design principles.

- To provide environments where temperature is both predictable and controllable and where all points enclosed within the retort achieve the same temperature at the same time so that the same quantity of heat is delivered to all containers at the same time, causing the probability of survival of target organisms to fall at the same rate in all containers (all within practical limits).
- To provide an environment that maintains the integrity of the sealed food container throughout the cycle, to the extent that the seal integrity is not threatened and the product not contaminated by ingress of retort fluids or subsequent infection as a consequence of weakened or breached seals.

### 9.3.1   Heating and cooling cycles

The retort cycle may be divided into two sections: a cooking section during which time sufficient thermal lethality is delivered to achieve commercial sterility and a cooling section to remove heat from the foods to minimise the detrimental effects of heat on certain aspects of product quality (over-cooking) and to avoid extended periods of time at temperatures likely to incubate any remaining viable or recoverable organisms.

The cooking section is usually preceded by a series of process control valve sequences and environment changes (variously called venting, pre-heat or come-up) that ensure heat is delivered at the same rate to all food containers enclosed within the retort. In some systems this sequence is required to remove air from the retort to achieve a pure steam environment (venting) and in others, the sequence excites and pre-heats a heat transfer fluid (water, air or a mixture of steam and air – pre-heating). Whatever the sequence, the effect is to increase the retort temperature to the cook temperature (come-up). Also during this time, an amount of food product pre-heating occurs. In some situations this can reduce the extent of initial temperature variability from one container to another (those containers that enter the retort early in the loading cycle may cool whilst others are loaded and the cycle start prepared). The start of the cooking period is usually defined as the point in time when the retort temperature achieves the required cook temperature and is stable within defined limits (generally regarded as $+1°C$ to $-0.5°C$) (DHSS (1994) & NFPA (1982)). During the cooking period, temperature is generally held constant for a defined period of time within defined tolerances.

In general, the delivery of lethal heat ('the effect of exposure to temperature, under specified conditions, transformed mathematically in order to give a measure of sterilisation achieved' (DHSS (1994)) occurs during the cooking period when retort temperature is controlled within the defined tolerances and the behaviour of the product and package is predictable and allowed for during thermal process design.

Populations of organisms located at the point of slowest heating within most food products in most containers, will continue to heat after the end of the cooking period (particularly if the onset of cooling occurs slowly), but the contribution that this period of heating makes to the total delivered lethality is generally not included when a given retort cycle is assessed against the target lethality, since temperature during these phases is generally not controllable or predictable to the required tight tolerances and because the behaviour of the product, and in particular semi-rigid and flexible packaging, is not predictable. Similarly the lethal contributions made during phases before the cooking period are generally not included. However, some thermal processes delivered in carefully controlled retorts may accumulate 'lethal heat' during other parts of the retort cycle (for instance, pre-heating, pre-cooling or cooling) but only if the temperature achieved in the retort falls within the required limits and the effect of those other parts of the retort cycle on the product and container are predictable and allowed for during thermal process design. The efficacy of the thermal process is required to achieve Commercial Sterility so the variables that govern the delivery of lethal heat become Critical Control Points and should be controlled and managed via a HACCP scheme.

The transition between cooking and cooling usually takes place very carefully since it is important to ensure all food containers stop heating and begin cooling at about the same time to reduce the variability of the effects of heat on quality, from one container to another (for instance if those containers close to the cooling water entry point cool faster than those further away – so those further away suffer the effects of heat for longer). Also during this transition time, the atmosphere inside the sealed food container may change rapidly and there is a risk that differential pressure changes (pressure inside the food container relative to that outside in the retort environment) across the container walls may pose a risk to the integrity of the container (if for instance sudden cooling causes retort steam to collapse and retort pressure to fall very quickly while there is still a pressure within the container). The cooling section is usually completed by a drain down/recovery sequence that returns the retort to its start conditions ready for the next cycle and allows an opportunity to unload one batch of food and load the next.

### 9.3.2    Atmospheric and pressurised systems

The pressure inside the sealed food container will change to reflect the temperature achieved inside the container, as the retort cycle progresses. The need to minimise the risk to container and seal integrity posed by differential pressures developed across the container walls and/or lid, usually requires a pressure to be developed within the retort to balance and even slightly exceed that developing within the food container. This retort over-pressure is often maintained throughout the cooking and cooling sections of the cycle and is often particularly carefully controlled during the transition from cooking to cooling. This maintains a prescribed differential pressure.

Retort overpressure is also applied to semi-rigid and flexible package formats to maintain their geometry throughout the retort cycle. Controlling package geometry in this way ensures that package geometry does not become a variable that may influence the rate of heat transfer to the food within the container and so does not influence the lethality actually achieved at the target population (e.g., ballooning pouches – where heat transfer rates will be slower than in pouches maintained in a parallel-sided 'slab' format).

There are occasionally situations where some retort cycles (e.g., some pasteurising processes in the order of 90°C) do not induce pressures inside containers likely to pose a risk to container seal integrity, particularly when those seals are very strong or when the container is sealed under vacuum. In these situations, it may be possible to achieve an acceptable retort cycle without the need for overpressure – or indeed any pressure above atmospheric pressure. In these situations, the food processor must be sure that in-container pressures pose no risk to container seal integrity and that container geometry is either constant or any geometry changes are taken into account when defining the thermal process.

### 9.3.3    Process control and process records

The amount of process control equipment required to perform the retort cycle, is generally proportional to the process cycle sophistication. The trend in recent years has been towards process automation using microprocessor-based systems. Bown (1985) describes one of the earlier such systems. Control system architectures tend to be distributed (for process integrity and autonomy) with centralised data handling. This approach also allows simpler operator interfaces and allows a system to grow and expand as process capacity expands. Local control systems, looking after a single or perhaps a small number of retorts, generally employ off-the-shelf microprocessor-based Programmable Logic Control systems with customised sequencing and control loop software. Central data handling computers use customised software to handle logistics, operational and supervisory tasks.

In some cases, control software automatically compensates for process deviations by adjusting live process temperature and/or process times according to prescribed rules. In particular, FMC employ systems in their 'Logtech' control system, to compare actual delivered lethality with that calculated by a numerical model to indicate live process deviations and to automatically adjust the thermal process to compensate for the deviation. Further information may be obtained from FMC (address given in 9.8.1) and the extensive bibliographies given in CCFRA (1997b) and (1997c).

Retort process controls of whatever complexity should conform to the established guidelines for accuracy, repeatability, safe and reliable operation and ensure that the required lethality is accurately and reliably delivered to every container of every load processed. Guidelines have been established to define control performance, data collection and process recording (DHSS 1994). Process control variables that need to be logged and recorded include retort temperature with time, cook temperature confirmed by the Master Temperature Indicator during the cook time, rotation speed (if rotary agitation is employed) and some unique process cycle identification that links a specific group of containers to an individual process cycle, in the event that the cycle is shown to be deficient and the group of containers needs to be withdrawn from saleable stock.

The tolerance for temperature control has generally fallen as control systems improve. The smaller the tolerance, the more opportunity there is to optimise the thermal process since the degree of overcook can be better controlled. In general, modern retorts are expected to achieve cook temperatures to better than $\pm0.5°C$ from process to process and retort to retort, and better than $\pm1°C$ from point to point in a given retort regardless of load, generally within two minutes of first achieving cook temperature.

### 9.3.4   Commercial sterility

An empirical approach is generally used to investigate the efficacy of a thermal process in a given practical situation, to determine if commercial sterility is achieved. Temperature measuring equipment is positioned at the point of slowest heating within a container (the point where the probability of survival for a given organism is greatest) and a method of 'lethal rate summation' at that point is used to determine the actual delivered lethality and hence the probability of survival of a target organism. This approach is used to develop thermal process designs to suit new products, packages and process systems. The approach is also used to establish and qualify new production scenarios ahead of commercial use and is used to validate all processes at regular and frequent intervals during the lifetime of the specific production and on every occasion when critical process parameters change.

CCFRA (1997b), CCFRA (1997c) and DHSS (1994) present the approach in practical detail and discuss the microbial connections between practical heat transfer and achieved lethality. Specialist instrumentation has been developed to assist process evaluation. Devices have been developed to measure temperature and pressure inside a container, to measure the deflection of container surfaces as they respond to changes in differential pressure (note: the physical and mechanical properties of most plastic containers are a function of their temperature) and to measure rotation. Further specifics can be obtained from equipment suppliers, contact details for one of the major suppliers is given in section 9.8.3.

A wide range of variables influence actual delivered lethality and each must be accounted for in the series of experiments that comprise the empirical approach described earlier. The series of experiments should extend to provide an understanding of all the variables connected with the thermal process, the package format and all the interactions with products and upstream/downstream processes. It is the duty of food processors to exercise Due Diligence in the establishment of thermal process regimes and to ensure their Duty of Care to the consumer is properly fulfilled.

A HACCP study conducted by those with a full understanding of both the HACCP concept and the thermal process situation may help determine which variables are most significant in a given situation. CCFRA (1997a) presents an example HACCP study for sterilising or pasteurising foods in a raining water/ spray water retort.

## 9.4    Using plastic packaging in retort operations

Food packaging is evolving, conventional cylindrical cans are changing shape and becoming thinner and so more susceptible to damage by inappropriate differential pressure during retorting. Retortable plastics are becoming commonplace and a growing number of new products are appearing in heat sealable semi-rigid plastic containers with multi-layer plastic lids or multi-layer, heat-sealed flexible pouches. Consequently, retort technology is evolving to match.

Process styles and process control systems are comprehensive and sophisticated and the 'furniture' of retorts (container specific trays, transport crates, etc.) is custom designed to accommodate many specific package shapes whilst maintaining adequate fluid spaces around packages to ensure the basic design criteria are met in terms of minimum permitted variation in achieved lethality from any point to any other point within the retort. These trends in packaging and retort styles are in line with the drive towards lower manufacturing cost and higher integrity processes to match the insatiable drive towards retail product differentiation and market share. Typically, retortable plastic containers are produced from co-extrusions or laminates of various polymers, including polypropylene, oriented polyamide, polyethylene-terephthalate (PET) and polyethylene. They generally have polymer oxygen and moisture barriers and have sophisticated peel systems and other easy open features.

The use of semi-rigid and flexible plastic packaging adds to the list of potential variables that influence achieved lethality. The interactions between product, package and process add still further to the list, making a thorough understanding of the situation even more necessary if sub-lethal processes are to be avoided. At one end of the scale is the potential to breach the heat seal and so induce leaks, by inappropriate differential pressure (both positive and negative differential pressure) whilst at the other is the need to achieve and maintain a predetermined container geometry to allow the movement of heating and cooling fluids around the outside of the container and to achieve expected heat transfer rates within the container. To further complicate the situation, variations in filled weight, headspace volume, headspace gas density, container volume, the physical behaviour of the container materials within the retort and other aspects of the pre-retort process and the package design, interact with the retort environment to produce influences on achieved lethality that have the potential to change an otherwise optimised thermal process into a sub-lethal process, with all the attendant risks to public health.

Whilst achieved lethality is a function of the interactions between the product, package, pre-retort production line processes and the delivered thermal process, semi-rigid and flexible plastic packaging formats have a greater influence on achieved lethality than rigid and metal containers simply because their geometry is not necessarily predictable or constant and is influenced by so many of the package and production line variables. It is true that the geometry of rigid metal containers is also sensitive to many of the same variables, but the influence of these variables on achieved lethality in rigid containers is generally far less significant.

The following discussion outlines some of the interactions between products, pre-retort processes, plastic packages and the retort process and relates them to their influence on achieved lethality. It should be noted that the relative significance of these variables and their influence on achieved lethality is specific to each production line, product and package.

### 9.4.1  Package geometry

The overall shape of a package can be such that it contributes to reducing the detrimental effects of the retort process on certain aspects of product quality, by minimising the time required to achieve target delivered lethality by reducing the distance heat is required to travel to reach the target site. This is particularly evident with flexible pouches where the surface to volume ratio is high and the overall thickness of the package is relatively thin. Semi-rigid containers, perhaps to a lesser extent, achieve the same effect. They tend to be basically flat cylindrical or rectangular shapes, some of which are multi-compartment trays that further increase the heating surface area and reduce the distance to the slowest heating point.

The headspace in flat cylindrical or rectangular shaped semi-rigid containers tends to have a large surface area contact with the food product and whilst the headspace volume may not be large compared to the volume of the container, it will have an insulating effect, resisting heat transfer to the upper surfaces of the product and so reducing the surface area of product in direct contact with the heated sidewalls of the container. The effect is reduced when semi-rigid containers are arranged 'lid down' whilst in the retort, particularly since the headspace volume will be contained in the smaller proportions of the base of the container. Faster heating and cooling and the consequentially reduced detrimental effects of heat on certain aspects of quality are often regarded as opportunities to claim improved production rates (shorter retort cycle times) and improved product quality compared to the same product in a cylindrical can.

The container designer and the food processor need to consider the likely changes to container geometry during retorting if container shape is to be optimised. It is therefore necessary to fully understand and control the variables that influence container geometry during retorting. A number of common variables and their means of control are included in later discussion. The following list outlines some of the variables considered most significant:

- Headspace volume (derived from container volume, filled volume, area of lid applied to a semi-rigid container, position of the heat seal on a flexible pouch relative to the edges of the plastic laminate).
- Headspace gas pressure (derived from flush gas pressure, sealing machine vacuum cycle (if any), gas composition (since some gases dissolve into the product), product fill temperature).
- Mechanical and physical properties of component polymers with temperature and with differential pressure (tendency to stretch or shrink, adjusting enclosed volume).
- Gas content of product (gas tends to be driven out of some products during retorting, adding to the gas pressure in the headspace).
- Retort pressure and temperature.

### 9.4.2    Interaction between temperature and pressure

Fundamental laws of thermodynamics link temperature and pressure. Of particular interest here is the saturated steam pressure for a given temperature since retort processes generally involve air, water and steam. Overpressure is generally regarded as that pressure applied by the retort above the saturated steam pressure appropriate for the environment temperature, at that moment in time. Overpressure may thus be constant even when retort pressure is a variable with time. In general, overpressure is applied either by the pressure of steam supplied into a gas space above water in a water immersion process vessel (for instance in a Stock Rotomat) or is applied by compressed air either mixed with steam in a process vessel (for example in a LaGuarde retort) or applied directly to the process vessel in the presence of heated water in a water spray style retort (for instance a Barriquand retort).

It is possible to superheat water in a retort. That is to maintain water as a fluid at temperatures above 100°C. Water spray retorts and water immersion retorts are operated at pressures above saturated steam pressure for the required retort temperature. Typically, a Barriquand retort circulates water at 121°C and about 3 ba (bar absolute) – according to the needs of the container (note: saturated steam pressure at 121°C is 2 ba so a retort pressure of 3 ba provides 1 ba overpressure).

### 9.4.3   Influence of pressure generated within a container

The absolute pressure generated inside a container is a function of the initial pressure in the headspace at the time of sealing (sometimes a vacuum is achieved) and the temperature achieved within the container (and other variables). The gases in a container headspace heat faster than the product and so it is likely that a pressure is generated within the container almost as soon as the retort temperature exceeds that of the headspace gases. The container walls and seals take the strains produced by this internal pressure. Given that seal strength is sometimes reduced at retort temperatures as plastics soften as they get hot, it is possible to breach the seal during the first few minutes of the retort cycle. The container may be 'inflated' during this part of the retort cycle and may be constrained by elements of the retort 'furniture'. This may help reduce the strain otherwise taken by the container walls, particularly if the container is a flexible pouch. The strain applied to the seals during this period of the retort cycle is likely to be increased if the retort overpressure is not yet established or adequate to maintain stable geometry. As the retort cycle progresses, entrapped gases are 'expanded out' of the product cellular structure and join the gases in the headspace already expanding and acting on the container, adding to the strains applied to the container walls and seals. As the product temperature passes 100°C, water begins to turn to steam and further pressure is developed in the headspace.

It is important to apply the appropriate amount of overpressure early enough to maintain container geometry and to reduce the differential pressure to minimise strains on heat seals. Appropriate overpressure is also required to prevent the component films of semi-rigid container lids and flexible pouches from stretching beyond their elastic limit (where deformation may be permanent or where the material may break) or beyond a point where internal strains are applied within the structure that may reduce or even overcome the bond strengths of adhesives that maintain the laminate integrity. Local or widespread delamination may occur in the laminate if bond strengths are exceeded by these internal strains, which will add to the risk to package integrity and may reduce the performance of barriers otherwise provided by the laminate.

### 9.4.4   Pressure considerations during cooling

At the onset of cooling several pressure-related aspects may change dramatically. Steam within the retort environment is likely to condense at the moment cold water is introduced so that retort pressure may fall dramatically if not otherwise controlled. In severe cases, the collapsing steam develops a vacuum within the retort suddenly increasing the differential pressure across container walls and seals by significant amounts (likely to be at least 1 bg and could be as high as 2 bg). The risk to seal integrity is very high if this occurs. Therefore, commercial retorts control the transition from heating to cooling very carefully and generally introduce an intermediate step to replace the pressure of live steam in the retort with air pressure.

The steam environment inside the container is also just as likely to collapse at the onset of cooling, however this collapse is likely to occur a few moments after cooling starts (assuming the seal has not been breached already by collapsing retort pressure) since the hot product will tend to replace heat taken out of a gaseous headspace by retort cooling water and will thus support headspace pressure. The containers most at risk are those very close to the cooling water entry where they may receive a 'direct hit' from inrushing cooling water. The gentle nature of commercial retorts generally ensures that incoming cooling water is distributed evenly throughout the retort and is cooled slowly from cooking temperatures to avoid just this situation.

Overpressure is generally maintained during cooling to avoid sudden retort pressure changes and to continue to act upon the container since, once the initial shock of the onset of cooling has passed, the still hot product inside the containers is likely to continue to generate steam or expand headspace gases and hence support headspace pressure for several minutes. The plastics of the container are also undergoing change during cooling. Just before cooling begins the plastics are likely to be under stress, either inflated because internal pressure is greater than retort pressure or deflated if the pressures are applied the other way round. Flexible plastic laminates are likely to be under tension or may even have stretched (but hopefully below their elastic limit) by the end of the heating phase.

At the onset of cooling, the thin plastic laminates of semi-rigid container lids and those of flexible pouches are 'frozen' at their current size and shape. If cooling continues and the laminates remain cold (likely as cooling progresses), the new 'shape and size' is likely to be fixed. If semi-rigid container lids are stretched when cooling water reaches them, they are likely to remain at this new surface area and so appear to be loose at the end of the retort cycle. Flexible pouches that may have been close fitting around the product may later appear looser too for the same reasons. Some polymer laminates may recover after a few days, depending on their structure and the degree to which they were stressed and may sometimes return to their pre-retort size and shape.

The relative size of the lid and its semi-rigid container is sometimes exaggerated if the container shrinks during the retort cycle. Round polypropylene container diameters may shrink as much as 5% depending on retort temperature and the residual stresses remaining in the structure from thermoforming. Shrinkage is often non-linear too, so that a round container may shrink more in one direction than another – leaving the container oval post retort. Thus even if the laminate of the lid recovers post retort, it still may appear 'looser' than it would otherwise.

In some situations, where internal pressure is significantly higher or significantly lower than retort pressure, the walls of semi-rigid containers may also stretch beyond their elastic limit, stretching either inwards or outwards. When the internal environment settles some time after retorting, the stretched area may appear as a dent in the container wall. Note that this dent may be the consequence of too much overpressure and so the cure for this situation is not always to increase overpressure as may be the cure for similar situations with cans!

Given the complexities of temperature and stress related plastic behaviour at the onset of cooling and during cooling, it is usual to maintain retort over-pressure, to attempt to retain the container geometry, until the temperature at the slowest cooling point within the container (not always the same point as that which heats slowest given the geometry changes that may have taken place during heating) falls below about 80°C and then to slowly reduce overpressure until about 0.3 bg remains to the end of cooling. This remaining pressure is often used to 'assist' the water from the retort during draining and so may help reduce cycle time.

## 9.5   Dealing with variables during processing

The degree of interaction between production line variables, achieved lethality and container integrity is specific to individual situations and in principle may be different for every single container, given the high number of influential variables and the wide range of conditions encountered along a commercial process line. The sensitivity of the retort process to these variables must be such that achieved lethality and container integrity is not compromised and so two things must be achieved for reliable commercial sterility.

- Production line variables must be monitored and controlled within prescribed limits.
- The retort process must be designed with sufficiently wide operating tolerances so that production line variables are not permitted to compromise container integrity and achieved lethality.

This generally requires in-line control systems to be established and maintained and generally implies a degree of overprocessing (extended cooking beyond the point at which Commercial Sterility is otherwise achieved) is included to account for the 'worst case' lethality scenario. The following discussions provide a guide to some of the most often-encountered influential production line variables that need to be considered when establishing an effective thermal process and when investigating process difficulties experienced from container to container.

### 9.5.1    Containers

Variations in container volume may influence headspace volume which, in turn may influence heat transfer rates and differential pressure across the container walls and hence package geometry during retorting and so ultimately may influence achieved lethality and pose a risk to seal integrity. The brim-full volume of semi-rigid containers is generally closely controlled by the thermo-forming or injection moulding process, nominal values and acceptable tolerances usually form part of the supplier's specification and so variations in brim-full volume are not normally significant sources of headspace volume variations. However, the total enclosed volume of a semi-rigid container can often become a significant variable if the area of lid applied during sealing is not a constant. This is discussed later with respect to filling since it is possible for filling conditions to influence the area of lid applied to the semi-rigid container. The brim-full volume of flexible pouches is also usually well controlled. In practice, there are sometimes small differences in brim-full volume between batches but variations in brim-full volume should not be significant sources of headspace volume variations.

The total enclosed volume of flexible pouches may be a larger variable since the position of the final (usually top) seal usually depends on the means by which the pouch is located in the sealing machine's sealing jaws, the geometry of the pouch when filled and the position of the gusset (in the case of a stand-up pouch) and hence its contribution to pouch volume, at the moment of sealing. Variations in the total enclosed volume of pouches may also occur because of variations in the position or efficacy of the guides or formers which help shape the pouch on its route through the sealing machine. Significant variations are also likely if no means are used to 'fix' or define filled pouch shape or total enclosed volume.

### 9.5.2    Filling

In general, containers are either filled by weight or by volume. The bulk density of the product and the relative size of the product particulates compared to the container, influence the filled volume of those containers filled by weight. Consequently headspace volume and headspace gas pressure (including effects due to variations in the volume of gas trapped in variable amounts of product) will be influenced. The filled weight of those containers filled by volume is likely to be influenced by the specific density of the product and so the heating characteristics of the product may be influenced. Containers filled by counting particulates into the container are likely to be influenced by both sets of variables, given that natural food products can rarely be cut into particulates with uniform volume and weight. Whichever filling method is adopted, under weight and over weight filling will influence the headspace volume and hence headspace gas pressures. Gross over filling may also cause product to stack above the normal fill level and may influence the shape of a pouch at the moment of sealing or even add to the surface area of a semi-rigid container lid, 'draped' over a too-high product.

At its simplest, under and over filling may influence the final container shape (e.g., loose lids, oversize pouches) but at its most severe, over filling may slow down heating rates to the point where the prescribed retort cycle fails to deliver a sufficiently lethal process. Both conditions are likely to threaten seal and container integrity.

- Additional product in over filled containers will carry with it additional entrapped gases that may occupy a smaller than normal headspace volume inducing higher than normal headspace pressures.
- Very large headspace volumes and lower than normal product levels in under filled containers, are less likely to support the concave shape of lids on semi-rigid containers during periods of overpressure in the retort, which may be stressed beyond their elastic limit (to the point where the material may permanently deform or may fail) or produce significant stresses at the heat seals.

In general most products comprise both solids and liquids. Variations in the solid to liquid ratio are likely to influence the rate of heating and hence delivered lethality.

### 9.5.3   Sealing conditions

The strength of the seal achieved in the sealing machine varies with changes in sealing conditions; seal time, seal face temperature and pressure applied during sealing. In situations where the production rate changes or when a production line stops and starts frequently, it is possible for the heat delivered to the seal face to change as the (usually) electrical heaters respond to changing demands for energy. This variable heat flux is particularly significant if the temperature controller has a simple 'proportional-only' or a rudimentary 'on/off' control response.

The valve sequences that perform gas-flushing operations during the sealing cycle generally rely on a combination of electronic control and pneumatic actuation via pilot valves. These pilot valves control air signals that are sent to actuate process valves and so control the flow of flush gases, the application of vacuum and the subsequent release of vacuum. The relative timing of these valves influences the conditions achieved within the container headspace.

The time taken for the electronics to pass electrical signals to the valves may be generally regarded as a constant; it is unlikely that there will be any significant variation in the timing of these signals unless a component fails. However, the same is not true of the pneumatic systems actuated by these signals, since the speed at which they respond is a function of internal lubrication, cleanliness and wear of moving parts and the cleanliness of connecting pipes supplying flush gases and vacuum. It is likely that worn valves or those with dirty or inadequately lubricated moving parts, influence headspace pressure, the blend of headspace gases (where more than one flush gas is used) and, where sealing heads and sealing chambers are moved by air-actuated cylinders, the actual seal time and seal pressure may also be influenced. In addition, if vacuum release systems are slow to re-pressurise the sealing chamber at the end of a vacuum sealing cycle and the chamber is opened mechanically, the sudden inrush of atmospheric pressure may damage the still hot and 'wet' seals, significantly reducing the newly-formed polymer bonds and weakening the seal. Similarly partially blocked air, gas and vacuum routes may influence headspace conditions and seal strength since the expected volumes of air/flush gases will not pass through the system. Good machine maintenance is the key to reducing these hidden but sometimes very significant production line variables and becomes important when the assumptions about worse case scenarios for delivered lethality are developed and when retort process conditions are defined.

Lethality variations as a consequence of mechanical variations at the heat sealer are often included in a food processor risk assessment or HACCP study. Generally, the critical control points and a set of operating tolerances and action limits are established. However, they are not always considered when establishing worst-case scenarios to test delivered lethality and to validate thermal processes.

### 9.5.4   Headspace control prior to sealing

When container and filling variables are controlled to the point where variations in headspace conditions are within controlled limits and they are no longer the source of unexpected variations in achieved lethality and seal integrity, aspects of the product pre-treatment and the sealing operation need to be considered and controlled to minimise their influence on achieved lethality and seal integrity. Headspace variables are essentially headspace volume, headspace pressure (vacuum) and headspace gas composition. Headspace volume is a function of container volume, filling variables, the performance of sealing machine valve sequences and the influences of retort pressure and retort 'furniture' design on container geometry, discussed earlier. Headspace volume is also a function of the gas content of food products (usually air) at the time of sealing and if required, the gases used to flush the headspace immediately prior to sealing.

If the product is likely to carry large or variable amounts of gas into the container, either trapped within the cell structure or dissolved in the liquid fractions, it is sometimes necessary to de-aerate the product. For most solid products, this may be achieved during the blanching or pre-cooking process that may also be used to pre-treat the products ahead of retorting (baked beans, recipe sauce products). For most liquid products, gentle heating may achieve de-aeration and gentle handling may avoid re-aeration. This too may also be part of the pre-treatment ahead of retorting (pre-cooking recipe sauces, formulations for soups, preparation of brine).

It is therefore necessary to ensure these pre-treatments achieve consistent effects on the volume of entrapped gases carried by food products into the container, so that variations in entrapped volumes of gases that later escape into the headspace, do not influence headspace volume or headspace pressure and hence container geometry and achieved lethality and seal integrity during retorting.

Headspace gas pressure prior to retorting is a function of the gases initially present in the food, the process that evacuates and/or flushes the headspace and the gas pressure at the time the container was closed.

In general, and assuming whatever pre-treatments are necessary to regulate gases contained within the products are complete, sealing machines adjust the headspace gas pressure and usually replace headspace oxygen with an inert gas (usually nitrogen). This may be achieved by evacuating the container before flushing with inert gases and controlling headspace pressure at the time sealing occurs. After sealing, when the sealing chamber is opened and atmospheric pressure is applied to the container surfaces, the headspace volume will adjust to the point where external atmospheric pressure is balanced by any residual internal partial pressure and stresses taken by the container, its contents and, in the case of semi-rigid containers, its lid. Generally, atmospheric pressure or a slight vacuum is achieved inside the container at the moment of sealing and the headspace gas is slightly compressed as atmospheric pressure is applied when the sealing tool opens. Usually this means that flexible pouches form themselves around the product and the lids of semi-rigid containers become dish shaped, perhaps supported by the product surface.

It is possible that atmospheric pressure will also induce dents in the sidewalls of semi-rigid containers, particularly if the headspace volume is large or if the material distribution in the container walls is poor. Alternatively, gas density may be adjusted according to the selection of flush gases since some gases may be dissolved into some products (e.g., $CO_2$), vacating the headspace after sealing and so lowering the partial pressure and increasing the likely compression when atmospheric pressure is applied to the outside of the container. Although this approach is sometimes used to balance the gas exchange that may take place post retort (when entrapped gases are released from the product into the headspace), it should be noted that it is likely these gases will all be present in the headspace during retorting, in addition to any escaping from the food products and so the design of the retort time/temperature/pressure control profiles needs to account for their contribution to headspace volume and the likely changes in headspace gas properties.

### 9.5.5   Heat seal integrity and retorting

The importance of the relationship between seal integrity and retorting is obvious and some areas of the relationship have been explored already.

However, a number of heat seal machine related aspects are discussed here. The heat seal needs time to cool before it may be strong enough to cope with the differential pressures and temperatures of the retort cycle. During this cooling time, the polymer bonds produced by the sealing process become stronger as the polymers revert to a solid phase. Some flexible pouch sealers include a cooling and seal-ironing stage to ensure the polymer bond strength is sufficient before the pouch is released for further processing.

Handling systems between sealing machines and retorts, need to be designed to permit sufficient seal cooling time and to induce least stress at the heat seal, particularly while the seal may still be hot and relatively weak. These systems include orientation, buffering and loading systems used to load the crates used in batch retorts. If a semi-rigid container is bumped into another along a conveyor or is pushed against a stop, then the container is likely to distort. The points of contact on the periphery of the container will be pushed closer together at the moment of impact. At this same moment, two points on the heat seal perpendicular to the contact points will be pushed further apart as the container distorts. The consequential shearing action at the seal between the lid and the container flange is likely to damage the seal, perhaps breaking some of the new polymer bonds and reducing seal strength or, in severe cases, the shearing action may cause the seal to break.

Post-retort inspection should detect those containers with broken seals (loss or gain in weight, seal damage, etc.). Those seals that have been weakened may be less easy to detect and given that subsequent handling in the factory, distribution chain, retail situation and consumer handling may not always be very gentle, weakened seals provide a greater risk to public health than those of normal strength. It is normal to measure seal strength prior to retorting. Usually a destructive test is carried out on containers sampled according to a prescribed plan and taken from production. The Burst Test is normally achieved by inflating the containers with air using a prescribed protocol, until the seal either supports a minimum pressure or fails. The test result is used to reflect container material properties and sealing conditions and is used to indicate that the seal is strong enough to survive subsequent handling and the retort process without presenting a risk to public health post-retort. The burst pressure, defined as a minimum – or a positive result, needs to be established in conjunction with the retort time/temperature/pressure profiles and with an understanding of the differential pressures likely to be applied to the seal during the retort process. Details of a company who builds Burst Testers is given in section 9.8.4. DHSS (1994) discusses a range of seal tests and integrity concerns.

### 9.5.6    Time between sealing and retorting
Whilst it is important to allow a period of time between sealing and retorting to permit minimum seal strength (polymer bond strength) to be achieved, delays between sealing and retorting can also influence initial product conditions and so influence achieved lethality. The effects of delays and hence changes in initial

product temperature and the in-container temperature gradients, whilst perhaps waiting for a full retort load of containers to be prepared, are likely to increase the range of delivered lethality.

In some situations it is necessary to introduce a waiting period before the retort process can begin, for instance, if there is a need to allow time for product components to interact at filling temperatures (e.g., partial re-hydration of dried ingredients to establish expected heat transfer rates or expected levels of water activity) or if a contact time between components is required to establish an equilibrium (e.g., acidification). Variations in headspace conditions may also occur during the period between sealing and retorting, particularly if the headspace contains gases that may be absorbed by the product changing the volume of gases, gas density and pressure in the headspace. The detail of these situations must be taken into account when establishing worst-case scenarios, analysing risks, conducting HACCP studies and establishing and validating thermal processes.

## 9.6    The strengths and weaknesses of batch retorts

Batch retort manufacturers appear adept at meeting the challenge of new container types and materials, the concerns for the environment and energy conservation, the growing demand for automation and the need to reduce product manufacturing costs. It is likely that the basic principles of energy transfer via condensing steam, perhaps via a heat exchanger and automatic batch control systems will be available to the food processor for many years to come. Food researchers and microbiologists are likely to keep pace with product developers and package designers to ensure that the food processor has the expertise available to ensure that coming generations of new food products, thermal processes and package formats will not pose a risk to public health.

It seems likely that the current momentum in these research and development areas, the growing public awareness of the risks of food poisoning and the commercial pressures to produce more and more high-quality, shelf-stable food, will encourage more computerised retort process control systems where the degree of over-cooking, normally associated with product and process variations, will be trimmed and optimised for the sake of product quality and process efficiency. It is probable that new forms of preservation may be combined with conventional retorting to further optimise the delivered lethality and maximise product quality whilst reducing manufacturing costs. Current developments in high-pressure pasteurisation are driven by the low energy cost and low manufacturing cost. Adding a pre-heat process and using 'adiabatic heat' is extending the application of high-pressure processing towards sterilisation so it seems likely that retort technologies and those of high-pressure processing may be combined to produce an energy-efficient, apparently continuous and automatically controlled sterilisation system.

### 9.6.1   Strengths

History supports batch retorts. Their longevity is testimony to their adaptability and their suitability for food pasteurisation and sterilisation. A new food processor can minimise his capital investment by purchasing only the processing capacity required to meet current production forecasts and can easily expand as demand rises. A food processor can reduce the heat treatment component of his manufacturing costs by adding automation and increasing capacity to the point where a collection of batch retort systems are synchronised to function as a continuous process facility, he can add 'artificial intelligence' to the loading and unloading systems to allow the process facility to handle several different products at one time with the minimum of human interaction and maximum process assurance.

It is also possible for food processors to mix and match retort styles to suit a particular range of products and package formats, without losses in overall operational efficiency. Engineering developments make it possible to improve plant reliability to the point where the utilisation of pumps, valves, instrumentation and support services (steam, air, water) is at a maximum, where components have built-in self-check systems to indicate the need for recalibration, maintenance or repair and where critical components are duplicated and arranged to switch over in the event of a malfunction. So when such systems support batch retorts, the utilisation and reliability of the retorts will also increase.

When things do fail, when process definitions are incorrect or inadequate to deliver a sufficiently lethal process, or component systems fail and give rise to concerns that adequate lethality was perhaps not delivered, the batch nature of the retort means that the number of containers is limited to those exposed to the risk – which in turn is a function of how early the risk was noticed. It is at this point that real-time modelling systems can recover their investment since they are likely to indicate a change in the risk to public health on a batch-by-batch basis so that those products that pose unacceptable risk are not released into the post-retort product flow. There are already some systems that will detect a process deviation in real time and will attempt to correct the deviation in real time, so reducing the risk to public health and the financial exposure of the food processor.

### 9.6.2   Weaknesses

Whilst the batch nature of retorts is one of their biggest strengths, it is also one of their biggest weaknesses; the stop/start arrangement of a retort process and the constant need to move from one environment to another inside the pressure vessels that comprise a bank of retorts will never reach the steady state efficiency of a continuous process in which an environment can be allowed to reach optimum stability as a constant procession of containers moves through. This implies both thermal and operational inefficiencies since retort pressure vessels and their supporting subsystems increase heating and cooling loads and the additional time required to provide these loads adds to cycle times. Both aspects contribute to additional processing costs.

The supply of steam, compressed air and cooling water requires considerable capital investment and adds to manufacturing overheads since each function requires maintenance and operational staff. Given that the inactivation of microbial populations in foodstuffs by heat remains the preferred approach, then other heating systems may prove to be of lower cost, particularly for those food processors new to the process. For instance, ohmic heating (in which a current is induced through a continuous stream of moving food product and heating is a function of electrical resistance) coupled to an aseptic filling system, has a potentially lower capital cost and a lower manufacturing cost – for a limited range of products and package types.

As the scale of retort vessels increases to improve operational efficiencies, process capacities or to improve the capacity/capital investment ratio, the difficulty of achieving the basic principles of temperature control and heat distribution become greater. Additional costs may be due to the additional means of distributing energy evenly throughout the process vessel. Process times and/or process temperatures may need to be increased to deliver a sufficiently lethal process to all the enclosed containers. This may impact on the quality of foods processed in these systems, since the lengthened process cycle or the higher than otherwise required process temperatures, may detract from heat-sensitive quality aspects (flavour, nutrition, texture) of the food products and is likely to limit operational and energy efficiencies.

Another major strength of the batch process may also be seen as a weakness since the ever increasing complexity of retort 'furniture' required to maintain the geometry of flexible and semi-rigid containers will add to the heating and cooling loads within the retort system, will add to investment and maintenance costs and will add to the complexity of loading and unloading handling systems.

## 9.7    Future trends

Given that the list of weaknesses is considerably smaller than it would have been some years ago, it is likely that batch retorts will continue to be developed since they appear to solve more problems than they create and seem to offer a reliable, generally low-cost means of delivering a sufficiently lethal thermal process to render most foodstuffs in most containers, safe for public consumption.

It is likely that the number of system-wide controls based on 'artificial intelligence', will increase to add to process assurance and to provide real-time, on-line process repeatability in terms of delivered lethality rather than a prescribed time/temperature profile. They may even model or monitor other heat sensitive attributes of the food so that they are optimised along with delivered lethality (given that the latter has priority) or may link with sub-systems distributed within the process vessel, to confirm that the required lethality has in fact been delivered.

The growing needs to control pressure and differential pressure in order to sustain the requirements of heat seals, the growing number of easy-open features and thinner-walled, perhaps more fragile semi-rigid and flexible plastic containers are likely to be addressed in the nearer future.

The many significant interactions between pre-retort processes, the package and the product are under current investigation and are likely to be more widely understood as these package-formats mature and evolve. Further economic and ecological pressures are likely to be reflected in more efficient process systems, improved energy recovery via downstream sub-systems and more widespread automation.

The skill and ingenuity of the retort manufacturer and rigorous attention to detail by the food processor will be required to ensure that an adequately lethal thermal process is delivered to every container in every process so that the reputation that heat processed food has achieved for public health and safety is maintained – or even improved.

## 9.8    Sources of further information and advice

### 9.8.1    Batch retort system suppliers

The following list of batch retort suppliers is intended as a guide and is not exhaustive.

| Company details | Process styles |
| --- | --- |
| Barriquand Steriflow Snc<br>32 Rue de Cambrai<br>75019 Paris<br>France<br>Tel: +33 (1) 40 37 08 45<br>http://www.steriflow.com | ● Raining/water spray<br>● Static and rotary<br>● Handling systems |
| ECPS SA<br>Steritech<br>ZI du Kochersburg<br>1 Rue De Furchhausen<br>F – 67700 Saverne<br>France<br>Tel: +33 388 710433<br>http://www.steritech-fr.com | ● Steam/air<br>● Static and rotary |
| FMC FoodTech<br>Food Processing Systems Division<br>Breedstraat 3<br>B-9100 Sint Niklaas<br>Belgium<br>Tel +32 3 780 1398<br>http://www.fmcfoodtech.com | ● Raining/water spray<br>● Process modelling |

| | |
|---|---|
| H G Molenaar & Co Ltd<br>PO Box 5, Paarl<br>7622 South Africa<br>Tel: +27 21 868 2210 | ● Water immersion |
| Hermann Stock Maschinenfabrik GmbH<br>Rendsburger Strasse 93,<br>D – 24537 Neumunster<br>Germany<br>Tel: +49 4321 1880<br>http://www.stocksterilisation.com | ● Water immersion<br>● Water spray<br>● Static and rotary<br>● Handling systems |
| Hisaka Works Ltd.<br>Konoike Plant<br>2-1-48 Higashi-konoike-cho Higashi<br>Osaka City<br>Osaka<br>Japan<br>Food & Chemical Machinery Division<br>Phone:81-729-62-1457<br>http://www.hisaka.co.jp | ● Raining/water spray<br>● Water immersion<br>● Handling systems |
| Maconse Maquinaria Conservera del Segura SA<br>30500 Molina de Segura<br>Murcia, Spain<br>Tel: +34 968 38 6030<br>http://www.maconse.com | ● Raining/water spray<br>● Water immersion<br>● Static and rotary |
| Societe Lagarde<br>Z.I. Les Plaines<br>N°5 bis<br>26780 Malataverne<br>France<br>Tel: +33 4 75 90 58 58<br>http://www.lagarde-autoclaves.com | ● Steam/air<br>● Hot water spray<br>● Full water immersion<br>● Static and rotary<br>● Handling systems |
| Surdry S.L.<br>P.I. Tranapadura,<br>S/n E – 48220<br>Abadiano,<br>Vizcaya<br>Spain<br>Tel +34 94 6814171<br>http://www.surdry.com | ● Raining/water spray<br>● Static and rotary<br>● Handling systems |

## 9.8.2   CCFRA

The Campden and Chorleywood Food Research Association is a centre of technical excellence for the food industry and has a wealth of expertise available to support food processors in all aspects of food technology and related sciences, in particular in connection with thermal processing and retort use.

Campden and Chorleywood Food Research Association,
Chipping Campden,
Gloucestershire, GL55 6LD
UK.
Tel: +44 (0) 1386 842 000
www.campden.co.uk

### 9.8.3    Data acquisition equipment

| Ellab A/S | Ellab (UK) Ltd |
|---|---|
| Krondalvej 9, | 3, Dundee Court, |
| Roedovre, | Hamburg Way, |
| DK-2610 | King's Lynn, PE30 2ND |
| Denmark | UK |
| Tel: +45 44 94 92 11 | Tel: +44 1553 769 143 |
| www.ellab.dk | ellab.uk@virgin.net |

### 9.8.4    Burst test equipment

INSTeng Process Automation
Unit 3, Moy Road Industrial Estate,
Taffs Well,
Cardiff, CF15 7QR
UK
Tel: +44 29 2081 5000
www.insteng.co.uk

## 9.9    References

BOWN, G. (1985). *Retort control. The application of a microcomputer based control system.* Technical Memorandum 391. CFFRA. Chipping Campden, Glos. UK

CCFRA (1997a). *Guidelines for batch retort systems – full water immersion – raining/ spray water – steam/air.* Guideline 13. CCFRA, Chipping Campden, Glos. UK.

CCFRA (1997b). *Guidelines for establishing heat distribution in batch overpressure retort systems.* Guideline 17. CCFRA, Chipping Campden, Glos. UK.

CCFRA (1997c). *Guidelines for performing heat penetration trials for establishing thermal processes in batch retort systems.* Guideline 16. CCFRA, Chipping Campden, Glos. UK.

DHSS (1994). Guidelines for the safe production of heat preserved foods. Department of Health, HMSO, London.

MAY, N.S. (2001), 'Retort Technology'. In Richardson P., *Thermal Technologies in Food Processing*, Cambridge, Woodhead, 7–28.

NFPA (1982). *Thermal processes for low-acid foods in metal containers.* Bulletin 26-L. 12th edn. National Food Processors Association, Washington, USA.

# 10

# Combining heat treatment, control of water activity and pressure to preserve foods

L. Beney, J.M. Perrier-Cornet, F. Fine and P. Gervais, ENSBANA (Université de Bourgogne), France

## 10.1  Introduction

To ensure a secure and steady food supply, food needs to be preserved and stabilised so it can be stored for extended periods. Extending food products shelf life requires inactivation of the spoilage or toxic microorganisms they contain and avoiding their subsequent proliferation. Food preservation thus implies exposure of microorganisms to hostile conditions. Heating is one of the most practical, efficient and inexpensive methods of disinfection and sterilisation. Thermal treatment leads either to pasteurisation, when only vegetative microorganisms are destroyed, or sterilisation, when spores are also destroyed. Heat treatments are characterised by the level of temperature reached in the product and by its duration.

However, thermal inactivation data are generally established in set conditions for water activity ($A_w$), pH, and pressure. A new era of research is to identify the potential synergies between these operating parameters. Synergies are particularly interesting because combination of processes, i.e., hurdle technology, are a promising means of enhancing safety whilst retaining food quality. In this chapter, special attention will be focused on the effects of temperature-$a_w$ and temperature-pressure interactions on microbial destruction. After a brief introduction to the thermal destruction of microorganisms, the second part of the chapter is devoted to the combined actions of water activity or pressure with temperature.

## 10.2  The thermal destruction of microorganisms

This section deals with the general characteristics of the thermal destruction of microorganisms, from the statistical destruction of individuals in a population to

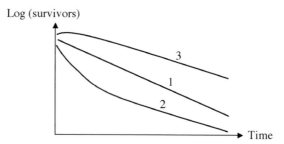

**Fig. 10.1**    Schematic representation of three types of microbial survival curves, representing the number of viable cells against time of exposure to heat. Curve type number 1 is typical of an homogeneous population of microorganisms homogeneously heat treated. Curve type number 2 is typical of a composite population of cells where thermosensitive and thermoresistant cells coexist. Curve number 3 is typical of microorganisms that are activated by short exposure to heat (e.g., germination of spores, fragmentation of chains).

the structural causes of cellular death under heating. The influence of water activity and of pressure conditions on cells and their implications for heat resistance will then be presented

The impact of heat treatment on microorganisms is estimated from the measurement of surviving cells against heating time. The destruction profile that is obtained allows the determination of the characteristics of resistance of the microorganism that are the basis for the designation of the operational requirements of a thermal process. Traditional estimations of the efficiency of preservation and disinfection processes are based on the assumption that microbial death follows a known evolution. As each species has its own particular heat tolerance, thermal operating conditions are determined experimentally and data are presented as the number of surviving organisms (generally judged according to the ability to multiply) or viable spores against the exposure time at a given temperature. Curves generally represent the log $_{10}$ of surviving cells as a function of time. In many cases this representation gives a linear relationship (Fig. 10.1) that implies that the thermal destruction phenomenon is a first order reaction. However, deviation from the linearity of thermal death curves are frequently observed and thermal death curves can also be characterised by shoulders and tails (Fig. 10.1). Deviation from linearity can be related to the composition of the microbial population, to the germination of sporulated forms or to the heterogeneity of the thermal treatment. Coexistence of strains having different thermoresistance (Cerf, 1977) gives segmented curves (line 2 in Fig. 10.1). Thermal activation of germination is responsible for maintaining the initial cell number (line 3 in Fig. 10.1). Adaptation to heat also leads to curve tailing (for a detailed review see Smelt *et al.*, 2002). In the straight part of these plots, the number of cells thermally destroyed at temperature $T$ and during the time interval $\Delta t$ (s) is given by the following equation:

$$X(t + \Delta t) - X(t) = -k \cdot X(t) \cdot \Delta t \qquad\qquad 10.1$$

where $X$ is the number of living cells and $k$ the destruction rate $(s^{-1})$.
So, from this equation:

$$X = X_0 \cdot e^{-kt} \tag{10.2}$$

Where $X_0$ is the number of cells (more exactly, unity forming colony) initially present and $X$ the number of survivors. $t$ corresponds to the exposure time and $k$ is the destruction rate $(s^{-1})$. Early research introduced the $D$-value, defined as the decimal reduction time (average time of exposure needed to reduce the number of microorganisms by a factor 10) which leads to the following relation:

$$X = X_0 \cdot 10^{-\frac{t}{D}} \tag{10.3}$$

$z$ (°C) is another characteristic value, corresponding to the increase in temperature that induces a reduction of $D$-value by a factor 10, and is given by the following equation:

$$D = D_{ref} \cdot 10 - \frac{T - T_{ref}}{z} \tag{10.4}$$

Where $T$ (°C) is the treatment temperature, $D_{ref}$ the thermal reduction time at the reference temperature $T_{ref}$. Reactions that have small $z$ values are highly temperature dependent.

Thermal calculations thus involve the need for knowledge of the concentration of microorganisms to be destroyed, the acceptable concentration of microorganisms that can remain, the thermal resistance of the target microorganisms (e.g., the most heat-tolerant pathogenic ones), and the temperature-time relationship required for destruction of the target microorganisms.

### 10.2.1   Destroying pathogenic microorganisms and retaining product quality

In milk, the pasteurization treatment required is determined from the heat resistance of *Mycobacterium tuberculosis*, the most resistant pathogen in milk, and gives the temperature/exposure time values proposed in Table 10.1.

**Table 10.1**   Thermal inactivation barems of *Mycobacterium tuberculosis*

| Temperature (°C) | Exposure time (seconds) | Remarks |
|---|---|---|
| 62.8 | 1800 | Barem used in the low-temperature long-time pasteurisation method of milk |
| 71.7 | 15 | Barem used in the high-temperature short-time method |
| 90 | 0.5 | |
| 100 | 0.01 | |

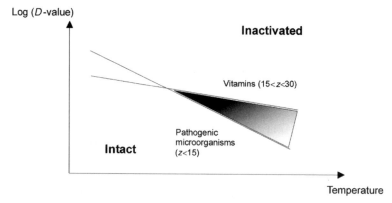

**Fig. 10.2**    Relative changes in time-temperature profiles for the inactivation of microorganisms and vitamins. The shadowed area represents the region where thermal parameters allow preservation of vitamins and destruction of microorganisms.

Pasteurisation of milk which still retains the nutritional and sensory qualities of the product is achieved by taking into account the heat resistance of other milk components. There are specific $D$ and $z$ values for the thermal inactivation and destruction of enzymes, vitamins, pigments, etc., and the differences in $z$ and $D$ values between unwanted elements (pathogenic cells, toxins, enzymes) and desirable ones (such as nutrients, flavour and colour) are exploited in order to optimise thermal treatments (see Fig. 10.2). For example, typical $z$ values of 10°C are characteristic of pathogenic bacteria whereas $z$ values of enzymes, vitamins and pigments are generally contained in the range 20 to 70°C. This difference allows the manufacturers to determine an optimal thermal process (temperature/exposure time). In the case of milk, for example, High Temperature Short Time (HTST) corresponds to the shadowed area located between the curves of pathogenic microorganisms and vitamins in Fig. 10.2.

## 10.3    The effects of dehydration and hydrostatic pressure on microbial thermotolerance

Knowing the exact mechanisms of death induction by heat of microorganisms is clearly important in optimising thermal processes but, as we will see, these mechanisms are not fully understood. According to Moats (1971), cell death results from the denaturation or inactivation of numerous critical sites (or a large number of the same site) in cells. Because target sites are not strictly identified and because numerous cellular structures are considered as critical sites a question emerges. Is there a cellular structure that is more critical than others?

In 1971, Rosenberg et al. demonstrated the existence of a good numerical correlation between some thermodynamic parameters in protein denaturation and in death rates of bacteria, yeast, viruses and drosophila. Information about the causes of thermal death also came from another approach that looked at the differences between thermophiles and other microorganisms. These studies also confirmed the potential role of proteins. However, many components in thermotolerant cells exhibit a particularly high resistance to elevated temperatures, suggesting that each of them should be a target of heating. Among them, one structure is of particular interest because it is exposed first to heat and may be seen as an indicator of thermal stress: the plasma membrane (Beney and Gervais, 2001). The structure of membrane components is known to be strongly influenced by temperature (Chapman *et al,*, 1967, Luzzati *et al,*, 1968, Chapman, 1994) and heating is particularly implied in the transition from lamellar to non-lamellar organisation of membrane lipids which alters the selective permeability properties of the membrane (Russell *et al.*, 1995). An interesting idea about the induction of cell death is given by Smelt *et al.* (2002). They distinguished between two temperature ranges, first between the normal physiological temperature and approximately 65°C, where proteins are not denatured and membrane lipids may be the main targets, and the second corresponding to temperatures above 65°C where both proteins and lipids are denatured. Additional arguments implying membrane denaturation in the first temperature range come from the dependence of cell survival to heat on heating rates (Gervais and Martinez de Maranon, 1995).

### 10.3.1   Effects of dehydration on cellular structures and constituents

Hydration of a food product is generally quantified by means of its water activity. This term corresponds, for ideal solutions, to the mole fraction of water in solution. In complex solutions and media, it is assumed to be equal to the relative humidity of the gaseous phase equilibrated over these media or solutions. As food products are represented across the whole water activity range (from 0 to 1), we will describe the main cellular input of partial and total dehydration. The influence of water activity on cells is complex because as we will see, hydration changes modify the entire cellular structure, from the cytoplasmic volume to the conformation of the molecular constituents.

Microbial cell structure and composition are closely dependent on the degree of hydration. The effects of dehydration on whole cells are first manifested by a volume decrease corresponding to an osmotic exchange, that can then be followed by a metabolic adaptation of cells. Placing microorganisms in low $a_w$ media results in passive and active mechanisms of adaptation. The adaptive response is mainly based on the intracellular accumulation of solutes that allows water retention in cells (Brown and Edgley, 1980, Blomberg and Adler, 1992). This response occurs at relatively high water activities (1 to 0.6, depending on cell type and growth phase) whereas cell metabolism is ineffective in more dehydrated media. The accumulation of carbohydrates and amino acids during adaptation to dryness may account for an increased thermotolerance (Piper, 1993, Benaroudj *et al.*, 2001, Cánovas *et al.*, 2001). During adaptation to dehydration, protein synthesis and phospholipid modification also occur and may also contribute to better resistance to heat (Santos *et al.*, 1998). Saccharide-like trehalose, accumulated during dehydration of some microorganisms, have a protective action on proteins and membranes against heating.

Osmotic exchanges are related to the osmotic pressure gradient between cells and the medium in which they occur (Gervais and Beney, 2001). They mainly consist of a water outflow from the cells that allows the restoration of the hydric potential equilibrium between cells and the medium. Volume decrease can be extremely important, representing more than 50% of the yeast physiological volume and up to 85% of bacterial volume (Marechal and Gervais, 1994, Poirier *et al.*, 1998). In case of marked medium dehydration, reduction of the cellular volume through water loss leads to increased internal solutes and structured concentration. Low internal water content has been related to thermoresistance and, accordingly, low water content in sporulated forms would explain their thermal resistance (Nakashio and Gerhardt, 1985, Beaman and Gerhardt, 1986).

Proteins have a structure and activities which are closely related to hydration. Optimal water activity levels depend on enzyme type. Lipase are known to optimally function in low $a_w$ media, for example, whereas ATPase have optimal activities in highly hydrated media. In general, studies of the thermostability of proteins in media with various $a_w$ show that the reduction of the water content induces a conformational modification of proteins (rigidification) that enhances their resistance. Hendricks *et al.* (1992) studied the influence of $a_w$ (between 0.1 and 0.9) on the thermal stability (between 140 and 160°C) of a peroxydase. They observed an increased stability at low $a_w$ and a maximal $z$ value of 44°C at $a_w$ around 0.8. Zaks and Klibanov (1988) and then Klibanov (1989) showed that, without water or hydrogen bonds-forming solutes such as glycerol or formamide, the conformational flexibility of enzymes is reduced. These studies emphasise the fact that the thermal denaturation of enzymes requires an important conformational mobility and thus a sufficient hydration.

Phospholipids are the main constituents of microbial membranes (McElhaney, 1984, 1989) and also adept in response to water activity in their environment. Phospholipids can undergo phase changes in response to external parameters such as hydration and temperature (Luzzatti and Husson, 1962; Chapman *et al.*,1967) (Fig. 10.3). These phenomena, widely studied in pure phospholipids, correspond to the transition from the fluid crystalline phase to the gel phase under cooling, drying or increased pressure and may account for the lethal effects of dehydration (Becker and Rapoport, 1987). Transitions from lamellar into non-lamellar configuration (Cullis and de Kruijff, 1979; Gawrisch *et al.*, 1992; Shaelev and Steponkus, 1999) have also been reported with drying and heating. Many authors describe the potential importance of these responses in cell activity (Lindblom and Rilfors, 1989; Lohner, 1996; De Kruijff, 1997; Luzzati, 1997). These could be implied in cell death caused by heating or dehydration (Russell *et al.*, 1995, Steponkus, 1999).

Dehydration can be detrimental to cells if it is extreme and rapid (Beney *et al.*, 2001). It is interesting to note that microorganisms are sensitive to the kinetics of osmotic pressure variation and that rapid variations are more detrimental to cells than gradual ones (Gervais *et al.*, 1992, Poirier *et al.*, 1997). Adaptative

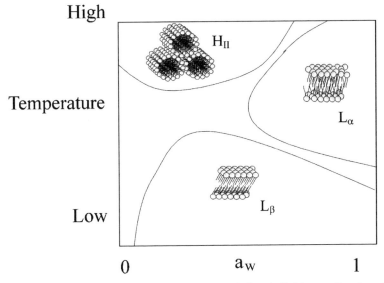

**Fig. 10.3**   Schematic and general organisation of phospholipids as a function of hydration and temperature.

mechanisms can occur during gradual dehydration, leading to cell content modification (accumulation of osmoprotectants) and also to cell remodelling (e.g., change in protein content and membrane composition). Gradual dehydration may also prevent cells from too rapid a decrease in volume, allowing cells to achieve smaller volumes without lethal damage (Marechal and Gervais, 1994). From a general point of view, dehydration is thought to stabilise proteins and cells and to preserve them against thermal effects. However, structures like membranes suffer from extreme dehydration and require a minimal quantity of water to adopt their functional structure. These opposite effects emphasise the complex influence of hydration on cell thermoresistance. Rapid and extreme dehydration can therefore be deleterious for cells. However, slow dehydration before thermal treatment can enhance the thermoresistance of microbial flora (adaptation to dryness) and, with their low water content, make them more difficult to eradicate.

### 10.3.2   Effects of hydrostatic pressure on cellular structures and constituents

Change in treatment temperature can modify high pressure effects on biological structures. The effects of hydrostatic pressure have been well described and reviewed (Heremans, 1982). They can be divided on two targets: biomolecules and biomembranes. This section provides an overview of the effects of hydrostatic pressure on both these structures.

Biomolecules, especially proteins, are structurally and functionally modified by the combined effects of pressure and temperature. The role of heat and

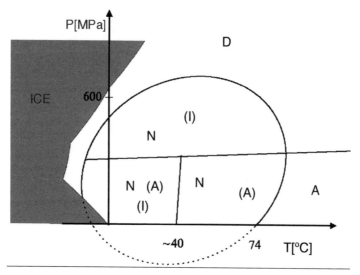

**Fig. 10.4** Extended phase diagram for myoglobin. The diagram includes both denaturation and aggregation phenomena, and therefore contains several metastable phases (enclosed in parentheses). N, native; D, denatured; A, aggregated; I, intermediate (adapted from Smelt *et al.*, 2002).

pressure in the denaturation of proteins is well known and is shown in Fig. 10.4 (Smeller, 2002). Similar patterns in synthetic polymer phase separation (Kunugi *et al.*, 2002) and starch gelatinisation (Douzals *et al.*, 2001) curves suggest the role of hydrogen bonds in the response to pressure-temperature effect. The similarity in the pattern of microorganism inactivation and protein denaturation suggests the role of different pressure-sensitive microbial protein structures like ribosomes (Niven *et al.*, 1999), metabolic enzymes (Simpson and Gilmour, 1997) and transport systems (Ulmer *et al.*, 2002) in microbial inactivation. There is a parallel between virus inactivation and protein denaturation especially at low temperature and high pressure (Oliveira *et al.*, 1999). However, most of the studies on these structures were undertaken *in vitro* and a greater resistance would be expected *in vivo* due to the interactions of proteins with intracellular solutes or membrane phospholipids.

Membrane damage has also been suggested as the main effect of pressure or temperature treatment. For these two parameters, phenomena like permeabilisation (Perrier-Cornet *et al.*, 1999a, Gervais and Martinez de Maranon, 1995), vesiculation (Steponkus and Lynch, 1989) and lysis (Asami and Yamaguchi, 1999, Gershfeld and Murayama, 1988) have been identified in different cellular models. Modifications of membrane structures, i.e., phase transition, are generally reported to be at the origin of this membrane damage. However, pressure could counterbalance the effects of elevated temperature. The pressure dependence of phase transition temperature is about a constant increase of 0.2°C/MPa (Macdonald, 1984). Ulmer and coworkers have recently shown a relation between the phase transition temperature of the membrane, the temperature of hydrostatic treatment and the inactivation of *Lactobacillus plantarum* (Ulmer *et al.*, 2002). Moreover the lysis of yeast spheroplasts induced by high pressure is also enhanced at subzero temperature (Beney *et al.*, 2003). These findings suggest a combined effect of pressure and low temperature on membrane related structure. Indeed, synergistic effects between pressure and temperature could probably affect cellular targets differently at low and high temperature. However, the molecular basis of this interaction is evidently much more complex on the whole cell than on isolated proteins. As an example, the functionality of integral proteins like carriers depends on both the structure of their lipidic environment and on their own structure, each of these structures being influenced by hydrostatic pressure.

## 10.4    Temperature variation and microbial viability

An intrinsic characteristic of thermal treatments that influences the viability of microorganisms is related to the kinetics of temperature variation. The phenomenon is discussed in the following section because it is essential to the optimisation of thermal treatments.

### 10.4.1    Heat shocks improve thermal death

In most studies, the determination of heat resistance involves the addition of a small volume of microbial suspension to large volumes of a heating medium. Cells are then removed at desired intervals and cooled. This means that, at the laboratory scale, the kinetics of temperature variation during a thermal process are often not considered as a technological variable.

As a result, contrary to temperature level and exposure time, literature dealing with the influence of the temperature variation rate on cellular resistance is scarce, Dowben and Weidenmuller (1968), who showed that the mesophilic bacteria *B.subtilis* can grow at elevated temperatures (72°C) after a progressive increase in temperature. Gervais and Martinez de Maranon (1995) have shown a variation in the resistance of the yeast *S.cerevisiae* (Fig. 10.5) when exposed in an optimal liquid media to a heat shock or to an optimal heat slope ($0.42°C.min^{-1}$) from 25 to 50°C. Such an observation showed that heat perturbation can lead to cell reactions and adaptation. In the case of heating rates slower than 0.42°C. $min^{-1}$, a decrease in viability is observed. The influence of the kinetics of temperature variation results from the effects of two opposite actions.

On the one hand a positive effect related to the slowness of the temperature variation may be linked to cell remodelling or adaptation, and on the other hand the negative influence of the exposure of cells over the critical temperature range which is located around 45°C (Coote *et al.*, 1991). These results show that between 25 and 50°C, the $D$ and $z$ values of *S.cerevisiae* are influenced by the rate of temperature variation during heating. Moreover, when the cell volume of the yeast *S.cerevisiae* was measured against an optimal heat slope and during a

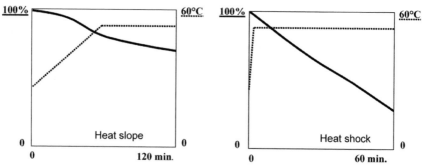

**Fig. 10.5** Evolution of temperature (dashed line) and viability of *S.cerevisiae* (continuous line) during a heat slope (0.42°C min⁻¹) and a heat shock from 25 to 50°C followed by an exposure of one hour at 50°C (from Gervais and Martinez de Maranon, 1995).

thermal shock, a difference in behaviour was observed. In the case of a heat shock, an important decrease in cell volume (20–25%) can be seen during the first hour after the heat exposure. This observation is probably related to the influence of heating on membrane structure as shown by experiments which reveal an important increase in fluidity and a release of internal solutes following exposure of cells to elevated temperatures (Laroche *et al.*, 2001; Gervais and Martinez de Maranon, 1995). For the case of the heat slope, the volume decrease is less important (10%) and occurs much more progressively. When ion leakage from *S.cerevisiae* is measured after a heat shock or after an optimal heat slope a significant difference is observed (Fig. 10.6). Heat shocked cells lose an important part of their ion content. These results have been interpreted as the consequence of the influence of the heating kinetics on the regulation of fluidity and permeability characteristics of the plasmic membrane of *S.cerevisiae*. The similar influence of heating rate on the viability of *E.coli* has been reported by Morozov and Petin (1998). These results strongly suggest that membrane rupture or permeabilisation is the first cause of *S.cerevisiae* and *E.coli* death under heat shock in the temperature range 25 to 50°C. In complementary experiments (Martinez de Maranon *et al.*, 1999), it has been demonstrated that the critical temperature range where heating rate is critical is between 40 and 50°C (Fig. 10.7). These experiments have demonstrated that controlling the heating rate in a small temperature interval of 10°C was essential for cell destruction or preservation. This observation, if extended to other bacteria, suggests one way of enhancing the performance of thermal treatments.

Yeast membrane destruction under heating shares a common characteristic with cell viability, a dependence on the level of temperature and the heating rate. The basis of this dependence on temperature kinetics may originate in the multitude of physico-chemical changes in the membrane in response to temperature in curvature and shape, in physical state and in spatial repartition of molecules. The membrane hypothesis is supported by studies of protein thermal denaturation (Grinberg *et al.*, 2000); (Burova *et al.*, 1990). This research

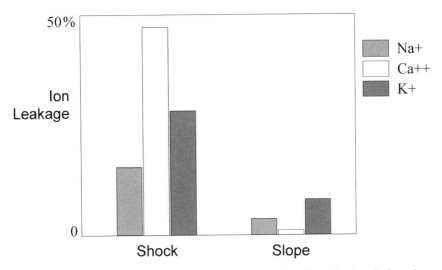

**Fig. 10.6**   Ion leakage from *S.cerevisiae* immediately after a heat shock and after a heat slope (0.42°C.min$^{-1}$). Initial temperature was 25°C and final one was 50°C. The viabilities of the yeast populations at the moment of the measurement were 96% for the shock and 82% for the slope (from Martinez de Maranon *et al.*, 1999).

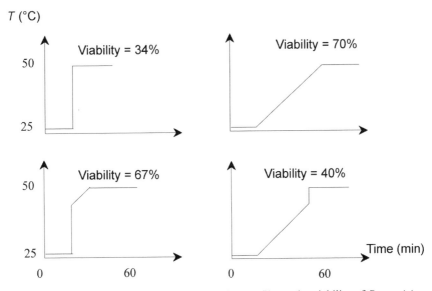

**Fig. 10.7**   Influence of the temperature variation profile on the viability of *S.cerevisiae*.

indicates that protein denaturation under thermal shock occurs at higher temperature than under progressive heating. This characteristic suggests that the dependence of the survival of microorganisms on the heating rate is not governed by an analogous dependence in proteins.

### 10.4.2    Applications: controlling the kinetics of heating to improve the performance of thermal processes

A direct consequence of this research is that powerful heating systems with high heat transmission capacity are expected to achieve more efficient thermal destruction of cells. Fast heating methods based on radio frequency and microwave energy application on food products could present high sterilisation efficiency compared to conventional methods. Results obtained by Tajchakavit *et al.* (1998) by heating *S.cerevisiae* and *L.plantarum* by a conduction/convection system, with a heating rate of approximately $1-2°C\,min^{-1}$, or by microwave ($10°C\,min^{-1}$), showed that an important decrease in D-values (Table 10.2) was observed between conventional and microwave heating methods. Values corrected by the exact time of exposure in both systems show that the D-value is 5 to 12 times higher for conventional heating than for microwave (Tajchakavit *et al.*, 1998). As the enhanced thermal effects associated with microwaves are still not clear they could at least partly be related to the influence of high heating rates. This phenomenon could also allow the reduction of the level/duration barems and improve the residual physicochemical quality of food products. The influence of kinetics of heating on the survival of microorganisms must be considered in slow heat transfers where the survival of microorganisms could be higher than expected.

### 10.4.3    Controlling the temperature variation rates to improve powder decontamination

Powder decontamination is a specific problem, firstly because any micro-organisms present are adapted to low $a_w$ and consequently more thermotolerant and secondly, because heating powders is more complicated than heating liquids. One application of the influence of the kinetics of heat stress on the destruction of dried microorganisms is based on the use of very short stresses (around a few seconds) at high temperatures (in the range 200 to 300°C) followed by an instantaneous cooling with a cold gas. The first hot step destroys

**Table 10.2**  Comparison of the D-values at different temperatures for *S.cerevisiae* and *L.plantarum* exposed to heat in a water bath or in a microwaves system (Data from Tajchakavit *et al.*, 1998)

|  | Microwave Time corrected D-values/temperature | Water bath Time corrected D-values/temperature |
|---|---|---|
| *S.cerevisiae* | 4.8 s/52.5°C | 58 s/50°C |
|  | 2.1 s/55°C | 25 s/55°C |
|  | 1.1 s/57.5°C | 10 s/60°C |
| *L.plantarum* | 14 s/57.5°C | 52 s/55°C |
|  | 3.8 s/60°C | 22 s/60°C |
|  | 0.79 s/62.5°C | 8.4 s/70°C |

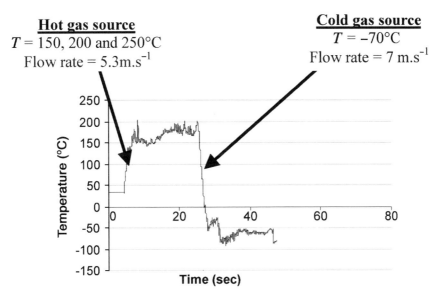

**Fig. 10.8**   Variation of temperature level during a run in a HTST process (Gervais *et al.*, 2002). In this case, the heating step was performed using gas heated at 200°C and the following cooling step used $CO_2$.

a large number of yeasts, moulds, bacteria and spores without burning treated powders. The cold step stops further damaging heat conduction into the product. A typical thermal profile is given in Fig. 10.8, where a heating rate of $50°C.s^{-1}$ was obtained and led to the destruction of total mesophilic flora of pepper or corns in the range 3 and 5 log. After treatment, residual yeasts, moulds and enterobacteria were below 50 per gram, whereas the organoleptic qualities of the decontaminated product were preserved. This process of decontamination of powdered products using the influence of heating rates is protected by a patent (Gervais *et al.*, 2002, French Patent no. FR02/00873).

As seen in the preceding section, thermal destruction, which is assumed to be a first order reaction, is generally related to temperature level and exposure time. However, we have shown that the kinetics of temperature variation, which is often not fully considered, is a key parameter influencing process efficiency. In the following section we will additionally see how other physical parameters, such as water activity and pressure, can influence thermal treatment efficiency and so how the classic models of destruction by heat may need to be modified.

## 10.5   Combining heat treatment, hydrostatic pressure and water activity

In this section, the combined effects of temperature, $a_w$ and hydrostatic pressure will be considered in order to show how they affect the input of heat on microbial destruction.

### 10.5.1    Combining $a_w$ and temperature actions on cell viability

Water activity has a well known influence on microbial activity. Lowering water activity by elimination of water or addition of solutes is extensively used in order to preserve food products (drying, salting or sugaring, for example) at ambient temperature. When heat treated products are dried their microbial stability is increased, thus improving shelf-life. The combined actions of temperature and water activity on the viability of microorganisms will be described in the next section, firstly considering the influence of $a_w$ on the thermal resistance of microorganisms and secondly the influence of temperature on resistance to dehydration.

### 10.5.2    Thermal death is related to medium hydration

It is generally observed that reducing the water content of microbial cells induces an increased thermal resistance. As an example, the survival of bacterial vegetative forms of *Salmonella typhimurum* is greatest at $a_w$ lower than 0.2 and decreases with increasing $a_w$ (Corry, 1975). The phenomenon is generally attributed to the stabilising or rigidifying effect of water removal from molecular structures.

However, more complex relations between temperature and hydration levels on cell inactivation have also been observed. Murrel and Scott (1966), observed that survival of bacterial spores to heat treatments achieved in the water activity range 0 to 0.998 exhibited a maximal resistance between 0.2 and 0.4. Their results, shown in Table 10.3, show that the D value of *Clostridium stearothermophilus* spores was greatest for water activity in the range 0.2 and 0.4. Similar results were obtained by Angelotti *et al.* (1968) and by Pfeiffer (1992) for *Bacillus subtilis* spores. Recently, we have obtained similar results with vegetative cells of *Saccharomyces cerevisiae* and *Lactobacillus plantarum* dried on flour and powdered milk. These microorganisms exhibited maximum heat resistance in the $a_w$ range 0.3 and 0.4 (Fig. 10.9). These thermal destruction curves show that the relation between temperature and hydration is complex and involves more than molecular stabilisation by water removal. If the increase in cell thermoresistance that is observed when $a_w$ is lowered from 0.9 to 0.4 can be attributed to the decrease of intracellular water content (which reduces the conformational flexibility of molecules), no explanation dealing with the low

**Table 10.3**   D-values (seconds) of two sub-species of *Clostridium* spores determined in different $a_w$ ranges (from Murrel and Scott, 1966)

|  | $a_w$ ranges | | |
|---|---|---|---|
|  | Near 0.0 | 0.2–0.4 | Near 1 |
| *Clostridium botulinum* | 0.3 | 110 | 0.001 |
| *Clostridium stearothermophilus* | 23 | 800 | 35 |

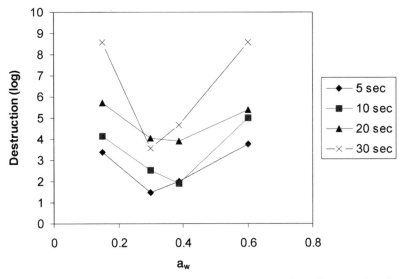

**Fig. 10.9**   Destruction of *Lactobacillus plantarum* dried on wheat flour as a function of
$a_w$ and heat duration at 300°C. For 30 seconds of treatment, the destruction level can
reach more than 8 log for $a_w = 0.15$ and 0.6 whereas 'intermediate' $a_w$ values limited
microbial destruction to 4 log for the same treatment conditions.

thermoresistance observed at very low $a_w$ levels is available. It can only be
speculated that drastic dryness could enhance the oxidation of cells. Enzymatic
oxidation is influenced by $a_w$ and is low at intermediate $a_w$ values (between 0.3
and 0.5) (Labuza, 1975, Leung, 1987). An alternative hypothesis is based on the
fact that extreme dehydration can destabilise the lamellar structure of cell
membranes (see Fig. 10.3).

### 10.5.3   Low temperatures enhance resistance to dehydration

Experiments in our laboratory with *S.cerevisiae* help to clarify the role played by
cell membranes in the combined effects of temperature and hydration (Beney *et
al.*, 2001). The extent of *S.cerevisiae* survival by exposure to osmotic stress of
100 MPa was increased by a factor of 2.5 after cooling of cells from 25°C to
10°C prior to osmotic stress (Fig. 10.10). Such enhancement of yeast
osmoresistance was attributed to the fact that that the cooling step at 10°C
reduced the osmotic destabilisation of the membrane by inducing a membrane
phase change. This assumption is supported by the phase transition temperature
of hydrated yeast membrane, estimated at 12°C by Crowe and Crowe (1992).
Parallel estimation of the yeast plasma membrane fluidity through fluorescence
and FTIR measurements suggests a direct relation beween yeast destruction
during dehydration and the occurrence of a membrane phase change during
contraction. New results obtained with other microorganisms shows that the
temperature at which osmotic shock occurs influences cell viability.

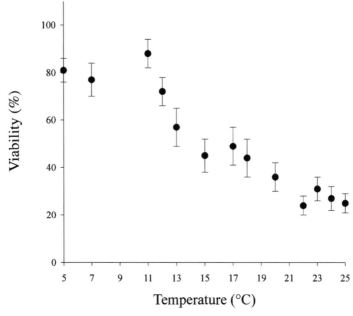

**Fig. 10.10**    Viability of *S.cerevisiae* after hyperosmotic shocks to 100 MPa achieved at temperatures ranging from 4 to 23°C. Depressor used: glycerol. Initial osmotic pressure: 1.38 MPa. Bars represent standard deviation.

Experiments with the gram-negative bacteria *Bradirhyzobium japonicum* and *Escherichia coli* (Mille *et al.*, 2002 ) showed that lowering the temperature prior to osmotic dehydration enhances cell survival after dehydration. The combined effects of temperature and osmotic pressure vary, however, depending on the microorganism considered (Fig. 10.11). Such results suggest the importance of the control of both $a_w$ and temperature during dehydration. Cell deaths could be related to the membrane phase changes that occur during dehydration because viability decreased when membrane phase transition occurred simultaneously with the cell volume decrease (Beney *et al.*, 2001; Laroche *et al.*, 2001). Viability was maintained when the membrane phase transition was induced by a first cooling step achieved prior to the osmotic shock. These results can be used to help improve preservation techniques where cells need to remain functional after dehydration, e.g., the production of dried yeasts.

The preceding examples demonstrate the importance of controlling temperature and $a_w$ during thermal processes. Such examples also illustrate the complexity that characterises the combined effects of $a_w$ and temperature. Our recent work on food powders has revealed the existence of optimal $a_w$ values for the thermal destruction of microorganisms, indicating that intermediate $a_w$ may enhance cell thermoresistance. The major role played by membrane phase changes in cell survival during dehydration reinforces the importance of dual control of temperature and $a_w$ in order to avoid membrane

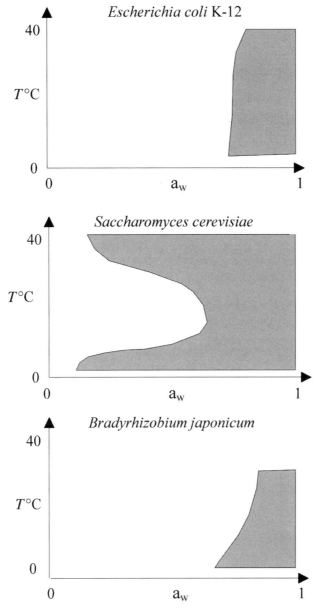

**Fig. 10.11**  Viability diagrams of 3 microorganisms in function of $a_w$ and temperature. Cells were first thermally equilibrated from their physiological temperature (25°C for *S.cerevisiae*, 28°C for *B.rhyzobium*, 37°C for *E.Coli*) to a desired temperature (between 40°C and 4°C) and then osmotically treated from their physiological $a_w$ (0.99 for all microorganisms) to a fixed $a_w$ (between 0.99 and 0.05). Cells were rehydrated at $a_w = 0.99$, returned to their physiological temperature and viability was assessed. Shaded areas correspond to the $a_w$ and thermal ranges where viability was found to be higher than 50%.

phase changes. In the following section, the combined effects of temperature and hydrostatic pressure are considered.

### 10.5.4    Combined effects of hydrostatic pressure and temperature on cell viability

As previously shown for $a_w$, combining temperature and high pressure can be used to improve food pasteurisation and even sterilisation. Numerous studies have shown the temperature dependence of microbial inactivation under pressure (Ludwig *et al.*, 1992, Patterson and Kilpatrick, 1998, Sonoike *et al.*, 1992). Microbial resistance to high pressure is optimum at a temperature near to ambient (Yayanos, 1999). Data for numerous microbial strains gives an elliptic curve as shown on Fig. 10.12 for *Escherichia coli* (Smeller, 2002). Increasing temperature can lead to greater inactivation at constant pressure level. For moderate temperature (50–60°C), this effect could be used to decrease pressure holding time or to stabilized non-acid foods (Patterson and Kilpatrick, 1998). The use of higher temperature (80–130°C) could allow the sterilisation of food products. Indeed, bacterial spores, which are generally not sensitive to pressure, could be affected by coupling pressure and high temperature (Wuytack and Michiels, 2001, Furukawa and Hayakawa, 2000). Nevertheless, even at high pressure, the temperature level to achieve sterility remains high (>100°C). Temperature increase obtained by adiabatic compression (about 4°C/100 MPa) could be used to reduce heating time and subsequent gradients (Meyer, 2000).

Decreasing temperature could also increase the inactivation of microorganisms. As shown on Fig. 10.13, in order to inactivate the yeast

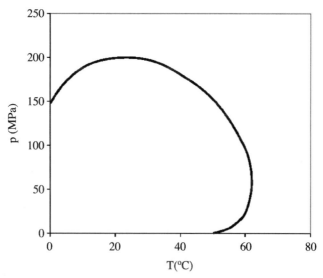

**Fig. 10.12**    The pressure-temperature stability diagram of *E. coli*, showing a decrease of bacterial count by two orders of magnitude within 5 min. (Smeller, 2002).

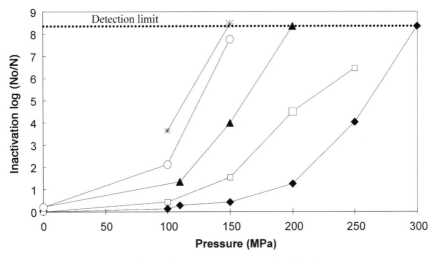

**Fig. 10.13**   Inactivation of *Saccharomyces cerevisiae* for 10 min pressure treatment at different pressure levels and various temperatures: 25°C (◆), 0°C (□), −10°C (▲), −15°C (O), and −20°C (*).

*Saccharomyces cerevisiae* a decrease of 10°C is equivalent to an increase of about 50 MPa. The use of subzero temperatures down to −25°C has improved the antimicrobial effect of pressure in keeping food product quality. Low temperature processing has not been currently used due to the lack of data on this treatment. Some experiments on high-pressure freezing do not seem to enhance spore inactivation significantly. Results vary between different microorganisms' nature and conditions before, during and after the treatment such as water activity (Perrier-Cornet *et al.*, 1999b) or pH (Hayert *et al.*, 1998). Low pH conditions have been shown to enhance the pasteurisation effect of pressure-temperature combined treatment (Alpas *et al.*, 2000). The inactivation mechanisms induced by pressure-temperature interaction, as well as pressure or temperature treatment alone are not clearly established. It is obvious that both pressure and temperature do not affect one specific site but many targets are involved (Smelt *et al.*, 2002). The combination of pressure and temperature could help to improve microbial inactivation in food products but before industrialisation is possible, more research on spore inactivation in different types of food is necessary.

## 10.6    Conclusions

This chapter is intended to show that classical inactivation models based on temperature level and exposure time are heavily influenced by intrinsic and environmental conditions during thermal treatment. Firstly, the heating rate, which is generally not taken into account in models of thermal destruction, has been found to be a determinant parameter affecting cell survival to heating. Accordingly, heat shocks were found to be more effective than progressive heating, enabling the optimisation of the thermal destruction process by increasing thermal gradients. At a fundamental level, the effects of heating rate on membrane permeability also emphasise the fact that cell membranes are probably structurally dependent on heating kinetics.

Secondly, environmental parameters such as water activity or hydrostatic pressure markedly affect thermal treatment effects on the viability of microorganisms. Microorganisms appear to be thermally stabilised by intermediary $a_w$ values (0.3–0.5) and the most favourable hydration conditions for their destruction correspond to fully hydrated or dehydrated media. As proteins are generally stabilised by extreme dehydration, we might speculate that the thermal destruction of cells in dehydrated media is enhanced by oxidation or by membrane destabilisation favoured by low hydration. The major role played by membrane destabilisation in the induction of cell death can be seen in the way that passing through the membrane phase transition using a cooling step enhances cell resistance to osmotic dehydration significantly. The main implication of these results is that thermal stabilisation of dehydrated products can be optimised, especially when high heating rates are used.

We have also shown that the association of hydrostatic pressure with temperature is an efficient means to control microbial survival. One very interesting aspect of this interaction comes from the elliptic shape of the viability curves on temperature-pressure diagrams. These curves, which are analogous to protein denaturation curves, suggest that the inactivation effects that are obtained by heating under pressure can be more efficiently obtained by cooling at negative temperatures under pressure. This cold temperature-high pressure inactivation effect is surely a promising means to provide safe but non-thermally affected food products. $a_w$ and hydrostatic pressure are two thermodynamic parameters, rarely taken into account in models of thermal inactivation, that greatly modify the thermal effects observed in classical conditions of hydration and pressure (i.e., $a_w \cong 1$ and atmospheric pressure). Hydration and hydrostatic pressure levels, as well as heating rate, strongly influence thermal stabilisation of food products, and these parameters could be more efficiently used to improve classical heating processes.

## 10.7  References

ALPAS, H, KALCHAYANAND, N, BOZOGLU, F and RAY, B (2000), 'Interactions of high hydrostatic pressure, pressurization temperature and pH on death and injury of pressure-resistant and pressure-sensitive strains of foodborne pathogens', *Int J Food Microbiol*, 60 (1), 33–42.
ANGELOTTI, R, MARYANSKI, J, BUTLER, T, PEELER, J and CAMPBELL, J (1968), 'Influence of spore moisture content on the dry-heat resistance of *Bacillus subtilis* var. *niger*', *Appl Microbiol*, 16(5), 735–745.

ASAMI, K and YAMAGUCHI, T (1999), 'Electrical and morphological changes of human erythrocytes under high hydrostatic pressure followed by dielectric spectroscopy', *Ann Biomed Eng*, 27 (4), 427–435.

BEAMAN, T C and GERHARDT, P (1986), 'Heat resistance of bacterial spores correlated with protoplast dehydration, mineralization, and thermal adaptation', *Appl Env Microbiol*, 52, 1242–1246.

BECKER, M J and RAPOPORT, A I (1987), 'Conservation of yeast by dehydration', *Adv Biochem Eng Biotechnol*, 35, 127–170.

BENAROUDJ, N, LEE, D H and GOLDBERG, A L (2001), 'Trehalose accumulation during cellular stress protects cells and cellular proteins from damage by oxygen radicals', *J. Biol Chem*, 276, 24261–24267.

BENEY, L and GERVAIS, P (2001), 'Influence of the fluidity of the membrane on the response of microorganisms to environmental stresses', *Appl Microbiol Biot*, 57, 34–42.

BENEY, L, MARECHAL, P A and GERVAIS, P (2001), 'Coupling effects of osmotic pressure and temperature on the viability of *Saccharomyces cerevisiae*', *Appl Microbiol Biotechnol*, 56 (3–4), 513–516.

BLOMBERG, A and ADLER, L (1992), 'Physiology of osmotolerance in funghi'. *Adv Microbial Phys*, 33, 145–212.

BROWN, A D and EDGLEY, M (1980), 'Osmoregulation mechanisms in yeast', in *Genetic Engineering of Osmoregulation*, Plenum Press, New York, 75–90.

BUROVA, T V, VARFOLOMEEVA, E P, GRINBERG, V IA, SUCHKOV, V V, PAPKOV, V S, BAUVE, KH and TOLSTOGUZOV, V B (1990), 'Interpretation of thermograms of protein denaturation in non-equilibrium conditions', *Biofizika*, 35, 222–227.

CÁNOVAS, D, FLETCHER, S A, HAYASHI, M and CSONKA, L N (2001), 'Role of trehalose in growth at high temperature of *Salmonella enterica* serovar *Typhimurium*', *J Bact*, 183, 3365–3371.

CERF, J (1977), 'Tailing of survival curves of bacterial spores', *J Appl Bacteriol*, 42(1), 1–19.

CHAPMAN, D (1994), 'The role of water in biomembrane structures', *J Food Eng*, 22, 367–380.

CHAPMAN, D, WILLIAMS, R M and LADBROOKE B D (1967), 'Physical studies of phospholipids. VI. Thermotropic and Lyotropic mesomorphism of some 1,2-diacylphosphatidylcholines (lecithin)', *Chem Phys Lipids*, 1, 445–475.

COOTE, P J, COLE, M B and JONES, M V (1991), 'Induction of increased thermotolerance in *Saccharomyces cerevisiae* may be triggered by a mechanism involving intracellular pH', *J Gen Microbiol*, 137, 1701–1708.

CORRY, J E L (1975), 'The effect of water activity on the resistance of bacteria', pp. 325–337, In 'Water relations of foods', ed. by Duckworth, R B, Academic Press, London.

CROWE, J H and CROWE, L M (1992), 'Membrane integrity in anhydrobiotic organisms: Toward a mechanism for stabilizing dry cells', in *Water and life*, Springer-Verlag, Berlin, Heidelberg.

CULLIS, P R and DE KRUIJFF, B (1979), 'Lipid polymorphism and the functional roles of lipids in biological membranes', *Biochim Biophys Acta*, 559, 399–420.

DE KRUIJFF, B (1997), 'Lipid polymorphism and biomembrane function'. *Curr Op Chem Biol*, 1, 564–569.

DOUZALS, J P, PERRIER-CORNET, J M, GERVAIS, P and COQUILLE, J C (2001), 'Pressure-temperature phase transition diagram for wheat starch', *J Agric Food Chem*, 49, 873–876.

DOWBEN, R M and WEIDENMÜLLER, R (1968), 'Adaptation of mesophilic bacteria to growth at elevated temperatures', *Biochim Biophys Acta*, 158, 255–261.

FURUKAWA, S and HAYAKAWA, I (2000), 'Investigation of desirable hydrostatic pressure required to sterilize bacillus stearothermophilus ifo 12550 spores and its sterilization properties in glucose, sodium chloride and ethanol solutions', *Food Research International,* 33 (10), 901–905.

GAWRISCH, K, PARSEGIAN, V A, HAJDUK, D A, TATE, M W, GRANER, S M, FULLER, N L and RAND, R P (1992), 'Energetics of a hexagonal-lamellar-hexagonal-phase transition sequence in dioleoylphosphatidylethanolamine membranes', *Biochemistry*, 31, 2856–2864.

GERSHFELD, N L and MURAYAMA, M (1988), 'Thermal instability of red blood cell membrane bilayers; temperature dependence of hemolysis', *J Membr Biol*, 101 (1), 67–72.

GERVAIS, P and MARECHAL, P A (1994), 'Yeast resistance to high levels of osmotic pressure: Influence of kinetics', *J Food Eng*, 22, 399–407.

GERVAIS, P and MARTINEZ DE MARANON, I (1995), 'Effect of kinetics of temperature variation on *saccharomyces cerevisiae* viability and permeability', *Biochim Biophys Acta,* 1235, 52–56.

GERVAIS, P and BENEY, L (2001), 'Osmotic mass transfer in the yeast *Saccharomyces cerevisiae*', *Cell Mol Biol*, 47, 831–841.

GERVAIS, P, MARECHAL, P A and MOLIN, P (1992), 'Effects of the kinetics of osmotic pressure variation on yeast viability', *Biotechnol Bioeng*, 40, 1435–1439.

GERVAIS, P, MARECHAL, P A, PERRIER-CORNET, J M, FERRET, E and LAROCHE, C (2002), 'Procédé de décontamination microbiologique de produits pulvérulents', French Patent no. FR02/00873, March 12, 2002.

GRINBERG, V Y, BUROVA, T V, HAERTL, T and TOLSTOGUZOV V B (2000), 'Interpretation of DSC data on protein denaturation complicated by kinetic and irreversible effects', *J Biotechnol*, 79, 269–80.

HAYERT, M, PERRIER-CORNET, J M and GERVAIS, P (1998), 'Cumulative effect of low acid pH and high pressure on the viability of *saccharomyces cerevisiae*', in Bennet, P B, Demchenko, I and Marquis, R E, *High pressure biology and medicine. Vth international meeting on high pressure biology*, St Petersburg, Rochester; New York, 44–51.

HENDRICKS, M, SARAIVA, J, LYSSENS, J, OLIVEIRA, J and TOBBACK P (1992), 'The influence of water activity on thermal stability of horseradish peroxidase', *J Food Sci Technol*, 27, 33–40.

HEREMANS, K (1982), 'High pressure effects on proteins and other biomolecules', *Ann. Rev. Biophys. Bioeng.*, 11, 1–21.

KLIBANOV, A M (1989), 'Enzymatic catalysis in anhydrous organic solvents.', *TIBS*, 14, 141–144.

KUNUGI, S, TADA, T, TANAKA, N, YAMAMOTO, K and AKASHI, M (2002), 'Microcalorimetric study of aqueous solution of a thermoresponsive polymer, poly(n-vinylisobutyramide) (pnviba)', *Polymer Journal*, 34 (5), 383–388.

LABUZA, T (1975), 'Oxydative changes in foods at low and intermediate moisture levels', pp 455–476, In *Water relations of foods*, ed. by Duckworth, R B, Academic Press, London.

LAROCHE, C, BENEY, L, MARECHAL, P A and GERVAIS, P (2001), 'The effect of osmotic pressure on the membrane fluidity of saccharomyces cerevisiae at different physiological temperatures', *Appl Microbiol Biotechnol*, 56 (1–2), 249–254.

LEUNG, H K (1987), 'Influence of water activity on chemical reactivity', pp 27–54, in *Water relations of foods*, ed. by Duckworth, R B, Academic Press, London.

LINDBLOM, G and RILFORS, L (1989), 'Cubic phases and isotropic structures formed by membrane lipids possible biological relevance', *Biochim Biophys Acta*, 988, 221–256.

LOHNER, K (1996), 'Is the high propensity of ethanolamine plasmalogens to form non-lamellar lipid structures manifested in the properties of biomembranes?', *Chem Phys Lipids*, 81, 167–184.

LUDWIG, H, BIELER, C, HALLBAUER, K and SCIGALLA, W (1992), 'Inactivation of microorganisms by hydrostatic pressure', in Balny, C, Hayashi, R, Heremans, K and Masson, P, *High pressure and biotechnology*, Montrouge, INSERM/John Libbey Eurotext Ltd, 25–32.

LUZZATI, V (1997), 'Biological significance of lipid polymorphism: the cubic phases', *Curr Op struct Biol*, 7, 661–668.

LUZZATI, V and HUSSON, F (1962), 'The structure of the liquid-crystalline phases of lipid-water systems', *Journal Cell Biol*, 12, 207–219.

LUZZATI, V, GULIK-KRZYWICKI, T and TARDIEU, A (1968), 'Polymorphism of lecithins', *Nature*, 218, 1031–1034.

MACDONALD, A G (1984), 'The effects of pressure on the molecular structure and physiological functions of cell membranes', *Philos Trans R Soc Lond B Biol Sci*, B 304, 47–68.

MCELHANEY, R N (1984), 'The structure and function of the *Acholeplasma laidlawii* plasma membrane', *Biochim Biophys Acta*, 779, 1–42.

MCELHANEY, R N (1989), 'The influence of membrane lipid composition and physical properties of membrane structure and function in *Acholeplasma laidlawii*', *Crit Rev Microbiol*, 17, 1–32.

MARECHAL, P A and GERVAIS, P (1994), 'Yeast viability related to water potential variation: Influence of the transient phase', *Appl Microbiol Biotechnol*, 42, 617–622.

MARTINEZ DE MARANON, I, CHAUDANSON, N, JOLY, N and GERVAIS, P (1999) 'Slow heat rate increases yeast thermotolerance by maintaining plasma membrane integrity', *Biotechnol Bioeng*, 6, 176–181.

MEYER, R S (2000), 'Ultra high pressure, high temperature food preservation process', US Patent 6017572A.

MILLE, Y, BENEY, L and GERVAIS, P (2002), 'Viability of Escherichia coli after combined osmotic and thermal treatment: a plasma membrane implication', Biochim Biophys Acta, 1567, 41–48.

MOATS, W A (1971), 'Kinetics of thermal death of bacteria', *J Bacteriol*, 105, 165–171.

MOROZOV, I I and PETIN, V G (1998), 'Modification of cell damage, caused by variable rate heating, by means of changes in osmotic pressure of the medium or using chloramphenicol', *Tsitologiia*, 40, 178–184.

MURRELL, W G and SCOTT, W J (1966), 'The heat resistance of bacterial spores at various water activities', *J Gen Microbiol*, 43, 411–425.

NAKASHIO, S and GERHARDT, P (1985), 'Protoplast dehydration correlated with heat resistance of bacterial spores', *J Bact*, 162, 571–578.

NIVEN, G W, MILES, C A and MACKEY, B M (1999), 'The effects of hydrostatic pressure on ribosome conformation in escherichia coli: an *in vivo* study using differential scanning calorimetry', *Microbiology*, 145 (Pt 2), 419–425.

OLIVEIRA, A C, ISHIMARU, D, GONCALVES, R B, SMITH, T J, MASON, P, SA-CARVALHO, D and SILVA, J L (1999), 'Low temperature and pressure stability of picornaviruses: Implications for virus uncoating', *Biophys J*, 76 (3), 1270–1279.

202    Food preservation techniques

PATTERSON, M F and KILPATRICK, D J (1998), 'The combined effect of high hydrostatic pressure and mild heat on inactivation of pathogens in milk and poultry', *J Food Protect*, 61 (4), 432–436.

PERRIER-CORNET, J M, HAYERT, M and GERVAIS, P (1999a), 'Yeast cell mortality related to a high-pressure shift: Occurrence of cell membrane permeabilization', *J Appl Microbiol*, 87 (1), 1–7.

PERRIER-CORNET, J M, HAYERT, M, SAURAT, E, MILESSE, C and GERVAIS, P (1999b), 'Interactions between osmotic and hydrostatic pressure in yeast inactivation', in Ludwig, H, *High pressure bioscience & biotechnology*, Heidelberg (Germany), Springer-Verlag, pp 27–30.

PFEIFFER, J (1992), 'Einfluβ der Wasseraktivität sowie des Milieus zwischen Dichtungen und Ditchflächen auf die Hitzeinaktivierung von Mikroorganismen, am Beispiel, bakterieller Sporen', Dissertation, Technische Universität München, Munich.

PIPER, P W (1993), 'Molecular events associated with acquisition of heat tolerance by the yeast *Saccharomyces cerevisiae*', *FEMS Microbiol Rev*, 11, 339–356.

POIRIER, I, MARECHAL, P A and GERVAIS, P (1997), 'Effects of the kinetics of water potential variation on bacteria viability', *J Appl Microbiol*, 82, 101–106.

POIRIER, I, MARÉCHAL, P A, EVRARD, C and GERVAIS, P (1998), '*Escherichia coli* and *lactobacillus plantarum* responses to osmotic stress', *Appl Microbiol Biotechnol*, 50, 704–709.

ROSENBERG, B, KEMENY, G, SWITZER, R C and HAMILTON, T C (1971), 'Quantitative evidence for protein denaturation as the cause of thermal death', *Nature*, 232, 471–473.

RUSSELL, N J, EVANS, R I, TER STEEG, P F, HELLEMONS, J, VERHEUL, A and ABEE, T (1995), 'Membranes as a target for stress adaptation', *Int J Food Microbiol*, 28, 255–261.

SANTOS, B C, CHEVAILE, A, KOJIMA, R and GULLANS, S R (1998), 'Characterization of the Hsp110/SSE gene family response to hyperosmolality and other stresses', *Am J Physiol*, 274, F1054-F1061.

SHALAEV, E and STEPONKUS, P L (1999), 'Phase diagram of 1,2-dioleoylphosphatidyl-ethanolamine (dope): Water system at subzero temperatures and at low water contents', *Biochim Biophys Acta*, 1419, 229–247.

SIMPSON, R K and GILMOUR, A (1997), 'The effect of high hydrostatic pressure on the activity of intracellular enzymes of listeria monocytogenes', *Lett Appl Microbiol*, 25 (1), 48–53.

SMELLER, L (2002), 'Pressure-temperature phase diagrams of biomolecules', *Biochim Biophys Acta*, 1595 (1–2), 11–29.

SMELT, J P, HELLEMONS, J C, WOUTERS, P C and VAN GERWEN, S J (2002), 'Physiological and mathematical aspects in setting criteria for decontamination of foods by physical means', *Int J Food Microbiol*, 78 (1–2), 57–77.

SONOIKE, K, SETOYAMA, T, KUMA, Y and KOBAYASHI, S (1992), 'Effects of pressure and temperature on the death rates of *lactobacillus casei* and *escherichia coli*', in Balny, C, Hayashi, R, Heremans, K and Masson, P, *High pressure and biotechnology*, Montrouge, INSERM/John Libbey Eurotext Ltd, 297–301.

STEPONKUS, P L (1999), 'Freeze induced dehydration and the cryostability of biological membranes', in Roos, Leslie Lillford eds, *Water management in the design and distribution of quality foods*, Technomic Publishing Company Inc. Lancaster, Pennsylvania, U.S.A.

STEPONKUS, P L and LYNCH, D V (1989), 'Freeze/thaw-induced destabilization of the plasma membrane and the effects of cold acclimation', *J Bioenerg Biomembr*, 21 (1), 21–41.

TAJCHAKAVIT, S, RAMASWAMY, H S and FUSTIE, P (1998), 'Enhanced destruction of spoilage microorganisms in apple juice during continuous flow microwave heating', *Food Res Int*, 31, 713–722.

ULMER, H M, HERBERHOLD, H, FAHSEL, S, GANZLE, M G, WINTER, R and VOGEL, R F (2002), 'Effects of pressure-induced membrane phase transitions on inactivation of hora, an atp-dependent multidrug resistance transporter, in *lactobacillus plantarum*', *Appl Environ Microbiol*, 68(3), 1088–1095.

WUYTACK, E Y and MICHIELS, C W (2001), 'A study on the effects of high pressure and heat on bacillus subtilis spores at low pH', *Int J Food Microbiol*, 64(3), 333–341.

YAYANOS, A A (1999), 'The properties of deep-sea piezophilic bacteria and their possible uses in biotechnology', in Ludwig, H, *Advances in high pressure bioscience and biotechnology*, Heidelberg, Springer.

ZAKS, A and KLIBANOV, A (1988), 'The effect of water on enzyme action in organic media', *J Biol Chem*, 263 (17), 8017–8021.

# 11

# Combining traditional and new preservation techniques to control pathogens: the case of *E. coli*

V. K. Juneja, US Department of Agriculture

## 11.1  Introduction

The contamination of the food supply with spoilage and pathogenic microorganisms continues to be a global problem despite the wide range of preservation methods employed. Traditional methods for successful and acceptable preservation of foods include heating, chilling, freezing, drying, curing, salting, preserving with sugar, direct acidification, natural fermentation, modified atmosphere packaging, and smoking. These processes have been developed empirically without a thorough understanding of the mechanisms of action of the antimicrobial processes or agents employed. Further, these processes are based on the use of relatively few preservation factors ('hurdles'), for example, temperature (D and z-value), acidity (pH), redox potential (Eh), preservatives, water content (water activity; $a_w$), and competitive microflora. Current consumer demand for fresh-tasting, high-quality, low-salt, preservative-free, microwavable meals, which have a high degree of convenience and require minimal preparation time, has resulted in an increased production of minimally processed, ready-to-eat, extended shelf-life refrigerated foods in the North American and European markets. The challenge remains to ensure the safety of such food products, known as 'new generation refrigerated foods'.

Interestingly, many of the factors used to destroy microorganisms or control microbial growth are also able to facilitate microbial survival and growth. These factors, which include pH, water content, temperature, Eh, preservatives, oxygen and other gases, competitive microorganisms, and nutrient content, can be manipulated and considered as prime determinants that foster an environment in which bacterial species will compete for dominance or die. Many of the microbial food preservation methods currently employed involve such manipulation. As such, the safety of minimally processed foods relies on combined preservative factors, i.e., a combination of two or more agents being more inhibitory than any of the agents alone (the 'hurdle effect'). Combining inhibitory factors can result in a significant improvement in securing microbial safety and stability as well as the sensory and nutritional quality of foods.

Recent research has focused on combining traditional inactivation, survival and growth-limiting factors at subinhibitory levels with emerging novel non-thermal intervention food preservation techniques using bacteriolytic enzymes (lysozyme), lactic cultures and culture products (e.g., bacteriocins), ionizing radiation, high hydrostatic pressure, or pulsed electric field (PEF). For example, the efficacy of high pressure is considerably enhanced when combined with heat, antimicrobials, or ionizing radiation. The effect of the combined intervention strategies is either additive, or synergistic in which the interaction leads to a combined effect of greater magnitude than the sum of the constraints applied individually.

Despite significant advances in food processing technologies, an annual estimated 76 million cases of foodborne illnesses occur in the U.S. resulting in approximately 5,000 deaths (Mead *et al.*, 1999). In the year 2000 alone, approximately 2.4 million pounds of beef were recalled due to possible contamination with *Escherichia coli* O157:H7. This chapter deals with the current knowledge of a wide range of traditional preservation factors and the additive/synergistic effects when used in combination with each other or with newly developed physical treatments to control pathogenic *E. coli* in foods, thereby enhancing the stability and safety of foods. The organism is a natural inhabitant of the gut of humans and warm-blooded animals and birds. The importance of *E. coli* ranges from its role as an indicator for fecal contamination to one of the most important foodborne pathogens. Since the voluminous published literature provides basic insights into the behavior and the physiology of stress responses of numerous bacteria, the focus of this chapter will be on *E. coli* O157:H7 because of its significance as a foodborne pathogen.

## 11.2    Pathogen growth conditions: the case of *E. Coli*

### 11.2.1    Temperature

The general growth and survival characteristics of *E. coli* O157:H7 are broadly the same as those of non-pathogenic *E. coli*. Buchanan and Klawitter (1992) reported that the growth range for *E. coli* O157:H7 is 10 to 42 °C, and there was no growth at 5 or 8 °C. The optimum temperature for growth is 37 °C and, under otherwise optimum conditions, the minimum growth temperature is 8 to 10 °C (Palumbo *et al.*, 1995; Rajkowski and Marmer, 1995). Palumbo *et al.* (1995) found that the lower and upper temperature limits for growth of *E. coli* O157:H7 was culture medium-dependent; all strains grew in brain heart infusion (BHI) broth between 10 and 45 °C, but 6 of 16 strains did not grow in *E. coli* broth at 45 °C, and 3 of 16 strains increased 1,000-fold in viable counts in 4 to 6 days at

10 °C. The growth kinetics of *E. coli* O157:H7 under temperature abuse conditions is an important food safety concern. Rajkowski and Marmer (1995) reported on the growth response of *E. coli* O157:H7 to nonisothermal and/or fluctuating temperature ranges and reported that the growth kinetics at fluctuating temperatures more closely approximated the higher temperature than the midpoint temperature of each cyclic range. These findings have significant food safety implications because transitory abuse could foster more rapid growth than that expected of *E. coli* O157:H7 in foods stored properly.

### 11.2.2   pH

The effect of pH on growth kinetics of *E. coli* O157:H7 is dependent on the type of acid (organic versus inorganic) and the acid concentration. Organic acids have been found to be more inhibitory than hydrochloric acid. Glass *et al.* (1992) found an increase in the inhibitory pH when lactic acid was used as the acidulant as compared to hydrochloric acid. Inhibition of growth rate by lactic acid was proportional to the concentration of undissociated acid (Pressor *et al.*, 1997). Abdul-Raouf *et al.* (1993) reported that in beef slurries, the relative inhibitory activity of organic acids on *E. coli* O157:H7 was acetic > lactic > citric. Although refrigeration is normally considered to provide a useful hurdle in delaying growth or inhibiting survival of pathogens, *E. coli* O157:H7 has been shown to survive better in an acid environment at 4 °C than at 10 °C (Conner and Kotrola, 1995). In a study on the effect of pH reduction with acetic (pH 5.2), citric (pH 4.0), lactic (pH 4.7), malic (pH 4.0), mandelic (pH 5.0), or tartaric (pH 4.1) acids on growth and survival of *E. coli* O157:H7 in tryptic soy broth held at 25, 10, or 4 °C for 56 days, Conner and Kotrola (1995) reported that the population increased by up to 4 $\log_{10}$ cfu/ml in all treatments except with mandelic acid, whereas no growth occurred at 4 or 10 °C in any treatments except the control. *E. coli* O157:H7 was able to survive acidic conditions ($\geq$ pH4.0) for up to 56 days, but survival was affected by the type of acidulant and temperature (Conner and Kotrola, 1995). Low pH and nitrite (200 mg/g) interacted synergistically to restrict growth of *E. coli* O157:H7 in tryptic soy broth (Tsai and Chou, 1996). Likewise, the combination of low pH and ethanol exhibited a synergistic effect in destruction of the pathogen in fermenting apple cider (Semanchek and Golden, 1996).

Because of the low infectious dose (< 100 cfu) of the pathogen (Griffin and Tauxe, 1991), survival of low numbers of *E. coli* O157:H7 in food products is undesirable. Researchers have assessed the survival of the pathogen in acidic foods and reported survival for several weeks to months in a variety of acidic foods such as apple cider (Zhao *et al.*, 1993; Besser *et al.*, 1993), fermented dairy products (Reitsma and Henning, 1996; Arocha *et al.*, 1992), mayonnaise (Raghubeer *et al.*, 1995; Weagnant *et al.*, 1994), and sausages (Clavero and Beuchat, 1996). Survival in acid foods stored at refrigeration temperatures is prolonged substantially compared to survival at ambient temperature. Zhao *et al.* (1993) reported survival of the pathogen in fresh unfermented apple cider (pH

3.7) for 10 to 31 days at 8 °C compared to 2 to 3 days at 25 °C; and for 21 days when supplemented with 0.1% sodium benzoate at 8 °C (Miller and Kasper, 1994). At 7 °C or −18 °C, survival was prolonged at a more acid, more suboptimal pH (pH 4.5 > pH 5.4 > pH 7.0) while at a defined pH (pH 4.5), better survival was observed at 7 °C than at 22 °C (Uyttendaele *et al.*, 2001). This suggests that application of the hurdle technology for food preservation may inhibit outgrowth but result in prolonged survival of *E. coli* O157:H7 in minimally processed foods.

### 11.2.3   Sodium chloride
The effect of sodium chloride in combination with other factors on *E. coli* has been investigated. The combination of reduced pH (to pH 4.5) and increased salt concentration (5% NaCl) inhibited growth of the pathogen at 22 °C in a beef gravy medium simulating fermented dried meat (Uyttendaele *et al.*, 2001). Gibson and Roberts (1986) examined the combined effects of pH, temperature, NaCl, and NaNO$_2$ on the growth of 10 pathogenic strains of *E. coli* and reported that the maximum NaCl concentration that permitted growth was 6% at pH values between 5.6 and 6.8 and temperatures between 15 and 30 °C. In this latter study, growth occurred in any combination of 0 to 4% NaCl and 0 to 400 mg/l of NaNO$_2$ at pH values between 6.2 and 6.8 and temperatures between 15 and 35 °C. However, a concentration of 8% or more of sodium chloride completely inhibited growth of enteropathogenic *E. coli* at different temperature and pH levels, while a concentration of 4% in combination with pH 5.6 and 200 ppm of nitrite did not (Gibson and Roberts, 1986). *E. coli* O157:H7 does not have an unusual salt tolerance. The pathogen was inhibited by 8.5% or more sodium chloride in trypticase soy broth (Glass *et al.*, 1992). A concentration of 2.5% NaCl did not have any inhibiting effect, while at 4.5% the generation time was longer and at 6.5% the lag time was very long (36h) which the authors attributed to the presence of a salt-tolerant population of the organism. In fermented sausage with 3.5% sodium chloride, 69 ppm sodium nitrite and pH 4.8, the *E. coli* population was reduced, but was not inhibited completely (Glass *et al.*, 1992). The survival of bioluminescent *E. coli* O157:H7 in BHI medium containing sodium chloride with other factors as well as in model systems representing fermented sausage was studied (Tomicka *et al.*, 1997). Sodium chloride at concentrations up to 3.5% did not inhibit growth in BHI. In American-style fermentation (high-temperature, short-time) with 2% sodium chloride, starter culture, dextrose and sodium nitrite, the organism survived for more than 51 days, and the authors explained that sodium chloride and sodium nitrite enhanced the survival of the organism in this system. In the European-style fermentation, at low inoculum levels of the organism there was inhibition after 9 days, while with high initial inoculum levels, there was survival for more than 30 days. The reason for this survival was attributed to possible inhibition of starter cultures by the salts added and hence lesser competition for *E. coli*. In skim milk (10% rehydrated nonfat dry milk), *E. coli* O157:H7 had up to a 3-log$_{10}$ reduction with 4% salt at pH 4.7 at different

times and temperatures, while 6% sodium chloride caused complete inhibition at all treatment conditions (Guraya *et al.*, 1998). It was concluded that sodium chloride at increasing concentrations enhanced inactivation at pH levels between 4.1 and 4.7. While the minimum $a_w$ for growth is 0.95 (ICMSF, 1996), Sperber (1983) reported that *E. coli* generally does not survive at an $a_w$ of < 0.95 (ca. 8.5% NaCl). However, a study on inoculated processed salami (pH 4.86 and 4.63 at $a_w$ values of 0.95 and 0.90, respectively) revealed that the pathogen at 4 to 5 $\log_{10}$ cfu/g survived storage at 5 °C for 32 days (Dev *et al.*, 1991). Thus, *E. coli* O157:H7 has an unusual tolerance to drying.

**11.2.4   Growth kinetic models**

Models have the ability to predict the growth of foodborne pathogens under conditions different from those tested experimentally, but within the experimental/studied range of parameters used to generate the data. These models are less useful close to the boundary between growth and no growth. This problem is alleviated by the use of probability models, where the objective is to determine whether or not the microorganisms can grow under specified conditions. As part of an effort to better characterize the behavior of *E. coli* O157:H7 and develop predictive models, several researchers (Buchanan *et al.*, 1993; Buchanan and Klawitter, 1992; Buchanan and Bagi, 1994; Sutherland *et al.*, 1995) have assessed the effects of incubation temperature, initial pH, sodium chloride content, and/or sodium nitrite concentration on growth of this pathogen. These researchers reported that as incubation temperature decreased, as sodium chloride concentration increased, and as pH increased, the growth of *E. coli* O157:H7 decreased. In a study by Buchanan and Klawitter (1992), the maximum population density (MPD) was largely dependent on pH, salt and temperature; however, MPD declined by 0.5 to 1.0 $\log_{10}$ units when *E. coli* O157:H7 was cultured anaerobically. Generation time and lag time were largely unaffected by initial pH at values ≥ 5.5. Increasing NaCl levels from 0.5 to 5% decreased the growth rate, particularly if the other variables were not optimal for growth. Sodium nitrite became an effective inhibitor of *E. coli* O157:H7 at < pH 5.5 in BHI broth (Buchanan and Bagi, 1994). In a study on the effects of three non-ionic humectants (mannitol, sorbitol, and sucrose) on the growth kinetics of *E. coli* O157:H7, Buchanan and Bagi (1997) concluded that while humectant differences occur at limiting $a_w$ values, differences among humectants were minimal at $a_w$ 0.98. A predictive model fitted using the Gompertz equation for the growth of *E. coli* O157:H7 as a function of temperature, pH and sodium chloride was developed by Sutherland *et al.* (1995) and has been extrapolated to a range of foods including meat, poultry, milk, cheese and tempeh.

Researchers have attempted to develop logistic regression models for 'growth-no growth' of *E. coli*. Pressor *et al.* (1998) modeled a nonpathogenic strain of *E. coli* as a function of temperature (10 to 37 °C), pH (2.8 to 6.9), lactic acid concentration (0 to 500 mM), and $a_w$ (0.955 to 0.999; NaCl used as humectant). In this study, the inhibitory effect of combinations of $a_w$ and pH varied with temperature, and predictions from the model for the growth/no growth interface were consistent with 95% of the experimental data set. The model described the influence of these factors on growth after 50 days of incubation and was based on modifications of the square root model with specific terms for undissociated and dissociated lactic acid. In another study, Salter *et al.* (2000) adopted a nonlinear logistic regression approach to model the response of Shiga toxin-producing *E. coli* to combinations of temperature (7.7–37 °C) and $a_w$ (0.943–0.987; NaCl as humectant). In this study, the minimum $a_w$ which allowed growth occurred in the range of 25–30 °C and at temperatures below this range, the minimum $a_w$ which allowed growth increased with decreasing temperature. McKellar and Lu (2001) developed a logistic regression model describing the growth-no growth interface of *E. coli* O157:H7 as a function of temperature, pH, salt, sucrose, and acetic acid and reported that acetic acid was the factor having the most influence on the growth-no growth interface; addition of as little as 0.5% resulted in an increase in the observed minimum pH for growth from 4.0 to 5.5. In this study, increasing the salt concentration also had a significant effect on the interface; at all acetic acid concentrations, increasing salt increased the minimum temperature at which growth was observed. Using logistic regression techniques, the effect of pH (3.1 to 4.3), storage temperature and time (5 to 35 °C for 0 to 6 or 12 h), preservatives (0, 0.05, or 0.1% potassium sorbate or sodium benzoate), and freeze-thaw treatment combinations on the probability of 5-$\log_{10}$ reduction in a 3-strain mixture of *E. coli* O157:H7 in cider was determined (Uljas *et al.*, 2001). In this study, statistical analyses revealed a significant ($p < 0.0001$) effect of all four variables, with cider pH being the most important, followed by treatment and time, and finally by preservative concentration. Thus, logistic regression approaches can be used to describe the effectiveness of multiple treatment combinations in pathogen control in cider making.

## 11.3   The heat resistance of *E. coli*

The heat resistance of the organism has been studied extensively in meat (Ahmed *et al.*, 1995; Ahmed and Conner, 1997; Doyle and Schoeni 1984; Kotrola and Conner, 1997; Line *et al.*, 1991; Jackson *et al.*, 1996; Juneja *et al.*, 1997) and apple juice (Splittstoesser *et al.*, 1996). These reports pertaining to the heat resistance of *E. coli* O157:H7 provide sufficient evidence that the pathogen does not have an unusually high heat resistance. Therefore, it is practically feasible to inactivate this pathogen by the type of mild heat treatment given to minimally processed foods, without negatively impacting the product quality.

### 11.3.1   Factors affecting heat resistance
An appropriate heat treatment designed to achieve a specified lethality of microorganisms is influenced by many factors. Some of these can be attributed to the

inherent resistance of microorganisms, while others are due to environmental influences. Examples of inherent resistance include the differences among species and the different strains or isolates of bacteria (assessed individually or as a mixture). Environmental factors include those affecting the microorganisms during growth and formation of cells (e.g., stage of growth, growth temperature, growth medium, previous exposure to stress, etc.) and those active during the heating of a bacterial suspension, such as the composition of the heating menstruum (amount of carbohydrate, proteins, lipids, and solutes, etc.), $a_w$, pH, added preservatives, method of heating, and methodology used for recovery of survivors, etc. This part of the chapter deals with the most significant research on the combination of preservation regimes affecting the heat resistance of E. coli O157:H7.

### 11.3.2    Effect of single and combined factors

The pH of the heating menstruum is recognized as one of the most important factors influencing the heat resistance of bacteria. Microorganisms usually have their maximum heat resistance at pH values close to neutrality; a decrease in the pH of the heating medium usually results in a decreased D-value. Reichart (1994) provided a theoretical interpretation of the effect of pH on microbial heat destruction and described a linear relationship between pH and the logarithm of the D-values for E. coli. The author stated that the logarithm of the heat destruction rate increases linearly in the acid and alkaline range and has a minimum at the optimum pH for growth. High pH interacts synergistically with high temperature to destroy gram-negative foodborne pathogens (Teo et al., 1996). Abdul-Raouf et al. (1993) demonstrated that the rate of thermal inactivation of E. coli O157:H7 in acidified beef slurry was dependent on the acidulant and increased in the order: citric acid, lactic acid and acetic acid. In a study by Reichart and Mohacsi-Farkas (1994), when heat destruction of E. coli as a function of temperature, pH, redox potential and $a_w$ was assessed in a synthetic heating medium, the heat destruction increased with decreasing pH and increasing $a_w$. Lower pH of the gravy tended to increase E. coli O157:H7 sensitivity to heat at 55 °C (Juneja et al., 1999). In this latter study, the observed D-values at 55 °C decreased (76.7%) from 12.0 to 2.8 as the pH of the gravy decreased from 8 to 4. The lethality of heat to E. coli O157:H7 increased when gravy (pH8) contained 1 to 6% salt (Juneja et al., 1999). However, the addition of salt in gravy exhibited a reverse trend at low pH, i.e., the salt effect was protective to E. coli O157:H7 against the lethal effect of heat in pH4 gravy. A combination of salt and sodium pyrophosphate (SPP) in gravy increased sensitivity of the pathogen to heat (Juneja et al., 1999). Thus, SPP interacted with salt, thereby reducing the protective effect of salt. In contrast, Blackburn et al. (1997) reported an optimum pH (5.2–5.9), dependent on temperature and NaCl, for survival of E. coli O157:H7, and increasing acidity or alkalinity increased the rate of thermal inactivation. Thus, the pH effect on heat resistance of E. coli O157:H7 depends upon the interaction of other variables (SPP, NaCl, etc.) in the heating menstruum.

In a study by Kotrola and Conner (1997), when the heat resistance of *E. coli* O157:H7 inoculated in ground turkey breast meat at various fat and salt levels was assessed, the D-values at 55 °C, obtained by linear regression, increased from 12.5 min (3% fat, no salt) to 26.1 min (3% fat, 8% salt); the D-values increased from 11.0 min (11% fat, no salt) to 20.4 min (11% fat, 8% salt). In the same study, the authors reported D-values at 55 °C of 23.0 and 17.9 min at levels of 3 and 11% fat in ground turkey breast meat containing the additive mix (8% NaCl + 4% sodium lactate + 0.5% polyphosphate), respectively. In conclusion, the D-values for turkey meat with these additives were higher than turkey meat without the additives, indicating that the additives enhanced survival of the organism.

It is feasible to produce a safe apple cider by combining heat with pH modification and preservative addition. Dock *et al.* (2000) investigated the effect of pH and preservatives on the heat resistance of *E. coli* O157:H7 in apple cider. The D-values at 50 °C of 65 min in apple cider were reduced to 13.9, 13.2 and 7.0 min in apple cider with addition of 0.5% malic acid, 0.1% sorbate and 0.1% benzoate, respectively. Addition of both 0.2% benzoate and 1% malic acid showed an additive effect, lowering the D-value to 0.3 min, and addition of a combination of 0.2% sorbate, 0.2% benzoate, and 1% malic acid resulted in a D-value of 18 s.

### 11.3.3   Heat inactivation kinetics predictive models

Juneja *et al.* (1999) employed a fractional factorial design to assess and quantify the effects and interactions of temperature, pH, salt and SPP levels and found that the thermal inactivation of *E. coli* O157:H7 was dependent on all four factors. Thermal resistance of cells can be lowered by combining these intrinsic factors. The following multiple regression equations, developed in these studies, predict D-values of *E. coli* O157:H7 for any combinations of heating temperature (55–62.5 °C), salt (0.0–6.0%, w/v), SPP (0.0–0.3%, w/v), and pH (4.0–6.5). The predicted D-values are for changes in the parameter values in the range tested from any combination of four environmental factors.

$$
\begin{aligned}
\text{Log}_e \text{ D-value} = {} & -43.0646 + 1.4868(\text{temp}) + 3.5737(\text{pH}) - 0.1341(\text{salt}) \\
& - 8.6391(\text{phos}) - 0.0419(\text{temp})(\text{pH}) + 0.0103(\text{temp})(\text{salt}) \\
& + 0.1512(\text{temp})(\text{phos}) - 0.0544(\text{pH})(\text{salt}) + 0.2253(\text{pH})(\text{phos}) \\
& - 0.2682(\text{salt})(\text{phos}) - 0.0137(\text{temp})^2 - 0.0799(\text{pH})^2 - 0.0101(\text{salt})^2 \\
& - 6.4356(\text{phos})^2
\end{aligned}
$$

The authors developed confidence intervals (95%) to allow microbiologists to predict the variation in the heat resistance of the pathogen. Representative observed and predicted D-values of *E. coli* O157:H7 are provided in Table 11.1. Predicted D-values from the model compared well with the observed thermal death values. Thus, the model provides a valid description of the data used to generate it.

**Table 11.1**    Observed and predicted D-values at 55 and 60 °C of *E. coli* O157:H7 in beef gravy

| Temperature (°C) | pH | % NaCl | % Phosphate | D-value Observed (min.) | D-value Predicted[1] (min.) |
|---|---|---|---|---|---|
| 55 | 4 | 0.0 | 0.0 | 2.8 | 4.1 |
| 55 | 4 | 0.0 | 0.30 | 1.9 | 2.7 |
| 55 | 4 | 6.0 | 0.30 | 3.5 | 4.3 |
| 60 | 4 | 3.0 | 0.15 | 2.1 | 2.2 |
| 60 | 6 | 3.0 | 0.30 | 1.8 | 2.1 |

Source: Juneja *et al.* (1999).
[1] Predicted D-values are the 95% upper confidence levels.

Blackburn *et al.* (1997) used a log-logistic function to develop a 3-factor thermal inactivation model for *E. coli* O157:H7 as affected by temperature (54.5–64.5 °C), pH (4.2–9.6 adjusted using HCl or NaOH) and NaCl concentration (0.5–8.5% w/w). In this study, 83% of *E. coli* O157:H7 survival curves represented a linear logarithmic death, with the remaining curves demonstrating shoulder and tailing regions.

Riondet *et al.* (2000) showed that in a pH range from 5.0 to 7.0, Eh (redox potential) had a complex interactive effect on heat resistance. Thus, developing a quadratic response surface inactivation model was inappropriate. In their study, the threshold for the Eh response and the amplitude of the variation of heat resistance varied with pH. Regarding the growth after heat treatment, a decrease in Eh and pH resulted in a longer duration of the lag phase and a slower exponential growth phase. Intracellular pH is a determining factor for *E. coli* growth (Booth 1985). Riondet *et al.* (1999) showed that a reducing Eh and an acid pH led to a decrease in the proton motive force, linked to a fall in intracellular pH.

## 11.4    Problems in combining traditional preservation techniques

Combined preservation factors for the control of foodborne pathogens include pH, $a_w$, Eh, competing microflora and added preservatives. The basic concept for ensuring microbiological safety is that growth, survival and inactivation of microorganisms in food are dependent on the cumulative effects of a number of factors such as temperature, pH, $a_w$, antimicrobials, etc. By manipulating more than one of these factors, it is possible to control microbial growth or render the pathogens more sensitive to intervention techniques. Much research is aimed at identifying combinations of these factors that are necessary for the safe production of foods. The use of inhibitory/preservation factors in combination is advantageous because they interact, sometime synergistically, enabling use of lower intensities of each factor rather than one preservative factor of larger intensity. As such, combinations of different mild preservation factors are used to achieve multi-target, preservation effects. Thus, food processors can produce products that are less acidic, more moist and refrigerated instead of frozen, and still maintain the microbial integrity of food.

The effectiveness of the individual effects of temperature, pH, salt, etc., with regard to pathogen growth or inactivation is maximized by conducting multiple factorial experiments in which the effects and interactions of these parameters in foods are assessed in extending the lag time, increasing the generation time, or lowering the heat resistance of foodborne pathogens. Subsequently, growth and inactivation kinetics, or thermal death models, are developed which predict the target pathogen's behavior within a specific range of food formulation variables. The inactivation kinetics models can help either to establish an appropriate physical intervention treatment, or to understand and determine the extent to which existing/traditional processes could be modified for a variety of processed foods. The models can contribute to more effective evaluation and assessment of the impact of changes in food formulations that could affect their microbiological safety or the lethality of pathogens. These predictive models enable food processors and regulatory agencies to ensure critical food safety margins by predicting the combined effects of multiple food formulation variables. The food processors are able to design appropriate processing times and temperatures for the production of safe food with extended shelf-life without adversely affecting the sensory quality of the product. However, it is of critical importance that the D-values predicted by the models first be validated with resistance data obtained by actual experiments in specific foods before the predicted values can be used to design physical processes for the production of a safe food.

It is logical to consider the stress responses of E. coli in the context of food formulation factors that have systematically been demonstrated to affect growth and survival in food systems. Food preservation factors, such as temperature, $a_w$, pH, etc., constitute environmental stresses to bacteria. If the stress is mild, it causes injury to the bacteria and if it is severe, it causes inactivation. Injured bacteria in food are of concern, since they can survive when favorable conditions are encountered, as well as multiply and grow in food. As consumers demand enhanced freshness and appeal, minimal processing is employed in which mild treatments are applied to the food products. As such, the bacteria are exposed to mild stress, which can induce resistance responses and compromise the safety and shelf-life of these food products.

One possible limitation of the food preserved by combined methods is that different microorganisms exhibit different physiological responses to stresses, in particular homeostasis, and stress reactions. Homeostasis is the tendency of microorganisms to maintain a stable and balanced (uniform) internal environment. Organisms tend to maintain intracellular pH between narrow limits even though the pH in the environment changes outside these limits. They synthesize stress-shock proteins that enable them to withstand hostile environments such as non-lethal heating or high-pressure stress. Bacteria balance the internal osmotic pressure to changes in $a_w$ due to drying or to changes in salt or sugar concentrations outside the cell (osmohomeostasis).

According to Gould (1995), homeostasis and stress reactions enable microorganisms to keep important physiological systems operating, in balance, and unperturbed even when the external environment is greatly perturbed. Homeostasis mechanisms that cells have evolved to survive extreme environmental stresses are energy dependent and allow bacteria to keep functioning. Combined preservation strategies are effective when they overcome, temporarily or permanently, the various homeostatic reactions that microorganisms have evolved to resist stresses (Gould, 1995). The goal of food preservation is to reduce the availability of energy (removing oxygen, limiting nutrients, and reducing the temperature) and/or increase the demand for energy (reducing $a_w$, reducing pH, and adding membrane active compounds). When the homeostasis of microorganisms is disturbed by food formulation variables, bacteria will not multiply but remain in the lag phase or even die before the homeostasis is re-established.

According to Archer (1996), the stresses that exist in foods, either naturally or through application of food preservation methods, have a major impact on gene expression in bacterial pathogens, promoting adaptive mutations that may select for strains with increased virulence. The presence of strains with enhanced virulence in foods is extremely serious for immuno-compromised consumers.

The application of multiple factors (hurdle technology) involving exposure of pathogens to combinations of sublethal conditions in foods could also result in the promulgation of adaptive stress responses (stress hardening) that can alter an organism's susceptibility to subsequent homologous as well as heterologous stress (cross protections) conditions (Archer, 1996; Leistner, 1995; Rowen 1999). In *E. coli*, the regulation of stress responses through the transcriptional control of alternate sigma factors encoded by *rpoS* and *rpoH* in response to general stress and heat, respectively, has been studied in great detail (Hengge-Aronis 1993; Yura *et al.*, 1984). Stress reactions may enable bacteria to minimize the effect of specific constraints, and there may also be non-specific effects, in which microorganisms adapt to a particular applied stress (hurdle) in food and become tolerant to other stresses. It is, therefore, likely that the use of a single preservation technique may not be able to overcome homeostasis mechanisms and stress reactions. Thus, several preservation techniques should be used in combination following the multiple-target approach. In other words, the simultaneous or sequential exposure to different stresses with different cellular targets is a valuable concept for optimal microbial stability, since to counter multiple stresses will involve the expenditure of energy on the part of the target organism.

Stress-responses and cross-protection have been studied extensively in both nonpathogenic and pathogenic *E. coli* (Finkel *et al.*, 2000; Rowbury, 1995). For example, acid adaptation is an important phenomenon that has been frequently observed. Outbreak strains of enterohaemorrhagic *E. coli* were reported to have greater acid resistance than natural isolates (McKeller and Knight, 1999). Various studies have demonstrated that induction of acid tolerance can enhance *E. coli* O157:H7 survival in acidic foods such as fermented dairy products and fermented meats such as shredded hard salami (Cheville *et al.*, 1996; Leyer *et al.*, 1995). While in acidic condiments such as mustard and sweet pickle relish, the pathogen dies within 1 h of storage at 5 and 23 °C, whereas survival of the pathogen in ketchup depends upon whether the cells have been preadapted to acidic conditions before inoculation into the condiment, together with the temperature of storage. Adaptation enhanced survival in ketchup at 5 °C but not at 23 °C, as measured by recovery on TSA (Tsai and Ingham, 1997). In this study, *E. coli* O157:H7 survived longer than the non-pathogenic strains, which may be a food safety concern. Acid adaptation of some strains of *E. coli* O157:H7 exhibited cross-protection against increased osmolarity (Garren *et al.*, 1998; Cheville *et al.*, 1996). In contrast, survival of *E. coli* O157:H7 in dried beef powder was not significantly enhanced by acid adaptation, suggesting that this stress response did not afford cross protection against dehydration or osmotic stresses (Ryu *et al.*, 1999). Dried beef powder has a complex composition and likewise, it is possible that several factors present in a particular food can have a substantial influence on survival. This contention implies that it is not logical to predict survival in different foods based on *in vitro* growth and survival responses, and that challenge studies are warranted to accurately assess the behavior of the pathogen in foods. Rowbury (1995) indicated that induction of acid tolerance also increases the resistance of *E. coli* to heating, radiation, and antimicrobials. In another study, Rowbury *et al.* (1996b) reported that the microorganism also possesses alkali tolerance response. Natural isolates of *E. coli* O157 also varied in resistance to hydrostatic pressure, heat, salt, hydrogen peroxide, and compounds causing membrane damage (Benito *et al.*, 1999). This indicates that the bacterial cell has a limited number of basic systems for eliciting gene expression; changes induced by one stress would protect cells against other environmental challenges. The mechanism of cross responses, known as global stress response, has received recent attention because of its implications for the safety of milder preservation technologies. Salt, heat and acid tolerances in *E. coli* 0157:H7 are regulated by the *rpoS* sigma factor (Cheville *et al.*, 1996). Lin *et al.* (1996) examined three mechanisms of acid resistance, i.e., oxidative, arginine-dependent, and glutamate-dependent, and found that all three contribute to the microorganism's overall acid resistance.

Exposure to NaCl has been reported to induce marked sensitivity to a subsequent acid challenge in *E. coli* (Rowbury *et al.*, 1994). This sensitivity is independent of both the NhaA and NhaR antiporters (Rowbury *et al.*, 1994) and high external osmotic pressure (Rowbury *et al.*, 1996a). Exposure to hydrochloric acid has been reported to diminish the tolerance of *E. coli* O157:H7 to subsequent elevated NaCl levels (Ryu and Beuchat, 1998); the reverse has been claimed for some *E. coli* O157:H7 strains when lactic acid was used as the acidulant, i.e., prior exposure to acid pH induced tolerance to high NaCl concentrations (Garren *et al.*, 1998). There have been investigations into the effect on pathogens on simultaneous exposure to organic acid and high NaCl levels; one of the few such reports suggested that an organic acid (in the form of vinegar) and NaCl had a synergistic inhibitory effect on *E. coli* O157:H7 (Entani *et al.*, 1997). However, such combinations of agents are not always more inhibitory to pathogens than one alone. Casey and Condon (2002) reported that NaCl reduces the inhibitory effect of lactic acid on *E. coli* 0157:H7, by raising the cytoplasmic pH, with approximately 1000-fold more survivors at pH 4.2 when 4% NaCl was added to the medium. This study suggests that *E. coli* can use NaCl to counteract acidification of its cytoplasm by organic acids, and in addition, that combinations of antimicrobial agents cannot always be relied upon to achieve additive antimicrobial effects.

In multiple food formulations, numerous antimicrobial combinations are suggested. This may be a reason for concern if bacteria can acquire some degree of resistance toward a particular antimicrobial agent. Stress responses elicited with application of food preservatives such as sorbate, benzoate, lactate, sulfite, nitrite, smoke, and other preservatives have not yet been established. Newer processing technologies such as treatment of foods with high pressure, pulsed electric field, and others would also be expected to induce stress responses, including novel or unexpected responses, but more research is needed in this area.

The intensity of a preservation factor may change during the shelf-life of the product and/or the initial intensity of the factor may be less than expected for the levels applied. This decreased efficacy may be attributed to several phenomena including binding to food components such as proteins and fats; chemical degradation; inactivation and/or biological destabilization by other ingredients or components; pH and temperature effects on hurdle stability and activity; physical losses by mass transport from the food to the environment; and poor solubility and uneven distribution in the food (Alzamora, 1998). For example, stability of sorbic acid primarily depends upon pH, $a_w$, temperature, light, presence of oxygen, type of packaging material and other components of the system. Many natural antimicrobials (e.g., bacteriocins, some phenolics) are less effective in food matrix than *in vitro* (Gould, 1996), with proteins, lipids, salts, pH and temperature affecting their antimicrobial activity.

## 11.5   Combining traditional and new preservation techniques

In general, preservation by a single factor is not sufficient to ensure completely safe products, and multiple hurdles are advised (Leistner and Gorris, 1995). Likewise, to avoid the undesirable effects of heat, one approach is to use mild heat in combination with other emerging preservation technologies. The use of multiple preservation techniques incorporating mild treatments, e.g., mild heat, can result in enhanced preservative action by having an additive or synergistic effect on microbial inactivation, particularly in foods with a high water content, and/or reduce the severity of one or all the treatments. For example, the lethal effect of heat is enhanced if bacterial cells have undergone ultrasound treatment (Wrigley and Llorca, 1992). The combination treatment of heat and ultrasound is termed 'thermosonication' (Hurst *et al.*, 1995). An interesting combination of low pressure (0.3 MPa), mild heat treatment, and ultrasonic wave treatment is effective for destruction of microorganisms (Knorr, 1995). Also, irradiation can sensitize cells to subsequent heating. Since the principal target of ionizing radiation is DNA, vegetative cells treated first by ionizing radiation experience DNA damage, and then subsequent heat treatment damages enzymes necessary for DNA repair. Finally, the efficacy of the lethal effect of heat on microorganisms is increased if the bacteria are subsequently exposed to organic acids. This is a consequence of prior heating causing damage to the cell membrane, making it easier for weak acids to penetrate into the cytoplasm.

Nonthermal processes show excellent promise for incorporation into combined preservation systems using the hurdle approach. The combined application of a number of variables to processing or preservation of food often allows for the development of foods with less product damage and greater consumer appeal. However, the protective effect of complex food matrices warrants the necessity to assess the efficacy of each combination process for a particular food product.

Researchers have shown that inactivation of *E. coli* increases with an increase in the applied electric field strength and treatment time and that higher temperatures act synergistically with PEF treatment (Vega-Mercado *et al.*, 1996a). Other factors that enhance PEF treatment are pH and the presence of antimicrobials that act as additional preservative factors (hurdles). Each factor imposes an additional stress to the microorganisms and the result is an increase in the total antimicrobial action of the combined treatment (Vega-Mercado *et al.*, 1996b). In a study on the effect of PEFs, pH and ionic strength on the inactivation of *E. coli* at temperatures ranging from 10 to 15 °C, up to 2.2-log reductions in plate counts were observed when both pH and electric field were modified (pH from 6.8 to 5.7 and electric field from 20 to 55 kV/cm) (Vega-Mercado *et al.*, 1996b). The authors reported that the electric field and ionic strength are more likely to be related to the poration rate and physical damage of the cell membranes, and pH is related to changes in the cytoplasmic conditions due to the osmotic imbalance caused by the poration. In another study (Liu *et al.*, 1995), when the combination of antimicrobial organic acids and PEFs were assessed, a high killing effect in pure cultures of *E. coli* O157:H7 was observed. At pH 3.4 (but not at pHs above 6.4), benzoic and sorbic acids reduced the population by 5.6 and 4.2 logs, respectively, with PEF compared with 2.9–2.5 and 0.6–1.1 $\log_{10}$ by acid alone and 1.1–1.6 $\log_{10}$ with a single high-voltage pulse alone. On surfaces such as those of beef steaks, the combination of organic acid, particularly acetic acid, with pulsed power electricity is reported as being statistically more effective in reducing the population of *E. coli* O157:H7 rather than either acid or pulsed power electricity treatment alone (Tinney *et al.*, 1997). An additive response of a 4-$\log_{10}$ cycle reduction in simulated milk ultrafiltrate media was accomplished with around 1,000 IU/ml (7.15 uM) of nisin and three pulses of 11.25 kV/cm or 500 IU/ml (nisin) for five pulses of the same intensity alone (Terebiznik *et al.*, 2000). These studies demonstrate that PEFs can be considered as a hurdle which, when combined with additional factors such as pH, ionic strength, temperature and antimicrobial agents, can be effectively used in the inactivation of microorganisms.

High pressure can also be used to reduce the intensity of factors traditionally used to preserve foods. In fact, attainment of synergistic antimicrobial action depends on identifying the factors or treatments that could sensitize microorganisms to pressure (Cheftel, 1995) or that could cause microbial death in sublethally pressure-injured microbial cells. Therefore, attempts have been made to inactivate *E. coli* using a combined pressure-temperature treatment. Bacterial cells are relatively less sensitive to hydrostatic pressure at 20–35 °C but more sensitive to pressurization above 35 °C, due to phase transition of membrane lipids (Kalchayanand *et al.*, 1998a and b). Synergy between hydrostatic pressure and several factors such as pressurization time and temperature, suspending media, and the presence of antimicrobial substances has been demonstrated (Kalchayanand *et al.*, 1998a and 1998b; Benito *et al.*, 1999).

The use of high pressure in combination with mild heat is promising (Patterson, *et al.*, 1995a). This strategy is successful because there is evidence that microbial injury can occur at significantly lower pressures than that required for inactivation (Patterson *et al.*, 1995b). *E. coli* cells surviving pressurization become sublethally injured and develop sensitivity to physical and chemical environments to which the normal cells are resistant (Kalchayanand *et al.*, 1998a; Hauben *et al.*, 1996). This suggests that exposing *E. coli* to a combination of different intervention strategies renders the bacterium sublethally injured and serves as an effective food preservation method. Hauben *et al.* (1996) assessed the destruction and sublethal injury of *E. coli* by hydrostatic pressure and by combinations of high pressure treatments with lysozyme, nisin, and/or EDTA. High pressure treatments (180 to 320 MPa) disrupt the bacterial cells outer membrane, causing periplasmic leakage and sensitization to lysozyme, nisin, and EDTA.

A 15-min treatment of 400 MPa at 50 °C resulted in approximately a 6.0-$\log_{10}$ reduction in CFU/g in poultry meat and a 5.0-$\log_{10}$ reduction in UHT milk, while only a $< 1$-$\log_{10}$ reduction was achieved by either treatment alone (Patterson and Kilpatrick, 1998). When *E. coli* O157:H7 cells were suspended in peptone solution and exposed to combination treatments of hydrostatic pressure (138 to 345 MPa), time (5 to 15 min), temperature (25 to 50 °C), and pediocin AcH (3,000 AU/ml), cell death increased as pressure, time and temperature increased; however, the cells developed proportionately greater sensitivity as the pressure increased to 276 MPa and higher and temperature increased above 35 °C ( Kalchayanand *et al.*, 1998b). These authors reported that an 8-$\log_{10}$ cycle viability loss could be achieved only when pediocin AcH was included during pressurization. The bactericidal effect of high pressure can be increased with heat, low pH, carbon dioxide, organic acids, and bacteriocins such as nisin (Mertens and Deplace, 1993). Sonoike (1992) studied the combined effect of various temperatures (0 to 60 °C) and pressures (0.01 to 400 MPa) on the inactivation of *E. coli* JCM 1649. They reported that death rates decreased with rising temperatures under a high pressure and that contours of constant death rates on the pressure-temperature plane were elliptical and similar to those of the free-energy difference for pressure-temperature-reversible denaturation of proteins.

To determine the conditions that would give a 6-$\log_{10}$ inactivation of *E. coli* O157:H7 in orange juice, Linton *et al.* (1999) investigated the combined effect of high pressure (400, 500, and 550 MPa) and temperature (20 and 30 °C) on the survival of *E. coli* O157:H7 in orange juice in the pH range of 3.4–5.0. In this study, a pressure treatment of 550 MPa for 5 min at 20 °C produced this level of kill at pH up to 4.5 but not at pH 5.0. Combining pressure treatment with mild heat (30 °C) did result in a 6–$\log_{10}$ inactivation at pH 5.0. Thus, time and temperature combination treatments play a significant role when pressure-treating orange juice to ensure microbiological safety.

Pressure has also been combined with other intervention technologies to achieve enhanced reduction of *E. coli*. Combined high pressure treatment and alternating current (AC) induced lethal damage to *E. coli*. Shimada (1992) subjected *E. coli* cells to 300 MPa for 10 min immediately after AC exposure at 0.6 A/cm$^2$ at 35 °C for 2 h and reported significant reductions of surviving fractions. Exposure of *E. coli* cells to an AC of 50 Hz caused the release of intracellular materials, causing a decrease in the resistance to basic dyes (Shimada and Shimahara, 1985; 1987). This was believed to result from loss and/or denaturation of cellular components responsible for normal function of the cell membrane, suggesting that the lethal damage to a microorganism may be enhanced when the organisms are exposed to AC before or after the pressure treatment. Shimada (1992) has also reported that the combined treatment also rendered the cells more sensitive to antimicrobial chemicals, suggesting that the combined use of pressure and AC also lowers the tolerance level of microorganism to other challenges.

## 11.6    Conclusions and future trends

Technologies employing combinations of existing and new preservation techniques to establish a series of preservative factors that microorganisms are unable to overcome are valuable tools and have enormous potential to improve the microbiological safety of minimally processed foods. The microorganism's physiological responses during food preservation are the basis for the application of these technologies. While microbial stress responses further complicate food preservation, the crucial phenomenon of food preservation is the homeostasis of microorganisms. Preservative factors functioning as hurdles can disturb one or more homeostasis mechanisms, thereby preventing microorganisms from multiplying and causing them to remain inactive or even die. Food preservation is in fact achieved by disturbing the homeostasis of microorganisms in foods, and the best way to do this is to deliberately disturb several of the homeostasis mechanisms simultaneously. This multi-targeted approach is the essence of combination preservation/intervention strategies. It allows the use of different preservative factors of low intensity, which not only have a minimal effect on the desirable organoleptic attributes of food but also are likely to act synergistically. Nevertheless, use of such technologies relies heavily on detailed knowledge of the effects of preservative factors individually or in combination, as well as on factors or processes that interfere with these effects. While much research in this field has been performed, many key issues still need to be addressed for combination preservation factors or technologies to be useful in the food industry to meet public demands for foods with enhanced safety, freshness and appeal. Published literature on microbial responses to multiple stresses and the interaction between stress factors and the food matrix is woefully lacking. Further studies on stress responses should increase our understanding of the microbiology of food systems and enhance the safety and quality of our food supply. A particular need is to conduct studies aimed at providing insight into the physiological and molecular mechanisms of microbial inactivation, microbial homeostasis mechanisms, stress responses and associated enhanced virulence, and pathogen emergence and interactions with food production processes, to assist in identifying potential new approaches concerning multiple factors and/or technologies for the safer production of foods.

For the purpose of identifying critical control points, developing intervention strategies, and constructing accurate models for risk assessments, research efforts should be aimed at gaining knowledge on strain-to-strain variations within bacterial species concerning their growth and resistance kinetics in food formulated with multiple variables. Emphasis should be on the use of molecular biology to understand the responses of food pathogens to food environments, including the role of signaling molecules produced by pathogenic and spoilage bacteria in food on the regulation of growth, survival, and virulence of pathogens. It would be logical to construct strains of a particular pathogen that possess mutations in single genes involved in specific and general stress responses, and then evaluate these mutants for their survival following application of combination techniques. Approaches relying on the tools of genomics and proteomics should lead to new understandings of physiological responses of pathogens in complex food ecosystems. This information will provide the basis for the more effective control strategies for bacterial pathogens. With certain pathogens, such as *E. coli* O157:H7, that are declared as an adulterant and with concerns associated with individuals susceptible to low infectious doses, research efforts should be focused on developing technologies that not only reduce or inhibit pathogens, but that destroy or eliminate pathogenic organisms to ensure a safer global food supply.

In terms of single and combined processes, current knowledge on the growth limits of *E. coli* is adequate, though primarily pragmatically and not systematically acquired. Accordingly, quantitative knowledge of the factors in food systems that interact and influence inactivation kinetics are required to estimate accurately how a particular pathogen is likely to behave in a specific food. There is a need for a better understanding of how interactions among preservation variables can be used for predicting the safety of minimally processed, ready-to-eat foods. The future of combined preservation processes for the production of stable and safe foods will be likely to rely on predictive growth, survival, and inactivation kinetics modeling. Synergistic effects of emerging technologies, in combination with complex multifactorial experiments and analyses to quantify the efficacy of both intrinsic and extrinsic factors such as prior history of pathogens, storage conditions, and potential temperature abuse, etc., as well as the development of 'enhanced' predictive models, are warranted to ensure the microbiological safety of minimally processed foods. Since the interactive effects of a number of factors are not always predictable, appropriately designed microbiological challenge tests must be conducted and should play an important role in the validation of processes and to verify that a specific process is in compliance with pre-determined performance standards.

In view of the continued interest that exists in employing milder preservation techniques and reducing levels of antimicrobials, it would be logical to define a specific lethality at low temperatures. It would be useful to determine the possible effects of injury to bacterial cells, that may result from mild physical treatments and factors in foods that influence the recovery of cells exposed to these low intervention techniques.

To summarize, as a result of the systematic study of the homeostasis mechanisms and stress responses of microorganisms together with the determination of the combined efficacy of multiple factors, including novel preservatives and technologies in real food systems, much more sophisticated combination strategies will emerge, resulting in new intervention approaches, processes, and products. The overall goal is to identify potential new approaches for the safer production of foods and to provide consumers with high quality ready-to-eat, processed foods, which are free of deadly pathogens, such as *E. coli* O157:H7, that are highly virulent for individuals susceptible to low infectious doses.

## 11.7   References

ABDUL-RAOUF, U. M., L. R. BEUCHAT and M. S. AMMAR. 1993. Survival and growth of *Escherichia coli* O157:H7 in ground roasted beef as affected by pH, acidulants and temperature. *Appl Environ Microbiol* 59: 2364–8.

AHMED, M. N., D. E. CONNER and D. L. HUFFMAN. 1995. Heat-resistance of *Escherichia coli* O157:H7 in meat and poultry as affected by product composition. *J. Food Sci.* 60, 606–10.

AHMED, M. N. and D. E. CONNER. 1997. Heat inactivation of *Escherichia coli* O157:H7 in turkey meat as affected by sodium chloride, sodium lactate, polyphosphate, and fat content. *J. Food Protect.* 60, 898–902.

ALZAMORA, S. M. 1998. Application of combined factors technology in minimally processed foods, pp. 274–290. In *Sous-vide and Cook-chill processing for the Food Industry.* Ghazala, S. (Ed.). Aspen Publishers, Inc. Gaithersburg, MD.

ARCHER, D. 1996. Preservation microbiology and safety: evidence that stress enhances virulence and triggers adaptive mutations. *Trends Food Sci. Technol.* 7: 91–5.

AROCHA, M. M., M. MCVEY, S. D. LODER, J. H. RUPNOW and L. B. BULLERMAN. 1992. Behavior of hemorrhagic *Escherichia coli* O157:H7 during the manufacture of cottage cheese. *J. Food Protect.* 55: 379–91.

BENITO, A., G. VENTOURA, M. CASADEI, T. ROBINSON and B. MACKEY. 1999. Variation in resistance of natural isolates of Escherichia coli O157:H7 to high hydrostatic pressure, mild heat and other stresses. *Appl. Environ. Microbiol.* 65: 1564–9.

BESSER, R. E., S. M. LETT, J. T. WEBER, M. P. DOYLE, T. J. BARRETT and J. G. WELLS. 1993. An outbreak of diarrhea and hemolytic uremic syndrome from fresh-pressed apple cider. *JAMA* 269: 2217–20.

BLACKBURN, C. DE W., L. M. CURTIS, L. HUMPHESON, C. BILLON and P. J. MCCLURE. 1997. Development of thermal inactivation models for *Salmonella enteritidis* and *Escherichia coli* O157:H7 with temperature, pH and NaCl as controlling factors. *Intern. J. Food Microbiol.* 38, 31–44.

BOOTH, I. R. 1985. Regulation of cytoplasmic pH in bacteria. *Microbial Rev.* 49: 359–78.

BUCHANAN, R. L. and L. K. BAGI. 1994. Expansion of response surface models for growth of *Escherichia coli* O157:H7 to include sodium nitrite as a variable. *Int. J. Food Microbiol.* 23: 317–32.

BUCHANAN, R.L. and L. K. BAGI. 1997. Effect of water activity and humectant identity on the growth kinetics of *Escherichia coli* O157:H7. *Food Microbiol.* 14: 413–23.

BUCHANAN, R. L., L. K. BAGI, R. V. GOINS and J. D. PHILLIPS. 1993. Response surface models for the growth kinetics of *Escherichia coli* O157:H7. *Food Microbiol.* 10: 303–15.

BUCHANAN, R. L. and L. A. KLAWITTER. 1992. The effect of incubation temperature, initial pH, and sodium chloride on the growth kinetics of *Escherichia coli* O157:H7. *Food Microbiol.* 9: 185–96.

CASEY, P. G. and S. CONDON. 2002. Sodium chloride decreases the bacteriocidal effect of acid pH on *Escherichia coli* O157:H45. *Int. J. Food Microbiol.* 76: 199–206.

CHEFTEL, J. C. 1995. High-pressure, microbial inactivation and food preservation. *Food Sci. Technol. Int.* 1: 75-90.

CHEVILLE, A. M., K. W. ARNOLD, C. BUCHREISER, C. M. CHENG and C. W. KASPAR. 1996. rpoS regulation of acid, heat, and salt tolerance in *Escherichia coli* O157:H7. *Appl. Environ. Microbiol.* 62: 1822–4.

CLAVERO, M. R. S. and L. R. BEUCHAT. 1996. Survival of *Escherichia coli* O157:H7 in broth and processed salami as influenced by pH, water activity, and temperature and suitability of media for its recovery. *Appl. Environ. Microbiol.* 62: 2735–40.

CONNER, D. E. and J. S. KOTROLA. 1995. Growth and survival of *Escherichia coli* O157:H7 under acidic conditions. *Appl. Environ. Microbiol.* 61: 382–5.

DEV, V. J., M. MAIN and I. GOULD. 1991. Waterborne outbreak of *Escherichia coli* O157:H7. *Lancet* 337, 1412.

DOCK, L. L., J. D. FLORES and R. H. LINTON. 2000. Heat inactivation of *E. coli* O157:H7 in apple cider containing malic acid, sodium benzoate, and potassium sorbate. *J. Food Protect.* 63: 1026–31.

DOYLE, M. P. and J. L. SCHOENI. 1984. Survival and growth characteristics of *Escherichia coli* associated with hemorrhagic colitis. *Appl. Environ. Microbiol.* 48: 855–6.

ENTANI, E., M. ASAI, S. TSUJIHATA, Y. TSUKAMOTO and M. OHTA. 1997. Antibacterial action of vinegar against food-borne pathogenic bacteria including *Escherichia coli*

O157:H7 (Part 2). Effect of sodium chloride and temperature on bactericidal activity (in Japanese, with English abstract). *Kansenshogaku Zasshi* 71, 451–8.

FINKEL, S. E., E. R. ZINSER and R. KOLTER. 2000. Long-term survival and evolution in the stationary phase, p. 231–238. In G. Storz and E. Hengge-Aronis, eds., *Bacterial Stress Responses*. ASM Press, Washington, D.C.

GARREN, D. M., M. A. HARRISON, M. A. and S. M. RUSSELL. 1998. Acid tolerance and acid shock response of *Escherichia coli* O157:H7 and non-O157:H7 isolates provide cross protection to sodium lactate and sodium chloride. *J. Food Protect.* 61, 158–61.

GIBSON, A. M. and T. A. ROBERTS. 1986. The effect of pH, water activity, sodium nitrite and storage temperature on the growth of enteropathogenic *Escherichia coli* and *Salmonella* in a laboratory medium. *Int. J. Food Microbiol.* 3: 183–94.

GLASS, K. A., LOEFFELHOLZ, J. M., FORD, J. P. and DOYLE, M. P. 1992. Fate of *Escherichia coli* O157:H7 as affected by pH or sodium chloride and in fermented, dry sausage. *Appl. Environ. Microbiol.* 58: 2513–16.

GOULD, G. W. 1995. Homeostatic mechanisms during food preservation by combined methods. In: G. V. Barbosa-Canovas and J. Welti-Chanes, (Eds.), *Food Preservation by Moisture Control: Fundamentals and Applications*, Technomics Publishing, Lancaster, Pennsylvania, pp. 397–410.

GOULD, G. W. 1996. Industry perspective on the use of neutral antimicrobials and inhibitors for food applications. *J. Food protect. Suppl.*, pp. 82–6.

GRIFFIN, P. M. and R. V. TAUXE. 1991. The epidemiology of infections caused by *E. coli* O157:H7, other enterohemorhagic *E. Coli* and the associated hemolytic uremic syndrome. *Epidemiol. Rev.* 13: 60–91.

GURAYA, R., J. F. FRANK and A. N. HASSAN. 1998. Effectiveness of salt, pH and diacetyl as inhibitors for *Escherichia coli* O157:H7 in dairy foods stored at refrigeration temperatures. *J. Food Protect.* 61: 1098–102.

HAUBEN, K. J. A., E. Y. WUYTACK, C. F. SOONTJENS and C. W. MICHIELS. 1996. High-pressure transient sensitization of *Escherichia coli* to lysozyme and nisin by disruption of outer-membrane permeability. *J. Food Protect.* 59: 350–355.

HENGGE-ARONIS, R. 1993. Survival of hunger and stress: the role of *rpoS* in early stationary phase gene regulation in *E. coli. Cell.* 72: 165–168.

HURST, R. M., G. D. BETTS and R. G. EARNSHAW. 1995. The antimicrobial effect of power ultrasound. R&D Report No. 4, Chipping Campden, Glos. UK.

ICMSF, 1996. Intestinally pathogenic *E. coli. Microorganisms in Foods 5*. Chapman & Hall, London, UK, pp. 126–140.

JACKSON, C. J., HARDIN, M. D. and ACUFF, G. R. 1996. Heat resistance of *Escherichia coli* O157:H7 in a nutrient medium and in ground beef patties as influenced by storage and holding temperatures. *J. Food Protect.* 59, 230–237.

JUNEJA, V. K., O. P. SNYDER, JR and B. S. MARMER. 1997. Thermal destruction of *Escherichia coli* O157:H7 in beef and chicken: Determination of D- and z-values. *Int. J. Food Microbiol.* 35: 231–237.

JUNEJA, V. K., B. S. MARMER and B. S. EBLEN. 1999. Predictive model for the combined effect of temperature, PH, sodium chloride, and sodium pyrophosphate on the heat resistance of *Escherichia coli* O157:H7. *J. Food Safety.* 19: 147–160.

KALCHAYANAND, N., SIKES, T., DUNNE, C. P. and RAY, B. 1998a. Factors influencing death and injury of foodborne pathogens by hydrostatic pressure-pasteurization. *Food Microbiol.* 15: 207–14.

KALCHAYANAND, N., SIKES, T., DUNNE, C.P. and RAY, B. 1998b. Interaction of hydrostatic pressure, time and temperature of pressurization and pediocin AcH on inactivation of foodborne bacteria. *J. Food Protect.* 61: 425–431.

KOTROLA, J. S. and D. E. CONNER. 1997. Heat inactivation of *Escherichia coli* O157:H7 in turkey meat as affected by sodium chloride, sodium lactate, polyphosphate and fat content. *J Food Protect.* 60: 898–902.

KNORR, D. 1995. New developments in non-thermal food processing. IFT Annual Meeting: Book of abstracts. pp. 187.

LEYER, G. J., L. L.WANG and E. J. JOHNSON. 1995. Acid adaptation of *Escherichia coli* O157:H7 increases survival in acidic foods. *Appl. Environ. Microbiol.* 61: 3752–3755.

LEISTNER, L. 1995. Principles and applications of hurdle technology, pp. 1–21. In G. W. Gould, ed., *New Methods in Food Preservation*, Blackie Academic & Professional.

LEISTNER, L. and L. M. G. GORRIS. 1995. Food preservation by hurdle technology. *Trends Food Sci. Technol.* 6: 35–67.

LIN, J., M. P. SMITH, K. C. CHAPIN, H. S. BAIK, G. N. BENNETT and J. W. FOSTER. 1996. Mechanisms of acid resistance in enterohemorrhagic *Escherichia coli*. *Appl. Environ. Microbiol.* 62: 3094–3100.

LINE, J. E., A. R. FAIN, A. B. MOGAN, L. M. MARTIN, R. V. LECHOWICH, J. M. CAROSELLA and W. L. BROWN. 1991. Lethality of heat to *Escherichia coli* O157:H7: D-value and z-value determination in ground beef. *J. Food Protect.* 54: 762–766.

LINTON, M., J. M. MCCLEMENTS and M. F. PATTERSON. 1999. Inactivation of Escherichia coli O157:H7 in orange juice using a combination of high pressure and mild heat. *J. Food Protect.* 62: 277–279.

LIU, X., A. E. YOUSEF and G. W. CHISM. 1995. Inactivation of *Escherichia coli* O157:H7 by the combination of antimicrobial organic acids and pulsed electric fields, *1995 IFT Annual Meeting: Book of Abstracts*, p. 29.

MCKELLAR, R. C. and K. P. KNIGHT. 1999. Growth and survival of various strains of enterohemorrhagic *Escherichia coli* in hydrochloric and acetic acid. *J. Food Protect.* 62: 1466–1469.

MCKELLAR, R. C. and X. LU. 2001. A probability of growth model for *E. coli* O157:H7 as a function of temperature, pH, acetic acid, and salt. *J. Food Protect.* 64: 1922–1928.

MEAD, P. S., L. SLUTSKER, V. DIETZ, L. F. MCCAIG, J. S. BRESEE, C. SHAPIRO, P. M. GRIFFIN and R. V. TAUXE. 1999. Food-related illness and death in the United States. *Emerg. Infect. Dis.* 5: 607-625.

MERTENS, B. and G. DEPLACE. 1993. Engineering aspects of high pressure technology in the food industry. *Food Technol.* 47(6): 164–169.

MILLER, L. G. and C. W. KASPAR. 1994. *Escherichia coli* O157:H7 acid tolerance and survival in apple cider. *J. Food Protect.* 57: 460–464.

PALUMBO, S. A., J. E. CALL, F. J. SCHULTZ and A. C. WILLIAMS. 1995. Minimum and maximum temperatures for growth and verotoxin production by hemorrhagic strains of *Escherichia coli*. *J. Food Protect.* 58: 352–356.

PATTERSON, M. F. and D. J. KILPATRICK. 1998. The combined effect of high hydrostatic pressure and mild heat on inactivation of pathogens in milk and poultry. *J. Food Protect.* 61: 432–436.

PATTERSON, M. F., M. QUINN, R. SIMPSON and A. GILMOUR. 1995a. Effects of high pressure on vegetative pathogens, *High Pressure Processing of Foods* (D. A. Ledward, D. E. Johnston, R. G. Earnshaw, and A. P. M. Hasting, eds.), Nottingham University Press, Nottingham, pp. 47–64.

PATTERSON, M. F., M. QUINN, R. SIMPSON and A. GILMOUR. 1995b. Sensitivity of vegetative pathogens to high hydrostatic pressure in phosphate-buffered saline and foods. *J. Food Protect.* 58: 524–529.

PRESSER, K. A. D. A. RATKOWSKY and T. ROSS. 1997. Modelling the growth of *Escherichia coli* as a function of pH and lactic acid concentration. *Appl. Environ. Microbiol.* 63: 2355–2369.

PRESSER, K. A., T. ROSS and D. A. RATKOWSKY. 1998. Modelling the growth limits (growth/ no growth interface) of *E. coli* as a function of temperature, pH, lactic acid concentration and water activity. *Appl. Environ. Microbiol.* 64: 1773–1779.

RAGHUBEER, R. V., J. S KE, M. L. CAMPBELL and R. S. MEYER. 1995. Fate of *Escherichia coli* O157:H7 and other coliforms in commercial mayonnaise and refrigerated salad dressing. *J. Food Protect.* 58: 13–18.

RAJKOWSKI, K. T. and B. S. MARMER. 1995. Growth of *Escherichia coli* O157:H7 at fluctuating incubation temperatures. *J. Food Protect.* 58: 1307–1313.

REICHART, O. 1994. Modeling the destruction of *Escherichia coli* on the base of reaction kinetics. *Int. J. Food Microbiol.* 23: 449–465.

REICHART, O. and MOHACSI-FARKAS, C. 1994. Mathematical modeling of the combined effect of water activity, pH and redox potential on the heat destruction. *Int. J. Food Microbiol.* 24, 103–112.

REITSMA, C. J. and HENNING, D. R. 1996. Survival of enterohemorrhagic *Escherichia coli* O157:H7 during the manufacture and curing of Cheddar cheese. *J. Food Protect.* 59: 460–464.

RIONDET, C., R. CACHON, Y. WACHE, G. ALCARAZ and C. DIVIES. 1999. Changes in the proton motive force in *E. coli* in response to external oxidoreduction potential. *Eur. J. Biochem.* 262: 595–599.

RIONDET, C., R. CACHON, Y. WACHE, E. SUNYOL, I. BERT, P. GBAUIDI, G. ALCARAZ and C. DIVIES. 2000. Combined action of redox potential and pH on heat resistance and growth recovery of sublethally heat damaged *E. coli. Appl Microbiol. Biotechnol.* 53: 476–479.

ROWBURY, R. J. 1995. An assessment of environmental factors influencing acid tolerance and sensitivity in *Escherichia coli, Salmonella* spp. and other enterobacteria. *Lett. Appl. Microbiol.* 20: 333–337.

ROWBURY, R. J., M. GOODSON and T. J. HUMPHREY. 1994. Sodium chloride induces an NhaA/ NhaR-independent acid sensitivity at neutral external pH in *Escherichia coli. Appl. Environ. Microbiol.* 60, 1630–1634.

ROWBURY, R. J., M. GOODSON, Z. LAZIM and T. J. HUMPHREY. 1996a. Sensitization to acid induced by sodium ions in *Escherichia coli*: dependence on (p)ppGpp and cAMP and suppression of the *relA*-associated defect by mutations in *envZ. Microbios* 85, 161–177.

ROWBURY, R. J., Z. LAZIM and M. GOODSON. 1996b. Regulatory aspects of alkali tolerance induction in *Escherichia coli. Lett. Appl. Microbiol.* 22: 429–432.

ROWEN, N. J. 1999. Evidence that inimical food-preservation barriers alter microbial resistance, cell morphology, and virulence. *Trends Food Sci. Technol.* 10: 261–270.

RYU, J.-H. and L. R. BEUCHAT, 1998. Influence of acid tolerance responses on survival, growth, and thermal cross-protection of *Escherichia coli* O157:H7 in acidified media and fruit juices. *Int. J. Food Microbiol.* 45, 185–193.

RYU, J. H., Y. DENG and L. R. BEUCHAT. 1999. Survival of *Escherichia coli* O157:H7 in dried beef powder as affected by water activity, sodium chloride content and temperature. *Food Microbiol.* 16: 309–316.

SALTER, M. A., D. A. RATKOWSKY, T. ROSS and T. A. MCMEEKIN. 2000. Modelling the combined temperature and salt (NaCl) limits for growth of a pathogenic *E. coli* strain using nonlinear logistic regression. *Int. J. Food Microbiol.* 61: 159–167.

SEMANCHEK J. J. and GOLDEN D. A. 1996. Survival of *Escherichia coli* O157:H7 during fermentation of apple cider. *J. Food Protect.* 59: 1256–1259.

SHIMADA, K. 1992. Effect of combination treatment with high pressure and alternating current on the lethal damage of *Escherichia coli* cells and *Bacillus subtilis* spores, in *High Pressure and Biotechnology*, Balny, C. *et al.*, eds., London: John Libbey and Co., Ltd., 49–51.

SHIMADA, K. and SHIMAHARA, K. 1985, Leakage of cellular contents and morphological changes in resting *Escherichia coli* B cells exposed to an alternating current. *Agr. Biol. Chem.*, 49: 3605–3607.

SHIMADA, K. and SHIMAHARA, K. 1987, Effect of alternating current exposure on the resistivity of resting *Escherichia coli* B cells to crystal violet and other basic dyes. *J. Appl. Bacteriol.*, 62: 261–268.

SONOIKE, K. 1992. Effect of pressure and temperature on the death rates of *Lactobacillus casei* and *Escherichia coli*, in *High Pressure and Biotechnology*, Balny, C. *et al.*, eds., London: John Libbey and Co., Ltd., 297–301.

SPERBER, W.H. 1983. Influence of water activity on foodborne bacteria – a review. *J. Food Protect.* 46: 142–150.

SPLITTSTOESSER, D. F., M. R. MCLELLAN and J. J. CHUREY. 1996. Heat resistance of Escherichia coli O157:H7 in apple juice. *J. Food Protect.* 59, 226–229.

SUTHERLAND, J. P., A. J. BAYLISS and D. S. BRAXTON. 1995. Predictive modeling of growth of *Escherichia coli* O157:H7: the effects of temperature, pH and sodium chloride. *Int. J. Food Microbiol.* 25: 29–49.

TEO, Y., T. J. RAYNOR, K. R. ELLAJOSYULA and S. J. KNABEL. 1996. Synergistic effect of high temperature and high pH on the destruction of *Salmonella enteritidis* and *Escherichia coli* O157:H7. *J. Food Protect.* 59: 1023–1030.

TEREBIZNIK, M. R., R. J. JAGUS, P. CERRUTTI, M. S. HUERGO and A. M. PILOSOF. 2000. Combined effect of nisin and pulsed electric fields on the inactivation of Escherichia coli. *J. Food Protect.* 63: 741–746.

TINNEY, K. S., M. F. MILLER, C. B. RAMSEY, L. D. THOMPSON and M. A. CARR. 1997. Reduction of microorganisms on beef surfaces with electricity and acetic acid. *J. Food Protect.* 60: 625–628.

TOMICKA, A., J. CHEN, S. BARBUT and M. W. GRIFFITHS. 1997. Survival of bioluminescent *Escherichia coli* O157:7 in a model system representing fermented sausage production. *J. Food Protect.* 60: 1487–1492.

TSAI, S. H. and C. C. CHOU. 1996. Injury, inhibition and inactivation of *Escherichia coli* O157:H7 by potassium sorbate and sodium nitrite as affected by pH and temperature. *J. Sci. Food Agric.* 71: 10–12.

TSAI, Y. W. and S. C. INGHAM. 1997. Survival of *Escherichia coli* O157:H7 and *Salmonella* spp. in acidic condiments. *J. Food Protect.* 60: 751–755.

ULJAS, H. E., D. W. SCHAFFNER, S. DUFFY, L. ZHAO and S. C. INGHAM. 2001. Modeling of combined processing steps for reducing *Escherichia coli* O157:H7 populations in apple cider. *Appl. Environ. Microbiol.* 67: 133–41.

UYTTENDAELE, M., I. TAVERNIERS and J. DEBEVERE. 2001. Effect of stress induced by suboptimal growth factors on survival of *Escherichia coli* O157:H7. *Intern. J. Food Microbiol.* 66: 31–7.

VEGA-MERCADO, H., O. MARTIN-BELLOSO, F.-J. CHANG, G. V. BARBOSA-CÁNOVAS and B. G.

SWANSON. 1996a. Inactivation of *Escherichia coli* and *Bacillus subtilis* suspended in pea soup using pulsed electric fields. *J. Food Process. Preserv.* 20: 501–10.

VEGA-MERCADO, H., U. R. POTHAKAMURY, F.-J. CHANG, G. V. BARBOSA-CÁNOVAS and B. G. SWANSON. 1996b. Inactivation of *Escherichia coli* by combining pH, ionic strength and pulsed electric fields hurdles. *Food Res. Int.* 29: 117–21.

WEAGNANT, S. D., J. L. BRYANT and D. H. BARK. 1994. Survival of *Escherichia coli* O157:H7 in mayonnaise and mayonnaise-based sauces at room and refrigerated temperatures. *J. Food Protect.* 57: 629–31.

WRIGLEY, D. M. and N. G. LLORCA. 1992. Decrease of Salmonella typhimurium in skim milk and egg by heat and ultrasonic wave treatment. *J. Food Protect.* 55: 678–80.

YURA, T., T. TOBE, K. ITO and T. OSAWA. 1984. Heat shock regulatory gene (*htpR*) of *Escherichia coli* is required for growth at high temperature but is dispensable at low temperature. *Proc. Natl. Acad. Sci.* (USA) 81: 6803–7.

ZHAO, T., M. P. DOYLE and R. BESSER. 1993. Fate of enterohemorrhagic *Escherichia coli* O157:H7 in apple cider with and without preservatives. *Appl. Environ. Microbiol.* 59: 2526–30.

# 12

# Developments in freezing

C. Kennedy, NutriFreeze Ltd, UK

## 12.1  Introduction

One of the key issues in maintaining the shelf-life and other quality attributes of frozen foods is ice crystallisation. Quality changes during the freezing process are related to the way in which ice crystals are made to grow (Kennedy, 1998). Typically, if plant or animal tissue is cooled, ice crystals will initially form on the surface. The way in which ice growth continues from this point depends largely on the rate at which heat is extracted from the freezing product. If the product is cooled slowly then the initial ice crystals continue to grow into the intercellular tissue. As they do so, the concentration of the unfrozen solution outside the cells increases, drawing water out of the cells by osmosis. This water in turn is added to the growing ice crystals. The net result is shrunken cells and a few large ice crystals which have grown between the cells, causing maximum disruption to the structure. If we cool at a faster rate then heat is removed ahead of the growing ice crystals and new nucleation sites can be found. This leads to more ice crystals being formed of a smaller average size and less shrinking of the cells. This has been shown to reduce the degree of freeze damage as it causes smaller changes to texture and less loss of nutrients through drip on thawing. The combination of rapid freezing and slow thawing also kills more bacteria (Bogh-Sorensen, 2000). This chapter looks at a range of developments in freezing, many of which exploit the benefits of rapid freezing on product quality. It also considers techniques which control other characteristics such as water activity and glass transitions to stabilise food products more effectively. A detailed review of advances in refrigeration is provided by Sun (2001).

## 12.2    Pre-treatments

During freezing and frozen storage, water contributes to cell rupture on a food and provides a medium for accelerating and spreading deterioration reactions. Water can also participate directly in deterioration reactions, including production of off-flavours and changes in colour due to enzymatic or non-enzymatic reactions (especially browning). The use of pre-freeze treatments can help, either by inactivating deterioration reactions directly or by reducing the water content in the material which facilitates these reactions. Conventional pre-treatments include washing, blanching and soaking, and treatments such as comminuting, coating, grinding and packaging. Currently there is renewed interest in implementing partial dehydration and formulation stages prior to freezing (Torreggiani *et al.*, 2000). Partial dehydration is generally achieved by air drying. The resulting process is termed dehydrofreezing. The advantages over conventional freezing include:

- energy savings, since the water load to the freezer is reduced, as well as transport, storage and packaging costs
- better quality and stability (colour, flavour), as well as thawing behaviour (lower drip loss) (Lazar, 1968; Huxsoll, 1982).

Partial air drying produces food ingredients with high water activity ($a_w > 0.96$), since water removal is limited to 50–60% of the original content. To avoid browning during air drying, blanching or other treatments such as dipping in antioxidant solutions (such as ascorbic or citric acid, or sulphur dioxide) can be used (Giangiacomo *et al.*, 1994).

Conventional air drying can be substituted by (or combined with) osmotic dehydration as a pre-freeze treatment. This process involves placing the solid food (whole or in pieces) into solutions of high sugar or salt concentration (FAIR, 1998). Le Maguer (1988), Raoult-Wack *et al.* (1992), Torreggiani (1993), Raoult-Wack (1994) and Lazarides *et al.* (1999) have reviewed the basic principles, modelling and specific applications of osmotic dehydration for fruit and vegetables. The main feature of osmotic pre-freeze treatment is the penetration of solutes into the food material. It is possible to adapt the functional properties of the dehydrofrozen fruit by:

- adjusting the physico-chemical composition of food through reducing water content, or adding water activity lowering agents;
- incorporating ingredients or additives with antioxidant, or other preservative properties (herbs, spices, sugars, ascorbic acid, sulphur dioxide, etc.) into the food prior to freezing (Saurel, 2002);
- adding solutes with nutritional, health or sensory benefits (Fito *et al.*, 2001).

The incorporation of different sugars into, for example, kiwi fruit slices modified their low temperature phase transitions, and significantly influenced chlorophyll stability during storage at $-10\,^{\circ}C$ (Torreggiani *et al.*, 1993). The technique also increased colour and vitamin C retention in osmodehydrofrozen apricot cubes

(Forni *et al.*, 1997) and anthocyanin stability in osmodehydrofrozen strawberry and cherry (Forni *et al.*, 1998; Torreggiani *et al.*, 1997). Osmotic dehydration has benefited from the development of vacuum infusion technology which both increases solute penetration and water extraction (Saurel, 2002). As an example, Matringe *et al.* (1999) used vacuum technology to introduce gelling hydrocolloids into fresh apple before freezing, significantly improving the texture on defrosting. Similar applications for fruit are described by Barat *et al.* (2000), Chafer *et al.* (2000), Moreno *et al.* (2000) and Chiralt *et al.* (2001).

The use of techniques such as dehydrofreezing and osmotic dehydration has also been extended by research into glass transitions in frozen foods. As a food freezes, the water molecules separate out into pure ice and an increasingly concentrated solution. If this solution contains large carbohydrate molecules, and if the solutes do not themselves crystallise, there is the possibility that at a specific, concentration-dependent temperature (the glass transition temperature), they will become locked together to form a glass (Oliveira *et al.*, 1999). Once the glass has formed, the mobility of the molecules is greatly reduced. This transition then will reduce the biochemical processes that cause deterioration of frozen foods by limiting the ability of the reactants to come in contact with each other.

Figure 12.1 shows a simplified phase diagram for the cooling of such an aqueous solution. Starting at point A the solution is cooled to the melting point B and then after a short period of supercooling to point C, ice formation begins.

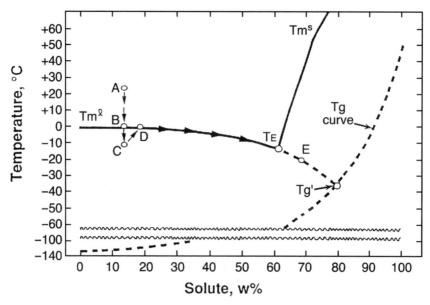

**Fig. 12.1**  Simplified phase diagram showing the glass transition for an aqueous binary system (see text for explanation).

**Table 12.1**   Glass transition temperature for some typical foodstuffs

| Food | $T_g'$ (°C) | | Food | $T_g'$ (°C) |
|---|---|---|---|---|
| *Fruit Juices* | | | *Fish* | |
| Orange | −37.5 | | Cod (81% water) | ca −77 |
| Pineapple | −37 | | Beef muscle | ca −60 |
| Pear | −40 | | | |
| Apple | −40 | | *Vegetables* | |
| Prune | −41 | | Sweetcorn | −15 |
| White Grape | −42 | | Potato, Russet Burbank | −12 |
| Lemon | −43 | | Cauliflower, stalk | −25 |
| | | | Peas | −25 |
| *Fruits, fresh* | | | Carrot | −26 |
| Strawberry | | | Green beans | −27 |
| Sparkleberry, centre | Centre | −41 | Broccoli, stalk | −27 |
| | Edge | −39 and | Broccoli, head | −12 |
| | | −33 | Spinach | −17 |
| Other cultivars | | −33 and | | |
| | | −41 | | |
| Blueberry, flesh | −41 | | *Frozen Desserts* | |
| Peach | −36 | | Ice cream | |
| Banana | −35 | | 3 commercial brands | −31 to −37 |
| Apple | −41 to −42 | | Ice milk | −30 |
| Tomato | −41 | | | |
| Cheese | | | | |
| Cheddar | −24 | | | |
| Provolone | −13 | | | |
| Cream cheese | −33 | | | |

The ice forms as pure water ice so that the remaining solution becomes increasingly concentrated. The composition of the unfrozen concentrated phase then follows the solubility curve as it is cooled to the eutectic temperature, $T_E$. At this point we might expect the concentrated phase to also solidify, however when reducing temperature at any reasonable speed we in fact see that the cooling and freeze concentration may continue, due to lack of nucleation in this phase, until we meet the glass transition curve at $T_g'$. Listed in Table 12.1 are the glass transition temperatures of a number of foods.

If foods can be formulated or infused with carbohydrates the glass transition temperature is raised and, if raised above the storage temperature, the stability and shelf-life of the products can be increased. Typical carbohydrates which have been shown to raise the glass transition temperature of foods include sucrose, fructose and maltodextrin. These carbohydrates have found use in the formulation of products such as ice cream to bring the glass transition up to the storage temperature. Products such as surimi which have a limited storage life at −20 °C are now transported at lower temperatures (−60 °C) in order to take them below their glass transition temperature (Zaritzky, 2000).

## 12.3   Developments in conventional freezer technology

Impingement technologies are being used to increase heat transfer during freezing (Newman, 2001). Impingement heat transfer is typically 3–5 times that of a conventional tunnel utilising axial flow fans. The increased heat transfer is achieved by forcing air at high velocity to impinge on the food perpendicular to the food surface. This breaks up the boundary layer of air, which would normally provide some insulation to the food when air is blown tangentially across the surface. With the increased overall heat transfer coefficient, it is possible to increase the freezing temperature or overall cryogen efficiency, or continue to run at very cold temperatures and dramatically increase the overall production rate. Impingement freezing is best suited for products with high surface area to weight ratios, for example hamburger patties. Testing has shown that thin products freeze most effectively in an impingement heat transfer environment (James and James, 2002). This is because in thin products the removal of heat is limited by heat transfer at the surface. As we go to larger products however the limiting factor increasingly becomes the conduction of heat across the product itself from the core to the surface. The process is also very attractive for products that require very rapid surface freezing and chilling.

Attempts have also been made to reduce cooling times by increasing the surface heat transfer coefficient, for example, by using radiative plates in conjunction with blast air (Gerosimov and Rumyanstev, 1972). The utilisation of a dynamic dispersion medium (DDM) as cooling medium has also been proposed as a way for intensifying air-blast freezing of foodstuffs (Ditchev and Richardson, 1999). However, most accelerated chilling systems rely on the maintenance of very low temperatures ($-15$ to $-70\,^{\circ}\text{C}$) during the initial stages of the chilling process. This can be achieved either by powerful mechnical refrigeration plant (Kerens, 1983; Union International Consultants, 1984) or by cryogenic liquids (Kerens, 1983; Bowling et al., 1987). Despite the considerable number of trials that have taken place and the cost advantages shown in feasibility studies (Bowater, 2001), few rapid-chilling commercial systems exist.

The potential benefits of more rapid freezing have led to increased interest in cryogenic techniques. Cryogenic freezing uses refrigerants, such as liquid nitrogen or solid carbon dioxide, directly. Owing to very low operating temperatures and high surface heat transfer coefficients between product and medium, cooling rates of cryogenic systems are often substantially higher than other refrigeration systems (Miller, 1998; Fellows, 2000). Cryogenic freezing is mainly used for small products such as burgers or ready meals. The most common method is by direct spraying of liquid nitrogen onto a food product while it is conveyed through an insulated tunnel. Most cryogenic tunnels have a single refrigerant spray zone, near the point where the product leaves the tunnel, and one or more gas transfer fans to move the cold gas along the tunnel to the product inlet. Newer designs have multiple liquid nitrogen spray zones, providing better control and eliminating the need for gas transfer fans. Increasing the distance between the fans and the products also provides a more uniform gas flow. These improvements give maximum heat transfer coefficients of 120 W/m$^2$K – up to twice the value for a standard cryogenic tunnel (Miller and Butcher, 2000).

Immersion chilling and freezing (ICF) is similar to osmotic dehydration in that both involve direct contact between food pieces and a concentrated solution. Solutions comprising 23% sodium chloride or 40% ethanol allow operating temperatures as low as $-20\,°C$ and $-30\,°C$ respectively (Lucas and Raoult-Wack, 1998). The ICF process offers numerous advantages that make it an interesting alternative to conventional freezing techniques; rapid heat transfer and lower operating and investment costs. The freezing time of small fruits and vegetables (from $0\,°C$ to $-7\,°C$) can be reduced by a factor of 4 to 7 when using ICF instead of air-blast freezing. Quick freezing preserves the texture of fruit and vegetable tissues more successfully and causes less dehydration during the freezing process. However, the ICF process has not been developed on an industrial scale, mainly because of an inadequate control of mass transfer (water and solutes) between the product and the refrigerating solution. Industrial applications remain centred on sodium chloride solutions used with products such as fish. However, the process is being developed for a wide range of fruit and vegetable products (Torreggiani et al., 2000).

Conventional freezing technologies are also being optimised through the increased use of modelling techniques (Pham, 2001). A number of models have been developed for meat chilling and thawing which are designed to optimise process efficiency or product qualities such as tenderness (Mallikarjunan and Mittal, 1994; Pham and Lovatt, 1996; Ditchev and Richardson, 1999). More recently, there have been developments in multi-objective optimisation techniques using evolutionary algorithms, which would be ideal for food refrigeration processes where weight loss, tenderness, microbial growth and other factors must be optimised simultaneously (Zitzler et al., 2000).

## 12.4    The use of pressure in freezing

This section discusses the following emerging technologies which exploit the effects of pressure on freezing:

- pressure shift freezing
- vacuum cooling
- the use of ultrasound.

The phase change temperature of water decreases when atmospheric pressure is increased. This phenomenon can be used to achieve rapid thawing or freezing of foods such as meat which contain a significant amount of water (Lamballerie-Anton et al., 2002). As has been noted, slow freezing results in larger ice crystals which generally damage the texture of the food, whereas a rapid freezing rate usually preserves food texture (Sanz et al., 1999). Rapid freezing of meat using high pressure can be achieved by cooling at $-20\,°C$ and 2 Kbar. In these conditions water remains in the liquid state. Upon release of pressure, instantaneous and homogeneous crystallisation occurs with formation of very small ice crystals. This method has been shown to improve the textural properties of frozen pork (Martino *et al.*, 1998). High-pressure freezing has also been used for some vegetables (Fuchigami *et al.*, 1997; Koch *et al.*, 1996). It has also been used to preserve fish products (Gudmundsson and Hafsteinsson, 2002). High pressures above 4 Kbar have been shown to inhibit enzymatic activities which cause undesirable changes in seafood quality, making products more stable during frozen storage. It has also been shown to produce kamaboko with a very fine surface and to produce novel fish gels.

High-pressure thawing also offers several advantages in comparison to thawing at atmospheric pressure, including the reduction of thawing times 2 to 5-fold and partial destruction or growth limitation of pathogens (Haack and Heinz, 2001). Zhao *et al.* (1998) have shown that high-pressure thawing maintains the organoleptic properties of bovine meat. High-pressure thawing has also been applied to seafood products (Kalichevsky *et al.*, 1995; Cheftel, 1995). However, further research is needed on water-holding capacity and protein denaturation during high pressure thawing (Knorr *et al.*, 1998).

As well as investigating the effects of increasing pressure, recent research has also highlighted the potential applications of reducing pressure to accelerate cooling. When the pressure drops, so does the boiling point of water. When pressure reaches 23 mbar, for example, the boiling point drops to 20 °C. At 6–8 mbar, water boils at 0-5 °C. At these low boiling points the latent heat inside cooked meat, for example, causes rapid evaporation and subsequent cooling (Wang and Sun, 2002a). Tests have shown that vacuum cooling can bring down the temperature of large joints in less than 2.5 hours (McDonald *et al.*, 2002). Ham and beef joints weighing between 4.5 and 4.9 kilos were, for example, brought to 10 °C in 2.3 hours (Kenny *et al.*, 2002). Blast chilling of similar sized joints can take over 9 hours and immersion chilling and slow air chilling both take over 14 hours to reach the target temperature (Wang and Sun, 2002b, 2002c).

Ultrasound, like all forms of sound, is a pressure wave. It has long been known that pressure waves passed through supercooled water can bring about the transition to ice. Under the influence of ultrasound a much more rapid and even seeding of ice crystals occurs. In addition, since there are a greater number of seeds the final size of the ice crystals is smaller and cell damage is reduced. Development of this technique in the future may offer the food industry an alternative way of creating a large number of nucleation sites within a frozen food (Leadley and Williams, 2002).

## 12.5   Developments in packaging

Active packaging, designed to perform some function in addition to physical and barrier properties, is rapidly emerging within several food sectors. Such developments can also potentially contribute improved quality retention to frozen foods (George, 2000). Developments such as modified atmosphere packaging (MAP) have provided significant extensions to the quality shelf-life of chilled agricultural and horticultural produce by the reduction of rates of respiration and ethylene production, and retarding biochemical and physical deteriorative processes (Day, 2003). Similarly, polymer films impregnated with chemically or physically active ingredients can function as oxygen/carbon dioxide/ethylene scavengers, moisture controllers/humidity buffers, taint removers and ingredient releasers (Vermeiren et al., 2003). Other innovative forms of packaging are edible films and coatings (Park, 2002). These can be used to control gas exchange (water vapour, oxygen, carbon dioxide, etc.) between the food product and the ambient atmosphere, or between mixed components in a food product.

Intelligent (or smart) packaging refers to packaging that 'senses and informs'. Intelligent packaging devices are capable of providing information about the function and properties of a packaged food and can provide assurance of pack integrity, tamper evidence, product safety and quality. Intelligent packaging devices include time-temperature indicators, gas-sensing dyes, microbial-growth indicators and physical shock indicators. Within this category of packaging are temperature and time-temperature indicators (TIs and TTIs). These devices are designed to monitor the temperature or time-temperature history of the product from the factory to the consumer (Taoukis and Labuza, 2003). TIs usually display either the current temperature, or respond to some pre-defined threshold temperature (e.g., freezing point). TTIs usually utilise a physico-chemical mechanism that responds to the temperature history to which the device has been exposed. Temperature control packaging includes the use of innovative insulating materials designed to guard against undue temperature abuse during storage and distribution. This may be in the form of 'thermal blankets' for wrapping over pallets of frozen food, or individual thermally lined food packages, designed to minimise temperature fluctuation in individual products.

## 12.6    Cryoprotectants

Cryoprotectants are compounds that improve the quality and extend the shelf-life of frozen foods. A wide variety of cryoprotective compounds are available. These include sugars, amino acids, polyols, methyl amines, carbohydrates, some proteins and even inorganic salts, such as potassium phosphate and ammonium sulphate. A newer area of cryoprotection is the use of antifreeze proteins (AFPs) (Hedges, 2002). The addition of AFPs to meat has been shown to control ice crystal size, reducing drip loss and maintaining textural quality (Payne et al., 1994; Payne and Young, 1995). However, the method of addition involved either soaking the muscle in an AFP solution, or injection of an AFP solution into the bloodstream pre-slaughter. For whole fish fillets and poultry muscle, a key difficulty is in finding an expedient route of perfusing AFP molecules into the muscle structure without causing disruption/damage.

Antifreeze proteins occur naturally in some fish (Payne and Wilson, 1994). Four quite different anti-freeze proteins have been identified in various fish species, known simply as AFP I, AFP II, etc. (Cheng, 1998). In the past decade it has become clear that similar proteins have evolved in a number of other environmental niches. In particular anti-freeze proteins have been extracted and identified in grasses such as winter rye, in carrots and in a number of insects. The largest degree of thermal hysteresis is currently seen in an anti-freeze protein extracted from the spruce bud worm. Further claims for anti-freeze activity have been made for extracts from many food plant materials including brussels sprouts. It may be possible in the future to breed plants selectively that are capable of expressing anti-freeze proteins and therefore could be expected to have a greater resistance to recrystallisation damage during frozen distribution, with the resultant effect of increased textural quality and retention of nutrients on thawing. Current research is focused on locating new sources of anti-freeze proteins and on understanding their expression and mode of action.

## 12.7   References

BARAT, J, CHIRALT, A and FITO, P (2000) 'Structural change kinetics in osmotic dehydration of apple tissue', *Proceedings of the 12th International Drying Symposium*, Elsevier Science, Amsterdam.

BOGH-SORENSEN, L (2000) 'Maintaining safety in the cold chain', in Kennedy, C (ed.), *Managing Frozen Foods*, Woodhead Publishing Limited, Cambridge.

BOWATER, F J (2001) 'Rapid chilling plant compared to conventional systems', in *Rapid Cooling of Food*, Meeting of IIR Commission C2, Bristol (UK).

BOWLING, R A, DUTSON, T R, SMITH, G C and SAVELL, J W (1987) 'Effects of Cryogenic chilling on beef carcass grade, shrinkage and palatability characteristics', *Meat Sci*, 21, 67–72.

CHAFER, M, GONZALEZ-MARTINEZ, C, ORTOLA, M *et al.* *(2000)* *'Osmotic dehydration of mandarin and orange peel by using rectified grape must'*, *Proceedings of the 12th International Drying Symposium*, Elsevier Science, Amsterdam.

CHEFTEL, J C (1995) 'Review: High pressure, microbial inactivation and food preservation', *Food Science and Technology International*, 1, 75–90.

CHIRALT, A, MARTINEZ-NAVARETTE, N, MARTINEZ-MONZO, J *et al.* (2001) 'Changes in mechanical properties through osmotic processes: cryoprotectant approach', *J Food Eng* 49: 129–35.

CHENG, C H C (1998) 'Evolution of fish antifreeze proteins', *Abstracts of Papers of The American Chemical Society*, 216(1), 44-AGFD.

DAY, M (2003) 'Novel PAP applications for fresh-prepared produce', in Ahvenainen, R (ed.), *Novel food packaging techniques*, Woodhead Publishing Limited, Cambridge.

DITCHEV, S and RICHARDSON, P (1999) 'Intensification of freezing', in Oliviera, F and Oliviera, J (eds), *Processing Foods: quality optimisation and process assessment*, CTC Press, Boca Raton.

FAIR (1998) 'Improvement of overall food quality by application of osmotic treatments in conventional and new process', Concerted action FAIR-CT96-1118 of the 4th Framework Program of the European Union: *http://www.uoguelph.ca/~odmlm/fair.html*.

FELLOWS, P (2000) *Food processing technology: principles and practice* (second edition), Woodhead Publishing Limited, Cambridge.

FITO, P, CHIRALT, A, BETORET, N et al. (2001) 'Vacuum impregnation and osmotic dehydration in matrix engineering: application in functional fresh food development', *J Food Eng* 49: 175–83.

FORNI, E, SORMANI, A, SCALISE, S and TOREGGIANI, D (1997) 'The influence of sugar composition on the colour stability of osmodehydrofrozen intermediate moisture apricots', *Food Res Int*, 30, 87–94.

FORNI, E, GENNA, A and TORREGGIANI, D (1998) 'Modificazione della temperatura di transizione vetrosa mediante disidratazione osmotica e stablitità al congelamento del colore delle fragole', in Porretta, S (ed.), Proceeding 3rd CISETA (Congresso Italiano di Scienza e Tecnologia degli Alimenti), *Ricerche e innovazioni nell'industria alimentare*, Pinerolo, Chiriotti Editori.

FUCHIGAMI, M, MIYAZAKI, K, KATO, N and TERAMOTO, A (1997) 'Histological changes in high pressure frozen carrots', *J Food Sci*, 62, 809–12.

GEORGE, M (2000) 'Selecting packaging for frozen foods', in Kennedy, C (ed.), *Managing Frozen Foods*, Woodhead Publishing Limited, Cambridge.

GEROSIMOV, N A and RUMYANSTEV, U D (1972) 'Heat exchange at radiation convective chilling of meat', *Khalo-tech*, 11, 31–4.

GIANGIACOMO, R, TORREGGIANI, D, ERBA M L and MESSINA, G (1994), 'Use of osmodehydrofrozen fruit cubes in yoghurt', *Italian J Food Sci*, 3, 345–50.

GUDMUNDSSON, M and HAFSTEINSSON, H (2002) 'New non-thermal techniques for processing seafood', in Bremner, H (ed.), *Safety and quality issues in fish processing*, Woodhead Publishing Limited, Cambridge.

HAACK, E and HEINZ, V (2001) 'Improvement of food safety by high pressure processing. II Studies on use in the meat industry', *Fleischwirtschaft*, 81(6), 38–41.

HEDGES, N (2002) 'Maintaining the quality of frozen fish', in Bremner, H (ed.), *Safety and quality issues in fish processing*, Woodhead Publishing Limited, Cambridge.

HUXSOLL, C C (1982) 'Reducing the refrigeration load by partial concentration of food prior to freezing', *Food Technol*, 5, 98–102.

JAMES, S and JAMES, C (2002) *Meat refrigeration*, Woodhead Publishing Limited, Cambridge.

KALICHEVSKY, M T, KNORR, D and LILLFORD, P J (1995) 'The effects of high pressure on water and potential food applications', *Trends in Food Science and Technology*, 6, 253–9.

KENNEDY, C J (1998) 'Formation of ice in frozen foods and its control by physical stimuli', in Reid, D S (ed.), *The Properties of Water in Foods ISOPOW 6*, London, Blackie Academic & Professional.

KENNY T, DESMOND, E, WARD, P and SUN, DA-WEN (2002) 'Rapid Cooling of cooked meat joints', Teagasc, Ballsbridge, Dublin, Ireland, 24 pp., ISBN 1 84170 277 3 (booklet).

KERENS, G (1983) 'Accelerated chilling of beef carcasses', FRIGAIR '83 *Symposium*, SIR, Pretoria.

KNORR, D, SCHLUETER, O and HEINZ, V (1998) 'Impact of high hydrostatic pressure on phase transitions of foods', *Food Technol*, 52, 42–5.

KOCH, H, SEYDERHELM, I, WILLE, P, KALICHEVSKY, M T and KNORR, D (1996) 'Pressure shift freezing and its influence on texture, colour, microstructure and rehydration behaviour of potato cubes', *Nahrung*, 40, 125–31.

LAMBALLERIE-ANTON, M, TAYLOR, R and CULIOLI, J (2002) 'High pressure processing of meat', in Kerry, J, Kerry J and Ledward, D (eds), *Meat processing: improving quality*, Woodhead Publishing Limited, Cambridge.

LAZAR, M E (1968) 'Dehydrofreezing of fruits and vegetables', in Tressler, D K, Arsdel, W B V and Copley M J (ed.), *The Freezing Preservation of Foods*, Westport CT, The AVI Publishing Company.

LAZARIDES, H, FITO, P, CHIRALT, A *et al.* (1999) 'Advances in osmotic dehydration', in Oliviera, F and Oliviera, J (eds), *Processing Foods: quality optimisation and process assessment*, CTC Press, Boca Raton.

LE MAGUER, M (1988) 'Osmotic dehydration: review and future directions', *Symposium on Progress in Food Preservation Processes*, Brussels, 1, 283–309.

LEADLEY, C and WILLIAMS, A (2002) 'Power ultrasound current and potential applications for food processing', Review No 32, Campden and Chorleywood Food Research Association Group.

LUCAS, T and RAOULT-WACK, A L (1998) 'Immersion chilling and freezing in aqueous refrigerating media: review and future directions', *Intnl J Refrig*, 21(6), 419–29.

MALLIKARJUNAN, P and MITTAL, G S (1994) 'Optimum conditions for beef carcass chilling', *Meat Sci*, 39, 215–23.

MARTINO, M N, OTERO, L, SANZ, P D and ZARITZKY, N E (1998) 'Size and location of ice crystals in pork frozen by high-pressure-assisted freezing as compared to classical methods', *Meat Sci*, 50, 303–13.

MATRINGE, E, CHATELLIER, J and SAUREL, R (1999) 'Improvement of processed fruit and vegetable texture using a new technology "vacuum infusion"', Proceedings of the International Congress 'Improved Traditional Foods for the Next Century', Institute de Agroquimica y Tecnologia de Alimentos, Valencia, Spain.

MCDONALD, K, SUN, DA-WEN and LYNG, J (2002) 'Effect of vacuum cooling on the thermophysical properties of a cooked beef product', *Journal of Food Engineering*, 52(2), 167–176.

MILLER, J (1998) 'Cryogenic food freezing systems', *Food Proc.* 67(8): 22–3.

MILLER, J and BUTCHER, C (2000) 'Freezer technology', in Kennedy, C (ed.), *Managing Frozen Foods*, Woodhead Publishing Limited, Cambridge.

MORENO, J, CHIRALT, A, ESCRICHE, I and SERRA, J (2000) 'Effect of blanching/osmotic dehydration combined methods on quality and stability of minimally-processed strawberries', *Food Res Internat* 33(7): 609–16.

NEWMAN, M (2001) 'Cryogenic impingement freezing utilizing atomized liquid nitrogen for the rapid freezing of food products', *Proceedings of the International Institute of Refrigeration Rapid Cooling – above and below zero*, Bristol.

OLIVIERA, J, PEREIRA, M, FRIAS, J *et al.* (1999) 'Application of the concepts of biomaterials science to the quality optimisation of frozen foods, in Oliviera, F and Oliviera, J (eds), *Processing Foods: quality optimisation and process assessment*, CTC Press, Boca Raton.

PARK, H (2002), 'Edible coatings for fruit' in Jongen, W (ed.), *Fruit and vegetable processing: improving quality*, Woodhead Publishing Limited, Cambridge.

PAYNE, S R and WILSON, P W (1994) 'Comparison of the freeze/thaw characteristics of Antarctic cod (*Dissostichus mawsoni*) and black cod (*Paranotothenia augusta*) – possible effects of antifreeze glycoproteins', *J Muscle Foods*, 5(3), 233–55.

PAYNE, S R and YOUNG, O A (1995) 'Effects of pre-slaughter administration of antifreeze proteins on frozen meat quality', *Meat Sci*, 41(2), 147–55.

PAYNE, S R, SANDFORD, D, HARRIS, A and YOUNG, O A (1994) 'Effects of antifreeze proteins on chilled and frozen meat', *Meat Sci*, 37(3), 429–38.

PHAM, Q (2001) 'Modelling thermal processes: cooling and freezing', in Tijskens, Hertog, M and Nicolai, B (eds), *Food Process Modelling*, Woodhead Publishing Limited, Cambridge.

PHAM, Q T and LOVATT, S J (1996) 'Optimisation of refrigeration processes by stochastic methods', *Food Australia*, 48(2), 64–9.

RAOULT-WACK, A L (1994) 'Recent advances in the osmotic dehydration of foods', *Trends in Food Sci and Tech*, 5(8), 255–60.

RAOULT-WACK, A L, GUILBERT, S and LENART A (1992) 'Recent advances in drying through immersion in concentrated solutions', in Mujumdar, A S (ed.), *Drying of Solids*, London, Elsevier Science, 21–51.

SANZ, P D, DE ELVIRA, C, MARTINO, M, ZARTZKY, N, OTERO, L and CARRASCO, J A (1999) 'Freezing rate simulation as an aid to reducing crystallization damage in foods', *Meat Sci*, 52(3), 275–278.

SAUREL, R (2002) 'Use of vacuum technology to improve processed fruit and vegetables', in Jongen, W (ed.) *Fruit and vegetable processing: improving quality*, Woodhead Publishing Limited, Cambridge.

SUN, DA-WEN (2001) *Advances in Food Refrigeration*, Leatherhead Food International, Leatherhead.

TAOUKIS, P and LABUZA, T (2003) 'Time-temperature indicators', in Ahvenainen, R (ed.), *Novel food packaging techniques*, Woodhead Publishing Limited, Cambridge.

TORREGGIANI, D (1993) 'Osmotic dehydration in fruit and vegetable processing', *Food Res Int*, 26, 59–68.

TORREGGIANI, D, FORNI, E and PELLICCIONI, L (1993) 'Modificazione della temperatura di transizione vetrosa mediante disidratazione osmotica e stabilità al congelamento del colore di kiwi', in S Porretta (ed.), *Ricerche e innovazioni nell'industria alimentare*, 1st Congresso Italiano di Scienza e Tecnologia degli Alimenti (CISETA), Pinerolo, Chiriotti Editori, pp. 621–30.

TORREGGIANI, D, FORNI, E and LONGONI, F (1997) 'Chemical-physical characteristics of osmodehydrofrozen sweet cherry halves: influence of the osmodehydration methods and sugar syrup composition', in *1st Int Cong Food Ingredients: New Technologies. Fruits & Vegetables*, Allione Ricerca Agroalimentare S.p.A., pp. 101–9.

TORREGGIANI, D, LUCAS, T and RAOULT-WACK, A (2000) 'The pre-treatment of fruits and vegetables', in Kennedy, C (ed.), *Managing Frozen Foods*, Woodhead Publishing Limited, Cambridge.

UNION INTERNATIONAL CONSULTANTS (1984) 'A study of the practical and economic considerations associated with high velocity and low-temperature air streams for chilling beef', *Proceedings of the 30th European Meeting Meat Research Workers*, Bristol, 2.1.

VERMEIREN, L, HEIRLINGS, L, DEVLIEGHERE, F and DEBEVERE, J (2003) 'Oxygen, ethylene and other scavengers', in Ahvenainen, R (ed.), *Novel food packaging techniques*, Woodhead Publishing Limited, Cambridge.

WANG, L J and SUN, DA-WEN (2002a) 'Modelling vacuum cooling process of cooked meat, part 2 – Mass and heat transfer of cooked meat under vacuum pressure', *International Journal of Refrigeration*, 25 (7), 861–72.

WANG, L J and SUN, DA-WEN (2002b) 'Modelling vacuum cooling process of cooked meat, part 1 – Analysis of vacuum cooling system', *International Journal of Refrigeration*, 25 (7), 852–60.

WANG, L J and SUN, DA-WEN (2002c) 'Evaluation of the performance of slow air, air-blast and water immersion cooling methods in the cooked meat industry by the finite element method', *Journal of Food Engineering*, 51(2), 329–40.

ZARITZKY, N (2000) 'Factors affecting the stability of frozen foods', in Kennedy, C (ed.), *Managing Frozen Foods*, Woodhead Publishing Limited, Cambridge.

ZHAO, Y, FLORES, R A and OLSON, D G (1998) 'High hydrostatic pressure effects on rapid thawing of frozen beef', *J Food Sci*, 63, 272–5.

ZITZLER, E, DEB, K and THIELE, L (2000) 'Comparison of multiobjective evolutionary algorithms: Empirical results', *Evolutionary Computation*, 8(2), 1–24.

# Part III

# Emerging preservation techniques

# 13

# Biotechnology and reduced spoilage

J. R. Botella, University of Queensland, Australia

## 13.1 Introduction: mechanisms of post-harvest spoilage in plants

Even though there are a number of efficient chemical and physical treatments that can be used to preserve fresh foods, the ideal solution would be to genetically programme the foods to do the job by themselves without any human intervention. Once plant tissues are harvested, they engage in an accelerated senescence process that leads to the spoilage of the nutritional and organoleptic qualities of the tissue. Plant organ senescence is a natural, genetically programmed developmental process that requires the co-ordinated expression of a large number of genes resulting in a remobilisation of cellular resources to other parts of the plant. Aside from this natural senescence, harvesting implies in many cases detaching specific organs from the main plant (fruits, leaves, tubers, flowers, etc.), adding a strong stress component that speeds up the decay process.

Genetic engineering has the potential to slow down the natural senescence processes as well as alleviate the stress responses from harvested tissues. The two leading problems faced today are the enormous variety of tissues and species used for human consumption and the relative lack of knowledge about the molecular mechanisms governing senescence and stress responses in plants.

Two of the major classes of unprocessed plant foodstuffs are fruits and vegetables. Fruits evolved as a seed dispersal mechanism and therefore their nutritional, flavour and aroma qualities are destined to entice animals into eating them and dispose of the seeds at relatively distant locations from the original source. In general, fruits were not designed to last long. If harvested when fully ripe, fruits senesce in a very short period of time, from 1–2 days to 1–2 weeks.

The senescence process can be accelerated by a variety of environmental factors such as temperature, humidity, atmosphere and pathogen attack.

Fruits can be classified into climacteric and non-climacteric depending on whether or not they exhibit a respiratory rise at the onset of senescence accompanied by an auto-catalytic production of ethylene. Climacteric fruits include cold, temperate and tropical species such as tomato, apple, melon, papaya and mango. Ethylene plays a pivotal role in the control of ripening in this kind of fruit and it has been established that upon ripening, there is a large increase in ethylene production as well as an increased sensitivity of the fruit tissue to this gaseous hormone. Exposure to internal or external ethylene can greatly accelerate the ripening process and bring about the decay of the fruit. This poses a number of practical problems during transport and storage of climacteric fruits since the presence of other ripening fruits (or any other ethylene-producing source) will act in a synergistic way to accelerate senescence.

The main changes taking place during the ripening of fruits are chemical and structural. Ripening involves a large number of chemical changes in the mature fruit tissue including the uploading and production of sugars and other nutritional compounds, development of colour and synthesis of taste-related chemicals. The peak nutritional, organoleptic and general consumer quality are achieved in a very narrow window of time. Structurally, the fruit undergo extensive changes at the microscopic level to achieve the right level of softness, but the softening process never stops and will eventually produce a fruit that is not acceptable for eating and is more susceptible to the attack of a number of pathogens.

In non-climacteric fruits ethylene does not seem to have the same control role observed in their climacteric counterparts but most of the processes taking place during ripening (sugar uploading, colour changes, volatile production, softening, etc.) are identical. Our understanding of the processes controlling and co-ordinating ripening in non-climacteric fruits is quite limited therefore more research is needed before we can practically manipulate the rate of ripening.

The mechanisms governing senescence in other edible plant organs such as tubers, roots, leaves and flowers are different from those in fruits although there are some common themes. Genetic engineering solutions need then to be devised on a case-by-case basis depending on the tissues and species considered.

Some vegetables are harvested while immature and rapidly developing (asparagus, broccoli and lettuce are an example). Biochemical analysis of these commodities has revealed that there are dramatic changes resembling starvation responses occurring soon after harvest.

## 13.2   Methods for reducing spoilage in fruits

The dependence of climacteric fruits on ethylene to regulate the ripening rate have made them the focus of much biotechnological research aimed at

**Fig. 13.1**    Ethylene biosynthetic pathway (Yang and Hoffmann, 1984). Met, methionine; SAM, S-adenosyl methionine; ACC, 1-aminocyclopropane-1-carboxylic acid.

increasing the shelf life while not affecting other quality characteristics. Most of the approaches have been aimed at controlling the amount of ethylene synthesised by the fruits or the sensitivity to the hormone in fruit tissues. Alternatively, fruit firmness, another critical parameter determining the fruit effective life has been targeted altering the expression of cell wall modifying enzymes.

Ethylene is synthesised in plants from the amino acid methionine in three steps (Fig. 13.1). The last two steps in the biosynthetic pathway, the conversion of S-adenosyl methionine (SAM) to 1-aminocyclopropane-1-carboxylic acid (ACC) and its oxidation to ethylene have been manipulated by conventional preservation techniques and more recently by biotechnological means. Conventional and modern techniques such as cold storage and modified atmosphere basically aim to control the expression[1] of the genes that will eventually produce the enzymes catalysing these two reactions or the activity of the enzymes themselves.

Most of the molecular biology and biotechnology studies have been performed in tomato, a model system that has been extensively studied at the physiological and biochemical levels. The earliest reports describing the biotechnological control of ethylene production in fruits and its effect on ripening were described by Hamilton *et al.* (1990) and Oeller *et al.* (1991). Oeller *et al.* (1991) produced transgenic tomato plants bearing inverted copies of a ripening-induced ACC synthase gene (LE-ACC2), a method known as 'antisense gene inactivation'. Some of the transgenic lines exhibited a strong reduction of LE-ACC2 gene activity leading to almost complete inhibition of endogenous ethylene production in the fruits. Antisense transgenic lines failed to ripen although they developed an orange colour when harvested and kept on air or left on the plant for up to 150 days after pollination compared to control plants that fully ripen 60 days after pollination and deteriorate soon after. The non-ripening phenotype was fully reversible by treatment with exogenous ethylene producing fruits that were indistinguishable from the controls even though the length of the treatment was longer for the transgenic lines (6 days) versus the controls (1–2 days) (Oeller *et al.*, 1991).

Reduction of ethylene production in ripening fruits has also been achieved by targeting ACC oxidase, the final enzyme on the biosynthetic pathway (Fig.

[1]  In molecular biology, gene expression is the process by which the original gene (DNA) is transcribed into an RNA molecule and this RNA molecule is translated into the final protein molecule.

13.1). Antisense suppression of the pTOM13 gene in tomato, later discovered to encode the ripening-related ACC oxidase gene, resulted in fruits producing reduced levels of ethylene and an extended ripening period (Hamilton et al., 1990, Hamilton et al., 1991). Further more complete studies showed that fruit ripening was delayed by the suppression of the ACC oxidase gene and that leaf phenotype was also affected (John et al., 1995, Picton et al., 1995). Levels of ACC oxidase have also been altered in melons (Ayub et al., 1996). Cantaloupe 'Chanterais' melons are a very appreciated variety due to the excellent eating quality and flavour. Nevertheless market expansion is constrained by the extremely poor post-harvest characteristics of the fruits. Genetically modified plants show a strong silencing of the ripening-related ACC oxidase gene with almost total suppression of ethylene production by the fruit. Transgenic fruits exhibited greatly enhanced storage capacity retaining eating quality when stored for ten days at 25°C, well after the control fruits had spoiled. As reported in tomato, softening had also been altered in the transgenic fruits remaining firmer for a longer period than the controls. Transgenic fruits were also resistant to chilling injury being able to survive storage at 2°C for up to three weeks without visible damage while controls developed extensive damage during the same storage period (Ben-Amor et al., 1999).

Reduction of ethylene production has also been achieved by depletion of the biosynthetic metabolites such as SAM and ACC. A bacterial gene coding for an enzyme that metabolizes ACC (ACC deaminase) was introduced in tomato (Klee et al., 1991). Transgenic fruit showed delayed ripening only when harvested from the plant but not when allowed to develop on the vine. Detached fruits showed reduced ethylene production and increased firmness (Klee et al., 1991, Klee, 1993). A gene encoding SAM hydrolase has been introduced in tomato with the objective of diverting the pool of SAM to other metabolites instead of being converted into ACC (Good et al., 1994). In this case a fruit ripening-specific promoter was used to direct the expression of the gene only to the desired tissue at the desired developmental stage (Deikman et al., 1992). The resulting fruits produced reduced amounts of ethylene during ripening and consequently the ripening process was extended and the fruits stayed firm for longer (Good et al., 1994).

The increase in ethylene production observed in climacteric fruits is accompanied by an increase in ethylene sensitivity by the fruit. Ethylene is perceived by the cell by a family of receptors (Good et al., 1994). In tomato the family comprises at least five different genes (Klee and Tieman, 2002). Conditional inhibition of ethylene perception could have great biotechnological potential and manipulation of the perception has already been achieved by suppressing the expression of Nr, one of the ethylene receptors in tomato (Tieman et al., 2000). Fruits with very low levels of the Nr gene expression showed delayed ripening (Tieman et al., 2000).

Even though enhanced firmness has always been observed in all transgenic fruits with impaired ethylene production or perception, this was an indirect consequence rather than the principal aim of the work. The softening process that accompanies ripening is one of the most important causes of post-harvest losses in fruits. A number of enzymes are responsible for the ripening-induced changes in texture that are due to extensive modifications in the architecture of the cell wall by changes in the polymer composition and structure. The cell wall changes are quite complex and greatly dependent on the species studied. Nevertheless there are a number of common enzymes that play important roles in the evolution of the fruit's texture. Manipulation of the genes encoding these enzymes has been reported in a number of fruits with varying results.

Endo-polygalacturonase (PG) catalyses the hydrolytic cleavage of galacturonic linkages in the cell wall and is one of the most extensively studied contributors to the changes in firmness that occur during ripening. Levels of PG greatly increase during ripening in many fruits such as tomato, peach and avocado although levels are quite low in other species such as strawberry and melon (Hadfield and Bennett, 1998, Huber and Odonoghue, 1993). Activity levels of the PG gene and the PG enzyme have been reduced in tomato using different genetic constructs and techniques (Sheehy *et al.*, 1988, Smith *et al.*, 1988, Smith *et al.*, 1990a, Smith *et al.*, 1990b). Surprisingly, transgenic fruits retaining as little as 0.5% of the total PG activity levels did not show any appreciable differences in overall fruit ripening and specifically in the softening characteristics (Smith *et al.*, 1990b). This result has been confirmed by experiments with other transgenic ripening-impaired tomatoes (Dellapenna *et al.*, 1990, Giovannoni *et al.*, 1989). Complete disruption of the PG gene by insertion of unrelated DNA molecules into its sequence confirmed that softening rate was no different in transgenic plants versus control wild-type (Cooley and Yoder, 1998). Nevertheless the transgenic low-producing PG fruits show a significant increase in fruit shelf life and noticeable improvements in the resistance to cracking and splitting as well as better handling characteristics and elevated resistance to some post-harvest pathogens such as *Rhizopus stolonifer* and *Geotrichum candidum*, two fungi causing Rhizopus soft rot and Sour Rot in tomatoes. Analysis of the fruits showed that they contain longer polygalacturonic acid molecules as a result of the genetic modification, and this increased cell adhesion properties making the fruits more robust. Transgenic low PG-producing fruits have also shown important applications for the processing industry due to the changes in fruit texture (Langley *et al.*, 1994, Kramer *et al.*, 1991, Schuch *et al.*, 1991).

Reduction in the activity of pectin methylesterase (which de-esterifies polyuronides in the cell wall), to 10% of normal levels did not affect ripening of transgenic tomatoes but had a devastating effect in overripe fruits with almost complete loss of tissue integrity (Tieman and Handa, 1994, Hall *et al.*, 1993, Tieman *et al.*, 1992). The enzyme $\beta$-galactosidase is also involved in cell wall metabolism and has been targeted for suppression using molecular biology techniques. Reduction of the activity by up to 75% resulted in no observable differences in fruit softening but transgenic tomato fruits deteriorated more slowly during long-term storage (Brummell and Harpster, 2001). In a different experiment, reduction of the activity by 90% in early ripening produced transgenic fruits with a noticeable reduction in softening during ripening (up to 40%) (Brummell and Harpster, 2001). Finally, reduction of the levels of expansin, an enzyme that is thought to loosen up the cell wall allowing the action of other enzymes, to less than 3% of wild-type levels reduced softening by 15–20% during fruit ripening (Brummell et al., 1999).

When compared to their climacteric counterparts, very little is known about the mechanisms controlling fruit ripening and senescence in non-climacteric fruits. Nevertheless, the economic importance of this group of fruits that include strawberry, grape, citrus and pineapple have driven an important research surge in recent years that have resulted in significant advances in our understanding of the ripening and eventually spoilage mechanisms. Ethylene is clearly not as important in non-climacteric fruits and other plant hormones such as auxins and abscisic acid have been implicated either directly or indirectly in the control of ripening (Manning, 1998).

One important agronomic trait influencing post-harvest life of non-climacteric fruits is firmness. As happens with climacteric fruits, ripening is usually accompanied by an increase of softening that eventually leads to the spoilage of the fruit. The enzymes involved in softening development are essentially the same already described for climacteric fruits, (endoglucanases, beta-galactosidases, expansins, etc.). Manipulation of fruit firmness can therefore lead to a longer effective period of consumer acceptability and reduced losses during transport and storage.

Manipulation of firmness has been attempted in strawberry by silencing an endo-beta-1,4-glucanase gene (cel1). Strong gene silencing was achieved although no effect on total endoglucanase activity was observed in the transgenic plants. No effect on firmness was observed in the transgenics either (Woolley et al., 2001). A possible explanation for the lack of success is the presence of a second endoglucanase gene in strawberry fruits that could compensate for the absence of cel1 (Llop-Tous et al., 1999).

An increase in fruit firmness was observed in transgenic strawberry plants in which a fruit-ripening-specific pectate liase gene had been silenced (Jimenez-Bermudez et al., 2002). No difference was observed in the colour, shape or weight of the transgenic fruits but a clear difference in firmness was observed (both external and internal). Microscopic analysis of the fruits showed that cell walls in transgenic fruits displayed a lower degree of swelling than control fruits. No differences were observed in fruit firmness during development up to the white fruit stage with the biggest differences in softening observed in the transition from white to red. Post-harvest softening was also reduced in transgenic fruits giving an indication that this strategy could be effectively used to reduce post-harvest fruit spoilage. An important drawback of the experiment was a dramatic reduction in yield observed in the plants transformed with the pectate liase genetic constructs. Anti-pectate liase lines showed a mean reduction in yield of 80.5% when compared to other transgenic controls containing the GUS gene that exhibited 30% reduction in yield vs. non-transformed lines. This yield reduction could be minimised or completely avoided by using tissue-specific promoters that would silence the pectate liase gene only in ripening fruits instead of the silencing induced by the authors in all plant tissues.

## 13.3    Methods for reducing spoilage in vegetables

Edible vegetables come in all shapes, developmental stages and colours. Leafy vegetables are arguably the most economically important type and include Lettuce (*Lactuca sativa*), Spinach (*Spinacea oleracea*), Endive (*Cichorium endivia*), Radicchio and Witloof (*Cichorium intybus*). In order to increase the life of these vegetables it is important to understand the mechanisms of leaf senescence. Contrary to the popular belief that senescence is a chaotic process, there is plenty of evidence to prove that senescence is a highly regulated stage in the life of the leaf and it is co-ordinated by a set of genes generally known as senescence-associated genes or SAGs (Gan and Amasino, 1997). Contrary to fruits (which abscise from the plant, fall to the ground and rot if not eaten in a relatively short period of time), very little is wasted in senescing leaves. A complete recycling process take place and most resources are redirected to other parts of the plants (Buchanan-Wollaston, 1997). The control of the senescence process is quite complex and a number of external and internal parameters can influence in various ways the rate of senescence (such as temperature, humidity, light, hormones, carbohydrates, etc. (Gan and Amasino, 1997).

Ethylene is intimately linked to senescence and its role as a senescence inducer has been firmly established (Buchanan-Wollaston, 1997). Therefore, in addition to the delayed fruit senescence observed in low-ethylene producing fruits, tomato plants with low ethylene synthesis in leaves also showed delayed leaf senescence symptoms (John *et al.*, 1995). A similar delay in leaf senescence was also observed in ethylene-insensitive Arabidopsis plants that had been mutagenised to disrupt ethylene perception by the cellular receptors (Grbic and Bleecker, 1995).

Cytokinins have shown an antagonistic role to ethylene, delaying the onset of senescence in leaves (Mok and Mok, 2001). During the senescence process, there is a drop in cytokinin levels, therefore several groups have attempted the manipulation of cytokinin biosynthesis with the aim of delaying senescence in leaves. The first reported attempt used a bacterial gene coding for isopentenyl transferase (IPT), a key enzyme in the biosynthesis of cytokinins, under the control of a heat shock promoter (Smart *et al.*, 1991). Transgenic plants contained elevated levels of cytokinins and exhibited a remarkable delay in leaf senescence. Unfortunately, cytokinins are involved in a large number of important cellular processes in plants and the high cytokinin levels present in the transgenic cytokinin-overproducing plants also induced a large number of developmental aberrations (Smart *et al.*, 1991). To avoid indiscriminate production of cytokinins all over the plant, Gan and Amasino (1995) linked the IPT gene to a very specific and highly regulated promoter that is active only in senescing leaf tissues. As a result they produced transgenic tobacco plants that could control the leaf senescence process by producing cytokinins only when and where they were needed. These plants showed a strong delay in leaf senescence without any other evident developmental abnormalities (Gan and Amasino, 1995, Gan and Amasino, 1997). Even though the results of this strategy are quite spectacular, it needs to be established whether the same method can be applied to edible vegetable crops without altering the nutritional quality of the food.

Flower vegetables such as cauliflower and broccoli are quite popular but the fresh market opportunities are limited by their poor post-harvest life, especially in broccoli. Broccoli (*Brassica oleracea* var. italica) deteriorates rapidly following harvest and requires refrigeration immediately after picking in the field. Ethylene has been proved to play a crucial role in the control of senescence in many flowers such as carnation and orchids (Woltering *et al.*, 1995, Borochov and Woodson, 1989, Woodson *et al.*, 1992). Transgenic petunias and carnations with impaired ethylene production or ethylene sensitivity show a longer vase life (Gubrium *et al.*, 2000, Bovy *et al.*, 1999). Broccoli produces a significant amount of ethylene after harvest and this has a strong influence on the rate of senescence. In order to manipulate the production of ethylene by the floret, Henzi *et al.* (1999) produced transgenic broccoli plants carrying antisense copies of a tomato ACC oxidase (ACO) gene. Transgenic broccoli lines showed a marked increase in ethylene production in the early phase of post-harvest with levels three times higher than control samples while in late harvest (72 hours after harvesting) transgenic plants showed clearly lower levels of ethylene than controls. Early respiration rates were comparable in control and transgenic samples but transgenic florets showed a linear decrease of respiration up to 98h after harvest.

Contrary to the aim of the experiment, the levels of ACO activity were higher in transgenic florets than in control samples. These apparent contradictions could be explained by the fact that the sequences used in the genetic constructs were not endogenous senescence-related ACC oxidase broccoli genes but tomato genes that will have only a limited homology to the broccoli counterparts. Agronomic evaluation of the transgenic lines has revealed some promising plants with significant improvements over the controls (Henzi *et al.*, 2000). In order to correct the problems encountered with this strategy, the same research group has recently produced plants with genetic constructs containing a senescence-related ACO gene from broccoli (Gapper *et al.*, 2002). No data is yet available about the post-harvest characteristics of these plants. The same constructs used by Gan and Amasino (1995) for tobacco has been transferred to broccoli in order to induce the production of cytokinins in early senescing tissue and subsequently stop the senescence process. Future analysis of the transgenic lines will provide useful information about the usefulness of this method in floral vegetables.

## 13.4   Enhancing plant resistance to diseases and pests

One of the main causes of post-harvest losses in fresh fruits and vegetables and any other foodstuff in general is the propensity of harvested and stored food to attract pathogens and pests.[2] Losses due to pathogen attack occur in all steps of the commercialisation chain, the farm, the transport and distribution, the shop or supermarket and the consumer home. Pathogens that attack harvested food do not necessarily infect the food after harvest but can be present in the plant before harvest and flourish as the fruit ripens or the vegetable is stored.

There are many types of plant pathogens but the most devastating are fungi, bacteria, viruses and insects. Plants have evolved a myriad of mechanisms to defend themselves but at the same time pathogens have evolved to circumvent the plant defence mechanisms. As a result there is a complicated situation in which different pathogens have different host ranges.

Due to the economic and social importance of plant pathogens, a great deal of research has been devoted to understanding the interactions between plants and pathogens. At the genetic and molecular level, the last 10–15 years have produced important advances in our understanding not only about the relationship but also about the strategies used by plants to fight pathogens. A pathogen is said to be compatible with a particular plant when it can successfully infect the plant. Resistance to a particular pathogen can be caused by many circumstances but the most common ones are:

1.  The plant cannot supply the necessary requirements (nutritional or structural) for a particular pathogen and therefore it is outside the host range of the pathogen (non-host).
2.  The plant has preformed physical (structural) or chemical (toxic) barriers that hinder successful infection by the pathogen (non-host resistance).
3.  The plant rapidly recognises the attacking pathogen and activates a number of defence mechanisms minimising the effectiveness of the pathogen attack by containing the invading pathogen to very limited regions or eliminating it altogether (host resistance).

### 13.4.1   Virus resistance

Viral resistance was the first successful example of plant disease resistance obtained by biotechnological means. To date, most of the available examples used genes from the pathogens in order to confer resistance in what is known as 'pathogen-derived resistance' (PDR). Transgenic tobacco plants resistant to the tobacco mosaic virus (TMV) were obtained by overexpression of the viral coat protein gene in what was named coat-protein-mediated resistance (CPMR) (Abel *et al.*, 1986). Subsequently, transgenic tomato plants containing a similar genetic construct proved to be highly resistant to TMV in field trials (Shah *et al.*, 1995). Since this pioneering work, many plants have been successfully modified

---

[2] For simplicity, we will include both pathogens and pests within the same word 'pathogen'.

to exhibit resistance to a wide variety of viruses including potato, papaya, melon and squash (Fitchen and Beachy, 1993).

Perhaps the most successful examples of commercialisation of virus-resistant plants are squash, zucchini and papaya. Squash and zucchini are highly susceptible to a series of viruses that can cause devastating effects in the crop's yield such as the zucchini yellow mosaic virus (ZYMV), Watermelon Mottle Virus 2 (WMV-2), and Cucumber Mosaic Virus (CMV). These viruses cause leaf mottling, stunted plant growth, and deformed inedible fruit and routinely reduce yields by 20–80%, depending on location and growing season. Resistant plants to these viruses are now available and commercialised by Asgrow seed (Kalamazoo, MI, USA) (Shah et al., 1995). The same kind of viruses also affect other related crops such as pumpkin, cucumber and watermelon and it is only a question of time when resistant commercial varieties will be developed for these commodities. The flourishing Hawaiian papaya industry was devastated by the appearance of the papaya ring spot virus (PRSV) in 1992. Following an extensive characterisation of the viral strains present in the islands, a CPMR strategy was used to produce highly PRSV-resistant papaya plants based on the commercial varieties already developed on the island by the local breeders (Lius et al., 1997, Tennant et al., 1994). After extensive field trials, the fruits named 'SunUp' and 'Rainbow', were commercialised in 1998 and are now available in supermarkets in the USA (Ferreira et al., 2002). In addition to the coat protein, other viral genes, such as the replicase gene, have been successfully used in the production of resistant tobacco, potato and tomato plants to TMV, potato virus Y (PVY), potato leafroll virus (PLRV) and potato virus X (PVX) (Shah et al., 1995, Baulcombe, 1994, Mueller et al., 1995).

The main drawback of CPMR and similar pathogen-derived strategies is the relatively narrow specificity of the protection conferred with transgenic plants being protected only against one or only a few viral strains (Baulcombe, 1996). Nevertheless, in some instances a broad protection has been achieved (Beachy, 1997). PDR has also been achieved using mutated viral movement protein with better results in terms of the range and specificity of the protection (Beachy, 1997). The differences observed among the different resistance methods could be due to our poor understanding of the molecular basis of the protection mechanism being activated in the host plant. A more comprehensive knowledge of such mechanisms will allow the increase both of the efficiency and the protection range in future crop varieties.

### 13.4.2   Insect resistance

The use of Bacillus thuringiensis (Bt) toxins to control insect pests has been known and practised by farmers since the 1950s. Bt toxins have several advantages over conventional insecticides such as the specificity of their action, restricting the target range and therefore not affecting 'beneficial insects'. Bt toxins are totally innocuous to humans and are biodegradable. More than 140 Bt toxins genes have been described from different Bacillus thuringiensis subspecies with different specificity and host range (Crickmore *et al.*, 1998). Nevertheless, the inherent technical and cost-related problems associated with the production and application of the toxin has restricted its widespread adoption by the industry. Genetic engineers attacked the problem from a different angle by cloning the toxin-producing genes and expressing them in plants. The first examples of insect-resistant plants using Bt toxins had limited success with low levels of protein produced in the plant mainly due to fundamental differences in gene structures between bacteria and plants. A completely redesigned artificially synthesised gene using plant consensus sequences corrected these problems (Perlak and Fishoff, 1993, Perlak *et al.*, 1991).

Transgenic cotton varieties carrying the Bt toxin gene isolated from *Bacillus thuringiensis* subs. Kurstaki (Btk) are highly resistant to cotton bollworm (*Helicoverpa zea*), tobacco budworm (*Heliothis virescens*) and pink bollworm (*Pectinophora gossypiella*) (Perlak *et al.*, 1990). However, in field conditions farmers may need supplemental insecticide applications to control cotton bollworm completely during the blooming period. A transgenic cotton variety carrying Bt genes is being commercialised by Monsanto with the name Bollgard® cotton. In addition to the pests already mentioned, Bollgard® provides a limited amount of protection against European corn borer (*Ostrinia nubilalis*), cabbage looper (*Trichoplusia ni*), saltmarsh caterpillar (*Estigmene acrea*) and cotton leafperforator (*Bucculatris thurberiells*). The incorporated protection has resulted in a dramatic reduction of insecticide applications with subsequent environmental benefits.

Maize elite varieties carrying different *Bacillus thuringiensis* toxin genes have been produced and are being commercialised or field tested by Syngenta, Monsanto, Aventis, Dekalb, Pioneer-Hibred and Mycogen. These products are resistant to European corn borer (*Ostrinia nubilalis*), southwestern corn borer (*Diatraea grandiosella*), Southern cornstalk borer (*Diatraea crambidoides*), and are partially effective against corn earworm (*Helicoverpa zea*), stalkborer (*Papaipema nebris*), and fall armyworm (*Spodoptera frugiperda*) (Koziel *et al.*, 1993, Armstrong *et al.*, 1995, Sims *et al.*, 1996, Pilcher *et al.*, 1997). Potato varieties are also commercially available with Bt genes that make them resistant to the Colorado potato beetle (*Leptinotarsa decemlineata*, Say) (Perlak *et al.*, 1993) (http://www.agbios.com/).

A large number of other crops such as rice, broccoli, oilseed rape, larch, poplar, sugarcane, peanut, chickpea, alfalfa and soybean have been transformed with Bt toxin genes with excellent results under laboratory or glasshouse conditions but their behaviour in large field planting conditions remains to be determined (Fujimoto *et al.*, 1993, Kleiner *et al.*, 1995, Delannay *et al.*, 1989, Hilder and Boulter, 1999). An artificial gene containing a fusion of two Bt toxins has been introduced into rice elite varieties and field tested. Natural and repeated heavy manual infestation of two lepidopteran insects, leaffolder and yellow stem borer was attempted with the transgenic hybrid plants showing high protection against both insect pests without affecting the total yield (Tu *et al.*, 2000). Apart from Bt, other sources for insect protection are being actively pursued. Several promising candidates such as lectins, amylase inhibitors and proteinase inhibitors have been studied with different degrees of success (Shade *et al.*, 1994, Hoffmann *et al.*, 1992, Gatehouse *et al.*, 1997, Schroeder *et al.*, 1995).

### 13.4.3    Fungal and bacterial resistance

Obtaining fungal-resistant crops has proved to be more difficult than for viruses and insects. Most of the difficulties are due to our lack of understanding of the molecular mechanisms controlling the interactions between the plant host and the fungus. In recent years, there has been an explosion in our knowledge of this interaction and several promising strategies are now being developed. One of the most promising resistance strategies is the use of cell wall lytic enzymes to degrade or damage the fungal cell wall, composed mainly of chitin and beta-1,3-glucan. Several kinds of chitinases and glucanases have now been cloned and transgenic plants expressing them have an increased degree of resistance to fungal pathogens. Nevertheless, the use of a single enzyme (either chitinase or glucanase), has been found to have only limited success while the simultaneous expression of both enzymes greatly increases the level of protection (Jach *et al.*, 1995).

Other classes of proteins with antifungal potential are the family of pathogenesis-related proteins (PRPs) and the plant defensins. The expression of different PRPs in transgenic plants has resulted in increased resistance against different fungal pathogens. Potatoes expressing a tobacco PRP showed significant delay in the infection and lesions produced by the fungus *Phytophthora infestans* (Liu *et al.*, 1994). Similarly, tobacco plants expressing the protein PR1-a were tolerant to the attack of *Peronospora tabacina* and *Phytophthora parasitica* var. *nicotinianae* (Alexander *et al.*, 1993). Defensins are small peptides that have been found to have a strong antifungal activity in *in vitro* assays. Many of these peptides have been identified and some have conferred protection when expressed in plant tissues such as the Rs-AFP2 protein from radish that can confer resistance to *Alternaria longipes* in transgenic tobacco plants (Terras *et al.*, 1995).

As is the case with fungi, bacterial resistance is proving difficult to accomplish although some bacterial-resistance genes have now been reported. There is not a predominant set of genes or proteins that can be used to fight bacterial infections although reports are available describing an efficient protection against *Pseudomonas syringae* and *Erwinia carotonova* among others (During *et al.*, 1993, Carmona *et al.*, 1993).

### 13.4.4    Other resistance approaches

One of the most common mechanisms of host resistance to pathogens follows the gene-for-gene model which postulates that resistance will occur when a plant contains a dominant resistance gene (known as R) and the pathogen a reciprocal dominant avirulence gene (known as Avr). Recognition of the Avr gene by the R gene rapidly triggers a defensive response in the plant at the point of infection. A number of cells surrounding the infection site engage in the production of metabolites, toxins and other chemical and enzymatic defence substances to fight the pathogen, detoxify harmful excretions and contain the spread of the pathogen. This response leads to localised cell death and is known as the hypersensitive response (HR). Manipulation of the HR is one of the most promising new strategies to confer broad-spectrum resistance to agricultural crops. Ubiquitous expression of the R and the corresponding Avr genes simultaneously would result in the death of the plant but expression of the Avr gene under the control of a pathogen-activated promoter could theoretically lead to protection. The idea is that upon infection, pathogen elicitors would trigger the Avr gene and therefore a comprehensive set of cell defensive responses as well as the localised cell death. This method has already been proved effective in transgenic tobacco plants to elicit non-specific disease resistance (Keller *et al.*, 1999). A number of resistance (R) as well as avirulence (Avr) genes have already been cloned in different plants and pathogens making the use of this strategy feasible (Ellis *et al.*, 2000).

## 13.5    Future trends

Genetic engineering cannot provide the perfect solution for the conservation of foodstuff. There is no substitute for good farming and commercial practices. The production of transgenic plants with improved lifespans will need to be combined with other technologies (irradiation, modified atmosphere, etc.) to achieve optimal practical results. Equally, disease resistant crops will still need to apply concepts of pathogen ecology to minimise the risk of infestation as well as the risk of development of resistance.

Even though it is progressing at a tremendous pace, plant genetic engineering is only in its infancy. Most of the useful examples of transgenic plants have been shown to work only under laboratory or glasshouse conditions. The different elements used in the construction of the genetic constructs and the transformation methods are continually improving allowing for a greater control of the genes transferred as well as a smaller phenotypic variation in the plants.

Fresh fruits and vegetables with a longer shelf life will be developed by controlling the master regulatory genes co-ordinating the senescence processes instead of single genes as is done now. A greater understanding of these senescence processes will also allow developing tailor-made solutions for individual crops and even individual varieties. Identification of the specific problems in the commercial post-harvest storage and distribution chain will allow targeting specific problems (such as water loss or firmness). New inducible promoter switches will allow the induction or repression of particular genes at will, thus stopping ripening or softening during the period needed for delivery to consumers' homes. It will also be important to address consumers' concerns about the use and consumption of genetically modified foods, especially in European countries. Safety as well as environmental concerns need to be addressed equally. The best method to achieve this is through strong institutional regulation and control of GM crops until all safety issues are satisfactorily settled. Nevertheless, reports indicate that the use of pest-resistant crops has resulted in a dramatic reduction of pesticide use that has a direct and beneficial impact on both human health and the environment.

Sophisticated plant protection strategies are now being developed to confer broad-spectrum resistance to crops and diminish the risk of development of pathogen resistance. New resistance genes are being cloned, expanding the potential for their use in unrelated crops by transferring them through molecular techniques. The next challenge is to produce crops with several useful built-in characteristics. Biotechnologists should soon be focusing on producing tomato fruits that last longer, are resistant to the main tomato pathogens and, most importantly, taste good.

## 13.6    Sources of further information and advice

The University of Cornell offers an outstanding source of information targeted to non-scientist audiences at http://www.comm.cornell.edu/gmo/gmo.html as part of their 'Genetrically Engineered Organisms, Public Issues Education Project'. Different sections within this site will answer questions such as 'Am I eating genetically engineered foods?' 'What traits have been engineered into plants?' and 'What are the risks and benefits of genetically engineered organisms?'.

The Agricultural Biotechnology Support Project (ABSP) is a USAID-funded project based in the Institute for International Agriculture at Michigan State University. The project aims to assist developing countries in the development and management of the tools and products of agricultural biotechnology. http://www.iia.msu.edu/absp/index.html

Companies involved in biotechnology research provide a good source of up-to-date information on existing commercial products as well as the next generation of products to come. Some of the most important agricultural biotech companies are Monsanto (http://www.biotechknowledge.com/), Syngenta (http://www.syngenta.com/), Aventis (http://www.aventis.com/) and Pioneer Hi-Bred International (http://www.pioneer.com/).

The National Centre for Food and Agricultural Policy (http://www.ncfap.org), an independent non-profit, non-advocacy research organisation, has performed a comprehensive study entitled 'Plant Biotechnology: Current and Potential Impact For Improving Pest Management in U.S. Agriculture: An Analysis of 40 Case Studies' (http://www.ncfap.org/40CaseStudies.htm).

Other sources of useful information are:

AgBiotechNet (http://www.agbiotechnet.com/)
AgBioWorld foundation (http://www.agbioworld.org/)

The American Society of Plant Biologists (http://www.aspb.org/)
The United States Department of Agriculture (http://www.aphis.usda.gov/ppq/biotech/)
The National Health Museum (http://www.accessexcellence.org/index.html).

## 13.7  References

ABEL, P. P., NELSON, R. S., DE, B., HOFFMANN, N., ROGERS, S. G., FRALEY, R. T. and BEACHY, R. N. (1986), 'Delay of Disease Development in Transgenic Plants That Express the Tobacco Mosaic-Virus Coat Protein Gene', *Science*, 232, (4751), 738–743.

ALEXANDER, D., GOODMAN, R. M., GUTRELLA, M., GLASCOCK, C., WEYMANN, K., FRIEDRICH, L., MADDOX, D., AHLGOY, P., LUNTZ, T., WARD, E. and RYALS, J. (1993), 'Increased Tolerance to 2 Oomycete Pathogens in Transgenic Tobacco Expressing Pathogenesis-Related Protein-1a', *Proceedings of the National Academy of Sciences of the United States of America*, 90, (15), 7327–7331.

ARMSTRONG, C. L., PARKER, G. B., PERSHING, J. C., BROWN, S. M., SANDERS, P. R., DUNCAN, D. R., STONE, T., DEAN, D. A., DEBOER, D. L., HART, J., HOWE, A. R., MORRISH, F. M., PAJEAU, M. E., PETERSEN, W. L., REICH, B. J., RODRIGUEZ, R., SANTINO, C. G., SATE, S. J., SCHULER, W., SIMS, S. R., STEHLING, S., TAROCHIONE, L. J. and FROMM, M. E. (1995), 'Field-Evaluation of European Corn-Borer Control in Progeny of 173 Transgenic Corn Events Expressing an Insecticidal Protein from Bacillus-Thuringiensis', *Crop Science*, 35, (2), 550–557.

AYUB, R., GUIS, M., AMOR, M. B., GILLOT, L., ROUSTAN, J. P., LATCHE, A., BOUZAYEN, M. and PECH, J. C. (1996), 'Expression of ACC oxidase antisense gene inhibits ripening of cantaloupe melon fruits', *Nature Biotechnology*, 14, (7), 862–866.

BAULCOMBE, D. (1994), 'Replicase-mediated resistance: a novel type of virus resistance in transgenic plants?', *Trends in Microbiology*, 2, (2), 60–63.

BAULCOMBE, D. C. (1996), 'Mechanisms of pathogen-derived resistance to viruses in transgenic plants', *Plant Cell*, 8, (10), 1833–1844.

BEACHY, R. N. (1997), 'Mechanisms and applications of pathogen-derived resistance in transgenic plants', *Current Opinion in Biotechnology*, 8, (2), 215–220.

BEN-AMOR, M., FLORES, B., LATCHE, A., BOUZAYEN, M., PECH, J. C. and ROMOJARO, F. (1999), 'Inhibition of ethylene biosynthesis by antisense ACC oxidase RNA prevents chilling injury in Charentais cantaloupe melons', *Plant, Cell and Environment*, 22, (12), 1579–1586.

BOROCHOV, A. and WOODSON, W. R. (1989), 'Physiology and biochemistry of flower petal senescence', *Horticultural Reviews*, 11, 15–43.

BOVY, A. G., ANGENENT, G. C., DONS, H. J. M. and VAN ALTVORST, A. C. (1999), 'Heterologous expression of the Arabidopsis etr1-1 allele inhibits the senescence of carnation flowers', *Molecular Breeding*, 5, (4), 301–308.

BRUMMELL, D. A. and HARPSTER, M. H. (2001), 'Cell wall metabolism in fruit softening and quality and its manipulation in transgenic plants', *Plant Molecular Biology*, 47, (1–2), 311–340.

BRUMMELL, D. A., HARPSTER, M. H., CIVELLO, P. M., PALYS, J. M., BENNETT, A. B. and DUNSMUIR, P. (1999), 'Modification of expansin protein abundance in tomato fruit alters softening and cell wall polymer metabolism during ripening', *Plant Cell*, 11, (11), 2203–2216.

BUCHANAN-WOLLASTON, V. (1997), 'The molecular biology of leaf senescence', *Journal of Experimental Botany*, 48, (307), 181–199.

CARMONA, M. J., MOLINA, A., FERNANDEZ, J. A., LOPEZFANDO, J. J. and GARCIAOLMEDO, F. (1993), 'Expression of the Alpha-Thionin Gene from Barley in Tobacco Confers Enhanced Resistance to Bacterial Pathogens', *Plant Journal*, 3, (3), 457–462.

COOLEY, M. B. and YODER, J. I. (1998), 'Insertional inactivation of the tomato polygalacturonase gene', *Plant Molecular Biology*, 38, (4), 521–530.

CRICKMORE, N., ZEIGLER, D. R., FEITELSON, J., SCHNEPF, E., VAN RIE, J., LERECLUS, D., BAUM, J. and DEAN, D. H. (1998), 'Revision of the nomenclature for the Bacillus thuringiensis pesticidal crystal proteins', *Microbiology and Molecular Biology Reviews*, 62, (3), 807–813.

DEIKMAN, J., KLINE, R. and FISCHER, R. L. (1992), 'Organization of Ripening and Ethylene Regulatory Regions in a Fruit-Specific Promoter from Tomato (Lycopersicon-Esculentum)', *Plant Physiology*, 100, (4), 2013–2017.

DELANNAY, X., LAVALLEE, B. J., PROKSCH, R. K., FUCHS, R. L., SIMS, S. R., GREENPLATE, J. T., MARRONE, P. G., DODSON, R. B., AUGUSTINE, J. J., LAYTON, J. G. and FISCHHOFF, D. A. (1989), 'Field Performance of Transgenic Tomato Plants Expressing the Bacillus-Thuringiensis Var Kurstaki Insect Control Protein', *Bio-Technology*, 7, (12), 1265–1269.

DELLAPENNA, D., LASHBROOK, C. C., TOENJES, K., GIOVANNONI, J. J., FISCHER, R. L. and BENNETT, A. B. (1990), 'Polygalacturonase Isozymes and Pectin Depolymerization in Transgenic Rin Tomato Fruit', *Plant Physiology*, 94, (4), 1882–1886.

DURING, K., PORSCH, P., FLADUNG, M. and LORZ, H. (1993), 'Transgenic Potato Plants Resistant to the Phytopathogenic Bacterium Erwinia-Carotovora', *Plant Journal*, 3, (4), 587–598.

ELLIS, J., DODDS, P. and PRYOR, T. (2000), 'Structure, function and evolution of plant disease resistance genes', *Current Opinion in Plant Biology*, 3, (4), 278–284.

FERREIRA, S. A., PITZ, K. Y., MANSHARDT, R., ZEE, F., FITCH, M. and GONSALVES, D. (2002), 'Virus coat protein Transgenic papaya provides practical control of Papaya ringspot virus in Hawaii', *Plant Disease*, 86, (2), 101–105.

FITCHEN, J. H. and BEACHY, R. N. (1993), 'Genetically-Engineered Protection against Viruses in Transgenic Plants', *Annual Review of Microbiology*, 47, 739–763.

FUJIMOTO, H., ITOH, K., YAMAMOTO, M., KYOZUKA, J. and SHIMAMOTO, K. (1993), 'Insect-Resistant Rice Generated by Introduction of a Modified Delta-Endotoxin Gene of Bacillus-Thuringiensis', *Bio-Technology*, 11, (10), 1151–1155.

GAN, S. and AMASINO, R. M. (1995), 'Inhibition of leaf senescence by autoregulated production of cytokinin', *Science*, 270, (5244), 1986–1988.

GAN, S. S. and AMASINO, R. M. (1997), 'Making sense of senescence – Molecular genetic regulation and manipulation of leaf senescence', *Plant Physiology*, 113, (2), 313–319.

GAPPER, N. E., MCKENZIE, M. J., CHRISTEY, M. C., BRAUN, R. H., COUPE, S. A., LILL, R. E. and JAMESON, P. E. (2002), 'Agrobacterium tumefaciens-mediated transformation to alter ethylene and cytokinin biosynthesis in broccoli', *Plant Cell Tissue and Organ Culture*, 70, (1), 41–50.

GATEHOUSE, A. M. R., DAVISON, G. M., NEWELL, C. A., MERRYWEATHER, A., HAMILTON, W. D. O., BURGESS, E. P. J., GILBERT, R. J. C. and GATEHOUSE, J. A. (1997), 'Transgenic potato plants with enhanced resistance to the tomato moth, Lacanobia oleracea: Growth room trials', *Molecular Breeding*, 3, (1), 49–63.

GIOVANNONI, J. J., DELLAPENNA, D., BENNETT, A. B. and FISCHER, R. L. (1989), 'Expression of a Chimeric Polygalacturonase Gene in Transgenic Rin (Ripening Inhibitor)

Tomato Fruit Results in Polyuronide Degradation but Not Fruit Softening', *Plant Cell*, 1, (1), 53–63.

GOOD, X., KELLOGG, J. A., WAGONER, W., LANGHOFF, D., MATSUMURA, W. and BESTWICK, R. K. (1994), 'Reduced Ethylene Synthesis by Transgenic Tomatoes Expressing S-Adenosylmethionine Hydrolase', *Plant Molecular Biology*, 26, (3), 781–790.

GRBIC, V. and BLEECKER, A. B. (1995), 'Ethylene regulates the timing of leaf senescence in Arabidopsis', *Plant Journal*, 8, (4), 595–602.

GUBRIUM, E. K., CLEVENGER, D. J., CLARK, D. G., BARRETT, J. E. and NELL, T. A. (2000), 'Reproduction and horticultural performance of transgenic ethylene-insensitive petunias', *Journal of the American Society for Horticultural Science*, 125, (3), 277–281.

HADFIELD, K. A. and BENNETT, A. B. (1998), 'Polygalacturonases: Many genes in search of a function', *Plant Physiology*, 117, (2), 337–343.

HALL, L. N., TUCKER, G. A., SMITH, C. J. S., WATSON, C. F., SEYMOUR, G. B., BUNDICK, Y., BONIWELL, J. M., FLETCHER, J. D., RAY, J. A., SCHUCH, W., BIRD, C. R. and GRIERSON, D. (1993), 'Antisense Inhibition of Pectin Esterase Gene-Expression in Transgenic Tomatoes', *Plant Journal*, 3, (1), 121–129.

HAMILTON, A. J., LYCETT, G. W. and GRIERSON, D. (1990), 'Antisense Gene That Inhibits Synthesis of the Hormone Ethylene in Transgenic Plants', *Nature*, 346, (6281), 284–287.

HAMILTON, A. J., BOUZAYEN, M. and GRIERSON, D. (1991), 'Identification of a tomato gene for the ethylene-forming enzyme by expression in yeast', *Proceedings of the National Academy of Sciences of the United States of America*, 88, (16), 7434–7437.

HENZI, M. X., MCNEIL, D. L., CHRISTEY, M. C. and LILL, R. E. (1999), 'A tomato antisense 1-aminocyclopropane-1-carboxylic acid oxidase gene causes reduced ethylene production in transgenic broccoli', *Australian Journal of Plant Physiology*, 26, (2), 179–183.

HENZI, M. X., CHRISTEY, M. C. and MCNEIL, D. L. (2000), 'Morphological characterisation and agronomic evaluation of transgenic broccoli (*Brassica oleracea* L. var. *italica*) containing an antisense ACC oxidase gene.', *Euphytica*, 113, 9–18.

HILDER, V. A. and BOULTER, D. (1999), 'Genetic engineering of crop plants for insect resistance – a critical review', *Crop Protection*, 18, (3), 177–191.

HOFFMANN, M. P., ZALOM, F. G., WILSON, L. T., SMILANICK, J. M., MALYJ, L. D., KISER, J., HILDER, V. A. and BARNES, W. M. (1992), 'Field-Evaluation of Transgenic Tobacco Containing Genes Encoding Bacillus-Thuringiensis Delta-Endotoxin or Cowpea Trypsin-Inhibitor – Efficacy against Helicoverpa-Zea (Lepidoptera, Noctuidae)', *Journal of Economic Entomology*, 85, (6), 2516–2522.

HUBER, D. J. and ODONOGHUE, E. M. (1993), 'Polyuronides in Avocado (Persea-Americana) and Tomato (Lycopersicon-Esculentum) Fruits Exhibit Markedly Different Patterns of Molecular-Weight Downshifts During Ripening', *Plant Physiology*, 102, (2), 473–480.

JACH, G., GORNHARDT, B., MUNDY, J., LOGEMANN, J., PINSDORF, P., LEAH, R., SCHELL, J. and MAAS, C. (1995), 'Enhanced Quantitative Resistance against Fungal Disease by Combinatorial Expression of Different Barley Antifungal Proteins in Transgenic Tobacco', *Plant Journal*, 8, (1), 97–109.

JIMENEZ-BERMUDEZ, S., REDONDO-NEVADO, J., MUNOZ-BLANCO, J., CABALLERO, J. L., LOPEZ-ARANDA, J. M., VALPUESTA, V., PLIEGO-ALFARO, F., QUESADA, M. A. and MERCADO, J. A. (2002), 'Manipulation of strawberry fruit softening by antisense expression of a pectate lyase gene', *Plant Physiology*, 128, (2), 751–759.

JOHN, I., DRAKE, R., FARRELL, A., COOPER, W., LEE, P., HORTON, P. and GRIERSON, D. (1995), 'Delayed leaf senescence in ethylene-deficient ACC-oxidase antisense tomato plants: Molecular and physiological analysis', *Plant Journal*, 7, (3), 483–490.

KELLER, H., PAMBOUKDJIAN, N., PONCHET, M., POUPET, A., DELON, R., VERRIER, J. L., ROBY, D. and RICCI, P. (1999), 'Pathogen-induced elicitin production in transgenic tobacco generates a hypersensitive response and nonspecific disease resistance', *Plant Cell*, 11, (2), 223–235.

KLEE, H. J. (1993), 'Ripening physiology of fruit from transgenic tomato (*Lycopersicon esculentum*) plants with reduced ethylene synthesis', *Plant Physiology*, 102, (3), 911–916.

KLEE, H. and TIEMAN, D. (2002), 'The tomato ethylene receptor gene family: Form and function', *Physiologia Plantarum*, 115, (3), 336–341.

KLEE, H. J., HAYFORD, M. B., KRETZMER, K. A., BARRY, G. F. and KISHORE, G. M. (1991), 'Control of ethylene synthesis by expression of a bacterial enzyme in transgenic tomato plants', *Plant Cell*, 3, (11), 1187–1194.

KLEINER, K. W., ELLIS, D. D., MCCOWN, B. H. and RAFFA, K. F. (1995), 'Field-Evaluation of Transgenic Poplar Expressing a Bacillus-Thuringiensis Cry1a(a) D-Endotoxin Gene against Forest Tent Caterpillar (Lepidoptera, Lasiocampidae) and Gypsy-Moth (Lepidoptera, Lymantriidae) Following Winter Dormancy', *Environmental Entomology*, 24, (5), 1358–1364.

KOZIEL, M. G., BELAND, G. L., BOWMAN, C., CAROZZI, N. B., CRENSHAW, R., CROSSLAND, L., DAWSON, J., DESAI, N., HILL, M., KADWELL, S., LAUNIS, K., LEWIS, K., MADDOX, D., MCPHERSON, K., MEGHJI, M. R., MERLIN, E., RHODES, R., WARREN, G. W., WRIGHT, M. and EVOLA, S. V. (1993), 'Field Performance of Elite Transgenic Maize Plants Expressing an Insecticidal Protein Derived from Bacillus-Thuringiensis', *Bio-Technology*, 11, (2), 194–200.

KRAMER, M., SANDERS, R. A., SHEEHY, R. E. and HIATT, W. R. (1991), 'Evaluation of Transgenic Tomatoes with Reduced Polygalacturonase', *Abstracts of Papers of the American Chemical Society*, 202, 57-AGFD.

LANGLEY, K. R., MARTIN, A., STENNING, R., MURRAY, A. J., HOBSON, G. E., SCHUCH, W. W. and BIRD, C. R. (1994), 'Mechanical and Optical Assessment of the Ripening of Tomato Fruit with Reduced Polygalacturonase Activity', *Journal of the Science of Food and Agriculture*, 66, (4), 547–554.

LIU, D., RAGHOTHAMA, K. G., HASEGAWA, P. M. and BRESSAN, R. A. (1994), 'Osmotin Overexpression in Potato Delays Development of Disease Symptoms', *Proceedings of the National Academy of Sciences of the United States of America*, 91, (5), 1888–1892.

LIUS, S., MANSHARDT, R. M., FITCH, M. M. M., SLIGHTOM, J. L., SANFORD, J. C. and GONSALVES, D. (1997), 'Pathogen-derived resistance provides papaya with effective protection against papaya ringspot virus', *Molecular Breeding*, 3, (3), 161–168.

LLOP-TOUS, I., DOMINGUEZ-PUIGJANER, E., PALOMER, X. and VENDRELL, M. (1999), 'Characterization of two divergent endo-beta-1,4-glucanase cDNA clones highly expressed in the nonclimacteric strawberry fruit', *Plant Physiology*, 119, (4), 1415–1421.

MANNING, K. (1998), 'Isolation of a set of ripening-related genes from strawberry: Their identification and possible relationship to fruit quality traits', *Planta*, 205, (4), 622–631.

MOK, D. W. S. and MOK, M. C. (2001), 'Cytokinin metabolism and action', *Annual Review of Plant Physiology and Plant Molecular Biology*, 52, 89–118.

MUELLER, E., GILBERT, J., DAVENPORT, G., BRIGNETI, G. and BAULCOMBE, D. C. (1995), 'Homology-Dependent Resistance – Transgenic Virus-Resistance in Plants Related to Homology-Dependent Gene Silencing', *Plant Journal*, 7, (6), 1001–1013.

OELLER, P. W., MIN WONG, L., TAYLOR, L. P., PIKE, D. A. and THEOLOGIS, A. (1991), 'Reversible inhibition of tomato fruit senescence by antisense RNA', *Science*, 254, (5030), 437–439.

PERLAK, F. J. and FISHOFF, D. A. (1993) *Advanced Engineered Pesticides*, Marcel Dekker.

PERLAK, F. J., DEATON, R. W., ARMSTRONG, T. A., FUCHS, R. L., SIMS, S. R., GREENPLATE, J. T. and FISCHHOFF, D. A. (1990), 'Insect Resistant Cotton Plants', *Bio-Technology*, 8, (10), 939–943.

PERLAK, F. J., FUCHS, R. L., DEAN, D. A., MCPHERSON, S. L. and FISCHHOFF, D. A. (1991), 'Modification of the Coding Sequence Enhances Plant Expression of Insect Control Protein Genes', *Proceedings of the National Academy of Sciences of the United States of America*, 88, (8), 3324–3328.

PERLAK, F. J., STONE, T. B., MUSKOPF, Y. M., PETERSEN, L. J., PARKER, G. B., MCPHERSON, S. A., WYMAN, J., LOVE, S., REED, G., BIEVER, D. and FISCHHOFF, D. A. (1993), 'Genetically Improved Potatoes – Protection from Damage by Colorado Potato Beetles', *Plant Molecular Biology*, 22, (2), 313–321.

PICTON, S., GRAY, J. E. and GRIERSON, D. (1995), 'The manipulation and modification of tomato fruit ripening by expression of antisense RNA in transgenic plants', *Euphytica*, 85, (1–3), 193–202.

PILCHER, C. D., RICE, M. E., OBRYCKI, J. J. and LEWIS, L. C. (1997), 'Field and laboratory evaluations of transgenic Bacillus thuringiensis corn on secondary lepidopteran pests (Lepidoptera: Noctuidae)', *Journal of Economic Entomology*, 90, (2), 669–678.

SCHROEDER, H. E., GOLLASCH, S., MOORE, A., TABE, L. M., CRAIG, S., HARDIE, D. C., CHRISPEELS, M. J., SPENCER, D. and HIGGINS, T. J. V. (1995), 'Bean Alpha-Amylase Inhibitor Confers Resistance to the Pea Weevil (Bruchus-Pisorum) in Transgenic Peas (Pisum-Sativum L)', *Plant Physiology*, 107, (4), 1233–1239.

SCHUCH, W., KANCZLER, J., ROBERTSON, D., HOBSON, G., TUCKER, G., GRIERSON, D., BRIGHT, S. and BIRD, C. (1991), 'Fruit-Quality Characteristics of Transgenic Tomato Fruit with Altered Polygalacturonase Activity', *Hortscience*, 26, (12), 1517–1520.

SHADE, R. E., SCHROEDER, H. E., PUEYO, J. J., TABE, L. M., MURDOCK, L. L., HIGGINS, T. J. V. and CHRISPEELS, M. J. (1994), 'Transgenic Pea-Seeds Expressing the Alpha-Amylase Inhibitor of the Common Bean Are Resistant to Bruchid Beetles', *Bio-Technology*, 12, (8), 793–796.

SHAH, C. M. T., ROMMENS, D. M. and BEACHY, R. N. (1995), 'Resistance to diseases and insects in transgenic plants: progress and applications to agriculture', *Trends in Biotechnology*, 13, 362–368.

SHEEHY, R. E., KRAMER, M. and HIATT, W. R. (1988), 'Reduction of polygalacturonase activity in tomato fruit by antisense RNA', *Proceedings of the National Academy of Sciences of the United States of America*, 85, (23), 8805–8809.

SIMS, S. R., PERSHING, J. C. and REICH, B. J. (1996), 'Field evaluation of transgenic corn containing a Bacillus thuringiensis Berliner insecticidal protein gene against Helicoverpa zea (Lepidoptera: Noctuidae)', *Journal of Entomological Science*, 31, (3), 340–346.

SMART, C. M., SCOFIELD, S. R., BEVAN, M. W. and DYER, T. A. (1991), 'Delayed leaf senescence in tobacco plants transformed with tmr, a gene for cytokinin production in *Agrobacterium*', *Plant Cell*, 3, (7), 647–656.

SMITH, C. J. S., WATSON, C. F., RAY, J., BIRD, C. R., MORRIS, P. C., SCHUCH, W. and GRIERSON, D. (1988), 'Antisense RNA Inhibition of Polygalacturonase Gene-Expression in Transgenic Tomatoes', *Nature*, 334, (6184), 724–726.

SMITH, C. J., WATSON, C. F., BIRD, C. R., RAY, J., SCHUCH, W. and GRIERSON, D. (1990a), 'Expression of a truncated tomato polygalacturonase gene inhibits expression of the endogenous gene in transgenic plants', *Molecular & General Genetics*, 224, (3), 477–481.

SMITH, C. J. S., WATSON, C. F., MORRIS, P. C., BIRD, C. R., SEYMOUR, G. B., GRAY, J. E., ARNOLD, C., TUCKER, G. A., SCHUCH, W., HARDING, S. and GRIERSON, D. (1990b), 'Inheritance and Effect on Ripening of Antisense Polygalacturonase Genes in Transgenic Tomatoes', *Plant Molecular Biology*, 14, (3), 369–379.

TENNANT, P. F., GONSALVES, C., LING, K. S., FITCH, M., MANSHARDT, R., SLIGHTOM, J. L. and GONSALVES, D. (1994), 'Differential Protection against Papaya Ringspot Virus Isolates in Coat Protein Gene Transgenic Papaya and Classically Cross-Protected Papaya', *Phytopathology*, 84, (11), 1359–1366.

TERRAS, F. R. G., EGGERMONT, K., KOVALEVA, V., RAIKHEL, N. V., OSBORN, R. W., KESTER, A., REES, S. B., TORREKENS, S., VANLEUVEN, F., VANDERLEYDEN, J., CAMMUE, B. P. A. and BROEKAERT, W. F. (1995), 'Small Cysteine-Rich Antifungal Proteins from Radish – Their Role in Host-Defense', *Plant Cell*, 7, (5), 573–588.

TIEMAN, D. M. and HANDA, A. K. (1994), 'Reduction in Pectin Methylesterase Activity Modifies Tissue Integrity and Cation Levels in Ripening Tomato (Lycopersicon-Esculentum Mill) Fruits', *Plant Physiology*, 106, (2), 429–436.

TIEMAN, D. M., HARRIMAN, R. W., RAMAMOHAN, G. and HANDA, A. K. (1992), 'An Antisense Pectin Methylesterase Gene Alters Pectin Chemistry and Soluble Solids in Tomato Fruit', *Plant Cell*, 4, (6), 667–679.

TIEMAN, D. V., TAYLOR, M. G., CIARDI, J. A. and KLEE, H. J. (2000), 'The tomato ethylene receptors NR and LeETR4 are negative regulators of ethylene response and exhibit functional compensation within a multigene family', *Proceedings of the National Academy of Sciences of the United States of America*, 97, (10), 5663–5668.

TU, J. M., ZHANG, G. A., DATTA, K., XU, C. G., HE, Y. Q., ZHANG, Q. F., KHUSH, G. S. and DATTA, S. K. (2000), 'Field performance of transgenic elite commercial hybrid rice expressing Bacillus thuringiensis delta-endotoxin', *Nature Biotechnology*, 18, (10), 1101–1104.

WOLTERING, E. J., SOMHORST, D. and VANDERVEER, P. (1995), 'The Role of Ethylene in Interorgan Signaling During Flower Senescence', *Plant Physiology*, 109, (4), 1219–1225.

WOODSON, W. R., PARK, K. Y., DRORY, A., LARSEN, P. B. and WANG, H. (1992), 'Expression of ethylene biosynthetic pathway transcripts in senescing carnation flowers', *Plant Physiology*, 99, (2), 526–532.

WOOLLEY, L. C., JAMES, D. J. and MANNING, K. (2001), 'Purification and properties of an endo-beta-1,4-glucanase from strawberry and down-regulation of the corresponding gene, cel1', *Planta*, 214, (1), 11–21.

YANG, S. F. and HOFFMAN, N. E. (1984), 'Ethylene biosynthesis and its regulation in higher plants', *Annual Review of Plant Physiology*, 35, 155–189.

# 14

# Membrane filtration techniques in food preservation

A. S. Grandison, The University of Reading, UK

## 14.1  Introduction

Commercial membrane processing has developed over the last 40 years, and is becoming increasingly important in the food industry for concentration and fractionation processes. The basic principle is to separate a single liquid feed into two liquid streams by means of a solid membrane. The membrane is selective, allowing some materials to pass through (the permeate stream), while other materials are retained (the retentate stream). In some cases it is the permeate stream that is desired, in others it is the retentate, while sometimes both products are of value. The main criterion for separation is size, although other factors, such as surface charge or shape of the molecule or particle, may have an effect. The driving force for the separation is pressure difference across the membrane.

Membrane processing holds several significant advantages over competing approaches to concentration or separation used in the food and biotechnology industries:

- membrane filtration is a purely physical operation and hence there are no chemical changes to the process streams
- the separations are pressure driven and no excessive heating is required, hence there is little risk of heat damage, resulting in flavour or other quality changes to food components, or heat denaturation of enzymes
- no phase changes are involved, which may lead to reduced energy use compared to operations involving evaporation
- the size spectrum of materials separated by membranes is enormous, ranging over several orders of magnitude from the smallest ions to particles such as fat globules or bacterial cells.

The use of membrane filtration in food preservation techniques can be considered from two approaches. On one hand membranes can be used to reduce bacterial numbers in a process stream, leading to a preservation technique *per se*. Alternatively, membrane concentrations and fractionations contribute to the production of many preserved food products. Both approaches will be discussed. The aim of this chapter is to provide information on the principles of membrane operations, and how they can contribute to food preservation techniques, with some ideas how they may develop in future.

## 14.2    General principles of membrane processing

The basic unit for separation is the membrane, whose properties determine the level of separation achieved. There are three classical membrane processes:

1.  Reverse osmosis (RO, sometimes referred to as hyperfiltration) is a concentration process in which even monovalent ions are retained by the membrane.
2.  Ultrafiltration (UF) operates in the approximate molecular weight cut-off (MWCO) range 500–500 000 Daltons. Generally, lower molecular weight species, such as simple sugars or amino acids, can pass through into the permeate, while macromolecules, such as proteins, polysaccharides or fats, will be retained.
3.  Microfiltration (MF) separates species in the approximate range 0.1–10 $\mu$m, such that some macromolecules may pass into the permeate, while larger macromolecules or colloidal structures and fat globules would be retained.

The sizes and types of particle undergoing separation are illustrated in Fig. 14.1. It should be noted that the distinction between the three separations is not exact, and the spectrum can be considered to be continuous. A further process, termed nanofiltration (NF) has recently been introduced, which lies between RO and UF, permitting separation of very small components such as simple ions and salts, from low molecular weight components such as mono- or disaccharides.

There are several related separation processes incorporating membranes. Diafiltration is an extension of UF or MF and is discussed on pages 267–8. Electrodialysis is a combination of membrane and ion-exchange separation which can be used for demineralisation of food materials, reviewed by Grandison (1996b). Dialysis is a concentration-driven membrane separation, which has medical and biochemical applications, but is unlikely to contribute to food preservation. Similarly, pervaporation is the separation of liquid mixtures with a permselective membrane, but is unlikely to have food applications.

### 14.2.1    Transport theory

Although there are many similarities between the equipment and operation of the different membrane processes, there is a fundamental difference between the

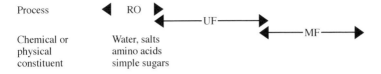

Fig. 14.1   The filtration spectrum and sizes of components.

mechanisms of transport in RO compared to UF or MF. Ultrafiltration and MF are believed to be true sieving processes, where the membrane has definite pores, which permit the passage of smaller particles but reject larger species. Reverse osmosis, however, is more difficult to explain in terms of sieving, not least because RO allows the permeation of water molecules, but rejects salt ions or molecules of approximately equal size. A useful parameter for all membrane processes is the concentration factor ($f$), where:

$$f = \frac{V_F}{V_R} \qquad\qquad 14.1$$

where $V_F$ = volume of feed; $V_R$ = volume of retentate.

*Reverse osmosis*
If a solution of, say salt or sugar, is separated from solvent by a semi-permeable membrane (permeable to solvent but not solute), there will be a flow of solvent to the solution (Fig. 14.2(a)). This is termed osmosis, and the extent of the process depends on the osmotic pressure ($\Pi$) of the solution. If a pressure greater than $\Pi$ is applied to the solution side of the membrane, then pure solvent will flow against the concentration gradient as indicated in Fig. 14.2(b), this is the principle of reverse osmosis.

For dilute solutions of non-ionised material, $\Pi$ can be obtained from the Van't Hoff equation:

$$\Pi = RT\frac{C}{M} \qquad\qquad 14.2$$

where R = gas constant; T = absolute temperature; C = concentration of solute; M = molecular weight of solute. For ionised solutes, this becomes:

$$\Pi = iRT\frac{C}{M} \qquad\qquad 14.3$$

where $i$ = degree of ionisation, e.g., for NaCl $i = 2$; for CaCl$_2$ $i = 3$.

However, care should be taken in making such calculations, as osmotic pressure actually rises in an exponential manner with increasing concentration,

(a) Osmosis

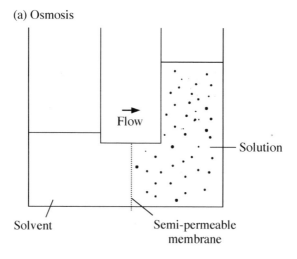

(b) Reverse osmosis

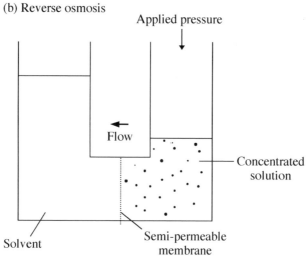

**Fig. 14.2** The principles of (a) Osmosis, and (b) Reverse osmosis.

and the Van't Hoff equation underestimates the osmotic pressures of more concentrated solutions. In many food fluids, osmotic pressure is derived from the combined contribution of many chemical species, and some examples are given in Table 14.1. The contribution of any species to total osmotic pressure is inversely proportional to its molecular weight, therefore small species such as salts and sugar contribute much more than do large molecules such as proteins. This is illustrated by the fact that seawater has a much greater osmotic pressure than a protein (casein) solution at the same solids concentration. Also, the osmotic pressures of whey and milk are identical, while the total solids content of milk is much greater than whey as it contains higher levels of protein and fat.

**Table 14.1** Osmotic pressures of some fluids (Data adapted from Cheryan (1986) and Lewis (1996a))

| Liquid | Approximate total solids (%) | Osmotic pressure (bar) |
|---|---|---|
| Milk | 11 | 6.7 |
| Whey | 6 | 6.7 |
| Orange juice | 11 | 15.3 |
| Apple juice | 14 | 20.0 |
| Sea water* | 3.5 | 14.1 |
| Casein solution* | 3.5 | 0.03 |

*Calculated from Van't Hoff equation.

The exact mechanism of transport is not clear and various theories are discussed elsewhere (Lewis, 1996a). A useful approach is to consider that the solvent (usually water) actually dissolves in the membrane material and diffuses through, under the driving force of pressure, whereas solutes are relatively insoluble and are held back. In any event, reverse osmosis requires that the applied pressure exceeds the osmotic pressure of the feed, and the rate of solvent transport across the membrane is proportional to the pressure difference, hence:

$$J_w \propto A(\Delta P - \Delta \Pi) \qquad\qquad 14.4$$

where $J_w$ = solvent flux, $A$ = membrane area, $\Delta P$ = applied pressure, $\Delta \Pi$ = osmotic pressure difference across the membrane-approximates to osmotic pressure of the solution. As the feed becomes more concentrated, the osmotic pressure rises and hence the applied pressure must be increased to maintain the flux. This limits the level of concentration possible. Applied pressures of up to 70 bar may be required in reverse osmosis.

*Ultrafiltration and microfiltration*
Ultrafiltration and MF are easier to understand in terms of pure sieving phenomena, the membranes having distinct pores. There is no definite distinction between the two processes, the only difference being the pore size, and even that is not an absolute distinction. Osmotic pressure is very much less important in UF and MF compared to RO, because UF and MF membranes are permeable to the smaller molecules and ionic species, which are the main contributors to osmotic pressure. Hence the osmotic pressure differences across the membrane are much smaller. For this reason the pressures, and hence pumping power, required for UF and MF are generally much lower than for RO. Typically, UF is carried out at 2–10 bar, with MF on the lower end of this range.

Performance during UF and MF can be described by two quantities – the permeate flux ($J$) which quantifies the rate of filtration, and the rejection ($R$) of the different components of the feed. For any molecule or ionic species:

$$R = \frac{C_F - C_P}{C_F} \qquad\qquad 14.5$$

where $C_F$ and $C_P$ are the concentrations of that component in the feed and permeate respectively. Therefore, if a component is completely rejected by the membrane, $C_P = 0$ and $R = 1$ (sometimes expressed as 100%). On the other hand, for components which freely permeate the membrane, $C_P = C_F$, and $R = 0$.

Ideally, during RO, all components would have $R = 1$. For UF, large molecules such as proteins would have values of $R$ approaching 1, whereas for small components such as dissolved salts or simple sugars, $R$ would approach 0. As UF and MF membranes in practice have a pore size distribution, and hence diffuse cut-off points, many species will have $R$ values between 0 and 1. The yield of any component is the quantity remaining in the retentate at the end of processing, and may be calculated from

$$C_1 = C_0 . f^R \qquad\qquad 14.6$$

where $C_1 = $ final concentration, $C_0 = $ initial concentration in feed. This relationship assumes that $R$ is constant throughout, which is not usually the case. Rejection frequently increases during processing.

Permeate flux during UF and MF is often modelled as a purely sieving process in terms of flow through a bundle of capillaries according to the Hagen-Poiseuille equation, where flux per unit area of membrane

$$J = \frac{d^2 \Delta P \Pi}{32 \mu L} \qquad\qquad 14.7$$

where $d = $ capillary (pore) diameter; $\mu = $ dynamic viscosity; $L = $ capillary length. In practice, this relationship is complicated by other properties of the membrane (porosity and tortuosity effects), and will change throughout processing due to concentration polarisation and fouling (discussed below). However, the relationship predicts the strong influence of pore diameter on flux as well as how increasing viscosity and membrane thickness would lead to reduced flux. It is notable that viscosity often increases during processing.

Diafiltration is an extension of UF, and to a lesser extent MF, in which water is added at some stage during processing. It can be carried out by continuous addition of water during processing, or discontinuously where water is added in batches after a certain level of concentration has been achieved. The net effect is to wash out lower molecular weight components so that a higher concentration of the retained species, as a proportion of total solids, can be obtained. It may also be useful where specific undesirable low molecular weight components need to be removed.

*Concentration polarisation and the crossflow principle*
In any membrane process when the feed is switched from water to a solution, there is a marked drop in permeate flux. The flux reduction may be as great as ten times when switching from water to milk. This phenomenon is caused by concentration polarisation, which is caused by a local increase in solids as

(a) In boundary layer

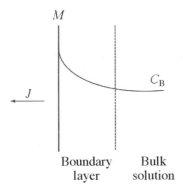

Boundary          Bulk
  layer          solution

(b) In associated gel layer

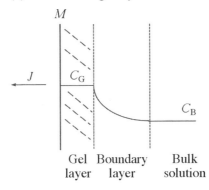

Gel   Boundary      Bulk
layer    layer     solution

$M$ = Membrane
$J$ = Permeate flux
$C_B$ = Concentration of bulk solution
$C_G$ = Gel concentration

**Fig. 14.3**  Concentration polarisation (a) in boundary layer, and (b) in associated gel layer.

permeate is removed from the feed stream. A concentration gradient is thus set up (Fig. 14.3(a)), which may even give rise to a gel layer (Fig. 14.3(b)). In both cases, the concentration polarisation layer becomes established as a dynamic equilibrium where convective flow of the component(s) to the layer equals the movement away, either into the permeate or back into the bulk solution. Concentration polarisation forms a very significant resistance to flux, especially if high molecular weight components are present in the layer. The extent of concentration polarisation depends on the chemical composition and physical properties of the feed, and is reversible if the feed is replaced by water, the original permeate flux should be restored (although in practice this may be limited by fouling).

**(a) Dead end filtration**

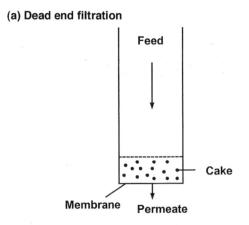

**(b) Cross-flow (shown for tubular membrane)**

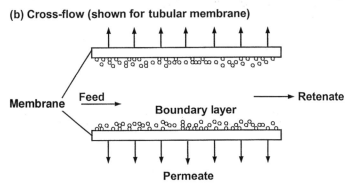

**Fig. 14.4** (a) Dead-end filtration; (b) Cross-flow filtration.

One major principle of improving membrane performance is to reduce the thickness of the concentration polarisation layer by increasing the flow at the membrane surface. Membrane systems can be operated in dead-end mode (Fig. 14.4(a)) resulting in the formation of a thick layer, which causes a large reduction in flux, and will build up further as processing continues. Alternatively, the crossflow system (Fig. 14.4(b)) produces turbulence or high shear rates in the feed, and hence minimises concentration polarisation. In fact the development of industrial membrane processing resulted from the development of crossflow systems permitting acceptable processing rates. Dead-end systems are largely confined to laboratory activities.

Concentration polarisation determines the relationship of permeate flux with pressure. At low pressure, especially where feed velocity is high and solute concentration is low, i.e., where concentration polarisation is minimal, flux is linearly related to transmembrane pressure. As pressure increases, a point will be found where flux deviates from the pressure-dependent region such that increasing pressure no longer produces increased flux. This is due to the formation of a consolidated polarised layer, which takes over control of the flux.

**Table 14.2**   Some factors which affect permeate flux rate during membrane processing

| Factor | Change | Effect on flux |
|---|---|---|
| 1. Properties of the membrane | | |
| Pore size | ▲ | ▲ |
| Thickness | ▲ | ▼ |
| Porosity | ▲ | ▲ |
| Tortuosity | ▲ | ▼ |
| Compaction | ▲ | ▼ |
| 2. Properties of feed | | |
| Concentration | ▲ | ▼ |
| Viscosity | ▲ | ▼ |
| Temperature | ▲ | ▲ |
| 3. Hydrodynamic effects | | |
| Transmembrane pressure | ▲ | ▲ |
| Crossflow velocity | ▲ | ▲ |

*Fouling*

Fouling is the deposition of solid material either on the surface or within the pores of a membrane, which produces a steady decline in permeate flux. The deposition may result from direct adsorption of molecules, such as proteins, to the membrane material, crystal formation on the surface or within the membrane pores, or formation of microbial colonies on the membrane. In any case the fouling is at least partly irreversible, and the membrane must be cleaned to restore the flux.

Flux during membrane processing is controlled by a number of factors, many of which are summarised in Table 14.2. One model for estimating permeate flux per unit area, which considers the resistances to flow in series, is:

$$J = \frac{\Delta P - \Delta \Pi}{\mu(R_m + R_f + R_p)}$$

14.8

where $R_M$ = membrane resistance; $R_f$ = fouling resistance; $R_p$ = resistance of concentration polarisation layer. The term $\Delta \Pi$ (osmotic pressure difference across the membrane) can usually be ignored in UF and MF.

## 14.3   Filtration equipment

### 14.3.1   Membranes

The development of membranes is often described in terms of first-, second- and third-generation. The first membranes to be used successfully on a large scale were composed of cellulose acetate. These are prepared as a thin (0.1–1.0 $\mu$m) 'skin' on a much thicker porous support. Their application, however, is limited to a narrow pH range (2–8 at most) and limited temperature (<40°C), which places a severe restriction on their use, especially on cleaning operations, which are vital to food processing. The second generation was the development of a range of polymer materials such as polyamide, polysulphone or polyvinylidine fluoride. These are again prepared as a skin on a porous support, and can be manufactured in a range of pore sizes. They are much more resistant to pH variation and can withstand much higher temperatures than cellulose acetate. The third generation are inorganic materials including glass, metals and compounds of aluminium, zirconium and titanium, again coated onto a solid support. They are very rugged with high mechanical, pH and temperature resistance.

Suppliers provide membranes with a range of specified rejection characteristics. Reverse osmosis (and nanofiltration) membranes are usually composed of cellulose acetate or polyamide, and are characterised in terms of rejection of particular components, e.g., 99% rejection of NaCl. UF membranes have pores in the range 2–20 nm diameter, but are normally classified in terms of the molecular weight cut-off, usually 500–500 000. The vast majority of commercial UF membranes are polymeric, although inorganic membranes in the UF range are emerging. MF membranes may be manufactured from any of the materials described above, but it is notable that the development of inorganic membranes has generally been towards MF applications. Microfiltration membranes are characterised in terms of pore size (0.01–10 $\mu$m diameter).

A very important, and often misunderstood, concept is that rejection characteristics and molecular weight or particle diameter cut-offs are, in reality, very inexact. The data provided by suppliers should be used only for preliminary selection of membranes. It is tempting to believe that, for example, a membrane with a molecular weight cut-off of 10,000 would reject all molecules greater than 10,000 Daltons ($R = 1$), while all species with lower molecular weight would be freely permeating ($R = 0$). This is not the case for a number of reasons. Molecular shape and charge, as well as interactions between feed components and the material of the membrane cause rejection to be inaccurate. Added to this, there is a range of pore diameters within any membrane, which causes the separation to be diffuse. Some membrane types will give a sharper cut-off than others with respect to any individual solute if they have a narrower distribution of pore sizes. Furthermore, rejection characteristics may actually change during processing. In most cases rejection increases due to changes in the concentration polarisation layer and development of fouling.

### 14.3.2   Membrane configurations and modules

In practice, membranes are configured into modules, the design of which must incorporate several features:

- support of membrane under required hydraulic pressures
- large surface area of membrane, preferably in compact volume

- flow streams must be established in which correct hydrodynamic conditions can prevail – e.g., flow rate, turbulence, pressure drop
- good hygienic conditions
- ease of cleaning and membrane replacement.

The major configurations are flat sheet and tubular designs (Fig. 14.5). Flat sheet geometries include plate-and-frame and spiral-wound, while tubular systems can be either hollow fibre (0.001–1.2 mm diameter) or wider tubular systems (0.6–2.5 cm). Each system has its own characteristics with respect to flow characteristics and hence recommended applications – e.g., hollow fibre systems have very narrow flow channels, which are unsuitable for viscous or particulate feeds. The subject is discussed in detail elsewhere (Cheryan, 1986; Lewis, 1996a; Grandison and Glover, 1994).

### 14.3.3   Machinery and systems

The basic requirements for membrane processing are a membrane module, feed tank, pump, flow control and pressure-retaining valves, along with appropriate flow rate, temperature and pressure monitoring devices. It is normal to include a heat exchanger to control the feed temperature. The choice of pump depends upon the pressure and flow rate required. Generally, centrifugal pumps are sufficient for UF and MF, while the higher pressures used in RO require positive displacement pumps. Delicate particulate or viscous feeds may require more specialised pumps. To achieve a useful degree of concentration, the feed must pass over the membrane surface many times – perhaps an average of 100 times – as single pass operations would require a massive membrane area. Plant may then be operated in either batch or continuous mode of operation.

*Batch operation*

In this mode of operation, the feed circulates round the whole plant and is returned to the feed tank. If necessary, the process volume can be increased by topping up the feed tank during processing, the concentration factor being calculated from the volume of permeate removed. It is suitable for processing small volumes, which can be wholly contained within the plant. In practice batch operations are more suited to small-scale or pilot plant operations. The basic requirements for batch operation are shown in Fig. 14.6(a).

*Continuous operation*

The design in Fig. 14.6(b) is a single stage internal recycle (or feed and bleed) system. In this system the feed is pumped round an inner loop consisting of the membrane module and circulation pump. The plant is first operated until the desired level of concentration is achieved. At this point a little of the retentate is bled off, the remainder returning to the circulation pump where more fresh feed is added from the feed pump to maintain the volume of concentrate. Fresh feed is continuously added at the same rate as concentrate is removed. This system

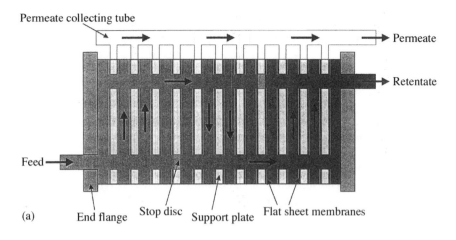

Permeate collecting tube

Permeate

Retentate

Feed

(a)   End flange   Stop disc   Support plate   Flat sheet membranes

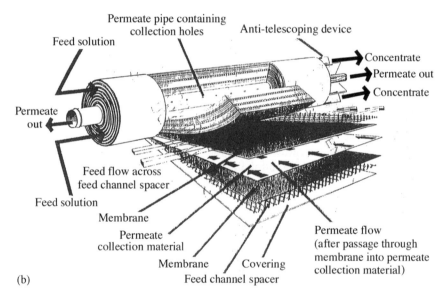

Permeate pipe containing
collection holes

Anti-telescoping device

Feed solution

Concentrate
Permeate out
Concentrate

Permeate
out

Feed flow across
feed channel spacer

Feed solution

Membrane

Permeate
collection material

Permeate flow
(after passage through
membrane into permeate
collection material)

Membrane   Covering
Feed channel spacer

(b)

**Fig. 14.5**   Some membrane configurations: (a) plate-and-frame (courtesy of DSS
SILKEBORG AS); (b) spiral wound (courtesy of Koch Membrane systems).

may be operated for quite long periods in commercial plants, say 20 h operation
followed by 4 h cleaning. This system holds major advantages over batch
systems in that the retention time in the plant is low (minutes rather than hours),
and that the internal loop is closed so the whole pressure is not lost on each
recycle, which conserves energy. The major disadvantage is that the continuous
operation is carried out at maximum product concentration so that permeate flux
is low.

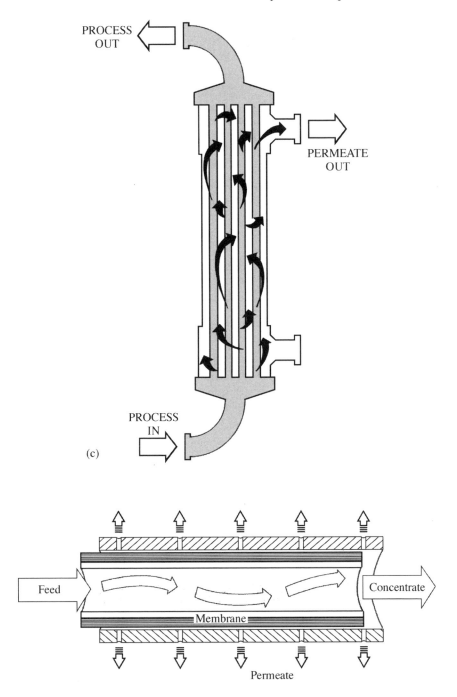

**Fig. 14.5 (cont.)**   (c) hollow fibre (courtesy of Koch Membrane systems); (d) tubular system (courtesy of PCI membranes).

An alternative design for very large-scale processing is a multi-stage plant, which may contain several hundred square metres of membrane. A single pump cannot provide the necessary power to drive the system, therefore plants are made up of repeating units, each with its own pump, arranged in series. Within each unit, the modules may be arranged in parallel or in series. Figure 14.6(c) shows a system with three units, although more may be possible in practice. The size of successive units would decrease in practice, as the volume of feed diminishes.

### 14.3.4   Hygiene and cleaning

In all membrane processes, all micro-organisms will be completely rejected by the membrane, and microbial numbers will therefore increase in the retentate in line with the concentration factor. There is also the likelihood that some microbial growth will occur during processing, depending on the temperature and residence time within the plant. In food processing operations with long residence times, it is advisable to operate at temperature above 50°C or below 5°C to prevent growth. Heat treatment before and/or following membrane processing may also be considered. The permeate, however, should be sterile on production, but may form a good medium for microbial growth. Hence membrane systems should be designed for cleaning and sterilisation on both retentate and permeate sides.

In addition to the requirement for good hygiene, regular cleaning is required to maintain the efficient operation of membrane systems. Fouling will develop during any food treatment (see page 271) and it is essential to remove completely any material that is irreversibly attached to the membrane, and hence restore the flux rate to the original. This is commonly assessed by measuring the water flux before processing and after cleaning. The precise cleaning regime depends on the nature of the feed and the resilience of the membrane. Developments in membrane materials have generally led to membranes that can survive harsher cleaning regimes. In dairy applications, for example, it is normal to clean with caustic solutions to remove fat and protein, followed by acid washing to remove minerals. Proteolytic enzymes and ion-sequestering chemicals may also be used.

## 14.4   Using membranes in food preservation

Membranes were first developed commercially as a means of purifying water by RO, and for purifying waste water. Applications in food processing have since widened considerably. Membrane techniques can contribute to food preservation in two ways. Firstly, membranes reject all micro-organisms within the retentate and thus the permeate will be sterile on production. Hence, provided that the relevant components of the food fluid permeate the membrane, then membrane processing can be used *per se* as a direct method of food preservation by reducing the number of micro-organisms in the feed. This approach is really

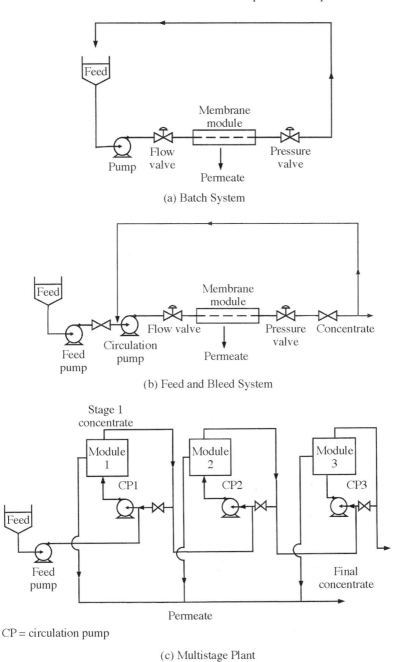

(a) Batch System

(b) Feed and Bleed System

CP = circulation pump

(c) Multistage Plant

**Fig. 14.6**  Membrane systems: (a) batch operation; (b) continuous internal recycle (feed and bleed); (c) continuous operation (multistage plant).

limited to microfiltration. On the other hand, all the membrane processes contribute to concentration or fractionation procedures, which form part of other food preservation activities.

### 14.4.1    Removal of micro-organisms by microfiltration

Microfiltration is a well-established laboratory technique for the removal of micro-organisms (both vegetative and spore forms), and hence the production of sterile fluids, without the application of heat. The advent of cross-flow MF has enabled the same concept to be applied on a commercial scale. The technique has been widely applied to the production of clarified beverages such as beer and cider (Finnegan and Skudder, 1989), wine (Palacios *et al.*, 2002) or fruit juices (Short, 1988). Microfiltration effectively removes cells and any other suspended solids, avoiding the use of clearing agents such as diatomaceous earth or enzymes, with excellent retention of colour.

Microfiltration of milk can be used with the aim of producing liquid milk with extended shelf-life either as a replacement for, or in addition to, heat treatment. Alternatively, MF milk with reduced bacterial numbers, can be used as an alternative to pasteurised milk in the manufacture of cheese. The problem with milk processing is that the size ranges of fat globules and bacteria overlap, such that much of the fat will be removed along with bacterial cells in the retentate. However, effective bacterial removal of cells from skim milk is possible. Guerra *et al.* (1997) claim that by use of careful control with 0.87 $\mu$m pore size membranes, bacterial spores can be reduced by a factor of $10^4-10^5$ with 100% transmission of casein at excellent permeate flux rates. Homogenisation of milk leads to reduction of fat globule size, which may permit half fat or full fat milks to be effectively treated if the globules are small enough to permeate the membrane. A product currently available in the UK is Cravendale 'Purfiltre' milk (marketed by Arla Foods, DK), which is a semi-skimmed product from which it is claimed 99.7% bacteria are removed by MF. The product is also pasteurised and has an increased shelf-life of 20 days. The combination of MF and pasteurisation reduces bacterial numbers by 99.99% (4D), (Grandison, 1996a). It is feasible that 'cold-pasteurised' liquid milks produced by MF alone will be available in future.

Removal of bacteria from skim milk for cheesemaking by MF, using ceramic membranes on a commercial scale has been described (Malmbert and Holm, 1988). The permeate may be recombined with heat-treated cream in the manufacture of full-fat cheese. There are a number of potential advantages, in particular the flavour characteristics of raw milk cheeses may be retained. The 'Bactocatch' system (marketed by Tetra Pak Inc., Vernon Hills, Il, USA) is claimed to hold further advantages in that bacterial contamination is reduced by 99.6% in either heat-treated or non-heated cheese milks, thus quality is improved generally and the incidence of blowing and the need to add nitrates to some cheeses are avoided. Reducing the bacterial load of cheese whey by MF prior to further processing is also a potential advantage.

Whole egg or egg whites are extensively used as ingredients, especially in the baking industry. The use of MF rather than heat pasteurisation of egg products is an obvious application, but the application is limited by fouling from ovomucins (Ferreira *et al.*, 1999).

### 14.4.2    Other concentration and separation processes

The application of the full range of membrane processes has been investigated in all sectors of the food processing industries, and detailed reviews can be found elsewhere (e.g., Cheryan 1998; Lewis 1996a and b; Kosikowski 1986). This section will take an overview of selected applications to illustrate the breadth and scope of the techniques as contributors to food preservation. Membranes are widely incorporated into fermentation or enzyme reactors in the biotechnology industries, UF or MF membranes being effective means of immobilising enzymes or cells and thus permitting continuous processing. This type of application will not be discussed further here.

*Concentration by membranes*

Reverse osmosis has made inroads into areas where evaporation is widely used – particularly the dairy, fruit juice and sugar processing industries. The level of concentration attainable is much less than with evaporation, but RO holds advantages in terms of the level of heat damage found in the products. Commercial applications may therefore be to increase the capacity of evaporation plants.

Possible applications of RO in the dairy industry (reviewed by El-Gazzar and Marth, 1991) include concentration of milk on-farm to reduce transportation costs, pre-concentration of milk for ice cream and yoghurt-making as an alternative to using expensive milk powders, concentrating milk for cheesemaking to increase the capacity of cheese vats. Whey may also be concentrated prior to transport or drying.

Fruit and vegetable juices are usually concentrated, either prior to frozen transport or in the manufacture of pulps and purees. Reverse osmosis can yield higher quality products compared to evaporation in terms of better retention of volatiles and minimising browning reactions. A limiting factor is the high osmotic pressure of the juices. The process is well established in the manufacture of concentrated tomato juice and puree, as well as citrus and many other fruit and vegetable concentrates (Medina and Garcia 1988; Koseoglu *et al.*, 1991). Other applications of RO include concentration of beet or cane sugar syrup, coffee extracts, egg white, and the manufacture of low-alcohol beer.

*Processes involving separation of food components*

Ultrafiltration and MF have been used in many diverse processes involving fractionation of the solids components. Separation of the larger components of milk (proteins and fat) from the smaller constituents such as lactose and minerals is exploited by UF in a variety of applications (reviewed by Renner and El-

Salam 1991). In the manufacture of cheese, the casein and fat form a gel from which the whey containing soluble whey proteins, lactose and soluble minerals is drained. By carrying out UF (or sometimes MF) prior to coagulation (up to $f = 5$), the whey drainage is greatly reduced and whey proteins are retained in the cheese, thus giving greater cheese yields. This technique is carried out commercially in the manufacture of many cheeses (e.g., Mozzarella, Feta, cottage cheese, fromage frais), although there may be loss of texture in hard cheeses such as Cheddar. A more limited level of concentration can be used either to standardise protein levels for cheese milks in continuous cheesemaking plants as used in Camembert manufacture, or to increase the yield per vat. Whey is a major by-product of cheesemaking, containing about 20% of the total milk protein. Liquid or dried whey is of limited value as the protein content is still quite low. However UF treatment of whey gives much higher protein levels, and if combined with diafiltration, can be used in the manufacture of whey protein powders containing up to 90% protein. These products have much wider applications in the meat processing, confectionery and baking industries.

There are numerous examples of applications of UF in situations where it is desirable to remove smaller species from food protein solutions (Lewis 1996b). Gelatin may be concentrated from dilute solutions with the removal of minerals, which gives an improvement in its gelling properties. The presence of glucose in egg whites gives rise to storage problems and excessive browning during baking processes. A solution is to carry out UF, possibly in conjunction with diafiltration to remove the glucose while retaining the egg white protein. Purifications of plant proteins such as soybean or rapeseed by UF have also been demonstrated.

Recovery of valuable proteins from waste water produced in the processing of fish, meat, milk and vegetables by UF has also been demonstrated. A further approach has been to incorporate UF or MF into refining of vegetable oils (Pioch et al., 1998). In this case the oil permeates the membrane while water-soluble impurities such as saponified fatty acids or phosphatides are removed in the retentate.

Microfiltration is a most efficient method of clarification of liquids, which can be applied to a range of juices and beverages as described in section 14.4.1. A most promising application of MF could be to replace carbonatation for clarification of beet juice in sugar manufacture. Hanemaaier (1985) has demonstrated the removal of residual fat from cheese whey, which dramatically improves the functionality of protein fractions produced from the clarified whey.

A promising application of MF is to the fractionation of macromolecules. Fractionation of milk proteins has usually involved separation of the proteins in the colloidal micellar phase from those in true solution. Hence, the casein micelles and whey proteins may be separated. For example Brandsma and Rizvi (2001) demonstrated improved quality Mozzarella cheese manufacture from MF milk depleted in whey protein. This approach can be taken further if different proteins are induced to associate with or diffuse from the micelles. For example, Pouliot et al. (1994) described dissociation of $\beta$-casein from micelles of a phosphocaseinate suspension, which can be microfiltered to produce $\beta$-casein enriched and $\beta$-casein depleted fractions. It is feasible that, in this way, milk could be tailored for specific products or dietary needs. Chove *et al.* (2002) have applied MF to soy protein isolates and demonstrated different functional properties in the subfractions. Fat may also be subfractionated by MF. Gouderanche *et al.* (2000) separated milk fat into globule size categories, which imparted different textural and organoleptic properties on the products.

## 14.5    Future trends

Membrane technology has made significant advances in applications contributing to food preservation in the past few decades. However, the techniques have yet to reach their full potential due to several reasons:

- the separations available with commercial membranes are often diffuse so that the levels of purification are not good enough to compete with existing techniques
- problems of low flux, or flux decline during processing, may render some operations non-economic
- many sectors of the food industry are very traditional and slow to embrace the opportunities presented by novel membrane techniques.

Advances in membrane design and greater understanding of operating parameters are leading to sharper, more accurate separations. For example, it is now feasible to separate mono-, di- and oligosaccharides using NF (Goulas *et al.*, 2002), or to fractionate the proteins in milk using MF (Le Berre and Daufin 1996). These possibilities would have been considered unlikely some years ago.

Improving flux rates has been the goal of much research in recent years. There have been several approaches that involve reducing the concentration polarisation layer and rate of fouling, or removing deposits from the membrane. Optimising pressures and feed flow rates too can be beneficial. The critical flux concept (Gesan-Guiziou *et al.*, 2000) in which permeate flux is maintained at a level below that at which fouling occurs, is a promising idea. Backflushing of some permeate into the retentate stream at intervals is a well-established method of clearing blocked pores and hence recovering flux during MF. Turbulence promoters can be used to minimise concentration polarisation. Other promising techniques include initiating toroidal vortices in the feed, the use of pulsatile flows, mechanically vibrating, or electrically charged membranes. These techniques have met with success on a research level and should lead to more commercial applications.

Membrane processing, being a purely physical technique, fits well into the philosophy of producing minimally processed foods and will probably continue to replace more severe techniques of concentration or separation involving heat or chemical interactions. Membranes could be used to produce purified proteins with specific functional properties, purified oligosaccharides with prebiotic properties or even long-life milk without any heat treatment.

## 14.6   Sources of further information and advice

There are several detailed works on the principles and equipment for membrane processing, including Cheryan (1986 and 1998), Gutman (1987), Lewis (1996a and 1996b), Winston Ho and Sirkar (1992). General information on membrane applications, developments and companies can be found on: www.membraneonline.com

Suppliers of membranes and equipment include the following:

Koch membrane systems, Wilmington, MA, USA.
PCI products, Whitchurch, Hants., UK.
Danish separations systems, Silkeborg, Denmark.
Osmonics, Minnetonka, MN, USA.
TAMI industries, Nyons, France.

## 14.7   References

BRANDSMA RL and RIZVI SSH (2001) 'Effect of manufacturing treatments on the rheological character of mozzarella cheese made from microfiltration retentate depleted of whey proteins', *International Journal of Food Science and Technology*, 36(6), 601–610.

CHERYAN M (1986), *Ultrafiltration: Handbook*, Basel, Technomic.

CHERYAN M (1998), *Ultrafiltration and Microfiltration: Handbook*, Basel, Technomic.

CHOVE BE, GRANDISON AS and LEWIS MJ (2002) 'Emulsifying properties of soy protein isolates obtained by microfiltration' *Journal of the Science of Food and Agriculture*, 82, 267–272.

EL-GAZZAR FE and MARTH EH (1991) 'Ultrafiltration and reverse osmosis in dairy technology; a review', *Journal of Food Protection*, 54, 801–809.

FERREIRA M, OLIVEIRA FAR and JOST R (1999) 'Application of microfiltration to egg white depleted in ovomucin', *International Journal of Food Science and Technology*, 34, 27–32.

FINNEGAN TJA and SKUDDER P (1989) 'The application of ceramic microfiltration in the brewing industry' Field RW and Howell JA *Process Engineering in the Food Industry*, London, Elsevier, 259–272.

GESAN-GUIZIOU G, DAUFIN G and BOYAVAL E (2000) 'Critical stability conditions in skimmed milk crossflow microfiltration: impact on operating modes', *Lait*, 80, 129–140.

GOUDERANCHE H, FAUQUANT J and MAUBOIS JL (2000) 'Fractionation of globular milk fat by microfiltration', *Lait*, 80, 93–98.

GOULAS AK, KAPASAKALIDIS PG, SINCLAIR HR, RASTALL RA and GRANDISON AS (2002) 'Purification of oligosaccharides by nanofiltration', *Journal of Membrane Science*, 209, 321–335.

GRANDISON AS (1996a) 'Microfiltration', in Grandison AS and Lewis MJ *Separation Processes in the Food and Biotechnology Industries*, Cambridge, Woodhead, 141–153.

GRANDISON AS (1996b) 'Ion-exchange and electrodialysis', in Grandison AS and Lewis MJ *Separation Processes in the Food and Biotechnology Industries*, Cambridge,

Woodhead, 155–177.

GRANDISON AS and GLOVER FA (1994) 'Membrane processing of milk', in Robinson RK *Modern Dairy Technology, Volume 1*, London, Chapman and Hall, 273–311.

GUERRA A, JONSSON G, RASMUSSEN A, WAAGNER NIELSEN E and EDELSTEN D (1997) 'Low cross-flow velocity microfiltration of skim milk for removal of bacterial spores', *International Dairy Journal*, 7, 849–861.

GUTMAN RG (1987) *'Membrane Filtration: The technology of pressure driven crossflow processes'*, Bristol, Adam Hilger.

HANEMAAIER JH (1985) 'Microfiltration in whey processing', *Desalination*, 53, 143–155.

KOSEOGLU SS, LAWHON JH and LUSAS EW (1991) 'Vegetable juices produced with membrane technology', *Food Technology*, 45, 124–130.

KOSIKOWSKI FV (1986) 'Membrane separations in food processing', in McGregor WC *Membrane Separations in Biotechnology*, New York, Marcel Dekker.

LE BERRE O and DAUFIN G (1996) 'Skim milk crossflow microfiltration performance versus permeation flux to wall shear stress ratio', *Journal of Membrane Science*, 117, 261–270.

LEWIS MJ (1996a) 'Pressure-activated membrane processes', in Grandison AS and Lewis MJ *Separation Processes in the Food and Biotechnology Industries*, Cambridge, Woodhead, 65–96.

LEWIS MJ (1996b) 'Ultrafiltration', in Grandison AS and Lewis MJ *Separation Processes in the Food and Biotechnology Industries*, Cambridge, Woodhead, 97–139.

MALMBERT R and HOLM S (1988) 'Producing low-bacteria milk by microfiltration', *North European Food and Dairy Journal*, 1, 1–4.

MEDINA BG and GARCIA A (1988) 'Concentration of orange juice by reverse osmosis', *Journal of Food Process Engineering*, 10, 217–230.

PALACIOS VM, CARO I and PEREZ, L (2002) 'Comparative study of crossflow microfiltration with conventional filtration of sherry wines', *Journal of Food Engineering*, 54, 95–102.

PIOCH D, LARGUEZE C, GRAILLE J, AJANA H and ROUVIERE J (1998) 'Towards an efficient membrane based vegetable oil refining', *Industrial Crops and Products*, 7, 83–89.

POULIOT M, POULIOT Y, BRITTEN M, MAUBOIS J.I. and FAUQUANT J. (1994) 'Study of the dissociation of $\beta$-casein from native phosphocaseinate', *Lait* 74, 325–332.

RENNER E and EL-SALAM MHABD. (1991) *Application of Ultrafiltration in the Dairy Industry*, London, Elsevier.

SHORT JL (1988) 'Newer applications for crossflow membrane filtration', *Desalination*, 70, 341–352.

WINSTON HO WS and SIRKAR KK (1992) *Membrane Handbook*, New York, Chapman and Hall.

## 14.8    Acknowledgement

The author would like to thank Mrs E. V. Gillham for her help with the illustrations.

# 15

# High-intensity light

S. Green, N. Basaran and B. G. Swanson, Washington State University, USA

## 15.1  Introduction

In response to the ever-present concern over potential foodborne illness and the universal expectation of consumers for wholesome foods, food scientists, engineers and processors are seeking more efficient, effective and feasible methods of reducing pests, spoilage organisms and pathogens from foods. High-intensity white light treatment, a non-thermal method for shelf life extension and pathogen control, offers food processors one such 'weapon' in the war on pests.

High-intensity light, also described as pulsed broad-spectrum white light, is a decontamination or sterilization technology that can be used for the rapid inactivation of microorganisms on food surfaces, equipment and food packaging materials. Surface decontamination of food products using pulsed high-intensity light has many potential benefits to the food industry. High-intensity light is a non-thermal food preservation intervention, with the ability to minimize the deleterious effects of thermal processing and chemical treatments on quality and sensory attributes. Two additional advantages of this technology are, first, it is cost effective, with minimal operating and maintenance costs once equipment is in place and secondly, it is regarded as a relatively safe and non-toxic treatment. Data submitted to the Food and Drug Administration (FDA) of the United States, for approval of UV light treatments for fruit juices, supports the claim that broad-spectrum white light provides sufficient antimicrobial inactivation and commercial sterilization with no known toxic effects (Food and Drug Administration, 2000).

The terms ultraviolet (UV) light,[1] broad-spectrum white light, pulsed white light, and near infra-red light are synonymous with high intensity light and

---

1.  Includes UVA and UVB light.

describe the range of light in which non-ionizing irradiation is emitted. Wavelengths in the range of X-rays and Gamma rays produce ionizing forms of irradiation and are not typically included under the heading of 'high-intensity light'. However, high-intensity light is occasionally referred to as a form of irradiation due to the fact that white light is a radiant light source. The electromagnetic spectrum (EM) (Fig. 15.1.) is expressed in terms of energy, wavelength, or frequency. Each segment of the continuum of the EM spectrum is related to the others in a precise mathematical way (Fig 15.2.).

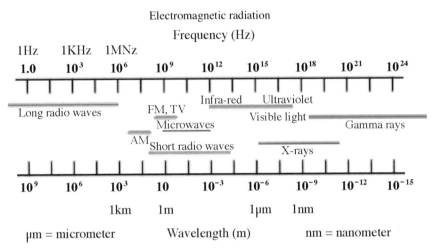

Courtesy of http://Kosmoi.com/Pictures/Science/Ermspectrum.gif

**Fig. 15.1**  Electromagnetic spectrum.

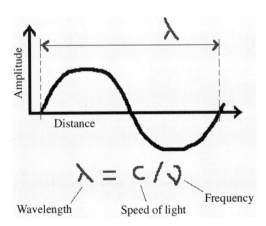

Courtesy of NASA (National Aeronautic and Space Agency). Website: http://imagine.gsfc.nasa.gov/docs/science/know_12/emspectrum. html

**Fig. 15.2**  The wavelength equals the speed of light divided by the frequency.

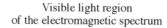

Visible light region
of the electromagnetic spectrum

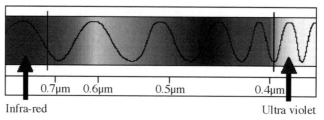

0.7μm    0.6μm        0.5μm            0.4μm

Infra-red                                    Ultra violet

Courtesy of http://imagers.gsfc.nasa.gov/ems/visible.html

**Fig. 15.3**   Visible light.

The relationships are:

The wavelength equals the speed of light divided by the frequency

or

$lambda = c/\text{nu}$

High-intensity white light and UV light food preservation methods employ light wavelengths ranging from ultraviolet to near infra-red (Fig. 15.3) in short intense bursts (or pulses). Pulses of light used for food processing applications typically emit one to twenty flashes per second of electromagnetic energy within the range of 170 to 2600 nm[2, 3] (Barbosa-Canovas et al., 1997, 2000). Analyses of various food surfaces, following exposure to high-intensity light in short rapid pulses demonstrate a varying range of antimicrobial efficacy from partial microbial inactivation to 7 log CFU[4] reductions, in some test situations (Dunn et al., 1988; Barbosa-Canovas et al., 2000; Food and Drug Administration, 2000).

Although the effect of high-intensity white light and UV light treatments on insect pests will not be the focus of this chapter, it should be noted that several genera are affected. In addition to being unsightly and damaging to the quality of food products, insects are often vectoring agents in the dissemination of disease and spoilage-causing microorganisms. Food processors must therefore take steps to inactivate all pests that might result in the deterioration of both the quality and the safety of their products.

Affected insects include representatives from the phyla *Nematoda* and *Arthropoda*.[5] Protozoan sporozoites and some algae (*Protista*), several genera of fungi (*Mycetae*), Gram-positive[6] vegetative cells, spores and Gram-negative

---

2. 1 nm ($10^{-9}$ cm) ($1.09361 \times 10^{-9}$ yards) = 10 Angstroms.
3. Typically, 70% of the electromagnetic energy generated in high-intensity light processes for food preservation applications fail within this range.
4. log = $\log_{10}$ scale; CFU = Colony forming unit.
5. Refer to additional information section for website of scanning electron microscopy images of organisms from these phyla.
6. Gram's Iodine Staining procedure determines the cell wall structure that differentiates this major taxonomical division. Gram-positive bacteria have thick cell walls in comparison to Gram-negative bacteria, which are described as having thin cell walls.

bacteria, as well as many viruses are inactivated to various degrees with high-intensity light treatments (Food and Drug Administration, 2000).[7]

## 15.2    Process and equipment

The principle involved in generating high-intensity light is that a gradual increase of low to moderate power energy can be harnessed and released in highly concentrated bursts of more powerful energy. Electromagnetic energy is accumulated in a storage capacitor[8] within fractions of a second and then released in the form of light within a millionth or billionth of a second, resulting in an amplification of power with a minimum of additional energy consumption (Dunn et al., 1995). Typically, equipment used to produce high-intensity light is composed of one or more adjustable lamp units, a power unit and a high-voltage connection that allows the transfer of a high-current electrical pulse. As the current passes through the gas chamber of the lamp unit, a short, intense burst of light is emitted.

There are numerous models of high-intensity light equipment for food treatment now under patent, each is designed to control unique treatment and product specifications. The advantages and disadvantages of the equipment (Fig. 15.4) design are described below.

> The lamp is mounted in a custom unit with a parabolic reflector with reflective sidewalls (at $90°$ to the electrodes). The reflector is coated with a vacuum spattered aluminum. To prevent an ozone build-up causing degradation of the reflector coating, the reflector is purged with nitrogen during lamp operations. Consequently, the lamp module is sealed; this is done with a 'window' of suprasil quartz plates over the reflector. The reflector contains aberrations and surface defects, the diffused reflected light comprises 20% of the reflected light at an angle of $120°$ from the quartz surface. This model features an anode-cathode component on the sides of the lamp module. However, the anode-cathode on the sides of the lamp module has no advantage since this light cannot be directed to the sample. A simpler reflector of far less cost can be purchased as an OEM product on the open market. The equipment's capacitor is $100\,\mu\text{F}$, charged by switching the mode of power supply to $\sim 3.5\,\text{kV}$. This capacitance gives a pulse energy of $500\,\text{J}$ and an absorbed radiant energy at the sample level of $\sim 0.6\,\text{J/cm}^2$. Corrections for reflector aberration and other losses reduce absorbed energy at the sample to $\sim 0.5\,\text{J/cm}^2$. One half Joule per square

---

7.  Refer to additional information section for address of the website with scanning electron microscopy images of these organisms and viruses.
8.  The energy stored in a capacitor can be expressed as $U = 1/2CV^2$, where $U$ = internal energy, $C$ = capacitance, and $V$ = electric potential.

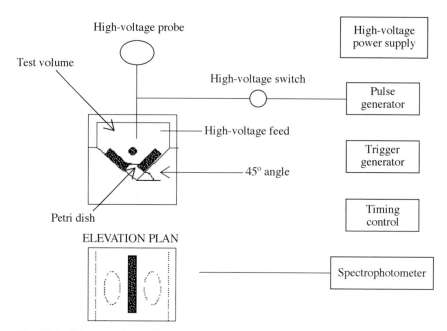

**Fig. 15.4**   Diagram of experiment with inoculated Tryptic Soy Agar Plates exposed to pulsed light.

centimeter of exposed sample provides a 2-log reduction in spore population measured. An efficient pulse duration was 400–500 $\mu$sec. This custom equipment has the same nature as that of a standard UV (254 nm) lamp, with the latter having the great advantage of being a few hundred times less expensive than the aforementioned custom-designed equipment (Wekhof, 2002).

Some factors that impact the type of equipment needed to achieve food preservation with high-intensity light are ozone build up, surface area of the food product and dimensions of each treatment unit and desired degree of decontamination.[9] A product that requires a specified temperature, during processing[10] to maintain optimal quality, may require a model of high-intensity light equipment that is fitted with a cooling unit (Fig. 15.5). For example, McGregor *et al.* (1998) developed a power light source equipment suitable for inactivation of microorganisms by utilizing a clear quartz tube filled within Xenon and subjected to 100 W of power.[11] This lamp equipment was attached to an inverting Marx pulse generator with a charge of 30 kV dc (U.S. Food and

---

9.  Decontamination requirements can range from 1–3 logs, 5 log reduction (for spoilage control) or 7 log reduction (for pathogen control and 'Commercial' sterilization).
10. An emulsion, for example.
11. High-pressure Xenon lamps produce a continuous spectrum of intense light.

**Fig. 15.5**   PurePulse Technology, Inc. lamp module. Above the module is the sample positioning equipment.

Drug Administration, 2000). Residual ozone build up and temperature can be controlled with this inverted Marx pulse equipment.

Food processing engineers and food scientists recognize that microbial inactivation is not the only issue when designing high-intensity and UV light irradiation equipment for foods. Designers of equipment used for food products must take into consideration the desirable texture, flavor, aroma and color attributes, as well as nutritional value of a given food and develop equipment that will preserve the highest possible quality. Lagunas-Solar and Pyne (1994) developed a model of high-intensity UV light treatment equipment specifically designed for use for food preservation applications that employs monochromatic excimer lamps set to wavelengths of approximately 247 nm. This equipment is currently under patent review in the United States and in use in Chile for decontamination of grapes for export to the United States.

## 15.3   Microbial inactivation

Wavelengths ranging from 170 to 800 nm result in detrimental changes to microbial cell structures and functions. Thus, wavelengths in this range of 170–800 are suitable for food preservation applications depending on the desired effect and the food equipment. The effects described below are generally observable when high-intensity light treatments are applied at wavelengths above 170 nm to product surfaces.

High-intensity light affects microbial cells by denaturation of proteins, including modification of or inactivation of functional enzymes and disruption of the functional components of nucleoproteins. Other affected functions and structures are enzyme directed DNA repair in microorganisms and the double

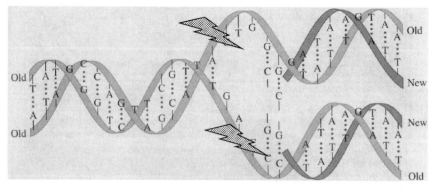

**Fig. 15.6**   Representation of destruction of DNA with high-intensity light.

helix structure of DNA, respectively; a result of damaging cleavage by high energy[12] (Fig. 15.6).

Loss of motility is observed in a wide range of microorganisms, in addition to alterations in a wide array of cellular structures from Gram-negative and Gram-positive bacterial cell walls,[13] to the oocysts of protozoan sporozoites treated with pulsed high-intensity light. UV wavelengths of 200–320 nm are highly effective through inducing structural alterations in DNA. Pulsed light treatments in these wavelength ranges inhibit both dark and light enzymatic DNA repair mechanisms[14] in microbial cells (PurePulse Technologies Inc., 1999). It is theorized that the high intensity of light combined with the rapid exposure renders the cell unable to repair or reproduce critical proteins, as well as DNA double helix structure and repair enzymes; in short, the cells are overwhelmed by irreversible damage to multiple structures and functions (Farkas, 1997; Barbosa-Canovas *et al.*, 2000; Food and Drug Administration, 2000). A complex sequence of events contributes to the loss of critical functions such as motility in flagellated bacteria due to disruption of any of the thirty genes that code for synthesis of flagellar proteins.

In contrast to other types of irradiation, such as electron acceleration, the activity of high-intensity broad spectrum light is thought to be non-ionizing.[15] Bintsis *et al.* (2000) attributes the lethality of long-wave UV light to cellular membrane damage, production of peroxyl radicals and concomitant exogenous photosensitization of microbial cells allowing absorption of peroxyl radicals. Oxygen radicals (•OH, for example) are known to initiate lipid oxidation and oxidative rancidity. The theory of production of deleterious oxygen radicals is refuted by Doyle (1999). In general, it is thought that UV exposures necessary for inactivation of bacteria, including pathogens such as *Listeria monocytogenes*, are not sufficient to cause deleterious effects on the color of

---

12.   This phenomenon is often referred to as causing 'nicks' in DNA.
13.   Such as *Escherichia coli*.
14.   Light enzymatic repair requires light and dark enzymatic repair occurs in the absence of light. Microorganisms may undergo either repair method dependent upon their environment.
15.   Non-ionizing means not directly due to the dissociation of excited molecules forming free radicals which react with the covalent bonds in the molecules of living cells.

red meats. Red meats readily undergo lipid oxidation and produce off-odors, off-colors, and textural changes in the presence of oxygen radicals. UV light applied in the range of 254–365 nm to red meats does not result in accelerated oxidative rancidity (Doyle, 1999). Further, Doyle (1999) suggests that the lethality of UV light treatments to bacterial cells is due to the formation of thymine dimers resulting in mRNA transcription failures (Doyle, 1999). Barbosa-Canovas *et al.* (2000) describe the photo-chemical changes in the UV range and photo-thermal changes occurring in the infra-red range.

Another theory behind the mode of antimicrobial action in high-intensity light treatments incorporates the absorption of UV light via highly conjugated carbon double bonds in nucleic acids and cellular proteins results in cellular damage (Jay, 2000). Another theory, that the physical disintegration of bacterial cells or spores occurs via intensive overheating of cells after absorption of pulsed UV light, is proposed by the Wek-Tec company in Germany (Wekhof, 2002).

### 15.3.1 Effectiveness of microbial inactivation

The effectiveness of high-intensity light as an antimicrobial intervention for foods is dependent upon multiple factors. Factors such as the initial microbial concentration, food surface constituents, presence of buffering compounds,[16] as well as the number, intensity and speed of pulses delivered and impact efficacy. An application of 20 flashes at 1 J/cm$^2$ using a single lamp/reflector or cavity treatment was applied after filling to achieve sterilization of inoculated saline and glucose solutions after filling on a blow-fill process line using low-density polyethylene containers. Researchers at a Japanese pharmaceutical corporation demonstrated adequate sterility of 160 containers of saline, water or glucose solutions after exposure to a single lamp cavity treatment for 10 flashes at 1 J/cm2 (Barbosa-Canovas *et al.* 2000; PurePulse Technologies Inc., 1999).

When exposed to intense electromagnetic energy in the form of high-intensity light, the viable microbial population on the surface of food products or food packaging materials is rapidly decreased. Inactivation of microorganisms may occur with as few as one pulse of 0.01 to 50 J/cm$^2$ with exposure times from 1 $\mu$s to 0.1 s at the food. Dunn *et al.*. (1995) found that the lethality of high-intensity light increases with increasing light intensity and frequency of pulses.

The shorter wavelengths (254 nm) are known to be more effective in microbial inactivation than longer wavelengths (Doyle, 1999). Likewise, each food and surface contaminant has a unique interaction and must be tested. Given the subtle genotypic, biochemical and morphological differences[17] between

16. Buffering compounds in dairy products protect microbial cells from attack and enhance the ability of certain microorganisms to recover from sub-lethal cell injury (Jay, 2000).
17. For example, *Salmonella enterica* subspecies, *E. coli* and *Shigella* spp. are typically difficult to isolate via microscopic examination and non-selective media. Identity confirmation is achieved with multiple subculture protocols on selective media and molecular typing methods (often not readily available to food processing facilities).

many spoilage and pathogenic strains of closely related microorganisms, it is suggested that high-intensity light will effectively inactivate both pathogenic and non-pathogenic indicator organisms in the same manner (Chang et al., 1985). The ability to reduce representative genera, species, strains or serovars from both the spoilage and pathogenic populations on the food surface is a key requisite for an effective preservation technology.

## 15.4   Inactivation of pathogens and spoilage bacteria

It is widely understood that the increase in the incidence of foodborne illness associated with consumption of fresh fruit and vegetable commodities is positively correlated with a shift in agricultural practices. This shift is due to the relatively[18] recent evolution of societies from subsistence farming to large-scale operations, as well as automation of harvesting, changes in processing and in consumer demands[19] (Seo and Frank, 1999). This statement also applies to foodborne illness associated with meat products, and other foods.

The predominant Gram-positive bacterial pathogens of concern are *Clostridium botulinum* (and *perfringens*), *Listeria monocytogenes* and *Staphylococcus aureus* and *Bacillus cereus*. *Clostridium botulinum*, the causative agent in botulism, is an anaerobic, spore-forming, Gram-positive bacilli, associated with low-acid, canned and modified atmosphere packaged (MAP) meats and vegetables. In the spore form, *Clostridium botulinum* is highly resistant to antimicrobial processes. *Clostridium botulinum* produces several of the most potent and deadly neurotoxins (BoNT) known. Purified type A toxin was reported to have a 50% lethal dose (in humans) of approximately 1 ng/kg of body weight (Jay, 2000). Botulism was at one time a frequent and life-threatening foodborne illness. Although less common today due to the establishment of the strict 12 D process for the inactivation of *Clostridia* in canned and MAP food products, occasional incidences of botulism are reported annually, due to mishandling during storage, transport or at the consumer end (Jay, 2000).

Another foodborne illness agent, frequently associated with dairy products, 'ready-to-eat' frankfurters and leaf vegetables is *Listeria monocytogenes (L. monocytogenes)*. *L. monocytogenes* is a Gram-positive, non-spore-forming bacilli, described as a facultative intracellular parasite ubiquitous in poultry, beef, pork (including processed deli meats) and dairy processing, in addition to fresh fruits, vegetation, nuts, seafood, water and soil. The growth range temperature is highly variable for this organism and *L. monocytogenes* has been cultured at 1 °C and up to 45 °C, however the standard laboratory incubation (in laboratory) temperature for optimal growth lies between 30 °C and 37 °C. *L.*

---

18.   'Recent' describes the period of time (within the last 2000–5000 years) with respect to the age of the earth.
19.   Trends, such as the increased demand for 'organic' and nutri-ceutical foods.

*monocytogenes* is able to survive pasteurization temperatures and may be considered a hardy organism, for this reason (Marth, 1994).

*Listeria monocytogenes* is one of the key foodborne pathogens of concern for modern food processors and a 'zero tolerance' policy is mandated for food processing plants in the United States and elsewhere. *L. monocytogenes* relies on a potent lippopolysaccharide toxin (LPS) to sensitize erythrocytes, leading to what is generally characterized as a granulomatosis in the host, also known as listeriosis. Listeriosis has a variable incubation period with onset usually within a few days and up to 28 days following ingestion of infected foods. The disease in humans is of particular concern to pregnant women, immuno-compromised individuals (such as persons undergoing chemotherapy or those suffering from diabetes, cirrhosis of the liver or AIDS).

*Listeria* spp. have two distinct advantages over other pathogens with regards to their ability to survive and proliferate in and on contaminated food products. First, *Listeria* spp. are psychrotrophic organisms that can proliferate at refrigeration temperatures (1 to 7 °C) and secondly, documented cases of *Listeria* spp. retaining viability and proliferating in temperatures as high as 45 °C (Jay, 2000) have appeared in literature. Some *Listeria* spp. strains are known to be catalase positive, thus resistant to attack by $H_2O_2$ and some are suspected of surviving pasteurization in dairy products (Jay, 2000). Because of the potential for surviving thermal pasteurization, resistance to high-intensity light is indicated.

*Staphylococcus aureus*, a non-spore-forming, Gram-positive cocci, produces the potent enterotoxin *staphylotoxin*. The toxin is produced as a result of reheating and holding buffet foods at temperatures below 60 °C. Deli meats, cheese fermentation brines and pre-packaged frozen meals are also a frequent vector for *Staphylococcus aureus* intoxication (Jay, 2000). *Staphylococcus aureus* intoxication is considered to be one of the most prevalent causes of food associated gastroenteritis (Jay, 2000). *Bacillus cereus*, a Gram-positive, spore-forming bacilli, is also a producer of both heat-stable and heat-labile enterotoxins. *B. cereus* toxins are responsible for gastro enteric illness in humans and viable cells are frequently isolated in low numbers from grains (rice), meat, raw milk and spices (Jay, 2000).

High-intensity light treatment is an appropriate intervention for pathogen control on foods such the surfaces of deli meat and cheese slices for control of *Listeria monocytogenes* and *Staphylococcus aureus*, particularly because deli meats are 'ready-to-eat' food items that are extensively handled during slicing and packaging, yet, no further cooking step is applied in most cases (Stermer *et al.*, 1987; Norje *et al.*, 1990). Likewise, high-intensity light may be less appropriate for control of *Clostridium botulinum* and *perfringens* in opaque and dense emulsion products such as canned vegetables and stews, but might be useful for inactivation of *Clostridia* from modified atmosphere packaged low-acid products such as corned beef slabs and sausage products in clear plastic packs.

Typically, 1 to 35 pulses of light in the range of 1 to 2 J/cm$^2$ are selected to inactivate bacteria. Researchers observed a 2 log reduction of the *Salmonella* population on chicken wings inoculated with either $1.0 \times 10^5$ CFU/cm$^2$ or $1.0 \times 10^2$ CFU/cm$^2$ after treatment with high-intensity light flashes (Dunn et al., 1995; Food and Drug Administration, 2000). Similarly, a 2 log reduction of Listeria innocua[20] on hot dogs treated with high-intensity pulsed light was reported. Reductions of Salmonella enterica (serovar Enteritidis) on egg shells, up to 8 logs were observed following exposure to 8 flashes at 0.5 J/cm$^2$ radiation value (Dunn, 1996; Kuo et al., 1997; Food and Drug Administration, 2000). High-intensity light is well suited to decontaminate processing equipment, a frequent vector for dissemination of Gram-negative bacteria in meat processing. Packaging materials treated with high-intensity light will also benefit by reducing cross-contamination.

Other microorganisms of concern are located in the protozoan group and include flagellate protozoans, such as Giardia lamblia (giardiasis causing agent), Entamoeba histolytica (amebiasis or amoebic dysentery causing agent) and Toxoplasma gondii (toxoplasmosis causing agent), the latter of which can produce a terminal secondary infection in immuno-compromised individuals. The protozoan group are typically associated with contaminated drinking and processing water and infected under-cooked meats (Jay, 2000). High-intensity light applied to transparent liquids is an effective decontamination treatment. PurePulse Technologies, Inc. is currently testing a model of high-intensity light treatment equipment that can effectively decontaminate water at a rate of four gallons per minute (PurePulse Technologies Inc., 1999). However, if water sources are turbid and contain abundant opaque organic materials or non-uniform particulates, high-intensity light treatment will not be appropriate.

Common fungal pathogens associated with food are producers of potent, concentrated mycotoxins. Mycotoxins are associated with foods such as cheese products, nut meals, beer, raisins, soybeans, coffee bean grains, country cured hams, fruits and vegetables. Mycotoxins frequently associated with foods are Aflatoxins, from the organism Aspergillus flavus, Ochratoxins, from organisms A. ochraceus, A. alliceus and other closely related species, Citrinins, from the organisms Penicillium citrinum and P. viridicatum, Patulins, from the organisms Penicillium expansum, P. patulum, some Aspergillus spp. and some Bsysochlamys spp.

High-intensity light is an effective method for reducing the mold spores, provided that they are on the food surface or in a clear medium. Mold spores of Aspergillus niger are readily reduced by greater than 7 logs following treatment with 'a minimal number of flashes' at 1 J/cm$^2$ power density (Dunn et al., 1995; Food and Drug Administration, 2000).

There are several notable human pathogens in the phylum Nematoda, including but not limited to Trichinella spiralis, causative agent of trichinosis in humans, resulting from eating undercooked meat products[21] derived from

20.  Listeria incocua is a non-pathogenic (to humans) species often used in testing as a 'surrogate' species; this species is closely related to pathogenic Listeria monocytogenes.
21.  Specifically pork and 'exotic meats', such as bear meat.

infected animals. Several agencies world wide, including the World Health Organization, as well as the Food and Drug Administration of the United States, reviewed and improved treatments for the control of *Trichinella spiralis* in swine and pork meat.[22] Due to the fact that *Trichinae* burrow deep into muscle tissue of infected animals and are not limited to the meat surface, high-intensity light is not currently used to inactivate microorganisms in intra-muscular meat tissue.

In a study at the University of Strathclyde, Royal College, Glasgow it was determined that viable counts of pathogenic bacteria such as *Listeria monocytogenes*, *Bacillus cereus*, *Staphylococcus aureus*, *Salmonella Enteritidis* and *Escherichia coli*[23] were reduced up to 2 log following exposure to 200 of low UV light pulses (each pulse duration approximately 100 ns) and up to 6 logs with high UV content light. The generator used was charged to a voltage of 30 kV, with a source capacitance of 6.4 nF and a source impedance of 3.25 $\Omega$. The duration of each pulse was 85 ns. There was no detected increase in the temperature of the food samples due to the fact that each pulse/sec consumed no more than 3 w of electricity, therefore energy absorbed at the food surface level was low.

To determine the comparative resistance of frequent food associated pathogens, representative Gram-positive and Gram-negative pathogens were grown on agar medium exposed to 100–1000 pulses/sec of a PPET (pulse power energizing technique) producing light at wavelengths of 254 nm and 365 nm, respectively. It was determined that *Listeria monocytogenes* is more resistant to UV light than *Staphylococcus aureus*, *Salmonella* Enteritidis,[24] *Escherichia coli* and *Bacillus cereus* in order of greatest to least resistant (Doyle, 1999). Further, a single pulse of 512 sec duration using PPET, was able to reduce the *Listeria monocytogenes* population on agar plates by 6 logs in 512 $\mu$s (Doyle, 1999). Gram-positive bacteria, and particularly Gram-positive bacterial spores, are more resistant to high-intensity and UV light treatments than vegetative cells, such as Gram-negative bacterial cells, due to the protective endospore coat of spores. Spores are highly heat resistant and tolerate desiccation far better than vegetative cells. Resistance of bacterial spores is somewhat a function of the medium or food equipment under analysis (Doyle, 1999).

22. The World Health Organization approved the use of 1–2 Kilograys of irradiation (typically from accelerated electron beam or Cobalt isotope source).
23. *Listeria* spp., *Bacillus* spp. and *Staphylococcus* spp. are Gram-positive bacteria, likewise, serovars of *Salmonella enterica* and *Escherichia* spp. are Gram-negative bacteria.
24. The genus *Salmonella* has undergone several taxonomical changes in recent years. Currently, there are only two species of *Salmonella (enterica)* and *Bongori*, *S. enterica* has 5 subspecies *(II. salamae, IIIa. arizonae, IIIb. diarizonae, IV. houtenae and VI. indica) with the former group V. subspecies transferred to the new species (Bongori)*. There are over 2,000 serovars (not italicized) such as 'Typhimurium', 'Mbandaka' and 'Havana'. Older literature may refer to *Salmonella enteritidis* (italicized) or *Salmonella* Typhimurium (not italicized) both designations now refer to *S. enterica* serovars.

### 15.4.1    Inactivation of spoilage microorganisms

The preservation of food that is already produced, i.e., control of food spoilage on minimally processed fruits and vegetables, is a current area of extensive research interests (Salunkhe and Desai, 1984; Shewfelt and Prussia, 1993). High-intensity light treatments for control of food spoilage and shelf life extension of smooth surface, non-opaque foods is proving to be an effective and versatile application of high-intensity light technology.

Key spoilage organisms involved in the deterioration of dairy, meats, fruit and vegetable products are lactic acid bacteria (LAB) and a smattering of Gram-negative bacteria and fungi. Notable examples of spoilage activities carried out by LAB are fermented beer spoilage caused by *Pediococcus damnosus*, *Leuconostocs mesenteroides* spoilage of sauerkraut[25] and sour rot caused by *Leuconostocs mesenteroides* in meats. Other Gram-positive bacteria associated with meat spoilage are *Clostridium perfringens*, *Bronchothrix* spp. *Lactobacillus* spp. and *Carnobacterium* spp. on meats. The Gram-negative bacteria frequently associated with spoilage of fruits and vegetables[26] are *Pseudomonas* spp.,[27] *Proteus* spp.,[28] *Klebsiella* spp., *Erwinia*, *Acinetobacter* spp. (or *Moraxella* spp.), *Flavobacterium* spp. on fish and vegetables and *Enterobacter* spp.

Some yeasts associated with spoilage of beer, wine, pickles and other low pH or fermented foods and beverages are *Brettanomyces* spp. (anamorph *Dekkera)*, and *Zygosaccharomyces bailii*, which spoils mayonnaise, salad dressing and wines (Jay, 2000). Spoilage molds are diverse in morphology and include *Botrytis cinerea*, responsible for gray mold rot[29] of grapes, tomatoes, apples and stone fruits, as well as, *Penicillium* spp. and *Cladosporium herbarum*, which produces 'black spot' on mutton, beef and 'restricted' rot on stone fruits (Jay, 2000).

## 15.5    Applications, strengths and weaknesses

Applications of high-intensity light are best suited for surface disinfection due to the restricted penetration of high-intensity light into opaque substances and irregular-surface foodstuffs such as comminuted meats, dairy products or other emulsions. In spite of the limited use in opaque foodstuffs, microbial loads on egg surfaces and in micropores of the eggs can be reduced 1 to 4 logs with high-intensity light treatments (Dunn *et al.*, 1995).

High-intensity light is a fast and highly effective processing step in food preservation, with relatively low operating costs. High-intensity light can be used in conjunction with other minimal processing steps to create a 'hurdle

25. Occurs if fermenting cabbage is not properly sealed in an anaerobic environment.
26. These organisms produce spoilage of meats and vegetables primarily.
27. *Pseudomonas* spp. and *Klebsiella* spp. are slime formers.
28. *Proteus* spp. are mesophilic spoilers associated with processing water that produce a distinctive offensive odor and swarming growth on plated agar media.
29. This rot is often seen on apples, grapes, raspberries, strawberries and some stone fruits.

effect'. 'Hurdle effect' refers to the theory that multiple intervention steps such as control of pH, Redox potential and antimicrobial treatments in combination create a series of hurdles. With enough hurdles, the microbial population cannot 'jump over' and effective preservation is achieved. Foods with smooth surfaces, such as fresh whole fruit and vegetable commodities, hard cheeses, or smooth-surface meat cuts, such as steaks or chops are ideally suited for treatment with high-intensity and UV light technology where surface contamination is a concern for microbial contamination. One challenge to this technology is that of logistics. High-intensity and UV light are well suited as final steps in minimal processing protocols, however, treatments that effectively penetrate packaging materials are ideal.

Foods with rough or uneven surfaces, crevices or pores are unsuitable for high-intensity light treatment because of the ability of microorganisms to harbor in small openings. Seo and Frank (1999) used confocal scanning electron microscopy to observe that viable *E. coli* 0157:H7[30] cells are able to attach to the surface, trichomes and stomata of cut lettuce leaves and accumulate in the stomata. Further, they observed that viable *E. coli* 0157:H7 cells are able to penetrate into cut leaf edges to a depth of 20 $\mu$m. Due to the opaque nature of cereals, grains and spices, high-intensity light is not an ideal technology for this application. However, high-intensity light is an effective method of decontaminating packaging materials, the smooth inner surface of storage bins and equipment such as blending spatulas.

Another challenge to high-intensity light technology is the production of off-colors, flavors and odors and was addressed in a study by Colchin *et al.* (2001). Researchers observed that modified atmosphere packaged shredded cheese was more susceptible to color loss and oxidation of the color pigment bixin when exposed to high-intensity light and $CO_2$ atmospheres. The production of volatile aldehydes increased by a factor of six under $CO_2$ and exposure to fluorescent light, with heptanal being the most abundant aldehyde present. Conversely, under high $N_2$ atmosphere and fluorescent light conditions, ketones were predominant. Following storage both aldehydes and ketones hydrolyzed into volatile alcohols such as 3-methyl-1-butanol, 2-pentenol, 2-heptanol and 1-octen-3-ol (Colchin *et al.*, 2001).

Currently there is no formulated predictive model for estimating the dose response of most microorganisms to high-intensity light treatment. Additional peer-reviewed data on the effectiveness of high-intensity light on foodborne viruses is needed. Currently, private sector[31] research has examined the effects

30.  *E. coli (Escherichia coli)* O157:H7 is associated with outbreaks of Hemolytic Uremic Syndrome (a sometimes fatal condition, particularly in children) and is the causative etiological agent in numerous outbreaks of foodborne illness (Toarmina *et al.*, 2001). Alfalfa, radish and other sprouts commonly eaten without prior heat treatment are frequent vectors (Toarmina *et al.*, 2001). *E. coli* O157:H7 is innocuous in the environments of warm-blooded farm animals, such as cattle and swine. This organism is also implicated in multiple foodborne illness outbreaks associated with hamburger meat and unpasteurized apple juice, where fatalities occurred (Jay, 2000).
31.  PurePulse Technologies Inc., PureBright Equipment[TM].

of high-intensity light treatment on a number of organisms, including, but not limited to:

| | |
|---|---|
| Hepatitis A Virus (HAV) | *Bacillus pumilus* spores |
| Simian Virus (SV40) | *Clostridium sporogenes* spores |
| Canine Parvovirus (CPV) | *Aspergillus niger* spores |
| Simian Rotavirus (SA11) | *Candida albicans* |
| *Bacteriophage* PRD-1 | *Deinococcus radiodurans* |
| Polio Virus Type 1 | *Staphylococcus aureus* |
| *Bacteriophage* MS-2 | *Enterococcus faecalis* |
| Human Immuno Deficiency Virus (HIV-1) | *Escherichia coli* |
| Bovine Viral Diarrhea (BVDV) | *Salmonella choleraesuis* |
| *Bacillus subtilis* | *Pseudomonas aeruginosa* |

Additional peer-reviewed research with a variety of food equipment and processing specifications is needed.

### 15.5.1  Improving the effectiveness of high-intensity light technology

Adjustment of the number of lamps, as well as their position, with respect to the food surface offers another way to improve the effectiveness of the treatment on the food surface. The number of pulses per second is also a factor that can be modified to increase microcidal efficacy. In determining the optimal wavelength, kilowatts and number of light pulses to apply, it is important to consider the cellular structure of the predominant types of microorganisms present on the food surface. High-intensity light treatment is potentially compatible with a variety of processing technologies such as bacteriocins, high hydrostatic pressure and modified atmosphere packaging (Table 15.1).

**Table 15.1**  Types of irradiation and potential compatibility with other treatments

| Types of irradiation | Thermal processing (final step) | Modified atmosphere packaging | High hydrostatic pressure | Antimicrobial chemical additives (BHA/BHT, nitrates) | 'Natural' antimicrobial essential oils extracts or bacteriocins |
|---|---|---|---|---|---|
| HIWL/UV light | +++ | $\theta$/+ | ++ | $\theta$/++ | $\theta$/++ |
| Gamma-ray | +++ | ++ | + | $\theta$/+ | $\theta$/++ |
| Electron acceleration | ++ | ++ | + | $\theta$/+ | $\theta$/+++ |

$\theta$ = Photosensitivity or ionizing of certain compounds may render them inactive in this combination.
+ = Potentially compatible (no research data available/further testing required).
++ = Preliminary research data/publications indicate compatibility of these treatments
+ + + = Substantial research to support compatibility of these treatment combinations.

### 15.5.2   Future research needs for high-intensity light technology

The U.S. Food and Drug Administration cites the following areas as critical research areas to be addressed:

- Identify critical processing factors and determine their effect on microbial inactivation.
- Assess the suitability of high-intensity light for solid foods, emulsions and non-clear liquids where penetration depth is critical.
- Assess the potential for formation of unpalatable and toxic by-products.
- Study the resistance of common pathogens or non-pathogenic surrogate organisms to pulsed light treatments.
- Determine the differences between high-intensity light technology and more conventional food preservation treatments.
- Elucidate the mechanisms of microbial inactivation to determine whether they are significantly different from those proposed for other food preservation treatments and develop predictive models to compare and quantify the potential benefit attributed to the high-intensity light disinfection.

## 15.6   Sources of further information and advice

### 15.6.1   Food processing safety and related microbiology

**Title:**  Food Safe Series
**Producer Name:**  Altschul Group Corporation
**Contact Information:** 1560 Sherman Ave., Suite 100, Evanston, IL  60201
**Email:** *agcmedia@starnetinc.com*
**Web site:** *http://www.agcmedia.com/*
**Format:**  Videocassette (4 videos, 10 min. each)
**Date Produced:**  1987
**Description:**  Each narrated video deals with a different topic, (1) receiving and storing, (2) facilities and equipment, (3) microbiology for foodservice workers, (4) housekeeping and pest control. Videos are available separately or as a set.
**Audience:**  Foodservice workers
**How to order:**  Order from above address or web site.
**NAL Call Number:**  Housekeeping & Pest Control videocassette no. 464, Foodservice Facilities & Equipment videocassette no. 470

**Title:**  Case History Series
**Producer Name:**  Altschul Group Corporation
**Contact Information:** 1560 Sherman Ave., Suite 100, Evanston, IL  60201
**Email:** *agcmedia@starnetinc.com*
**Web site:** *http://www.agcmedia.com/*
**Format:**  Videocassette (set of 8 videos, 10 min. each)
**Date Produced:**  1985

**Description:** Each video covers a specific pathogen: *Staphylococcus aureus*, Hepatitis A, *Staphylococcus aureus*, *Bacillus cereus*, *Salmonella*, *Campylobacter, Clostridium botulinum*. Scenarios take place in a restaurant with background narration. The series also includes the following titles: 'Food service facilities and equipment', 'Receiving and storage', 'Microbiology for food service workers' and 'Housekeeping and pest control'. Videos demonstrate what went wrong and how the problem should have been avoided.

**Audience:** Foodservice workers

**How to order:** Order from above address or web site.

**NAL Call Number:** Videocassette no.1670 - Hepatitis A #2, B cereus #4, *Salmonella* (eggs) #5, *Campylobacter* #6, *C botulinum* #7, *Salmonella* (meat) #8. To borrow *S. aureus* in sauces video individually, request Videocassette no. 469.

**Title:** Micro-Facts

**Producer Name:** American Institute of Baking

**Contact Information:** 1213 Bakers Way, Manhattan, KS  66505-3999

**Telephone:** 800-242-2534

**Fax:** (785) 537-1493

**Web site:** *http://www.aibonline.org*

**Format:** Manual, fact sheets

**Date Produced:** 1996

**Description:** A compact resource for personnel involved in food quality assurance and hygiene. Describes all major pathogenic microorganisms with an impact on food safety and discusses sources of the bacteria, symptoms of foodborne illnesses, and growth and survival characteristics of the illnesses. Includes descriptions of the bacteria viruses, and protozoa that may cause illnesses.

**Audience:** Foodservice, food processors

**How to order:** Order from above address. Item #6100

### 15.6.2   Pest management and entomology

**Title:** Integrated Fly Management

**Producer Name:** Actron, Inc.

**Contact Information:** P.O. Box 55655, Santa Clarita, CA  91385

**Telephone:** 661-287-3335

**Fax:** 661-287-3339

**Email:** flymaster@actroninc.com

**Web site:** *http://www.actroninc.com/flash/index.html*

**Date Produced:** 1999

**Description:** Multi-media instruction on the problem of flies with emphasizing their role in the transmission of foodborne illness and less hazardous IPM control methods appropriate for sensitive food-handling areas.

### 15.6.3   High-intensity light equipment
PurePulse Technologies, Inc, San Diego, California, USA

### 15.6.4   Educators, experts and universities emphasizing high-intensity light research for food preservation
Washington State University
Professor Gustovo V. Barbosa-Canovas, Ph.D., Department of Biological Systems Engineering, Washington State University, Pullman, WA 99163, USA

Professor Barry G. Swanson, Ph.D., Department of Food Science and Human Nutrition, Washington State University, Pullman, WA 99163, USA

## 15.7   References

BANK, H.L., SCHMEHL, J.J. and DRATCH R.J. 1990. Bactericidal effectiveness of modulated UV light. *Appl. Environl. Microbiol.* 56: 3888–3889.

BARBOSA-CANOVAS, G.V., PALOU, E., POTHAKAMURY, U.R. and SWANSON, B.G. 1997. Application of light pulses in the sterilization of foods and packaging materials. *Nonthermal Preservation of Foods.* Ch. 6, 139–161. Marcel-Dekker. New York.

BARBOSA-CANOVAS, G.V., SCHAFFNER, D.W., PIERSON, M.D. and ZHANG, Q.H. 2000. Pulsed Light Technology. *J. Food Safety Suppl. Kinetics of Microbial Inactivation for Alternative Food Processing Technologies.* 82–85.

BINTSIS, T., LITOPOULOU-TZANETAKI, DAVIES, R. and ROBINSON, R.K. 2000. The antimicrobial effects of long-wave ultraviolet light and furocoumarins on some micro-organisms that occur in cheese brines. *Food Microbiol.* 17: 687–695.

CHANG, J.C.H., OSSOFF S.F., LOBE, D.C., DORFMAN, M.H., DUMAIS, C.M., QUALIS, R.G. and JOHNSON, J.D. 1985. UV inactivation of pathogenic and indicator microorganisms. *Appl. Environl. Microbiol.* 49: 1361–1365

COLCHIN, L.M., OWENS, S.L., LYUBACHEVSKAYA, G., BOYLE-RODEN, E., RUSSEK-COHEN, E. and RANKIN, S.A. 2001. Modified atmosphere packaged cheddar cheese shred: influence of fluorescent light exposure and gas type on color and production of volatile compounds. *J. Agric. Food Chem.* 49: 2277–2282.

COLEMAN, G.J. and DEWAR, D. 1997. *The Addison-Wesley Science Handbook.* Addison-Wesley. Reading, MA.

DOYLE, M.E. 1999. Use of ultraviolet light to control Listeria in meat. UV light. *Food Research Institute Letters.* p. 1.

DUNN, J. 1996. Pulsed light and pulsed electric field for foods and eggs. *Poul. Sci.* 75(9): 1133–1136.

DUNN, J., CLARK, R.W., ASMUS, J.F., PEARLMAN, J.S., BOYER, K., PAIRCHAUD, F. and HOFMANN, G. 1988. Methods and apparatus for preservation of foodstuffs. US Int. Pat. Appl. No. WO 88/03369.

DUNN, J., CLARK, W. and OTT, T. 1995. Pulsed-light treatment of food and packaging. *Food Technol.* 49(9): 95–98.

FARKAS, J. 1997. Physical methods of food preservation. *Food Microbiology Fundamentals and Frontiers.* M.P. Doyle, L.R. Beuchat, T.J. Montville (eds). Washington, D.C. ASM Press. 497–519.

FOOD AND DRUG ADMINISTRATION 2000. *Code of Federal Regulations* (CFR) *Title 21 Part*

*179. Irradiation in the production, processing and handling of food.* Office of the Federal Register, US Government Printing Office, Washington DC.

JAY, J.M. 2000. Radiation preservation of foods and nature of microbial radiation resistance, p. 304–323. In J.M. Jay (6th edn), *Modern Food Microbiology.* Chapman & Hall, New York, NY. Chs. 1–9, 13–15, 22–31.

KUO, F.L., CAREY, J.B. and RICKE, S.C. 1997. UV irradiation of shell eggs: effect of populations of aerobes, molds and inoculated *Salmonella typhimurium. J. Food Prot.* 60: 639–643.

LAGUNAS-SOLAR, M.C. and PYNE, A.W. 1994. Method of controlling microorganisms by pulsed ultraviolet laser radiation. US Patent No. 5.364,645. Novemeber 15, 1994. http://vm.cfsan.fda.gov/~comm/ift-puls.html.

MACGREGOR, S.J., ANDERSON, J.G., FOURACRE, R.A., FARISH, O., MCILVANEY, L. and ROWAN, N.J. 1998. Light inactivation of food-related pathogenic bacteria using a pulsed power source. *Lett. Appl. Microbiol.* 27: 67–70.

NORJE, G.L., NEL, L., JORDAAN, E., BADENHORST, K., GOEDHART, E. and HOLZAFEL, W. H. 1990. Aerobic psychrotrophic populations on meat and meat contact surfaces in meat production equipment and on meat stored at chilled temperatures. *J. Appl. Bacteriol.* 68(4): 335–344.

OECHSLI, R. and MARG, E. 1960. A Servo-Method for Producing Equal-Energy, or Equal-Response Spectra. School of Optometry, University of California, Berkeley, California.

MARTH, E.H. 1994. Listeriosis. *Handbook of Zoonoses.* CRC Press. pp. 321–329.

PURE PULSE TECHNOLOGIES INC.. 1999. PureBright® CoolPure® advanced sterilization, decontamination and preservation technology for the food and food packaging industry. San Diego, CA. PurePulse Technologies, Inc. Brochure. http://www.packaging2000.com/purepulse/PurePulse.html

SALUNKHE, D.K. and DESAI, B.B. 1984. *Postharvest Biotechnology of Fruit.* Vol. II. CRC Press. Boca Raton, FL.

SHEWFELT, R.L. and PRUSSIA, S.E. 1993. Challenges in handling fresh fruits and vegetables. *Postharvest Handling: an Equipment Approach.* Shewfelt and Prussia eds. Academic Press. Ch. 2: 27–41.

SEO, K.H. and FRANK, J.F. 1999. Attachment of *Escherichia coli* 0157:H7 to lettuce leaf surfaces and bacterial viability in response to chlorine treatment as demonstrated by using confocal scanning laser microscopy. *J. Food Prot.* 62(1): 3–9.

STERMER, R.A., LASATER-SMITH, M. and BRASINGTON, C.F. 1987. Ultraviolet radiation – an effective bacteriocide for fresh meat. *J. Food Prot.* 50: 108–111.

TOARMINA, P.J., BEUCHAT, L.R. and SLUTSKER, L. 2001. Infections associated with eating seed sprouts: an international concern. CDC. *Emerg. Infect. Disease.* 5(5).

WEKHOF, A. 2002. Does the Engineering of the PureBright Sterilization Equipment Match the Pulsed Light Sterilization Process? Published in the Proceedings of the International Conference on Pulsed Power Applications, Gelsenkirchen, March 29–30, Germany, Presentation B-10.

## 15.7.1   www reference sites: for figures and images only

http://Kosmoi.com/Pictures/Science/Emspectrum.gif

http://imagers.gsfc.nasa.gov/ems/visible.html

http://imagine.gsfc.nasa.gov/docs/science/know_12/emspectrum.html

# 16

# Ultrasound as a preservation technology

**T. J. Mason and L. Paniwnyk, University of Coventry, UK and F. Chemat, University of Réunion, France**

## 16.1 Introduction

The use of ultrasound within the food industry is an active subject for research and development (Povey and Mason, 1998). As is the case in other areas of processing technology, the sound ranges employed can be broadly divided into high frequency, low energy, diagnostic ultrasound in the MHz range and low frequency, high energy, power ultrasound which is in the kHz range (Fig. 16.1). There is an increasing interest in the effect of different frequencies on processing and as a result of this the gap between the ranges used for analytical and processing applications is diminishing.

Until recently the majority of applications and developments in food technology involved non-invasive analysis with particular reference to quality assessment, e.g., by monitoring the attenuation of an ultrasound pulse it has been proved possible to determine the degree of homogenisation of fat within milk (Miles *et al.*, 1990). The extent of emulsification in such materials can also be estimated by the measurement of ultrasound velocity in conjunction with attenuation (Javanaud *et al.*, 1991). It is also possible to determine factors such as the degree of 'creaming' (or 'settling') of a sample, measurements which reflect the movement of solid particles/fat droplets to the surface (or to the base) (Gartside and Robins, 1990). Such information gives details, for example, of the long-term stability of fruit juices and the stability of emulsions such as mayonnaise. The combination of velocity and attenuation measurements shows promise as a method for the analysis of edible fats and oils (McClements and Povey, 1992) and for the determination of the extent of crystallisation and melting in dispersed emulsion droplets (McClements *et al.*, 1993).

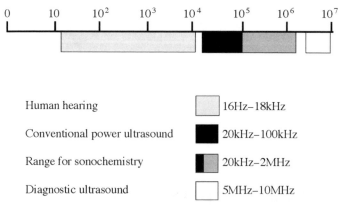

**Fig. 16.1**   Frequency ranges of sound.

More recently, food technologists have discovered that it is possible to use ultrasound to aid processing. The type of ultrasound used in these applications is more powerful and at a lower frequency than that used in diagnostic applications. Generally it is referred to as power ultrasound and its history is shorter than that of diagnostic ultrasound. As far back as 1927 a paper was published entitled 'The chemical effects of high frequency sound waves: a preliminary survey' by Richards and Loomis which described the development of power ultrasound for use in a range of processing including emulsification and surface cleaning (Richards and Loomis, 1927). By the 1960s the uses of power ultrasound in the processing industries were well accepted (Brown and Goodman, 1965; Frederick, 1965) and this interest has since continued (Abramov, 1998; Mason and Lorimer, 2002). A summary of the breadth of interest of the food industry in power ultrasound appears in Table 16.1, however, in this chapter we will explore only those effects of ultrasound that can be used to improve food preservation.

**Table 16.1**   Some uses of power ultrasound in food processing

| Mechanical effects | Chemical and biochemical effects |
| --- | --- |
| Accelerated freezing | Accelerated oxidation and ageing |
| Crystallisation of fats, sugars, etc. | Alteration of enzyme activity |
| Degassing | Bactericidal action |
| Destruction of foams | Effluent treatment |
| Extraction of flavourings | Modification of growth of living cells |
| Filtration and drying | Sterilisation of equipment |
| Mixing and homogenisation | |
| Precipitation of airborne powders | |
| Ultrasonic cutting | |

## 16.2     Principles: acoustic cavitation

Power ultrasound enhances chemical and physical changes in a liquid medium through the generation and subsequent destruction of cavitation bubbles. Like any sound wave ultrasound is propagated via a series of compression and rarefaction waves induced in the molecules of the medium through which it passes. At sufficiently high power the rarefaction cycle may exceed the attractive forces of the molecules of the liquid and cavitation bubbles will form. Such bubbles grow by a process known as rectified diffusion, i.e., small amounts of vapour (or gas) from the medium enters the bubble during its expansion phase and is not fully expelled during compression. The bubbles grow over the period of a few cycles to an equilibrium size for the particular frequency applied. It is the fate of these bubbles when they collapse in succeeding compression cycles that generates the energy for chemical and mechanical effects (Fig. 16.2). Cavitation bubble collapse is a remarkable phenomenon induced throughout the liquid by the power of sound. In aqueous systems at an ultrasonic frequency of 20 kHz each cavitation bubble collapse acts as a localised 'hotspot' generating temperatures of about 5,000 K and pressures around 2000 atmospheres (Neppiras, 1984; Henglein, 1987; Suslick, 1990).

Whatever application is to be studied or developed, two essential components are required, namely a liquid medium and a source of high-energy vibrations. The liquid medium is necessary because sonochemistry is driven by acoustic cavitation and this can occur only in liquids. The source of the vibrational

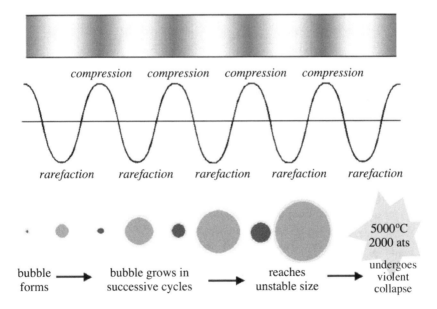

**Fig. 16.2**   The acoustic generation of a cavitation bubble.

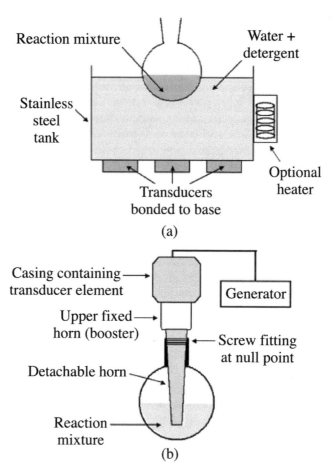

**Fig. 16.3**   Diagrams of common laboratory ultrasonic equipment (a) bath (b) probe.

energy is the transducer of which there are three main types: liquid driven, magnetostrictive and piezoelectric. The two most common pieces of equipment that are used for the generation of acoustic cavitation are the ultrasonic cleaning bath and the more powerful probe system (Fig. 16.3) (Mason, 1999). Larger-scale equipment will be dealt with later in the chapter. The cavitation bubble has a variety of effects within the liquid medium depending upon the type of system in which it is generated. These systems can be broadly divided into:

- homogeneous liquid
- heterogeneous solid/liquid
- heterogeneous liquid/liquid.

Each of these classifications is of interest in food processing.

### 16.2.1   Homogeneous liquid-phase reactions

It is not absolutely correct to describe any system within which cavitation occurs as homogeneous since bubbles must be present. However in this case 'homogeneous' refers to the state of the system *before* ultrasound is introduced. There are two major zones in which cavitation collapse can influence such systems (Fig. 16.4):

• in the bulk liquid immediately surrounding the bubble where the rapid collapse of the bubble generates shear forces which can produce mechanical effects and
• in the bubble itself where any species introduced during its formation will be subjected to extreme conditions of temperature and pressure on collapse leading to chemical effects.

The shear forces in the surrounding bulk liquid are so powerful that they can cause the breaking of chemical bonding in polymeric materials dissolved in the fluid. This was one of the early uses of power ultrasound (Price, 1990).

If the liquid in which cavitation is induced contains a gas then ultrasonic degassing will take place very readily. In the rarefaction phase any gas in the medium will enter the newly forming cavitation bubble. Such bubbles are not easily collapsed in the compression cycle of the wave due to the fact that they contain gas and they will continue to grow during further rarefaction cycles. As they fill with more gas they eventually float to the surface. Since the rarefaction cycles are taking place extremely rapidly (around 20,000–40,000 times per second using normal power ultrasonic frequencies) the bubbles grow so quickly that degassing appears to occur almost instantaneously. Ultrasonic degassing has found applications in many areas. In its simplest form it is used to degas solvents for use in high performance liquid chromatography (hplc) but industrially the potential applications are broad from the removal of air from a hot viscous material such as molten glass to the defobbing of beer.

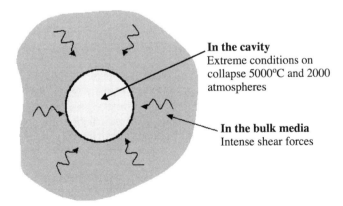

**In the cavity**
Extreme conditions on collapse 5000°C and 2000 atmospheres

**In the bulk media**
Intense shear forces

**Fig. 16.4**   Acoustic cavitation in a homogeneous liquid medium.

Ultrasound has also been used to influence crystallisation. In conventional crystallisation techniques a solution containing materials to be crystallised is super-saturated either by cooling or by evaporation and is then seeded. The problem with seeding is that it may be initiated non-uniformly and this can result in crystal growth proceeding at different rates at different nuclei sites. The resulting crystals may then show an unwanted broad and uneven crystal size distribution. It is also of con-siderable practical importance to be able to control the onset of crystallisation in a large-scale production process because this often occurs in an uncontrolled manner simply due to a slight change in external factors such as a temperature or pressure fluctuation. Ultrasound has proved to be extremely useful in crystallisation processes since it can initiate seeding and control subsequent crystal growth in a saturated or supercooled medium. This is thought to be due to cavitation bubbles themselves acting as nuclei for crystal growth and to the disruption of seeds/nuclei already present within the medium thus increasing the number of nuclei present in the medium. Through the correct choice of sonication conditions it is possible to produce crystals of a uniform and designated size that is of great importance in pharmaceutical preparations (Price, 1997). Power ultrasound also has an additional property which is particularly beneficial in crystallisation operations namely that the cleaning action of the cavitation effectively stops the encrustation of crystals on cooling elements in the crystallisation vat and thereby ensures continuous efficient heat transfer.

When water is sonicated the extreme conditions generated on collapse of the cavitation bubbles are sufficient to cause rupture of the O-H bond itself. This results in the formation of radical species and the production of oxygen gas and hydrogen peroxide (Makino $et$ $al.$, 1983):

$$H_2O \rightarrow OH^. + OH^.$$
$$OH + OH^. \rightarrow H_2O_2$$
$$OH^. + OH^. \rightarrow H_2 + O_2$$
$$H^. + O_2 \rightarrow HO_2^.$$
$$HO_2^. + H^. \rightarrow H_2O_2$$
$$HO_2^. + HO_2^. \rightarrow H_2O_2 + O_2$$
$$OH^. + H_2O \rightarrow H_2O_2 + O^.$$
$$H_2O^. + O^. \rightarrow H_2O_2$$
$$H^. + H^. \rightarrow H_2$$
$$H^. + OH^. \rightarrow H_2O$$

Any species dissolved in the water is clearly going to be subject to chemical reaction with these ultrasonically produced radicals. This is the reason why ultrasonic irradiation has been extensively investigated for chemical remediation of water. In fact both chemical and biological remediation are actively under investigation at this time (Mason and Tiehm, 2001).

### 16.2.2   Heterogeneous solid surface-liquid reactions

Unlike cavitation bubble collapse in the bulk liquid, collapse on or near to a surface is unsymmetrical because the surface provides resistance to liquid flow

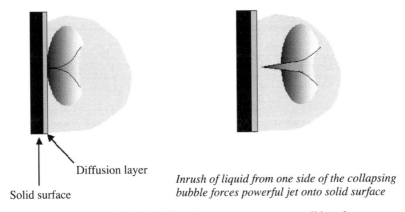

Diffusion layer

Solid surface

*Inrush of liquid from one side of the collapsing bubble forces powerful jet onto solid surface*

**Fig. 16.5**   Cavitation bubble collapse at or near to a solid surface.

from that side. The result is an inrush of liquid predominantly from the side of the bubble remote from the surface resulting in a powerful liquid jet being formed, targeted at the surface (Fig. 16.5). The effect is equivalent to high-pressure jetting and this is the reason why ultrasound is used extensively for cleaning. This effect can also increase mass and heat transfer to the surface by disruption of the interfacial boundary layers.

For similar reasons the classical techniques for the solvent extraction of materials from vegetable sources can be improved by sonication (Vinatoru *et al.*, 1999). The principle of the enhancement is that the 'jet' produced on bubble collapse can provide excellent penetration of the material coupled with the disruption of cells and release of contents. Ultrasonically assisted extraction can also be applied to the isolation of medicinal compounds such as helicid from plant material (Zhao *et al.*, 1991) or tea solids from the leaf (Mason and Zhao, 1994). Conventional extraction of helicid involves refluxing in ethanol followed by purification by crystallisation. When ultrasound (20 kHz at 40 °C) is used the crude product yield is lower than that obtained under conventional conditions (Table 16.2). However the amount of pure helicid that can be obtained from this crude yield is actually up to 50% higher yield in half the extraction time.

Another example is the enhanced extraction of essential oils from dill seed Table 16.3 (Toma *et al.*, 2001). An improved yield in a shorter time is obtained when the ultrasonic method is compared with the classical Soxhlet method.

### 16.2.3   Heterogeneous particle-liquid reactions

Acoustic cavitation can produce dramatic effects on particulate material or agglomerates in a liquid. In this case the solid surface is not the continuous surface as above but is a small powder fragment suspended in the medium, under these conditions cavitation can achieve both a reduction in particle size and efficient dispersion (Fig. 16.6). Surface imperfections or trapped gas can act as the nuclei for cavitation bubble formation on the surface of a particle and

**Table 16.2**   Extraction of helicid from dried seed

| Sonication time (minutes) | Crude yield[a] | Pure helicid[a] |
|:---:|:---:|:---:|
| 40 | 0.61 | 1.3 |
| 55 | 0.90 | 1.5 |
| 70 | 0.72 | 1.0 |

[a] Yields quoted are normalised to a standard of that obtained after a 2 hour reflux (= 1).

**Table 16.3**   Comparison of different extraction methods of dill seeds (100 g) with hexane

| Method used | Oil amount (g) | Extraction time (h) | Limonene % | Carvone % |
|:---:|:---:|:---:|:---:|:---:|
| Soxhlet | 3.00 | 4.0 | 40.79 | 47.29 |
| Ultrasonic | 3.40 | 0.5 | 49.63 | 48.15 |
| Ultrasonic | 3.40 | 1.0 | 51.22 | 45.84 |

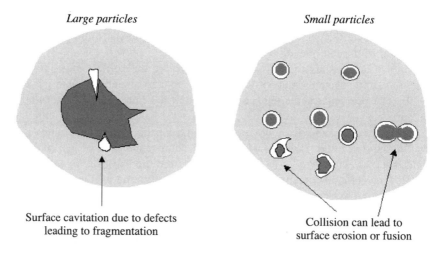

*Large particles*                    *Small particles*

Surface cavitation due to defects          Collision can lead to
leading to fragmentation                 surface erosion or fusion

**Fig. 16.6**   Cavitation collapse in the presence of a suspended powder.

subsequent surface collapse can then lead to shock waves which break the particle apart. Cavitation bubble collapse in the liquid phase near to a particle can force it into rapid motion. Under these circumstances the general dispersive effect is accompanied by interparticle collisions that can also lead to erosion, surface cleaning and wetting of the particles and particle size reduction. It is also possible to use ultrasound to adjust the particle size of sugar after crystallisation (Roberts and James, 1992). When a 74% sucrose solution is crystallised and then treated with ultrasound (20 kHz, 11 Wcm$^{-2}$ for 15 minutes) the particle size is considerably reduced.

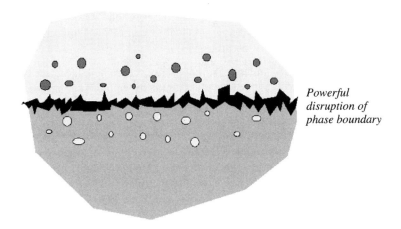

*Powerful
disruption of
phase boundary*

**Fig. 16.7**  Cavitation effects on a heterogeneous liquid/liquid system.

### 16.2.4  Heterogeneous liquid-liquid reactions

In heterogeneous liquid/liquid reactions, cavitational collapse at or near the interface will cause disruption and mixing, resulting in the formation of very fine emulsions (Fig. 16.7). Ultrasonic homogenisation has been used for many years in the food industry for the production of tomato sauce, mayonnaise and other similar blended items. In chemistry such extremely fine emulsions provide enormous interfacial contact areas between immiscible liquids and thus the potential for greater reaction between the phases. This effect has been utilised in the basic hydrolysis of waxes in aqueous ethanolic solution. The conventional process generally leads to discoloured products but sonication allows the use of lower temperatures with faster reaction times, leading to considerably purer products (Davidson *et al.*, 1987).

## 16.3  Ultrasound as a preservation technology

The destruction of microorganisms by power ultrasound has been of considerable interest since the 1920s when the work of Harvey and Loomis (1929) was first published. Their work examined the reduction in light emission from a seawater suspension of rod shaped *Bacillus Fisheri* caused by sonication (which they called 'raying') at 375 kHz under temperature controlled conditions. They showed that heating appeared to injure the bacterial colonies but that ultrasound appeared to have a greater effect. Reducing the temperature during sonication and maintaining it at 19 °C prevented re-growth of the bacteria as all the bacteria appeared to be dead when viewed under a microscope. The final sentence of the paper read:

> In conclusion we can state that, under proper conditions of raying,
> luminous bacteria can be broken up and killed by sound waves of

approximately 400,000 Hz frequency and the solutions sterilized, but that the method is not one of any practical or commercial importance because of the expense of the process.

Nowadays ultrasonic technology is much more commonplace, costs have reduced and applications have become economically viable. The various effects of cavitation outlined in section 16.2 can be utilised in food preservation. Applications include the long-established surface cleaning where the powerful jet generated on collapse will dislodge dirt and bacteria from surfaces. The particular advantage of ultrasonic cleaning in this context is that it can reach crevices that are not easily reached by conventional cleaning methods. Once dislodged into the bulk solution any harmful species are subject to ultrasonically assisted disinfection. In solution ultrasound can be of great use in the general sterilisation and disinfection of food materials particularly where ultrasound is used in conjunction with a conventional sterilisation technology, e.g., heat or the use of a biocide. Research studies to date have focused on a range of different experimental procedures, and biological systems to study the inactivation effect of ultrasound. There are several theories that have been proposed to explain how ultrasound might kill microorganisms with or without heat and/or pressure and these have been summarised in several review articles (Hughes and Nyborg, 1962; Earnshaw et al., 1995; Sala et al., 1995).

The following section will review the ways in which ultrasound alone or together with heat and/or pressure can inactivate microbes, enzymes, and spores in model and real foods. Microbial challenge tests have been conducted to determine the effect of ultrasound on the inactivation kinetics of selected organisms inoculated in model or real foods. These tests are conducted by applying ultrasound energy that results in the inactivation of a maximum number of microorganisms without ultrasonic breakdown of the food. The many and varied ways in which ultrasound has been used to affect microorganisms of interest in food technology are summarised in the papers itemised in Table 16.4.

### 16.3.1    Ultrasound induced cell damage: possible mechanisms

It is not possible to deduce a global conclusion as to the effect of ultrasound on living cells even from the large number of results presented in this chapter. There is however evidence of ultrasound lethality over a great variety of microorganisms, some enzymes, and even a few bacterial spores (Table 16.4). Different species of microorganisms differ in their resistance to ultrasound, larger cells appear to be more sensitive to ultrasound, coccal forms are more resistant than rod shaped bacteria and aerobic are more resistant than anaerobic species.

The mechanical effects of power ultrasound on chemical systems in a liquid medium are mainly attributed to cavitation and these forces have a dramatic effect on biological systems. Acoustic cavitation can be broadly divided into two types, transient and stable. The former occurs when the cavitation bubbles, filled with gas or vapour, undergo irregular oscillations and finally implode. This produces high local temperatures and pressures that would disintegrate biological cells and/or denature any enzymes present. The imploding bubble also produces high shear forces and liquid jets in the solvent that may also have sufficient energy to physically damage the cell wall/membrane. Mechanical effects of this type have been used on a small scale for the disinfection of water contaminated with microbial spores, e.g., cryptosporidium although the acoustic energy required is high. Stable cavitation, on the other hand, refers to bubbles that oscillate in a regular fashion for many acoustic cycles. The bubbles induce microstreaming in the surrounding liquid which can also induce stress in any microbiological species present. The microstreaming effect therefore provides a large force, without the bubbles having to burst and this type of cavitation may well be important in a range of applications of ultrasound to biotechnology (Reynolds and Willis, 1974).

The inactivation effect of ultrasound has also been attributed to the generation of intracellular cavitation and these mechanical shocks can disrupt cellular structural and functional components up to the point of cell lysis (Butz and Tauscher, 2002; Grahame, 1996; Abee and Wouters, 1999). Figure 16.8 represents a proposed mechanism of ultrasound-induced cell damage.

Scherba *et al.* exposed aqueous suspensions of specific bacteria, fungus and viruses to ultrasound at 26 kHz frequency. They discovered that the relative percentage of bacteria killed increased with an increase in exposure time and increased ultrasonic intensity. They suggested that the inner cytoplasmic membrane may be the point of ultrasonic damage since there appeared to be no significant difference in kill rate for either gram +ve or gram −ve bacteria (Scherba *et al.*, 1991).

Spores appear to be more resistant than vegetative forms whilst enzymes are reported to be inactivated by ultrasound due to a depolymerisation effect, however, the effectiveness of the depolymerisation varies. Cavitation is the formation, growth and, sometimes, the implosion of micro-bubbles created in a liquid when ultrasound waves propagate through it. The collapse of the bubbles leads to energy accumulation in hot spots (Suslick, 1990). This phenomenon can cause enzyme inactivation through three possible mechanisms, which can act

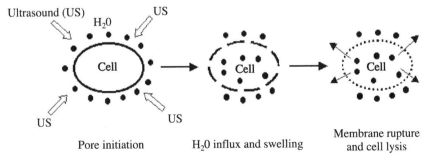

**Fig. 16.8**   Mechanism of ultrasound-induced cell damage.

**Table 16.4** Summary of some experiments that show the effects of ultrasound energy in food preservation

| No. | Object studied | Suspension media | $f$(kHz) | $P$(W) | Remarks | $T$(°C) | $t$(mins) | Ref. |
|---|---|---|---|---|---|---|---|---|
| 1 | tomato pectinmethylesterase | tomato juice | 20 | 450 | heat and pressure combination | 70 | 1 | Vercet et al., 2002 |
| 2 | Saccharomyces cerevisiae | sabouraud broth | 20 | 0–600 | heat and pH combination | 35–55 | 10–30 | Lopez-Malo et al., 1999 |
| 3 | Phospholipase | milk and salts buffer | 20 | 450 | heat and pressure combination | 50–130 | 1–5 | Vercet et al., 2001a |
| 4 | α-chymotrypsin | milk and salts buffer | 20 | 450 | heat and pressure combination | 50–130 | 1–5 | Vercet et al., 2001a |
| 5 | trypsin | milk and salts buffer | 20 | 450 | heat and pressure combination | 50–130 | 1–5 | Vercet et al., 2001a |
| 6 | porcine pancreatic lipase | milk and salts buffer | 20 | 450 | heat and pressure combination | 50–130 | 1–5 | Vercet et al., 2001a |
| 7 | Escherichia coli | water | 20–1071 | 80–140 | dissolved gas (O$_2$, Ar…) | 20–29 | 60 | Hua and Thompson, 2000 |
| 8 | Escherichia coli | biofilm | 70–500 | 0–100 | No | 37 | 120 | Peterson and Pitt, 2000 |
| 9 | alkaline phosphatase | skim and whole milk | 20 | 150 | heat combination | 61–75 | 1–2 | Villamiel and de Jong, 2000a |
| 10 | γ-glutamethyltranspeptidase | skim and whole milk | 20 | 150 | heat combination | 61–75 | 1–2 | Villamiel and de Jong, 2000a |
| 11 | lactoperoxidase | skim and whole milk | 20 | 150 | heat combination | 61–75 | 1–2 | Villamiel and de Jong, 2000a |
| 12 | α-lactalbumin | skim and whole milk | 20 | 150 | heat combination | 61–75 | 1–2 | Villamiel and de Jong, 2000a |
| 13 | β-lactoglobulin | skim and whole milk | 20 | 150 | heat combination | 61–75 | 1–2 | Villamiel and de Jong, 2000a |
| 14 | casein | skim and whole milk | 20 | 150 | heat combination | 61–75 | 1–2 | Villamiel and de Jong, 2000a |
| 15 | Pseudomonas fluorescens | trypticase soy broth | 20 | 150 | heat combination | 45–76 | 1–2 | Villamiel and de Jong, 2000b |
| 16 | Streptococcus thermophilus | trypticase soy broth | 20 | 150 | heat combination | 45–76 | 1–2 | Villamiel and de Jong, 2000b |
| 17 | Salmonella typhimurium | egg | 20 | 150–450 | heat and pressure combination | 40 | 1 | Manas et al., 2000 |
| 18 | Salmonella enteridis | egg | 20 | 150–450 | heat and pressure combination | 40 | 1 | Manas et al., 2000 |
| 19 | Salmonella senftenberg | egg | 20 | 150–450 | heat and pressure combination | 40 | 1 | Manas et al., 2000 |
| 20 | Peroxidase | water | 20–60 | 0–120 | heat combination | 80 | 30 | de Gennaro et al., 1999 |
| 21 | Listeria monocytogenes | tryptic soy broth | 20 | 450–2000 | heat and pressure combination | 30–70 | 1–10 | Pagan et al., 1999 |
| 22 | Saccharomyces cerevisiae | water | 20 | 300 | heat combination | 20–49 | 10–80 | Petin et al., 1999 |
| 23 | Pectinmethylesterase | orange juice | 20 | 450 | heat and pressure combination | 72 | 1–5 | Vercet et al., 1999 |
| 24 | Saccharomyces cerevisiae | citrate phosphate buffer | 20 | 150–450 | heat combination | 45–55 | 1–20 | Lopez-Malo et al., 1999 |

| No. | Substance | Medium | P | f | Method | T | t | Ref |
|---|---|---|---|---|---|---|---|---|
| 25 | Pectinmethylesterase | tomato juice | 20 | 450 | heat and pressure combination | 37–86 | 1 | Lopez et al., 1998 |
| 26 | Polygalacturonases | tomato juice | 20 | 450 | heat and pressure combination | 37–86 | 1 | Lopez et al., 1998 |
| 27 | Saccharomyces cerevisiae | water | 20 | 100 | heat combination | 50–55 | 10 | Ciccolini et al., 1997 |
| 28 | lipase from Ps. fluorescens | skim milk | 20 | 450 | heat and pressure combination | 110–140 | 1–10 | Vercet et al., 1997 |
| 29 | protease from Ps. fluorescens | skim milk | 20 | 450 | heat and pressure combination | 110–140 | 1–10 | Vercet et al., 1997 |
| 30 | Zygosaccharomyces bailii | orange juice | 20–800 | 0–150 | heat combination | 55 | 10 | Earnshaw et al., 1995 |
| 31 | Listeria monocytogenes | UHT milk or rice pudding | 20–800 | 0–150 | heat combination | 60 | 10 | Earnshaw et al., 1995 |
| 32 | Bacillus subtilus spores | milk | 20 | 150–450 | heat and pressure combination | 104 | 5 | Sala et al., 1995 |
| 33 | Bacillus stearothermophilus | potassium phosphate buffer | 20 | 150–450 | heat and pressure combination | 104 | 5 | Sala et al., 1995 |
| 34 | Bacillus coagulans | potassium phosphate buffer | 20 | 150–450 | heat and pressure combination | 80–100 | 5 | Sala et al., 1995 |
| 35 | Saccharomyces cerevisiae | potassium phosphate buffer | 20 | 150–450 | heat and pressure combination | 80–100 | 5 | Sala et al., 1995 |
| 36 | Aeromonas hydrophila | potassium phosphate buffer | 20 | 150–450 | heat and pressure combination | 80–100 | 5 | Sala et al., 1995 |
| 37 | Bacillus cereus | potassium phosphate buffer | 20 | 150–450 | heat and pressure combination | 104 | 5 | Sala et al., 1995 |
| 38 | Lipoxygenase | potassium phosphate buffer | 20 | 150–450 | heat and pressure combination | 67–77 | 5 | Sala et al., 1995 |
| 39 | Peroxidase | potassium phosphate buffer | 20 | 150–450 | heat and pressure combination | 121–142 | 5 | Sala et al., 1995 |
| 40 | Polyphenol oxidase | potassium phosphate buffer | 20 | 150–450 | heat and pressure combination | 71 | 5 | Sala et al., 1995 |
| 41 | Staphylococcus aureus | UHT milk | 20 | 150 | heat combination | 11–56 | 8 | Ordonez et al., 1987 |
| 42 | Staphylococcus aureus | phosphate-buffered saline | 40 | 150 | ozone combination | 25 | 1 | Burleson et al., 1975 |
| 43 | Salmonella typhimurium | phosphate-buffered saline | 40 | 150 | ozone combination | 25 | 1 | Burleson et al., 1975 |
| 44 | Escherichia coli | phosphate-buffered saline | 40 | 150 | ozone combination | 25 | 1 | Burleson et al., 1975 |
| 45 | Shigella flexneri | phosphate-buffered saline | 40 | 150 | ozone combination | 25 | 1 | Burleson et al., 1975 |
| 46 | Pseudomonas fluorescens | phosphate-buffered saline | 40 | 150 | ozone combination | 25 | 1 | Burleson et al., 1975 |
| 47 | Vibrio cholearae | phosphate-buffered saline | 40 | 150 | ozone combination | 25 | 1 | Burleson et al., 1975 |
| 48 | Bacillus cereus | Ringer solution | 20 | 264 | No | 10–12 | 1–12 | Burgos et al., 1972 |
| 49 | Bacillus licheniformis | Ringer solution | 20 | 264 | No | 10–12 | 1–12 | Burgos et al., 1972 |
| 50 | baker's yeast | salt solution | 20 | 60 | pressure combination | 0–7 | 5 | Neppiras and Hughes, 1964 |

P: ultrasound power (watts); f: ultrasound frequency; T: temperature; t: preservation/reaction time; Ref: references.

alone or combined (Hughes and Nyborg, 1962; Vercet *et al.*, 1997; Raso *et al.*, 1999; Vercet *et al.*, 1998):

- purely thermal, due to the enormous temperatures achieved during cavitation
- through free radicals generated by water sonolysis
- due to the mechanical forces (shear forces) created by micro-streaming and shock waves.

### 16.3.2   Effect of heat and pressure on ultrasound induced cell damage

The effectiveness of ultrasound in food preservation can be increased by combination with other treatments. The resistance of microorganisms and enzymes to ultrasound is very high and it may require several hours of ultrasonication to achieve the desired results. Such prolonged treatments will produce extensive changes in the food and the quality of treated food will be severely affected (Vercet *et al.*, 2001b; Villamiel *et al.*, 1999; Miles *et al.*, 1999; Vercet *et al.*, 2002; Villamiel and de Jong, 2000a). Increased effectiveness of ultrasound preservation in combination with heat and pressure opens new possibilities. The use of ultrasound with moderate heating is known as thermosonication (TS). A combination of ultrasound and moderate pressure is known as manosonication (MS) and finally the full combination of heat, ultrasound irradiation and moderate pressure is known as manothermosonication (MTS) (Earnshaw *et al.*, 1995; Sala *et al.*, 1995; Earnshaw, 1998). MTS treatment facilitates the inactivation of several enzymes at lower temperatures and/or in a shorter time than thermal treatments at the same temperatures. Table 16.5 compares the strengths and weaknesses of ultrasound alone and MTS as a preservation technology.

At the moment MTS is employed on a laboratory or pilot scale, but may well have potential as an alternative pasteurisation or sterilisation method for liquid foods in the future. Its application for solid foods is less likely because solid or viscous materials do not easily support cavitation and in economic terms the energies required would be very high (Gould, 1996).

Research over the past 50 years strongly supports the hypothesis that several different factors contribute to the overall efficiency of a preservation process involving ultrasound and these include frequency, intensity, treatment time, temperature, pressure and the media to be treated. Once identified however the preservation and the inactivation kinetics of vegetative cells, spores, and

**Table 16.5**   Effects of ultrasound in combination with heat and pressure

| Inactivation by | Vegetative cells | Spores | Enzymes |
| --- | --- | --- | --- |
| Ultrasound alone | + | − | − |
| Ultrasound + heat (TS) | + | + | − |
| Ultrasound + heat and pressure (MTS) | + | + | + |

enzymes can be optimised (de Gennaro *et al.*, 1999; Neppiras and Hughes, 1964; Vercet *et al.*, 2001a).

## 16.4   Ultrasonic inactivation of microorganisms, spores and enzymes

There are many examples of microorganisms inactivated using ultrasound (Table 16.4). Some of these have been studied in culture media and others in food. The most frequently studied microorganisms, not only in the field of power ultrasound, but also among other methods of food preservation are *Saccaromyces cerevisiae* and *Escherichia coli*. The former has been found to be less resistant to ultrasound than other vegetative cells, which is mostly attributed to its larger size. The inactivation of this microorganism has been proven in such food models as water, phosphate buffers, and sabouraud broth (Sala *et al.*, 1995, Ciccolini *et al.*, 1997; Guerrero *et al.*, 2001; Petin *et al.*, 1999; Lopez-Malo *et al.*, 1999). Examples of inactivation studies of *Escherichia coli* cells include investigations of suspensions in a variety of media under different treatment conditions including frequency, power, heat and the presence of dissolved gases (Burleson *et al.*, 1975; Hua and Thompson, 2000; Peterson and Pitt, 2000).

The inactivation of *Staphylococcus aureus* has been proven in water and phosphate buffers, as well as in such foods as UHT milk (Burleson *et al.*, 1975; Ordonez *et al.*, 1987). When applying ultrasound in combination with heat the kill rates were increased when compared to rates of thermal treatment alone and a synergistic rather than an additive effect was observed. Ultrasound produced a good level of inactivation under different treatment conditions and media for *Bacillus* species (Scherba *et al.*, 1991).

The inactivation of *Salmonella typhimurium* (Burleson *et al.*, 1975; Manas *et al.*, 2000) suspended in phosphate buffer or egg product was achieved by applying a heat and pressure combination treatment to the microorganism. *Salmonella typhimurium* suspensions in brain heart infusion broth, skim milk and liquid whole egg have been treated with ultrasound (Wrigley and Llorca, 1992). In brain heart infusion broth up to 99% reduction was observed and viability of the *S. typhimurium* decreased with an increase in temperature. In skim milk the reduction observed was over 2 log units at 40 °C. However in liquid whole egg the levels reduced were less than 1 log cycle. Indirect sonication reduced the numbers of *S. typhimurium* in both brain heart infusion broth and skim milk at temperatures below those required for pasteurisation. As the temperature of the medium was increased the numbers of surviving organisms decreased. Suggestions were made that the viscous nature and high lipid content of egg made cavitation less effective in the liquid egg medium allowing for the survival of greater numbers of organisms. *Pseudomonas fluorescens* suspended in phosphate buffers or Trypticase soy broth has been inactivated by ultrasound in combination with heat or ozone (Burleson *et al.*, 1975; Villamiel and de Jong, 2000a).

The inactivation of *Listeria monocytogenes* by high-power ultrasonic waves (20 kHz) at ambient temperature and pressure has been found to be low with decimal reduction values in 4.3 minutes. This could be improved however by either an increase in pressure (manosonication) or by increasing the power of sonication. Inactivation by manothermal sonication (MTS) proved to be more effective (Earnshaw *et al.*, 1995; Pagan *et al.*, 1999). By combining sub-lethal temperatures and higher pressures of 200 kPa the decimal reduction value fell dramatically over 1.5 minutes. Further increases in pressure to 400 kPa reduced the effect from 1.5 minutes to 1.0 minute. An advantage of using manosonication instead of heat alone to inactivate bacteria was that recovery of the bacteria was far lower and did not appear to be dependent upon the treatment medium employed. Manosonication at 40 °C and 200 kPa decreased the decimal reduction times of *Streptococcus faecium*, *Listeria monocytogenes*, *Salmonella enteritidis*, and *Aeromonas hydrophila* (Pagan, 1999). Increasing the ultrasonic amplitude reduced these levels even further. Increasing the pressure from 200 to 400kPa also resulted in a reduction in the decimal reduction rates. Cells grown at 37 °C were twice as heat resistant as those grown at 4 °C. At higher viscosities cavitation is harder to achieve but the final collapse of the bubble is more violent. By employing a calorimetric method of monitoring the power applied directly to the medium they discovered a linear relationship between power entering the medium and decimal reduction times (Manas *et al.*, 2000). This suggests that greater rates of kill could be achieved by using higher ultrasonic power that in turn would be dependent upon the frequency and intensity of the ultrasonic power entering the system.

*Yersinia entercolitica* inactivation has been examined at constant temperature and pressure but with increasing ultrasonic power (Raso *et al.*, 1998). The decimal reduction time was decreased from 4 minutes to 0.37 minutes when the power, as measured by the amplitude of vibration of the ultrasonic radiating source, was increased from 21 to 150 $\mu$m. Increasing the external applied pressure to 600 kPa at 30 °C decreased the decimal reduction time from 1.52 minutes to 0.2 minutes. At lethal temperatures of 58 °C a combination of ultrasound and pressure resulted in lower decimal reduction times when compared to thermal treatment alone. Increasing the temperature further reduced the beneficial effect of the ultrasound and pressure treatments.

Bacterial cells differ in their sensitivity to ultrasound treatment. In general, larger cells are more sensitive to ultrasound (Ahmed and Russell, 1975) and this may be due to the fact that larger cells have an increased surface area, making them more vulnerable to the high pressures produced during acoustic cavitation. Gram-positive cells appear to be more resistant to ultrasound than gram-negative cells; this may be due to the structure of the cell walls. Gram-positive cells have thicker cell walls that provide the cells with some protection against ultrasonic treatment. However, in other studies there appears to be no significant difference between the percentage of gram-positive and gram-negative cells killed by ultrasound (Ahmed, 1975). Cell shape has been investigated and it has been found that spherical shaped cells (cocci) are more resistant to ultrasound than

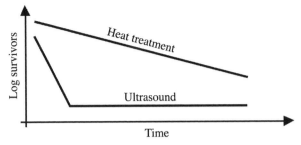

**Fig. 16.9**   Qualitative representation of the difference in the effects of ultrasound and heat treatments on the inactivation of vegetative cells with time.

rod-shaped cells (Alliger, 1975). *Bacillus* and *Clostridium* spores have been found to be more resistant to sonication than vegetative bacteria and many of the bacteria known to be resistant to heat are similarly resistant to ultrasound (Sanz *et al.*, 1985). Figure 16.9 represents the dramatic difference in the effects of ultrasonic and heat treatment on vegetative cells as a function of time. Ultrasonic treatment gives the more immediate and rapid effect.

### 16.4.1   Ultrasonic spore inactivation

Microbial spores are resistant to extreme conditions such as high temperatures and osmotic pressures, high and low pHs, and mechanical shocks. Those bacterial spores that survive heat treatment may severely restrict the shelf-life of thermally processed foods because of spoilage and poisoning. The endospores of *Bacillus and Clostridium* species are very resistant to extreme conditions; for example *Bacillus thermophilus* spores are destroyed by heating only at 100 °C for four hours.

*Bacillus subtilis* spores are notoriously difficult to denature. As a result they are often employed to determine the efficiency of various treatment/sterilisation processes as, being highly resistant, the success of the process can be weighed clearly against the kill rate of the bacillus spore. Combining the effect of a 20 kHz ultrasonic probe on samples under static pressure indicated that an increase in static pressure resulted in an increased level of spore inactivation (Raso *et al.*, 1998). Manosonication treatment at 500 kPa for 12 minutes inactivated over 99% of the spores. Increasing the amplitude of ultrasonic vibration of the transducer, i.e., the acoustic power entering the system, increased the level of inactivation, for example, a 20 kHz probe at 300 kPa, 12 minutes sonication at 90 $\mu$m amplitude inactivated 75% of the spores. Raising the amplitude to 150 $\mu$m resulted in 99.5% spore inactivation. Finally increasing the thermal temperature of the treatment resulted in greater rates of inactivation certainly at 300 kPa compared to thermal treatment alone.

The pathogens *Bacillus cereus* and *licheniformis* spores have been found to be resistant to ultrasonic treatment alone (Burgos *et al.*, 1972). However under

Viable count
100ml x 1000

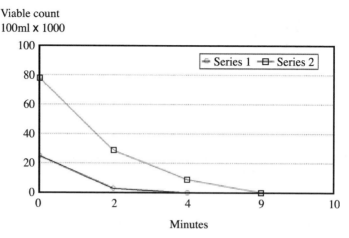

**Fig. 16.10**   Effect of ultrasound (20 kHz) on water inoculated with *Cryptosporidium* oocysts.

MTS treatment chemicals are released from the spores including dipicolinic acid and low molecular weight peptides (Palacios *et al.*, 1991).

The protozoa, Cryptosporidium parvum, has become recognised as a cause of the water-borne disease Cryptosporidiosis in humans and many cases have been reported in the news over the last decade. These outbreaks have occurred throughout Europe as well as the USA and are not just associated with the developing countries. The main concern of water suppliers is that conventional treatment methods are inadequate and are not a sufficient barrier in preventing the water-borne transmission of cryptosporidiosis. The most commonly used disinfectant techniques used in water treatment, i.e., chlorination and ultraviolet light is ineffective but ozone seems to be able to destroy some of these oocysts.

It has been found that sonication of batch samples of water containing 25,000 cryptosporidia oocysts per 100 ml (series 1) or 78,000 oocysts per 100 ml (series 2) is capable of reducing the viable count of oocysts (Fig. 16.10) (Biwater, 1993). In flow tests ($19 \, \text{lh}^{-1}$) with samples of tap water at 7 °C, previously spiked with purified oocysts and with a contact time of approximately 3.6 seconds within a flow cell (20 kHz, 140 W), only $2.5 \times 10^2$ oocysts per litre were recovered from an initial concentration of around $2.4 \times 10^5$.

### 16.4.2   Ultrasonic enzyme inactivation

To prevent denaturation, an enzyme has to maintain its native structure. Hydrophobic interactions, hydrogen bonding, van der Waals interactions, ion pairing, electrostatic forces, and steric constraints stabilise the three-dimensional molecular structure of globular proteins. Enzyme inactivation is a requisite for stabilisation of some food materials. Although it can be easily achieved by heat treatment, there are some cases where the high heat resistance of some enzymes can adversely influence food properties such as flavour, colour or nutritional value.

Ultrasonic enzyme inactivation depends on the conditions of the treatment (McClements, 1995), as well as on the nature of the enzyme. MTS treatment has an increased effectiveness of enzyme inactivation compared with ultrasound alone (Earnshaw *et al.*, 1995). The effect of MTS on lypoxygenase, peroxidase, and polyphenoloxidase, as well as heat-resistant lipase from *Pseudomonas fluorescens*, have been studied in model systems and whey (Manas *et al.*, 2000). Within the temperature range of 110–140 °C manothermosonication inactivated the enzymes more effectively than heat treatment alone (Vercet *et al.*, 1997). Manothermosonication at 650 kPa and 140 °C reduced the levels of protease activity to 6% and lipase to 7% when compared to activity levels obtained when employing thermal treatment alone. However, the effective improvement achieved using this combined treatment decreased as the treatment temperature increased. Manothermosonication could be useful to inactivate those enzymes within food materials that do not require such high temperatures for preservation.

MTS allows the inactivation of several enzymes at lower temperatures and/or in a shorter time than thermal treatments at the same temperature. It is possible to quantify the effect of such treatments by calculating the activation energy (*Ea*) for the process.

$$k = A.exp(-Ea/RT) \hspace{4cm} 16.1$$

*Ea* is obtained from the Arrhenius equation, shown above, by plotting log *k* (*k* is the rate of reaction), in this case inactivation against the inverse of the absolute temperature (*T*). The activation energy is the amount of energy required for the reaction to proceed. Figure 16.11 represents activation energy for enzyme inactivation by heat and manothermosonication.

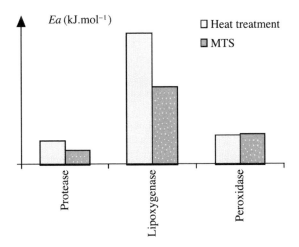

**Fig. 16.11**   Energy diagram for enzyme inactivation by heat and MTS.

Alkaline phosphatase, γ-glutamyltranspeptidase and lactoperoxidase, milk proteins and milk fat have all been examined using both whole and skim milk (Abee and Wouters, 1999). Complete inactivation of alkaline phosphatase was observed at 75.5 °C after thermal treatment alone for 102 seconds in both whole and skim milk. Ultrasonic treatment alone did not inactivate the enzyme, however, a combination of ultrasound and thermal treatment at 61 °C achieved 49% inactivation of the enzyme with whole milk (levels of 24% for thermal treatment alone at this temperature) and 44% for skim milk. Less than 0.9% activity was observed at 70 °C after ultrasonic treatment of 70 seconds. Similar results for γ-glutamyltranspeptidase were obtained. Ultrasound treatment for 102 seconds in the absence of heating produced only 22% inactivation. Thermal treatment at 75.5 °C resulted in less than 8.5% inactivation but a combination of thermal treatment and ultrasound at similar temperatures, and sonication treatment times, produced complete inactivation. For all processes concerned ultrasound alone produced very low levels of inactivation but the addition of heat to the treatment produced synergistic effects. Some differences in levels of inactivation were observed for skim and whole milk and this was attributed to the composition of the medium. Some denaturisation of whey proteins was also observed when employing ultrasound and the effect was greater with whole than with skim milk.

Burgos *et al.* examined the inactivation of lipoxygenase enzyme via manothermosonication under various parameters (Lopez and Burgos, 1995). They determined that its inactivation increased with ultrasonic power and pH affected the rate of enzyme inactivation with resistance increasing when the pH was altered from 5.2 to 8. The presence of glucose, sucrose and glycerol also increased resistance to both treatments. This group also studied peroxidase which is a heme containing enzyme from horseradish, polyphenol oxidase a copper containing enzyme from mushrooms and lipoxygenase containing iron and obtained from soybeans (Lopez *et al.*, 1994). The greater the ultrasonic power the higher the inactivation rate and increasing the pressure resulted in higher rates of inactivation up to a point after which it began to decrease. This point depended upon the ultrasonic power employed. It was postulated that inactivation of these enzymes was probably due to severe shear stresses due to cavitational collapse, inactivation of enzymes in cavitation hotspots and also free radical formation and resultant scavenging of amino acid residues of the enzymes used in structure stability, binding and catalytic activity.

Orange juice is usually heated to aid preservation but various thermoresistant enzymes prove to be difficult to denature by thermal treatment alone. Pectinmethylesterase (PME), from oranges, is strongly protected by its substrate pectin against thermo-inactivation, however, MTS treatment is unaffected by the presence of that molecule and enzyme inactivation is effective (Vercet *et al.*, 1999). PME present in oranges was treated by manothermosonication at pressures of 200 kPa in citrate buffer and also in orange juice. At 35.5 °C the inactivation of the enzyme using manothermosonication was estimated to be approximately seven times greater than thermal treatment alone.

The viscosity of processed tomatoes is very important to food processors as high viscosity is usually associated with a higher quality and hence a less concentrated amount of the tomato would be required to maintain quality within the foodstuff, whether it be in tomato puree, salsa, ketchup or sauce form. As pectin is associated with maintaining viscosity the depolymerisation of pectin by pectolytic enzymes is therefore of great concern to processors and any such enzymes liberated during processing must be inactivated as quickly as possible. This is usually achieved by 'heat shocking' the processed material to temperatures of up to 104 °C. Lopez *et al.* (1998) investigated the effect of manothermosonication on tomato pectin enzymes PME, Polygalacturonases I and II (PG I and PG II). PME was sonicated at 62.5 °C and 37 °C at pressures of 200 kPa and an ultrasonic frequency of 20 kHz. At 37 °C the combination of ultrasound and increased pressure produced higher levels of inactivation compared with those achieved at 62.5 °C with thermal treatment alone. Similar results observed for PG I and PG II suggested that manothermosonication provided a synergistic effect to the inactivation of such enzymes. For PG I to achieve 99% thermal inactivation the sample would need to be heated at 86°C for 40 minutes. The same effect could be achieved by employing manothermosonication at 86 °C for only 30 seconds, a substantial saving of time.

### 16.4.3   Effect of ultrasound on the anti-oxidant activity of milk

Milk is susceptible to oxidative degeneration and heating milk as a method of sterilisation often results in alterations to its flavour. Taylor and Richardson examined anti-oxidant activity in skim milk. Raw skim milk subjected to ultrasound for five minutes had 3.65 times higher levels of anti-oxidant activity when compared to non-sonicated milk. Beneficial effects were even observed when the milk was subjected to sonication times of only five seconds. The increased anti-oxidant activity was still retained even during storage at 40 °C for 40 hours. The casein fraction provided similar results to the sonicated skim milk hence it was suggested that casein provides protection against oxidation. As casein exists as micelles it was postulated that the ultrasound is able to disrupt the micellar structure to reduce larger micelles into smaller structures and as a result increase the availability of casein.

## 16.5   Ultrasound in combination with other preservation techniques

While the main research effort in food preservation using ultrasound has concentrated on either ultrasound alone, thermosonication or manothermosonication there are a range of studies which have examined ultrasound in combination with other techniques. Amongst these it is being employed in combination with disinfecting chemical agents including antibiotics, chlorine and ozone as an alternative synergistic method of pathogen destruction. There are also some studies of ultrasound in combination with freezing for improved food preservation.


### 16.5.1    With a bactericide in surface cleaning

One of the major long-established industrial applications of power ultrasound is in surface cleaning and it has proved to be an extremely efficient technology. Ultrasound is particularly useful in surface decontamination where the inrush of fluid that accompanies cavitational collapse near a surface is non-symmetric (Fig. 16.5). The particular advantage of ultrasonic cleaning in this context is that it can reach crevices that are not easily reached by conventional cleaning methods. Objects that can be cleaned range from large crates used for food packaging and transportation to delicate surgical implements such as endoscopes. This was recognised some years ago, see for example a general patent that relates to the use of ultrasound as a method of pasteurisation, sterilisation and decontamination of instruments and surfaces used within the medical, surgical, dental and food processing industries (Boucher, 1980). The use of ultrasound allows the destruction of a variety of fungi, bacteria and viruses in a much reduced processing time when compared to thermal treatment at similar temperatures. The removal of bacteria from various surfaces is of great importance to the food industry and can be efficiently accomplished with the combined use of sonicated hot water containing biocidal detergents (Quartly-Watson, 1998). Typical examples of items requiring repeated regular cleaning are plastic baskets, shackles (the hooks used for hanging poultry on a production line) and conveyer belts.

Chemicals such as chlorine are often used to clean and decontaminate food products and food processing surfaces. The effects of ultrasound on the surface contamination of poultry drumsticks have been examined (Sams and Feria, 1991). An increase in levels of bacteria, such as *Salmonella*, was observed during the pre-chilling stage possibly due to the dispersion of bacterial aggregates and their subsequent growth. Sonication post chilling also did not appear to reduce levels of bacteria. In this case sonication alone had little benefit in the preservation process, nevertheless, it was suggested that in combination with additional techniques it could prove to be beneficial. They postulated that the shape of the drumstick may have been detrimental to effective use of ultrasound with the formation of standing waves as a result of reflection from an uneven poultry surface resulting in reduced levels of effectiveness. Lillard examined the disinfection of flat poultry skin inoculated with *Salmonella* with a combination of ultrasound and chlorine (Lillard, 1993). The best results were obtained when employing ultrasound simultaneously with chlorine solution with levels reduced by 2.5 to $4.0 \log_{10}$. It was suggested that the enhancement arose through a combination of the release of *Salmonella* cells from the skin by bombardment with ultrasound and the ultrasonically increased penetration of chlorine into the cells.

In most countries the use of antibiotics in foods is strictly forbidden. Nevertheless, there have been several reports of the use of ultrasound to improve the effects of antibiotics in surface cleaning, particularly in the removal of biofilms. Thus ultrasound is able to promote the effectiveness of various antibiotics at concentrations that do not, on their own, reduce bacteria viability in biofilms (Qian *et al.*, 1997). This synergy reduced the viability by several orders of magnitude for cultures of *Pseudomonas aeruginosa*, *Escherichia coli*, *Staphylococcus epidenmidis* and *Staphylococcus aureus*. Measurements of the bactericidal activity of gentamicin against *P. aeruginosa* and *E. coli* demonstrated that simultaneous application of 67 kHz ultrasound enhanced the effectiveness of the antibiotic. As the age of these cultures increased, the bacteria became more resistant to the effect of the antibiotic alone and the application of ultrasound appeared to reverse this resistance. The ultrasonic treatment-enhanced activity was not observed with cultures of gram-positive *S. epidermidis* and *S. aureus*. The synergy was confirmed in studies of biofilms of *Escherichia coli* (Peterson and Pitt, 2000). The biofilms were up to 300 $\mu$m thickness, far greater than those previously examined with *Pseudomonas aeruginosa*. Treatment with ultrasound alone did not appear to enhance killing rate even after two hours sonication. Antibiotic alone killed only 82% of the cells within two hours. A combination of ultrasound and antibiotic killed 99% of the cells within two hours with the best results obtained employing high power densities and low ultrasonic frequencies. Improvement in the killing rate may be due to the ability of ultrasound to introduce the antibiotic further into the biofilm than it would normally have reached on its own.

The use of ultraviolet light as an aid to disinfection and to aid food preservation is well known and well used within the food industry. Ultraviolet light has been used to inactivate *Salmonella* in thin aqueous and chocolate films (Lee *et al.*, 1989). They compared the results obtained with those from the use of ultrasound as a method to inactivate the bacteria. Serotypes such as the heat-sensitive *S. eastbourne* to the less sensitive *S. senftenberg* were examined. They discovered that the thermal resistance of salmonella was greater in the chocolate than in the aqueous media. Decimal reduction times at 71 °C were 4.5 hrs, 4.6 hrs and 6.6 hrs for thermal treatment of *S. eastbourne*, *S. senftenberg* and *S. typhimurium* serotypes. Using ultrasound a $4 \log_{10}$ reduction was observed at 5 °C after only 10 minutes sonication in peptone water whilst a $0.78 \log_{10}$ reduction of the bacteria was observed in milk chocolate after 30 minutes. High temperatures were observed in the chocolate medium and this may have had some contributory lethal effect. This could be in some part due to the viscosity and thermal conductivity of the chocolate being detrimental to efficient sonication and cavitation production. Use of ultraviolet light killed 75% of the salmonella within 10 minutes when the chocolate thickness was 0.5 mm. Increasing chocolate film to 1 mm resulted in minimal destruction of the bacteria. They concluded that ultrasound produced high temperatures during the sonication process and that its bactericidal effect may be advantageous in the chocolate conching process.

### 16.5.2    In combination with pH

Bacterial spores are highly resistant to destruction due to their nature and structural design, *Bacillus.subtilis* being one of the most resistant to denaturisation. Sterilisation can be defined as the killing of 100% of microbiobial life and as a result often requires harsh conditions to achieve. Sterilisation of equipment is often carried out by heating, however, in order to achieve full kill rates high temperatures must be employed which may also cause damage to surrounding materials such as rubbers and plastics. Various chemicals can also be used to sterilise equipment/machinery but these can be difficult to handle and involve health and safety considerations. Glutaraldehyde is used as a chemical steriliser and it is usually employed at room temperature and at a pH greater than 7.4, where it is most efficient. Sierra and Boucher (1971) discovered that when employing glutaraldehyde solution in combination with ultrasound the efficiency of the sterilisation process is enhanced and neither is it dependent upon the actual pH of the solution employed when used at 70 °C. Ultrasound reduced the time required for glutaraldehyde sterilisation at 25 °C from 3 hours to just 30 minutes at pH 8. At pH 2.2 and temperatures of 60 to 65 °C the time required to inactivate the spores was reduced from 10 minutes to 4 minutes when employing 20 kHz ultrasound. The authors suggest that a synergisic effect is involved with ultrasound aiding the penetration of glutaraldehyde into the spore where it then acts upon the spore site of inactivation. They also suggest that combining ultrasound with glutaraldehyde at 54 °C is a quick and efficient method of surface sterilisation/de-contamination when using a liquid phase process.

### 16.5.3    In combination with ozone

In 1982 the U.S. Food and Drug Administration (FDA) granted ozone treatment GRAS status (Generally Regarded As Safe) for use as a method of preservation of bottled water. In order that ozone can be used as a method of food preservation the food processors must still apply for separate FDA approval. In August 2000 a broad-ranged petition for use of ozone as a method of food preservation within the meat, poultry, fruit and vegetable arena was filed with the FDA and a ruling is awaited. This will open up the way for widespread use of ozone throughout the food industry, for example, ozone saturated ice cubes for use in supermarket storage may become more commonplace. Ultrasound may be employed to inject the ozone into the water during the freezing process and the resultant ozone acts as an antibacterial agent. Ultrasonic ozone saturated water sprays have also been used by the food industry during various cleaning processes.

The inactivation of various bacteria and viruses including *Staphylococcus aureus*, *Pseudomonas fluorescens*, *Salmonella typhymurium* and the *Vesticular stomatitis*, have been investigated in the presence of ozone alone, sonication alone, ozone and sonication combined and finally oxygen and sonication combined (Burleson *et al.*, 1975). Using a frequency of 40 kHz at the base of a Plexiglas column they discovered that ozone inactivated the bacteria but contact time and concentration of ozone varied with the type of medium used. For example, a contact time of only 15 seconds was required for a medium of phosphate buffered solution but longer times were required in secondary effluent due to the extra oxygen demand required. Ozone and sonication combined both reduced the contact times and concentration of ozone necessary for complete inactivation. Sonication alone or oxygenation combined with sonication did not inactivate the microorganisms with no inactivation even after ten minutes of treatment. Inactivation patterns appeared the same for all the microorganisms studied. After-growth was not observed, even after 72 hours of further incubation, in the ozone alone and the combined ozone with sonication treatments. This suggests that ozone acts as a bactericide.

The effect of the combination of ultrasound and ozone on water and wastewater treatment has been reported (Dahi, 1976). Redistilled water and two versions of secondary effluent were subjected to sonication at 20 kHz frequency, 160 W power and the effect on *Escherichia coli* (bacterial contaminant) and Rhodamine B (chemical contaminant) were monitored. Ultrasound increased the anti-bacterial/oxidative nature of the ozone as it appears to increase the rate of ozone decomposition as well as increasing the rate of medium aeration.

### 16.5.4   In combination with ethylene oxide

Synergistic effects occurred when the gaseous sterilants ethylene oxide and propylene oxide were used to treat *Bacillus subtilis* var. *niger* in the presence of ultrasound (Boucher *et al.*, 1967). In this instance airborne ultrasound was applied in both the presence and absence of the sterilant gas and plate counts of the spores were monitored.

When employing ethylene oxide alone plate counts between 2200 and 6200 spores/ml were noted at a 125 mg/litre concentration of gas. When combining the gas with airborne ultrasound (30.4 kHz) these plate count levels fell to between only 3 and 4 spores/ml, a substantial improvement. When combining the sterilant propylene oxide with airborne sonication 1 spore out of 10 survived at 40 °C after 40 minutes of airborne sonication. This number fell to only 1 spore out of 1,000 surviving at 60 °C under similar sonication conditions.

The advantages of simultaneous sonication were illustrated in a set of experiments performed at 60 °C with an 80 minutes treatment time. Using propylene oxide alone at a concentration of 500 to 1,000 mg/litre 89.8% kill was achieved and using ultrasound alone at an acoustic intensity 161 to 162 db (db is decibel, the conventional unit of sound intensity in air) only 10% kill resulted. However when employing the two techniques simultaneously the kill rates were increased to 98.1%.

### 16.5.5   In combination with cooling and heating

Freezing food at source slows down the deterioration process and maintains the shelf life of the product as it slows down the growth rate of bacteria and various pathogenic microorganisms. The quality of 'fresh' thawed foods preserved through freezing can be somewhat disappointing in terms of texture. This is particularly true of soft fruits such as strawberries. The problem arises because the small ice crystals that are formed initially inside of the cellular material of the food continue to grow. As these crystals increase in size they break some of the cell walls leading to a partial destruction of the structure of the material. This deleterious growth occurs during the 'dwell time' between the initiation of crystallisation (usually at about $-3\,^\circ\mathrm{C}$) and complete freezing at which point the temperature of the whole item can fall. To avoid this problem food must be frozen quickly to encourage mass nucleation of ice crystals and reduce crystal size. Under the influence of ultrasound a much more rapid and even seeding occurs and this leads to a much shorter dwell time (Acton and Morris, 1992). In addition, since there are a greater number of seeds the final size of the ice crystals is smaller and cell damage is reduced.

The use of heat either alone or in combination with ultrasound for sterilisation has been described above. However, there is another aspect of ultrasound in combination with heating (or cooling) that is also of importance, improved heat transfer. In simple terms ultrasound is able to disturb the liquid layer surrounding the heating (or cooling) surface and hence increase heat transfer with the bulk liquid. An improvement in the convective heat transfer coefficient between aluminium particles and heated water from 500 to $1200\,\mathrm{Wm^{-2}K^{-1}}$ has been reported (Sastry *et al.*, 1989). It is somewhat surprising that there have been very few reports of any follow-up to this potentially important aspect of ultrasound in food processing (Leadley and Williams, 2002).

## 16.6    Ultrasonic equipment

There can be little doubt that ultrasound offers a range of development possibilities for the food industry. Some of these have already been realised in the cleaning and decontamination of equipment to avoid cross-contamination (Quartly-Watson, 1998), others are proven on a laboratory scale and are simply awaiting the investment required to marry these results to large-scale equipment.

There are essentially two types of large-scale plant: batch and flow types (Mason and Lorimer, 2002). Sometimes the flow system will form a part of batch processing as a loop attached to the main vat. The results from successful small-scale experiments can be adapted for large-scale work providing that information is available on power input and volume treated. However, the majority of reported small-scale studies have not been optimised and thus the calculated powers required for scale-up, based on such studies, will almost certainly be unrealistically high. Several scale-up designs are available which can be broadly divided into batch and flow systems.

### 16.6.1   Batch systems

Batch systems will generally be based upon the ultrasonic cleaning bath (Fig. 16.3) using the whole bath as the reactor. Such systems can be many thousands of litres in capacity and are often purpose built as part of an automated cleaning train. Alternatively it is possible to use a submersible transducer to convert any tank into an ultrasonic reactor (Fig. 16.12) – this offers somewhat greater flexibility in use than the purpose-built bath. The submersible is essentially a sealed box containing transducers bonded to the inside of one face. This face then reverberates when the transducers are activated thus providing a large surface area as the source of ultrasound.

### 16.6.2   Flow systems

One of the oldest devices that used cavitation to achieve a mechanical action was the liquid whistle. Devices of this type are particularly useful in applications where homogenisation and efficient mixing are important. Process material is forced under pressure generated by a powerful pump through an orifice from which it emerges into a mixing chamber (Fig. 16.13). There are two ways in which cavitational mixing can occur at this point. First, through the Venturi effect as the liquid rapidly expands into a larger volume on exiting the orifice and, secondly, the jet impacts upon a thin steel blade in the mixing chamber which is caused to vibrate and thereby produce further mixing of the process material flowing over it. With no moving parts, other than a pump, the system is rugged and durable. Typical examples of the uses of such whistles include the preparation of emulsion bases for soups, sauces or gravies which consist of a premix of water, milk powder, edible oil and fat together with flour or starch as thickening agent. After passing through the homogeniser a fine particle size

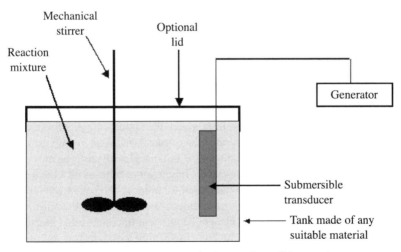

**Fig. 16.12**   Batch system employing a submersible transducer.

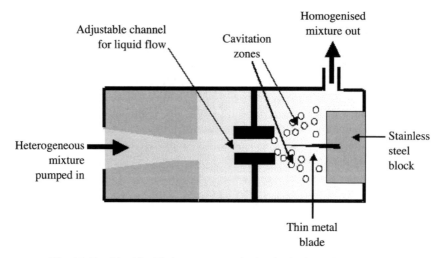

**Fig. 16.13**   Liquid whistle system employing hydrodynamic cavitation.

emulsion is generated with a smooth texture. Another example is the production of ketchup as a smooth product with increased thickness and improved taste compared with conventional mixers as a result of the complete dispersion of any clumps of tomato pulp.

For large-scale operations where higher-intensity ultrasound is required the source of power ultrasound is best used as part of a flow loop outside the main reactor. This permits the processing of large volumes and provides major advantages over the batch configuration for the probe system.

- High-intensity sonication is provided for a continuously flowing liquid reaction at controllable power by the adjustment of either input power to the transducer or the flow rate through the cell.
- Temperature control is provided through the circulating reaction mixture or a pulse option.

*Resonating tube reactors*
This type of system provides the greatest hope for general usage of ultrasound in the food industry. Essentially, the liquid to be processed is passed through a pipe with ultrasonically vibrating walls. In this way the sound energy generated from transducers bonded to the outside of the tube is transferred directly into the flowing liquid. Two design engineering problems are associated with this type of sonicator; (a) the correct mounting of the transducers on the outer tube and (b) the length of the tube must be such that the ends are at a null point in the sound wavelength in the unit. This will eliminate vibrational problems associated with the retrofitting of the unit to existing pipework. Generally the commercial tube reactors are constructed of stainless steel and the choices for pipe cross-section are generally one of four: rectangular, pentagonal, hexagonal and circular (Fig. 16.14).

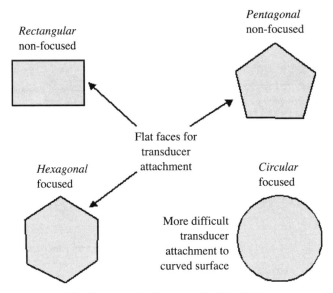

**Fig. 16.14**    Cross-sectional geometries for tubular reactors.

*Resonating bar inserts*

In order to introduce ultrasound into a medium flowing through a tube it is only necessary to place a vibrating source (e.g., probe) in contact with that liquid. A neat method of doing this is via the coaxial insertion of a radially emitting bar into the pipe containing the flowing liquid; this would require minimal change to existing pipework. This type of system was originally developed as a form of submersible transducer for cleaning the inside of barrels and tubes immersed in a cleaning fluid.

One system consists of a hollow gas filled tube sealed at one end and driven at the other by a standard piezo transducer (Fig. 16.15). This device looks like a conventional probe system but is significantly different in that the sealed end is at a null point and is not the major source of vibrational energy. Instead the ultrasound is emitted radially at half-wavelength distances along its length. There is the potential to unblock the end and use the system as a flow tube. Designed and marketed for cleaning there is currently no information on its potential for chemical applications.

Another concept involves a cylindrical bar of titanium (cut to a precise number of half-wavelengths at the frequency used). Opposing piezoelectric transducers are attached at each end connected through a central wire (Fig. 16.16). With these transducers operating together in a push-pull mode the 'concertina' effect makes the bar of metal expand and contract at half-wavelength distances along the entire length. Any erosion in this system would not affect the resonant length and, since the bar is essentially solid metal, material loss by erosion is not a major problem.

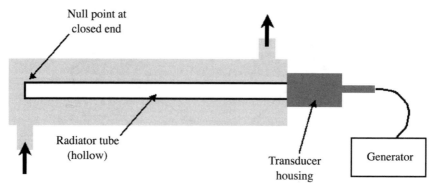

**Fig. 16.15**   The Telsonic tubular insert.

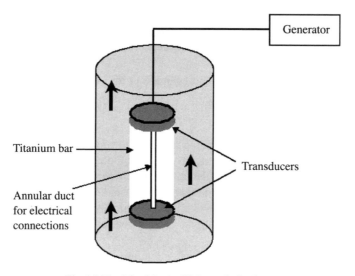

**Fig 16.16**   The Martin Walter tubular insert.

## 16.7   Conclusions

The US Food and Drug Administration examined ultrasound as a basis for use in the food industry. Their conclusions were that ultrasound used alone was insufficient to inactivate many bacterial species and would therefore not be effective as a method of food preservation alone. However, it had, in some cases, synergistic effects with other methods of food preservation and as such could be explored for its potential as a significant aid to food preservation techniques. Unfortunately, one of the major problems in writing a chapter such as this is that it is well known that several large food and drink companies do have significant investment in ultrasound but, unfortunately, none of them is willing to reveal details of their work.

# 16.8   References

ABEE T and WOUTERS J A (1999), 'Microbial stress response in minimal processing', *International Journal of Food Microbiology*, 50, 65–91.

ABRAMOV O V (1998), *High-Intensity Ultrasound: Theory and Industrial Applications*, London, Gordon and Breach.

ACTON E and MORRIS G J (1992), W.O. 99/20420.

AHMED F K I and RUSSELL C (1975), 'Synergism between ultrasonic waves and hydrogen peroxide in the killing of microorganisms', *Journal of Applied Bacteriology*, 39, 31–40.

ALLIGER H (1975), 'Ultrasonic disruption', *American Laboratory*, 10, 75–85.

BIWATER TREATMENT LTD (1993), European Patent 0 567 225 A1.

BOUCHER R M G (1980), US Patent 4, 211, 744.

BOUCHER R M G, PISANA M A, TORTORA G and SAWACKI E (1967), 'Synergistic effects in sonochemical sterilisation', *Applied Microbiology*, 15, 1257–1261.

BROWN B and Goodman J E (1965), *High Intensity Ultrasonics*, London, Iliffe Books.

BURGOS J, ORDONEZ J A and SALA F (1972), 'Effect of ultrasonic waves on the heat resistance of *Bacillus cereus* and *Bacillus licheniformis* spores', *Applied Microbiology*, 24: 497–498.

BURLESON G R, MURRAY T M and POLLARD M (1975), 'Inactivation of viruses and bacteria by ozone, with and without ultrasound', *Applied Microbiology*, 29, 340–344.

BUTZ P and TAUSCHER B (2002), 'Emerging technologies: chemical aspects', *Food Research International*, 35, 279–284.

CICCOLINI L, TAILLANDIER P, WILHEM A M, DELMAS H and STREHAIANO P (1997), 'Low frequency thermo ultrasonication of Saccharomyces cerevisiae suspensions: effect of temperature and of ultrasonic power', *Chemical Engineering Journal*, 65, 145–149.

DAHI E (1976), 'Physicochemical aspects of disinfection of water by means of ultrasound and ozone', *Water Research*, 10, 677–684.

DAVIDSON R S, SAFDAR A, SPENCER J D and LEWIS D W (1987), 'Applications of ultrasound to organic chemistry', *Ultrasonics*, 25, 35–39.

DE GENNARO L, CAVELLA S, ROMANO R and MASI P (1999), 'The use of ultrasound in food technology I: inactivation of peroxydase by thermosonication', *Journal of Food Engineering*, 39, 401–407.

EARNSHAW R G (1998), 'Ultrasound: a new opportunity for food preservation' in Povey M J W and Mason T J, *Ultrasound in food processing*, London, Blackie Academic and International, 183–192.

EARNSHAW R G, APPLEYARD J and HURST R M (1995), 'Understanding physical inactivation processes: combined preservation opportunities using heat, ultrasound and pressure', *International Journal of Food Microbiology*, 28, 197–219.

FREDERICK J R (1965), *Ultrasonic Engineering*, London, Wiley.

GARTSIDE C S and ROBINS M M (1990), 'Ultrasound in Diagnosis, Inspection and Monitoring' in Mason T J, *Sonochemistry, the uses of ultrasound in chemistry*, London, Royal Society of Chemistry, 27–46.

GOULD G W (1996), 'Methods for preservation and extension of shelf life', *International Journal of Food Microbiology*, 33, 51–64.

GRAHAME G W (1996), 'Methods for preservation and extension of shelf life', *International Journal of Food Microbiology*, 33, 51–64.

GUERRERO S, LOPEZ-MALO A and ALZAMORA S M (2001), 'Effect of ultrasound on the survival of Saccharomyces cerevisae: influence of temperature, pH and amplitude', *Innovative Food Science & Emerging Technologies*, 2, 31–39.

HARVEY E N and LOOMIS A L (1929), 'The destruction of Luminous bacteria by high frequency sound waves', *Journal of Bacteriology*, 17, 373–379.

HENGLEIN A (1987), 'Sonochemistry – Historical developments and modern aspects', *Ultrasonics*, 25, 6–16.

HUA I and THOMPSON J E (2000), 'Inactivation of Escherichia coli by sonication at discrete ultrasonic frequencies', *Water Research*, 34, 3888–3893.

HUGHES D E and NYBORG W L (1962), 'Cell disruption by ultrasound', *Science* 138, 108–114.

JAVANAUD C, GLADWELL N R, GOULDBY S J, HIBBERD D J, THOMAS A and ROBINS M M (1991), 'Experimental and theoretical values of the ultrasonic properties of dispersions – effect of particle state and size distribution', *Ultrasonics*, 29, 331–337.

LEADLEY C and WILLIAMS A (2002), 'Power ultrasound – current and potential applications for food processing', Review No 32, Campden and Chorleywood Food Research Association Group.

LEE B H, KERAMASHA S and BAKER B E (1989), 'Thermal, ultrasonic and ultraviolet inactivation of Salmonella in thin films of aqueous media and chocolate', *Food Microbiology*, 6, 143–152.

LILLARD H S (1993), 'Bactericidal effect of chlorine on attached *Salmonellae* with and without sonication', *Journal of Food Protection*, 56, 716–717.

LOPEZ P and BURGOS J (1995), 'Lipoxgenase inactivation by manothermosonication', *Journal of Agricultural and Food Chemistry*, 43, 620–625.

LOPEZ P, SALA F J, FUENTE J L, CONDON S, RASO J and BURGOS J (1994), 'Inactivation of peroxidase, lipoxygenase and polyphenol oxidase by manothermosonication', *Journal of Agricultural and Food Chemistry*, 42, 252–256.

LOPEZ P, VERSET A, SANCHEZ A C and BURGOS J (1998), 'Inactivation of tomato pectin enzymes by manothermosonication', *Zeitschrift für Lebensmittel – Untersuchung und Forschung*, 207, 249–252.

LOPEZ-MALO A, GUERRERO S and ALZAMORA S M (1999), 'Saccharomyces cerevisiae thermal inactivation combined with ultrasound', *Journal of Food Protection*, 62, 1215–1217.

MCCLEMENTS D J (1995), 'Advances in the application of ultrasound in food analysis and processing', *Trends in Food Science & Technology*, 6, 293–299.

MCCLEMENTS D J and POVEY M J W (1992), 'Ultrasonic analysis of edible fats and oils', *Ultrasonics*, 30, 383–388.

MCCLEMENTS D J, POVEY M J W and DICKINSON E (1993), 'Absorption and velocity dispersion due to crystallization and melting of emulsion droplets', *Ultrasonics*, 31, 433–437.

MAKINO K, MOSSOBA M M and RIESZ P (1983), 'Chemical effects of ultrasound on aqueous-solutions – formation of hydroxyl radicals and hydrogen-atoms', *J. Phys. Chem.*, 87, 1369–1377.

MANAS P, PAGAN R, RASO J, SALA F J and CONDON S (2000), 'Inactivation of *Salmonella enteridis*, *Salmonella thyphimurium* and *Salmonella seftenberg* by ultrasonic waves under pressure', *Journal of Food Protection*, 63, 451–456.

MASON T J (1999), *Oxford University Primer Series No 70, Sonochemistry*, Oxford, Oxford University Press.

MASON T J and LORIMER J P (2002), *Applied Sonochemistry*, Weinheim, Wiley VCH.

MASON T J and TIEHM A (2001), *Ultrasound in Environmental Protection*, Advances in

Sonochemistry 6, Amsterdam, Elsevier.

MASON T J and ZHAO Y (1994), 'Enhanced extraction of tea solids using ultrasound', *Ultrasonics*, 32, 375–377.

MILES C A, SHORE D and LANGLEY K R (1990), 'Attenuation of ultrasound in milks and creams', *Ultrasonics*, 28, 394–400.

MILES C A, MORLEY M J and RENDELL M (1999), 'High power ultrasonic thawing of frozen foods', *Journal of Food Engineering*, 39, 151–159.

NEPPIRAS E A (1984), 'Acoustic cavitation series 1. Acoustic cavitation – an introduction', *Ultrasonics*, 22, 25–28.

NEPPIRAS E A and HUGHES D E (1964), 'Some experiments on the desintegration of yeast by high intensity ultrasound', *Biotechnology and Bioengineering*, 6, 247–270.

ORDONEZ J A, AGUILERA M A, GARCIA M L and SANZ B (1987), 'Effect of combined ultrasonic and heat treatment (thermoultrasonication) on the survival of a strain of *Staphylococcus aureus*', *Journal of Dairy Science*, 54, 61–67.

PAGAN R, MANAS P, ALVAREZ I and CONDON S (1999), 'Resistance of *Listeria monocytognes* to ultrasonic waves under pressure at sublethal (manosonication) and lethal (manothermosonication) temperatures', *Food Microbiology*, 16, 139–148.

PALACIOS P, BURGOS J, HOZ L, SANZ B and ORDONEZ J A (1991), 'Study of the substances released by ultrasonic treatment from *Bacillus stearothermophilus* spores', *Applied Microbiology*, 71, 497–498.

PETERSON R V and PITT W G (2000), 'The effect of frequency and power density on the ultrasonically enhanced killing of biofilm sequestered Escherichia coli', *Colloids and surfaces B: Biointerfaces*, 17, 219–227.

PETIN V G, ZHURAKOVSKAYA G P and KOMAROVA L N (1999), 'Mathematical description of combined action of ultrasound and hyperthermia on yeast cells', *Ultrasonics*, 37, 79–83.

POVEY M J W and MASON T J (1998) *Ultrasound in Food Processing*, London, Blackie Academic and Professional.

PRICE G (1990), 'The use of ultrasound for the controlled degradation of polymer solutions' in Mason T J, *Advances in Sonochemistry 1*, London, JAI Press 231–287.

PRICE C J (1997), 'Take some solid steps to improve crystallisation', *Chemical Engineering Progress*, 34–43.

QIAN Z, SAGERS R D and PITT W G (1997), 'The effect of ultrasonic frequency upon enhanced killing of P-aeruginosa biofilms', *Annals of Biomedical Engineering*, 25, 69–76.

QUARTLY-WATSON T (1998), 'The importance of power ultrasound in cleaning and disinfection in the poultry industry – a case study', in Povey M and Mason T J, *Ultrasound in Food Processing*, London, Blackie Academic and Professional.

RASO J, PALOP A, PAGAN R and CONDON S (1998), 'Inactivation of *Bacillus subtilis* spores by combining ultrasonic waves under pressure and mild heat treatment', *Journal of Applied Microbiology*, 85, 849–854.

RASO J, MANAS P, PAGNAN R and SALA F J (1999), 'Influence of different factors on the output power transferred into medium by ultrasound', *Ultrasonics Sonochemistry*, 5, 157–162.

REYNOLDS C and WILLS C D (1974), 'The effect of irradiation on lysomal activation in hela cells', *Int. J. Radiat. Biol.*, 25, 113–120.

RICHARDS W T and LOOMIS A L (1927), 'Chemical effects of high frequency sound waves', *J. Am. Chem. Soc.*, 49, 3086–3100.

ROBERTS T and JAMES M J (1992), Research Report No. 544, Leatherhead FRA.

SALA F J, BURGOS J, CONDON S, LOPEZ P and RASO J (1995), 'Effect of heat and ultrasound on microorganisms and enzymes' in Gould W, *New methods of food preservation*, London, Blackie Academic & Professional, 176–204.

SAMS A R and FERIA R (1991), 'Microbial effects of ultrasonication of broiler drumstick skin', *Journal of Food Science*, 56, 274–275.

SANZ P, PALACIOS P, LOPEZ P and ORDONEZ J A (1985). 'Effect of ultrasonic waves on the heat resistance *of Bacillus stearothermophilus* spores'. in Dring G J, Elars D J and Gould G W, *Fundamental and Applied Aspects of Bacterial Spores*, Academic Press, New York, 251–259.

SASTRY S K, SHEN G Q and BLAISDELL J L (1989), 'Effect of ultrasonic vibration on fluid to particle convective heat transfer coefficients – a research note', *Journal of Food Science*, 54, 229–230.

SCHERBA G, WEIGEL R M and O'BRIEN J R (1991), 'Quantitative assessment of the germicidal efficacy of ultrasonic energy', *Applied and Environmental Microbiology*, 57, 2079–2084.

SIERRA G and BOUCHER R (1971), 'Ultrasonic synergistic effects in liquid phase chemical sterilisation', *Applied Microbiology*, 22, 160–164.

SUSLICK K S (1990), 'Sonochemistry', *Science*, 247, 1439–1445.

TAYLOR M J and RICHARDSON T (1980), 'Antioxidant activity of skim milk', *Journal of Dairy Science*, 63, 1938–1942.

TOMA M, VINATORU M, PANIWNYK L and MASON T J (2001), 'Investigation of the effects of ultrasound on vegetal tissues during solvent extraction', *Ultrasonics Sonochemistry* 8, 137–142.

VERCET A, LOPEZ P and BURGOS J (1997), 'Inactivation of heat resistant lipase and protease from Pseudomonas fluorescens by manothermosonication', *J. Dairy Sci.*, 80, 29–36.

VERCET A, LOPEZ P and BURGOS J (1998), 'Free radical production by mano-thermosonication', *Ultrasonics*, 36, 615–618.

VERCET A, LOPEZ P and BURGOS J (1999), 'Inactivation of heat resistant pectin-methylesterase from orange by manothermosonication', *J. Agric. Food. Chem*, 47, 432–437.

VERCET A, BURGOS J, CRELIER S and LOPEZ-BUESA P (2001a), 'Inactivation of proteases and lipases by ultrasound', *Innovative Food Science & Emerging Technologies*, 2, 139–150.

VERCET A, BURGOS J and LOPEZ-BUESA P (2001b), 'Manothermosonication of foods and food-resembling systems: effect on nutrient content and nonenzymatic browning', *J. Agric. Food. Chem.*, 49, 483–489.

VERCET A, SANCHEZ C, BURGOS J, MONTANES L and BUESA P L (2002), 'The effects of manothermosonication on tomato pectic enzymes and tomato paste rheological properties', *Journal of Food Engineering*, 53, 273–278.

VILLAMIEL M, VAN HAMERSVELD E H and DE JONG P (1999), 'Review: effect of ultrasound processing on the quality of dairy products', *Milchwissenschaft*, 54, 69–73.

VILLAMIEL M and DE JONG P (2000a), 'Inactivation of Pseudomonas fluorescens and Streptococcus thermophilus in Trypticase® soy broth and total bacteria in milk by continuous flow ultrasonic treatment and conventional heating', *Journal of Food Engineering* 45: 171–179.

VILLAMIEL M and DE JONG P (2000b), 'Influence of high intensity ultrasound and heat treatment in continuous flow on fat, proteins and native enzymes of milk', *J. Agric.*

*Food. Chem.*, 48, 472–478.

VINATORU M, TOMA M and MASON T J (1999), 'Ultrasonically assisted extraction of bioactive principles from plants and their constituents' in Mason T J, *Advances in Sonochemistry 5*, London, JAI Press, 209–248.

WRIGLEY D M and LLORCA N G (1992), 'Decrease of *salmonella-typhimurium* in skim milk and egg by heat and ultrasonic wave treatment', *Journal of Food Protection*, 55, 678–680.

ZHAO Y, BAO C and MASON T J (1991), 'The isolation of effective compositions from traditional Chinese medicines by ultrasound', *Ultrasonics International '91 Conference Proceedings*, Oxford, Butterworths, 87–90.

# 17

# Modified atmosphere packaging (MAP)

B. Ooraikul, University of Alberta, Canada

## 17.1 Introduction

The agri-food industry has undergone a profound change during the 20th century. Early in the century efforts were concentrated on finding ways to increase agricultural production in order to feed the world's rapidly growing population. Not many people foresaw the effectiveness of the two-pronged attack on the problems mounted by scientists, bureaucrats and politicians around the world. The average population growth rate in the past 30 years has been 1.7%, giving rise to the current world population of around 6 billion. The rate is expected to drop to 1.1% during the next 30 years, thus increasing the world population to 8.3 billion in 2030.

At the same time, an increasing share of the world's population is well fed, resulting in the decrease in world demand for agricultural products from current 2.2% annually to 1.5% for each of the next 30 years (FAO, 2002). Governments have to subsidize their agricultural industries to make them globally competitive. The rapid rate of scientific and technological progress which has driven the increase in food production occurred largely in the second half of the 20th century. Modified atmosphere packaging (MAP) for example, has seen an unprecedented growth in research and development. From a modest beginning with Brown (1922) demonstrating the effect of different concentrations of $CO_2$ and $O_2$ at various temperatures on the growth of fungi, many have since built on his success to make MAP what it is today. Some of the more recent notable works include those of Seiler (1965), experimenting on the extension of shelf life of cake with MAP; Ooraikul (1988), working extensively on MAP of various types of bakery products; Kader *et al.* (1989), on fruits and vegetables; Gill (1995), on fresh meats; and Hotchkiss and Langton (1995), on meat and poultry products. MAP has now been commercially applied to practically all fresh produce and processed products. It has been accepted as an important element in hurdle technology (Leistner and Gorris, 1995).

Some confusion does exist in defining terms that describe the use of gas atmospheres different from air to extend shelf life of foods. These terms include controlled atmosphere storage (CAS), controlled atmosphere packaging (CAP), vacuum packaging (VP), and modified atmosphere packaging (MAP). CAS normally refers to the use of a precisely defined atmosphere, which is continuously maintained, in a storage chamber. The atmosphere includes gas composition as well as humidity, and the technology applies generally to produce such as fruits or vegetables. CAP, on the other hand, is a misnomer for MAP, since it is practically impossible to continuously control the atmosphere in the package once it is sealed. VP is created by removing air from the headspace of a package. Young *et al.* (1988) defined MAP as 'the enclosure of food products in gas-barrier materials, in which the gaseous environment has been changed'. This seems to imply that VP is a variation of MAP. Ooraikul and Stiles (1991) preferred the definition of MAP provided by Hintlian and Hotchkiss (1986), i.e., 'the packaging of a perishable product in an atmosphere which has been modified so that its composition is other than that of air'. This definition implies that VP is not MAP since a vacuumized package does not have any headspace or atmosphere.

## 17.2   The use of MAP to preserve foods

Safety and perishability are the two most important concerns in any food product. Safety is determined principally by the presence of a pathogen or toxic chemical in the food. Perishability is caused by microbial degradation, enzymatic activities and/or chemical reactions, which may result in undesirable changes in sensory, physical and nutritional properties of the product. Foods vary in their perishability, depending on their composition and how they are processed, packaged and stored. The main purpose of MAP technology is to extend shelf life of food products by slowing down their rates of spoilage while maintaining their safety and general quality. Therefore, in designing a MAP regime for any product, factors that need to be controlled are microbial, physiological, chemical and physical changes.

### 17.2.1   Microbial factors

The rate of microbial development on food is affected by factors such as pH, $a_w$, redox potential ($r_h$), composition, physical characteristics, temperature, packaging, the presence of preservatives and competitive microflora in the product, etc. These factors are considered hurdles, which may be applied individually or in combination to a food product to inhibit microbial growth, thereby extending its shelf life (Leistner and Gorris, 1995).

When MAP is applied as a hurdle to extend shelf life of a food product one must first determine the types of microorganisms common to that product that may cause spoilage and safety problems. A suitable gas atmosphere, packaging film, and storage temperature are then chosen to stop or slow down the growth of those microorganisms. Various combinations of $CO_2$, $O_2$ and $N_2$ are usually used as gas atmospheres of choice.

In general, Gram-negative bacteria are more sensitive to $CO_2$ than Gram-positive bacteria. Gram-negative bacteria such as *Pseudomonas* spp, Enterobateriaceae, *Acinetobacter* spp. and *Moraxella* spp. are also inhibited by low temperature. Therefore, products packaged with a high concentration of $CO_2$ and stored at low temperature would normally allow Gram-positive bacteria, such as lactic acid bacteria, to grow and become dominant organisms (Church, 1994). This was clearly shown by Smith *et al.* (1983) who found *Bacillus licheniformis* and *Leuconostoc mesenteroides* to be dominant microorganisms in English-style crumpets packaged in the atmosphere of 60% $CO_2$ and 40% $N_2$. Gibson *et al.* (2000) have shown that 100% $CO_2$ slows the growth rate of *Clostridium botulinum*, and that this effect is enhanced by appropriate NaCl concentrations and chilled temperatures. Although it is more resistant, *Listeria monocytogenes* can also be inhibited by combining $CO_2$ with low temperature, decreased water activity and the addition of sodium lactate (Devlieghere *et al.*, 2001). Similarly, $CO_2$ retards the growth of *Yersinia enterocolitica* and *Aeromonas hydrophilia* at refrigerated temperatures (Doherty *et al.*, 1995; Bodnaruk and Draughton, 1998; Devlieghere *et al.*, 2000a). The combined hurdles of salt, sodium lactate, lowering $a_w$, and the use of refrigerated storage, for example, are required to control *C. botulinum* and *Y. enterocolitica* in MAP meat products (Devlieghere *et al.*, 2000b).

The absence of $O_2$ in the atmosphere would, of course, inhibit the growth of aerobic microorganisms. The removal of $O_2$ can be used to effectively control obligated aerobes such as moulds. This was demonstrated by Smith *et al.* (1986), who used an $O_2$ scavenger, Ageless, to control mould problems on baked products. Unfortunately, anaerobic atmosphere also favours the growth and toxin production of *C. botulinum* (O'Connor-Shaw and Reyes, 2000). It has been demonstrated in a challenge study that even a product not traditionally known for botulinal problems such as crumpets can sustain the growth and toxin production if *C. botulinum* spores are present (Daifas *et al.*, 1999). An anaerobic atmosphere must be used with extreme caution in MAP products. Other hurdles, such as pH, preservatives, and low temperature, should also be applied to inhibit anaerobic spore formers and other pathogens (Dufresne *et al.*, 2000). Quality assurance programmes, such as Good Manufacturing Practice (GMP) and Hazard Analysis Critical Control Point (HACCP), need to be prerequisites in the manufacture of MAP products.

### 17.2.2    Physiological factors

Physiological changes continue after fruit and vegetables have been harvested or animals slaughtered. These have profound effects on shelf life and quality of fresh or minimally processed products under MAP, therefore for these types of product, data on their physiological changes under various gaseous environments and storage temperatures should be obtained to assist in designing MAP regimens for them.

Fresh fruits and vegetables undergo perhaps the most complex physiological changes after harvest. These changes are related to oxidative metabolism, which is affected by environmental conditions such as gas atmosphere, humidity, temperature, and their physical condition. For example, respiration rate increases with increasing storage temperature, resulting in a faster breakdown of sugar and other components, and a quicker loss of moisture, leading to wilting or tissue softening. Accumulation of ethylene in the atmosphere will accelerate the ripening process of climacteric fruits. Increased $CO_2$ or reduction of $O_2$ concentration in the atmosphere may cause stressed metabolism in fruits or vegetables, resulting in the production of undesirable compounds, which affect their taste and/or aroma. Chilling-sensitive fruits or vegetables undergo physicochemical changes at temperatures lower than their tolerant limits. All these changes may be accentuated if the produce is damaged during harvesting and subsequent handling, which ultimately lead to the reduction of its quality. Minimal processing of fruits and vegetables do not stop these changes. In fact, rates of respiration and ethylene production of some fruits, e.g., Kiwi fruit and melon, increase after they are peeled and cut into small pieces (Cantwell, 1995).

After slaughter, a series of chemical reactions take place in animal tissue. Physiological changes in fresh meat are related to the changes in skeletal muscles after the onset of *rigor mortis*, the time for which varies with type and size of animal. The storage temperature and time, i.e., the ageing process, affect these changes after the onset of *rigor mortis*. These changes affect the organoleptic quality, especially the tenderness, juiciness and aroma of meat. Being high in protein and fat with relatively high pH, meat is also an excellent growth medium for spoilage and pathogenic microorganisms. Furthermore, red meat requires $O_2$ to maintain its bright red colour. Therefore, MAP must be applied with extreme caution and requires a strict quality control programme to extend the shelf life of meat while ensuring safety.

Due to its physical and chemical characteristics, fish may be the most perishable among the fresh commodities. Fish have a much shorter *rigor mortis* than warm-blooded animals. Lengthy struggle during catching will shorten the *rigor mortis* and adversely affect fish quality (Belitz and Grosch, 1986). Microbial contamination can occur quite easily through the mucous layer on the skin and through faecal matter. Fish lipids are largely unsaturated and, hence, are highly susceptible to oxidative rancidity. Therefore, many complex problems need to be controlled to extend the shelf life of fresh fish. This is largely responsible for the fact that commercial application of MAP to fresh fish appears to lag behind other commodities.

### 17.2.3    Chemical factors

Many chemical changes affect the quality of stored food products. Many of these reactions are oxidative in nature, e.g., lipid oxidation, Maillard or non-enzymatic browning, oxidation of pigments, e.g., chlorophyll, carotenoids and flavonoids, oxidation of myoglobin to oxymyoglobin or metmyoglobin in red meat, etc. Lipid oxidation causes the breakdown of unsaturated fatty acids, resulting in the production of malodorous compounds, e.g., aldehydes, ketones, and short-chain fatty acids. The Maillard reaction, with reducing sugars and amino acids as major reactants, may be detrimental to the product if it destroys essential amino acids such as lysine, or if it produces undesirable colour and flavour. In some foods, however, brown colour and 'baked' aroma may be quite desirable, and some of the compounds produced may have antioxidant or antimicrobial properties. Oxidation of chlorophyll, carotenoids and flavonoids would result in changes in the colour making the products rich in these pigments become generally less attractive. On the other hand, red meat becomes less attractive without $O_2$ to oxidize myoglobin to oxymyoglobin to maintain the bright red colour.

These reactions are affected by factors such as temperature, $a_w$, pH, $r_h$, and the presence of preservatives. For example, lipid oxidation is favoured by high temperature, low $a_w$, presence of Cu or Fe and light, but is inhibited by antioxidants such as BHT, BHA, or tocopherol. The Maillard reaction, on the other hand, occurs more readily at relatively high $a_w$ and temperatures, but is inhibited by $SO_2$. Reducing $r_h$ will also slow down the rates of these reactions. In designing a MAP system for a product, its effect on chemical reactions in the product must also be taken into account.

### 17.2.4    Physical factors

Physical characteristics of a food product play a very important role in consumer's perception of its freshness. Wilted or soft fruits or vegetables, for example, would be viewed as old or over-ripe. The loss of glossiness on the surface of fresh meat may be associated with toughness or loss of juiciness. Most baked products lose their freshness during storage through staling, caused principally by the retrogradation of starch fraction. Thus, breads become dry or leathery, cakes, waffles and crumpets become crumbly after a long storage, especially at low temperatures. The shell of apple turnovers, butter tarts or apple pies tends to be lighter in colour, and more crumbly, while the surface of cake doughnuts becomes sticky when packaged under the atmosphere of 60% $CO_2$ and 40% $N_2$ and stored at room temperature for a few weeks (Ooraikul, 1991) therefore, the physical reactions of the products must be taken into account when designing a MAP system for them. For example, packaging films with low vapour transmission rate may be used to package fruits, vegetables, or meats to reduce moisture loss. Surface active agents such as mono- or diglycerides, or lecithin, or antistaling amylase (e.g. Novamyl) may be added to baked products to minimize their textural changes during storage.

### 17.2.5   Shelf life extension

The shelf life of a food product is the period of time between harvest or manufacture to consumption during which the food remains safe and wholesome (Day, 1993). It is determined by the characteristics of the product, and the production and storage conditions. Fresh or minimally processed products can be expected to have a shorter shelf life under MAP than a more fully processed product. Mixed vegetable salad, for example, has an expected shelf life of about ten days, though two or more weeks are possible with improved minimal processing and MAP technology. Fresh fruits keep longer under controlled atmosphere storage (CAS) than under MAP. This is because optimum atmosphere and storage conditions can be maintained throughout the storage period under CAS. Such control is not possible with MAP since the metabolic process and microbial activities will continually change the composition of the headspace atmosphere once the product is packaged and sealed. Unfortunately, not all fruits can be preserved under CAS, especially tropical fruits such as mangoes, papayas, lychee, longan, durian, etc. For these fruits, minimal processing in combination with MAP would be an excellent alternative for their shelf life extension and maintenance of freshness. However, due to their more complex composition and metabolic process, shelf life of minimally processed, modified atmosphere packaged and refrigerated fruits is normally shorter than that of vegetables.

Fresh meat and seafood are other highly perishable commodities. According to Stiles (1991), fresh beef, pork, lamb, chicken, and rabbit meat have been shown to benefit from MAP in combination with refrigerated storage. Optimum gas combination varies with types of meat, with $CO_2$ and $N_2$ being the major gases used. Low levels of $O_2$ may be required for some meat, e.g., beef, to maintain red colour. A storage life of 24 weeks or more has been achieved at about 3 °C if the meat is properly prepared, packaged and stored. Fresh fish, on the other hand, requires a substantially higher $CO_2$ concentration (25–100%) for MAP and lower storage temperature ($\leq 0$ °C) to extend its shelf life to two or more weeks (Skura, 1991). Dipping fish fillets in solutions of acids, antioxidants or preservatives prior to packaging may slightly improve the quality of the product.

For more fully processed products, e.g., baked products, sandwiches, processed meats, intermediate moisture foods, and dried products, a considerably longer shelf life is possible under MAP. For example, English-style crumpets packaged under 60% $CO_2$ and 40% $N_2$ and stored at room temperature can expect a shelf life of more than one month. Meat sandwiches packaged under similar gas atmosphere and stored under refrigerated temperature claim to have a shelf life of about 30 days.

Some dairy products, e.g., cheeses, with the exception of those relying on mould cultures (e.g., blue cheese and Camembert), are susceptible to mould spoilage. Packaging them in the atmosphere of $CO_2$ and $N_2$ may extend the refrigerated shelf life of these products. Mould-free shelf life of shredded cheese, for example, can be extended with MAP using 30% $CO_2$ and 70% $N_2$.

Flushing the headspace of yogurt and sour cream have been practised in Europe to prolong their shelf life (Fierheller, 1991).

Intermediate moisture foods and dried products with $a_w$ below 0.9 are normally quite shelf stable. Nevertheless, they would benefit from MAP if their storage problems are aerobic spoilage and/or oxidative chemical reactions. Therefore, packaging in an atmosphere devoid of $O_2$ would inhibit mould growth in partially dried fruits or vegetables, or prevent oxidative rancidity in beef or pork jerky high in fat, for example. Vacuum packaging may be as effective, but some dried products may suffer physical damage under vacuum. $CO_2$ alone or in combination with $N_2$ would be necessary to inhibit mould growth, while either $CO_2$ or $N_2$ would suffice for the prevention of oxidative reactions.

## 17.3    MAP gases

In general, three major gases are used, singly or in combination, for most MAP products. These include $CO_2$, $N_2$ and $O_2$. Other gases that have had some experimental successes are CO, $SO_2$, $N_2O$, NO, He, $H_2$, Ar, ethylene oxide, propylene oxide, and $Cl_2$. It has been suggested, for example, that Ar can effectively inhibit enzymatic activities, microbial growth and chemical spoilage reactions in perishable foods (Brody and Thaler, 1996; Spencer, 1999). It has also been indicated that Ar can reduce the respiration rates of fresh produce and thus extend their shelf life (Spencer, 1999). However, their commercial applications have been very limited owing to the various safety, legal, organoleptic and technical problems associated with them (Church, 1994, Day, 2003).

### 17.3.1    Oxygen ($O_2$)

Oxygen is required in the metabolic processes of animals, plants, and aerobic microorganisms. It is also required in many chemical reactions. Absence or excessive reduction of $O_2$ in the atmosphere may cause death, growth retardation, unusual metabolic processes or physiological changes in these organisms. Therefore, for most MAP products, except fresh fruits, vegetables and certain meats, $O_2$ is either excluded or significantly reduced from the atmosphere. Strict aerobes, such as moulds, are inhibited in the absence of $O_2$. However, the presence of some $O_2$ at the beginning may encourage the growth of competitive microflora such as lactic acid bacteria, thus helping prevent the development of some anaerobic pathogens, notably *C. botulinum*.

Solubility of $O_2$ in water or lipid is quite low as compared to other gases, e.g., $CO_2$ ($CO_2$ is about 28 times more soluble in water than $O_2$ at 20 °C). Thus, ordinarily, the $O_2$ level in headspace atmosphere, if not utilized by microorganisms or product, is not expected to change much over time. However, the permeability of packaging films toward this gas will determine the rate of change in the composition of $O_2$ in the headspace. It should be kept in mind, also, that film permeability is dependent on ambient temperature and relative humidity. Of course, a leak on the package will nullify all the foregoing principles. Thus, package integrity is an extremely important parameter in the success or failure of MAP products.

More recently, there has been an interest in the use of $O_2$ at high concentrations as MAP gas. High $O_2$ concentrations (70–100%) have also been shown to inhibit *Y. enterocolitica*, Pseudomonas and Enterobacteriaceae (Gonsales Roncero and Day, 1998; Amanatidou, 2001). High $O_2$ MAP has been found to be particularly effective in inhibiting enzymatic discolouration, preventing anaerobic fermentation reactions and inhibiting microbial growth (Day, 2003). It has been used to extend the shelf life of fresh produce such as meat, lettuce, strawberries, raspberries, grapes and oranges.

### 17.3.2   Carbon dioxide ($CO_2$)

Carbon dioxide constitutes less than 0.05% by volume in air. It has a strong bacteriostatic effect on aerobic microorganisms, especially gram-negative bacteria, and inhibitory effects on some enzymes. It is soluble in both water and lipids, more so at reduced temperatures. Though the precise mechanism of its effectiveness against microorganisms is still largely unknown, Devlieghere *et al.* (1998) have demonstrated that it is determined by the concentration of dissolved $CO_2$ in the product. $CO_2$ forms $H_2CO_3$ with water, thus reducing the pH of the product. However, the concentration of the acid is very small as compared to that of dissolved $CO_2$ gas, and it is this gaseous fraction that is thought to be active in the inhibition of microbial growth in food. Devlieghere *et al.* (2000b) listed four proposed mechanisms of action attributed to $CO_2$:

1.  lowering the pH of the food
2.  cellular penetration followed by a decrease of the cytoplasmic pH of the cell
3.  specific actions on cytoplasmic enzymes
4.  specific actions on biological membranes.

It is still not clear which of these mechanisms plays the most important role in inhibiting microbial growth. Devlieghere (2000) has developed predictive models for the safety and spoilage of cooked meat products using dissolved $CO_2$ as an independent variable. $CO_2$ is also used to replace air to prevent oxidative off flavour in some dry products, e.g., ground coffee, or for insect and pest control in the packaging and storage of cereals and grains. Care must be taken, however, to ensure that the flavour and taste of the products are not compromised by the gas.

### 17.3.3   Nitrogen ($N_2$)

Nitrogen is an inert and tasteless gas, which has very low solubility in either water or lipids. It has no bacteriostatic effect except to provide an anaerobic environment, thus delaying oxidative reactions or inhibiting the growth of aerobes. Therefore, it is used principally to replace $O_2$ in the headspace, or as a filler gas to prevent the collapse of the package when high $CO_2$ concentration is used (Church, 1994). Ooraikul (1991) reported that crusty rolls packaged in 100% $N_2$ had a mould-free shelf life at ambient temperature of 9–11 days as compared to 5–6 days when packaged in air or 16–18 days when packaged in 60% $CO_2$ and 40% $N_2$.

### 17.3.4    Atmosphere modifiers

Another method of providing modified atmosphere in the package is to use atmosphere modifiers. The modifiers are separate products, which normally come in small sachets. These sachets are packaged together with the food product and will actively modify the headspace atmosphere, as the products are packaged and stored. In more recent developments some of these atmosphere modifiers are incorporated directly onto the surface of packaging films. The atmosphere modifiers currently in use in some countries, notably Japan, include $O_2$ absorbents, $CO_2$ absorbents or generators, ethylene absorbents or generators, and ethanol generators (Smith *et al.*, 1995; Vermeiren *et al.*, 1999). Examples of these products are: $O_2$ absorbents – Ageless (Mitsubishi Gas Chemical Co., Japan), Freshilizer Series (Toppan Printing Co., Japan), FreshPax (Multiform Desiccants, USA); ethanol vapour generators – Ethicap (Freund Industrial Co., Ltd., Japan), Fretek Wafer (USA); ethylene absorbents – Ethysorn (StayFresh Ltd., UK), Ageless C (Mitsubishi Gas Chemical Co., Japan). Ageless C, which contains $Ca(OH)_2$ can also absorb $CO_2$.

Ageless, which contains active iron oxide, has been shown capable of reducing $O_2$ in headspace atmosphere to <0.05% within 9 hours and, thus, is very effective in preventing the growth of aerobes such as moulds (Ooraikul, 1991). Ageless is particularly effective in extending mould-free shelf life of bakery products having a porous texture such as crusty rolls or hotdog buns. This is because it is extremely difficult to remove all the residual $O_2$ entrapped in the structure of these products by simply drawing vacuum from the package and replacing it with $CO_2$ and $N_2$. Ooraikul (1991) showed that crusty rolls packaged with Ageless stored at ambient temperature was mould free for more than 60 days while those packaged in 60% $CO_2$ and 40% $N_2$ lasted only 16–18 days.

Ethicap is a food-grade ethyl alcohol microencapsulated in silicon dioxide, packaged in a small sachet designed to slowly release ethanol vapour into the headspace of MAP products. Food-grade flavours are also added to Ethicap to mask the ethanol smell and enrich the flavour of the products. The manufacturer claims that it is effective against a wide range of microorganisms and can also prevent food from hardening. The effectiveness of Ethicap is dependent on the amount of ethanol vapour emitted into the atmosphere, which, in turn, is affected by the $a_w$ of the product. The higher the product $a_w$ the more ethanol is absorbed, thus a greater quantity of Ethicap is required to be packaged with the product. Ooraikul (1991) reported that a minimum of 1.1% (v/v) of ethanol vapour is necessary to completely inhibit yeast growth. He found Ethicap effective in suppressing yeast growth on bakery products such as doughnut, layer cake, apple turnover, and cherry cream cheesecake, thus extending their ambient shelf life to at least 21 days.

## 17.4   Packaging materials

In the development of a MAP product, a suitable packaging film or container must be chosen based on the nature of the product to be packaged. Products requiring an exclusion of gases such as $O_2$ and/or high retention of gases such as $CO_2$ must have very low permeability toward these gases under the intended storage temperature and relative humidity. For example, for most bakery products appropriate laminates or co-extruded films with polyvinyl chloride (PVC), polyvinylidene chloride (PVDC), nylon, ethylenevinyl alcohol (EVOH), or aluminum foil as the main barrier layer, have been used successfully.

Fresh produce, on the other hand, requires a certain level of $O_2$ to maintain physiological activities such as respiration, ripening, etc. Anaerobic atmosphere would cause the production of stress metabolites, which may adversely affect organoleptic properties of the produce. For example, MAP with $<3\%$ $O_2$ may initiate the production of ethanol, aldehydes and other chemicals causing off-odours, off-flavours, and discolouration in some minimally processed fruits and vegetables (Varoquaux and Wiley, 1994). Red meat needs $O_2$ to maintain its bright red colour. Therefore, packaging materials for such products must be selectively permeable toward $O_2$, $CO_2$ and moisture vapour to allow adequate diffusion of $O_2$ from the air into the package while preventing excessive loss of $CO_2$ and moisture vapour from the package headspace.

There have been a number of new technological developments in the packaging film industry to produce films that meet the varied requirements of MAP products. Among these are the technologies that would allow the production of films with high $O_2$ transmission rate (OTR) and a wide range of $CO_2/O_2$ permeability ratios (Zagory, 1997). Metalocene technology by Dow Chemical Co. and Exxon Chemical Co. uses single site catalysts to develop polymer resins that can produce films with very high OTR, low vapour transmission rate (VTR), enhanced clarity, superior strength, low seal initiation temperature and very rapid bonding of the seal.

For most plastic films, $CO_2$ permeability is 2–6 times greater than that of $O_2$, which provides a range of $CO_2/O_2$ permeability ratios. This allows the selection of films of suitable ratios for some products. However, in some other products, a relatively constant $CO_2/O_2$ ratio in the headspace is desirable. For such products, microperforated and microporous films are available for desired OTRs and $CO_2/O_2$ ratios. Landec Corp. has developed a side-chain polymer technology that allows the film OTR to increase rapidly as temperature increases, thus avoiding anaerobic conditions due to loss of temperature control. They also provide very high OTRs, adjustable $CO_2/O_2$ permeability ratios, and a range of VTRs

(Zagory, 1997). Other film characteristics to be taken into account in making the choice are strength, clarity, antifogging property, microwavability, recyclability, printability, heat sealability, etc. Technical data on each film should be available from the supplier to aid in the selection of the film.

## 17.5    Quality assurance

Strict application of quality assurance programmes is crucial to the success of MAP operations. MAP products are not sterilized, therefore their quality and safety during the extended storage life are dependent on how strictly the operations adhere to quality assurance programmes. Good Manufacturing Practice (GMP) and Hazard Analysis Critical Control Point (HACCP) are programmes of choice for the assurance of quality and safety in MAP operations. International organizations, such as the World Health Organization (WHO), Codex Alimentarius, and the International Association of Milk Food and Environmental Sanitarians (IAMFES), endorse the use of HACCP as a means to ensure microbiologically safe foods (Alli, 1993). Most MAP products are highly perishable and the conditions under which some products are packaged, stored and marketed may be suitable for growth and development of some pathogens while common spoilage microorganisms are suppressed. Therefore, potential for an outbreak of food-borne disease from the consumption of infected MAP products is extremely high. GMP will ensure that the facilities and the environment in which the MAP products are manufactured are of the highest standard, while HACCP will provide procedures for the identification and control of the steps in the entire processing and marketing chain that have the potential for causing health hazards.

Some of the parameters that need to be monitored in the routine quality control programme include microbial quality of raw materials and product, package integrity, headspace gas combination, and storage temperature. These factors directly influence the shelf life and quality of the products. Fast in-line, non-destructive leak detectors are now available to continuously monitor package integrity, using acoustic emissions, pressure differentials, gas detection, or friction methods (Church, 1994). Shelf life dating is extremely important for MAP products, since it informs the vendors and the consumers of the expiry date of the product. Therefore, shelf life testing of samples from each batch of the products should be a part of the routine quality control procedures. Handling and temperature abuse can occur in retail stores as well as in consumers' kitchens. Therefore, education of the vendors and the consumers with respect to proper product handling and storage is a necessary part of the marketing of MAP products. Time-temperature and freshness indicators have been developed for use with MAP products to monitor quality changes, which may be caused by temperature abuse during storage and marketing. This is an additional measure to safeguard the public from any potential health hazards posed by the consumption of these otherwise very high quality products. It will also ensure the survival and growth of this valuable technology.

## 17.6   Using MAP and other techniques to preserve fresh and minimally processed produce

Whenever possible, fresh produce is usually preferred to processed products by the consumers because of its freshness, which implies higher sensory and nutritional quality. Thus, fresh markets will always be with us despite the fact that most foods are now available in many convenient, processed forms, and their quality continues to improve with new processing and preservation technologies. Unfortunately, freshness is normally parallel with perishability, which implies short shelf life and wastefulness due to post-harvest losses caused by microbial, physiological and physical deterioration. Fresh produce in this context includes whole, unprocessed (except cleaning and washing) fruits, vegetables, and whole fish and other seafood. Fresh whole meats are not included under this category, since the animals are usually slaughtered and cut prior to marketing. The shelf life of these commodities in ambient atmosphere is only days, even under refrigerated temperatures.

CAS and MAP have been used to extend the shelf life of a variety of fresh produce. CAS, in particular, has been used extensively with fruits such as apples, peaches and pears. Lopez *et al.* (1999) reported that the highest emission of volatile components was obtained after five-month storage of Golden Delicious apples under 2% $O_2$ and 2% $CO_2$ at 1 °C and 92–94% RH, when they are removed from CAS and kept at 20 °C for ripening. Drake (1999) found that Bosc pears were firmer, had less decay, and retained the ability to ripen better when stored in 3% $CO_2$, 1.5% $O_2$ at 1 °C as compared to those in 1% $CO_2$ and 1.5% $O_2$. MAP has only limited success with whole fruits or vegetables. For example, shelf life of Kolikuttu bananas could be extended to 30 days when packaged in 0.75 mm low density polyethylene (LDPE) with ethylene scavengers such as potassium permanganate and stored at 14 °C and 94% RH (Chamara *et al.*, 2000). Arango *et al.* (1999) extended the shelf life of naranjilla fruits to a maximum of 50 days when packaged in 29 $\mu$m polyethylene (PE) bags with potassium permanganate and stored at 7.5 °C. Yun and Lee (1999) suggested packaging fresh Korean ginseng roots in 0.1 mm PE rather than storing them in air to retain their ginsenoside content. Thongsook *et al.* (2001) vacuum packaged Echinacea roots in 76 $\mu$m LDPE and stored them at 4 °C for 28 days without microbial spoilage or significant reduction in echinacoside content.

For some fruits, the problems are more complex and neither CAS nor MAP would adequately prolong their shelf life for extended marketing periods, especially for overseas markets. Mangoes, for example, are susceptible to infestation by black rot (anthracnose) and fruit flies. Any of these problems would render mangoes unmarketable within 7–10 days. Treatments with fungicides, e.g. benlate, may delay black rot for about a week, but most importing countries now prohibit the use of the fungicides commonly used on mangoes. Hot water or steam treatment is required to kill fruit fly eggs, but the high temperature treatments may affect the physiological properties of the fruit, especially the ability to ripen normally. Zenklang (2001) has used a combination of fungicide dipping and packaging in $CO_2$ for fresh mangoes to reduce the black rot and fruit fly problems with some success.

There has been a very limited application of MAP to fresh whole fish and other seafood. Principally, this is due to the highly perishable nature of the produce. Skura (1991) reviewed the use of MAP to extend refrigerated (1–4 °C) shelf life of trout, eviscerated salmon, scallops and prawns and concluded that $CO_2$ or $CO_2$ and $N_2$ can extend the shelf life of this fresh produce at least a few days longer than when they are packaged in air. The refrigerated shelf life of fish fillets can be extended under the atmosphere of $CO_2$ and $N_2$, with or without low concentration of $O_2$. Their quality can be further improved by dipping them in acidic or potassium sorbate solution prior to MAP (Fey and Regenstein, 1982; Powrie et al., 1987).

For the produce whose shelf life cannot be sufficiently extended by MAP and refrigerated storage, the use of other preservation technologies in combination with MAP should be explored. One promising technology is irradiation. However, the use of irradiation for food preservation is currently approved only by some countries and only for a limited number of products or produce. Recently, Canada has proposed the extension of the list of food that can be irradiated to include fresh and frozen ground beef, fresh and frozen poultry, pre-packaged fresh, frozen, prepared and dried shrimp and prawns, and mangoes (FoodNavigator.com, 2002). The use of MAP in conjunction with irradiation may become the technology of choice for much fresh produce in the future.

Lactic acid bacteria (LAB) grow well under MAP packaging and storage conditions and have been credited with the inhibition of pathogens common to meats, e.g., C. botulinum and Listeria spp. Extensive research has been focused on the use of suitable strains of LAB or the bacteriocins they produce to treat fresh meats and their products in conjunction with MAP to prolong their shelf life and ensure their safety (Schillinger et al., 1996).

Vegetables, which are minimally processed under strictly controlled aseptic environment, are usually dipped in antimicrobial and anti-browning solutions before the removal of excess liquid by centrifugation, and then packaged. The product is normally packaged in semi-rigid trays and over-wrapped with a clear, permeable plastic film. This is a form of passive MAP in which the headspace atmosphere is modified through the respiration of the fresh-cut vegetable until an equilibrium gas combination is reached. Under refrigerated temperature, these products have an average shelf life of about ten days to two weeks, long enough for companies such as those in Thailand to profitably airfreight their tropical vegetable products and market them through their agents in Europe (Chuenprayoth, 2002). Longer shelf life is possible with properly designed active MAP, but this benefit has to be weighed against the higher packaging cost.

Minimally processed fruits, especially those of tropical origin, have an excellent potential in the markets of Europe and North America. However, fruits pose different and unique sets of problems for shelf life extension while maintaining their fresh or near-fresh quality and safety. Physiology of fruits is much different from that of vegetables. Respiration rates of fruits are usually higher than those of vegetables, especially during ripening. Fruits may be classified as climacteric or non-climacteric, depending on their rate of $C_2H_4$ production and how sensitive they are to the level of $C_2H_4$ gas in the atmosphere with respect to their ripening process. Fruits are also variously sensitive to storage temperature. Generally, tropical fruits are subject to greater chilling injury than those grown in temperate climates. Some fruits may undergo anaerobiosis at low $O_2$ and high $CO_2$ concentrations in the atmosphere, producing metabolites with undesirable odours and flavours (Day, 1993). Peeled and sliced fruits may behave differently from whole fruits. For example, sliced apple, kiwi fruit and banana have higher respiration rates compared to intact fruits, whereas that of sliced cantaloupe remains unchanged. Similarly, ethylene production of sliced banana, cantaloupe and kiwi fruit increases 4 to 8 times over the intact fruits (Cantwell, 1995).

Minimal processing and headspace gas atmosphere may affect the ripening process. If the tissue is damaged during processing and subsequent handling, microbial and enzymatic activities may be accelerated. These are some of the major problems that have to be taken into account when MAP is designed for minimally processed fruits if their shelf life, quality and safety are to be optimized. Ngarmsak *et al.* (2002) have recently applied for a patent in Thailand on the method for minimally processing and MAP of tropical fruits. The products, including pineapple, papaya, pomelo and mangoes, are now being market tested in England, with expected refrigerated shelf life of about three weeks.

## 17.7   Using MAP and other techniques to preserve processed meat, bakery and other products

Processed products are much less perishable since processing has significantly modified their microbial, chemical and physical characteristics. Many hurdles have been incorporated through processing to make them more shelf stable than fresh or minimally processed products. With a judicious application of MAP, the shelf life of these products can be extended further, thus expanding their marketability.

### 17.7.1   Meat products

Stiles (1991), Church (1993), and Hotchkiss and Langton (1995) have adequately reviewed the applications of MAP to processed meat and poultry products. Generally, cured and cooked meats such as sliced bacon and ham and cooked poultry are vacuum packaged. MAP does not offer longer shelf life to these products than vacuum packaging, but MAP sliced meats can be separated from one another more easily. LAB are found to be predominant microorganisms in MAP processed meats and may cause spoilage after several weeks of refrigerated storage, when the counts have reached $10^8$–$10^9$ cfu/g (Church, 1993). In raw meats, especially beef, a minimum amount of $O_2$ in the headspace is needed to maintain a bright red colour, and to reduce potential botulinal hazard. In processed meats, red colour is no longer desired and botulinal hazard is quite low, especially when LAB are predominant microorganisms. In fact, a high concentration of $O_2$ can cause oxidative instability in processed meats with high fat content. For example, Moller *et al.* (2000) found that MAP of sliced and pasteurized ham retained colour and flavour best at <0.1% residual $O_2$.

Meat sandwiches packaged in 50–60% $CO_2$ and $N_2$ as the balancing filler gas, have a refrigerated shelf life of about 30 days. 'Lunchables' containing processed meat such as sliced ham or sausages, crackers, sliced cheese, and fresh-cut vegetables such as carrot fingers or celeries, each MA packaged in a separate compartment of a semi-rigid tray with suitable heat-sealed lidding web, are also gaining popularity among schoolchildren. Their refrigerated shelf life is dictated by the most perishable component, which is normally the fresh-cut vegetable.

### 17.7.2   Bakery products

Seiler (1989), Ooraikul (1991), Smith (1993) and Smith and Simpson (1995) have extensively discussed the applications of MAP to bakery products. Shelf stability of bakery products is dependent on their composition, chemical, physical and microbial characteristics. Simple products such as bread, buns, and crumpets are made from wheat flour and yeasts or leavening agents. They usually have neutral pH, relatively high $a_w$, and porous structure. Their spoilage is caused, primarily, by mould growth, though for high-moisture products like crumpets, excessive growth of LAB may cause off-odour and swelling of the package. More complicated products, e.g., muffins, cakes and pies, may contain sugar, dairy products such as butter, cheese or cream, and fruit fillings, in addition to wheat flour. They may have neutral to relatively low pH, high moisture content and high $a_w$, brown and flaky crust, very moist and may be highly pigmented fruit fillings. For these types of products, causes of spoilage are more complex. They may be mould, yeast or bacterial growth, chemical and/or physical changes, or a combination of some or all of these. Therefore, in designing a MAP regime for a bakery product, these characteristics have to be evaluated to determine possible causes of spoilage before choosing appropriate packaging materials and gas combination. Other hurdles such as preservatives or atmosphere modifiers may also be incorporated into the product or the packaging, where possible.

Ooraikul (1991) discussed various methods to control mould and yeast problems in bakery products. The outgrowth of mould on product surface can occur when residual $O_2$ in the headspace is >0.5%. The problem is quite common when products with porous textures such as bread or buns are packaged in barrier films with 60% $CO_2$ and 40% $N_2$. Air cannot be efficiently evacuated from the porous structure of the products before $CO_2$ and $N_2$ are admitted into the package, leaving enough residual $O_2$ to initiate the germination of mould spores. For such products, packaging them with $O_2$ scavengers such as Ageless is more effective in controlling mould growth than $CO_2$ and $N_2$ alone.

In dealing with excessive yeast growth, which is quite common with products containing sugar and/or fruit fillings, MAP with $CO_2$ and $N_2$ alone can extend their shelf life for only 1–2 weeks. This is because yeasts, like LAB, are facultative aerobes and therefore are not inhibited by $CO_2$. Excessive yeast growth can cause off-odours and swelling of the package due to $CO_2$ production. Incorporating preservatives such as parabens or natamycin (e.g., Delvocid) into the product, together with the use of MAP, is more effective in controlling yeast growth than MAP alone. An even more effective method is packaging the products with ethanol generators, e.g., Ethicap, either in air or $CO_2$ and $N_2$. In fact, ethanol vapour in the headspace at a concentration of about 2% can inhibit the growth of yeasts, moulds and bacteria.

A wide variety of MAP bakery products are now available on the store shelves of many countries around the world. MAP bakery products normally do not require refrigerated storage. However, temperatures above 25 °C may shorten their shelf life and cause textural problems such as softening of pie shells or stickiness of product surface. Refrigerated temperature, on the other hand, may cause crumbliness of product texture due to the retrogradation of the starch fraction in the products (Weatherall, 1986). Daifas *et al.* (1999), as a result of their challenge studies on crumpets, cautioned that high moisture bakery products stored at ambient temperature, if contaminated with *C. botulinum* spores, could pose a public health hazard irrespective of how they are packaged. Therefore, plant sanitation and a strict quality assurance programme are of paramount importance in producing MAP products. Though not essential to shelf life extension of most MAP bakery products, but for safety reasons, refrigerated storage may need to be considered for all MAP products.

### 17.7.3   Other products

Most processed food products having microbial or oxidative problems can benefit from the applications of MAP. Intermediate moisture fruit and vegetable products, for example, may be spoiled by yeast or mould growth, and/or non-enzymatic browning discolouration. Dried fruits and vegetables may undergo undesirable oxidative changes if they contain unsaturated fats or bright coloured pigments such as chlorophylls, carotenoids or flavonoids. Vacuum packaging or MAP under which $O_2$ is removed or excluded from the headspace can maintain quality and extend shelf life of these products. Vacuum packaging or $N_2$ flushing has been used extensively for high-value commodities such as freeze-dried products, ground coffee, roasted nuts, whole-milk powder, potato flakes, and many snack foods (Fierheller, 1991).

High-protein foods such as shredded cheese and beef jerky have also been packaged in high $CO_2$ atmosphere to prevent mould growth. For low moisture products, $a_w$ is an important factor affecting not only shelf life, but also their organoleptic quality. Beef jerky, for example, is more organoleptically acceptable at $a_w \geq 0.8$ than when it is dry. However, at this level of $a_w$, moulds and yeasts can still grow. Therefore, other hurdles such as preservatives, pH, storage temperature, etc., may have to be considered in conjunction with MAP in the extension of shelf life of these types of products.

## 17.8   Future trends

MAP technology provides great opportunities as well as challenges to scientists, engineers and food manufacturers. Markets will continue to grow for high quality, fresh or near-fresh, and convenient foods. The growth area with respect to MAP products is in minimally processed produce, especially vegetables and fruits. The major challenge is how to produce the products so that we can ensure quality, safety and reliability at competitive prices.

The application of hurdle technology in conjunction with MAP is necessary to ensure adequate shelf life, safety and reliability at reasonable costs. Thus, at product development stage, suitable hurdles such as pH, $a_w$, antimicrobials (especially naturally occurring ones), chemical preservatives, and minimum heat treatment may be incorporated into the product prior to MA packaging. Preservation technologies such as fermentation, irradiation, high hydrostatic pressure, pulsed light, and ultrasound may be used as pre- or post-packaging treatments for MAP products.

Environmental concerns have become major political and consumer issues. The Kyoto Accord has stirred up fierce debates on 'clean' and 'dirty' energy. The types of packaging applied to food products will be closely scrutinized both by lawmakers and consumers since the production of packaging materials and the packaging operations themselves, consume substantial amounts of energy. Barrier films such as PVC or PVDC, commonly used in many MAP operations are considered environmentally unfriendly since they are not easily recyclable. Therefore, to attract environmentally conscious consumers, packaging materials used for MAP will necessarily be more environmentally responsible. Future packaging materials for MAP will have to be either reusable or at least recyclable. There will be an increasing use of biodegradable and/or edible packaging films or containers for some MAP products.

MAP still has not reached its full potential in research and development and commercialization. We still do not fully understand the effects of MAP on various spoilage and pathogenic microorganisms. We do not understand the interactions of various microorganisms present on MAP products and how they affect product shelf life and safety. We need to understand the effect of various MAP gases on chemical, physical and sensory properties of the products to be able to design MAP regimes to minimize changes in these properties. We need to have adequate and accurate data on these various parameters that influence the quality, shelf life, and safety of the products to be able to develop workable mathematical predictive models to assist in the design of an optimum MAP system for each product.

For successful commercialization, further technical progress needs to be made on the following in order to transform the scientific principles into product reality:

- atmosphere modifiers, to produce desired atmospheres accurately and cheaply
- packaging materials that are more responsive to the requirements of the products, the packaging technology, the environmental regulations, and are cost-effective
- atmospheric change and temperature/time indicators to assist in the monitoring of handling abuse, product shelf life, and safety
- packaging technology that would handle a wide variety of products with different MA requirements and package types economically and with minimum adjustments between products
- quality control equipment that can, non-destructively, monitor seal integrity, leaks, and headspace atmosphere on-line
- marketing infrastructure needed for MAP products, especially with respect to post-process handling of the products, reliable temperature control system throughout the marketing chain, regulations relating to labeling and marketing of the products, and consumer education on proper handling of the products.

Food scientists and engineers have to work closely together to develop the whole MAP system that is based on solid scientific data to produce high quality, safe and reliable MAP products.

## 17.9   References

ALLI I (1993), 'Quality control of MAP products', in Parry R T, *Principles and Applications of Modified Atmosphere Packaging of Food*, London, Blackie Academic & Professional, an imprint of Chapman & Hall, 101–114.

AMANATIDOU A (2001) High oxygen as an additional factor in food preservation, PhD thesis, Wageningen University, The Netherlands.

ARANGO H, VAILLANT F, VELEZ C, MILLAN P and REYNES M (1999), 'Evaluation of post-harvest performance of naranjilla (*Solanum quitoense* Lam.) fruits packed under modified atmosphere', *Fruits*, 54(4). *http://www.ifis.org/hottopics/MAP2_abst.html.*

BELITZ H-D and GROSCH W (1986), *Food Chemistry*, Hadziyev D translated, Berlin, Springer Verlag.

BODNARUK P and DRAUGHTON, F (1998) 'Effect of packaging atmosphere and pH on the virulence of and growth of *Yersinia enterocolitica* on pork stored at 4 degrees centigrade' *Food Microbiol* 15(2): 129–36.

BRODY, A L and THALER C (1996) 'Argon and other noble gases to enhance MAP', in *Proceedings of IoPP Conference on Advanced Packaging Technology*, Illinois.

BROWN W (1922), 'On the germination and growth of fungi at various temperatures and in various concentrations of oxygen and carbon dioxide', *Ann Bot*, 36, 257–283.

CANTWELL M (1995), 'Fresh-cut products', in *Perishable Handling Newsletter,* Issue #81, California, UC Davis, 4–6.

CHAMARA D, ILLEPERUMA K, GALAPPATTY P T and SARANANDA K H (2000), 'Modified atmosphere packaging of Kolikuttu bananas at low temperature', *J Hort Sci Biotech*, 75(1), 92–96.

CHURCH P N (1993), 'Meat products', in Parry R T, *Principles and Applications of Modified Atmosphere Packaging of Food*, London, Blackie Academic & Professional, an imprint of Chapman & Hall, 229–269.

CHURCH N (1994), 'Developments in modified-atmosphere packaging and related technologies', *Trends Food Sci Technol*, 5, 345–352.

CHUENPRAYOTH C (2002), Personal communication, Kamphaeng-Saen Commercial Co. Ltd., Thailand. *http://www.kcfresh.com.*

DAIFAS D P, SMITH J P, BLANCHFIELD B and AUSTIN J W (1999), 'Growth and toxin production by *Clostridium botulinum* in English-style crumpets packaged under modified atmospheres', *J Food Prot*, 62(4), 349–355.

DAY B P F (1993), 'Fruit and vegetables', in Parry R T, *Principles and Applications of Modified Atmosphere Packaging of Food*, London, Blackie Academic & Professional, an imprint of Chapman & Hall, 114–134.

DAY B P F (2003), 'Novel MAP applications for fresh-prepared produce', in Ahvenainen, R (ed.), *Novel food packaging techniques*, Woodhead Publishing Limited, Cambridge.

DEVLIEGHERE F (2000), 'Predictive modelling of the spoilage and the microbial safety of modified atmosphere packaged cooked meat products', PhD thesis, University of Ghent.

DEVLIEGHERE F, DEBEVERE J and VAN IMPE J (1998), 'Effect of dissolved carbon dioxide and temperature on the growth of *Lactobacillus sake* in modified atmospheres', *Int J Food Microbiol*, 41, 231–238.

DEVLIEGHERE F, LEFEVERE I, MAGNIN A and DEBEVERE J (2000a) 'Growth of *Aeromonas hydrophila* on modified atmosphere packaged cooked meat products' *Food Microbiol* 17: 185–96.

DEVLIEGHERE F, JACXSENS L and DEBEVERE J (2000b), 'Modified atmosphere packaging: state of the art', *FoodInfo Online, IFIS Publishing. http://www.foodsciencecentral. com/library.html#ifis/3340.*

DEVLIEGHERE F, GEERAERD A H, VERSYCK K J, VANDEWAETERE B, VAN IMPE J and DEBEVERE J (2001), 'Growth of Listeria monocytogenes in modified atmosphere packaged cooked meat products: a predictive model', *Int J Food Microbiol* 18: 53–66.

DOHERTY A, SHERIDAN J, ALLEN P, MCDOWELL D A, BLAIR I S and HARRINGTON D (1995), 'Growth of *Yersinia enterocolitica* 0:3 on MAP lamb', *Food Microbiol* 12(3): 251–7.

DRAKE S R (1999), 'Quality of Bosc pears as influenced by elevated carbon dioxide storage', *J Food Qual*, 22(4), 417–425.

DUFRESNE I, SMITH J, JUIN-NI-LIU and TARTE I (2000), 'Effect of headspace oxygen on toxin production by *Clostridium botulinum* type E in rainbow fillets stored under modified atmospheres', *J Food Safety* 20(3): 157–75.

FAO (2002), 'World agriculture 2030: main findings', *FAO*, 2002. *http://www.fao.org/ english/newsroom/2002/7833-en.html*

FEY M S and REGENSTEIN J M (1982), 'Extending shelf-life of fresh red hake and salmon using $CO_2$-$O_2$ modified atmosphere and potassium sorbate at 1 °C', *J Food Sci*, 47, 1048–1054.

FIERHELLER M G (1991), 'Modified atmosphere packaging of miscellaneous products', in Ooraikul B and Stiles M E, *Modified Atmosphere Packaging of Foods,* London, Ellis Horwood, 246–260.

FOODNAVIGATOR.COM (2002), 'Canada extends food irradiation use', *FoodNavigator.com Breaking News & Analysis on Food Ingredients*, *http://www.foodnavigator.com/ news/printnews.asp?id=6496*.

GIBSON A M, ELLIS-BROWNLEE R C L, CAHILL M E, SZABO E A, FLETCHER G C and BREMER P J (2000), 'The effect of 100% $CO_2$ on the growth of non-proteolytic *Clostridium botulinum* at chill temperatures', *Int J Food Microbiol* 54: 39–48.

GILL C O (1995), 'MAP and CAP of fresh, red meats, poultry and offals', in Farber J M and Dodds K L, *Principles of Modified-Atmosphere and Sous Vide Product Packaging,* Langcaster, Technomic Publishing Co. Inc., 105–136.

GONSALES RONCERO M and DAY, B P F (1998), 'The effects of novel MAP on microbial growth in fresh-prepared produce', *Proceedings of the Cost 915 Conference*, Madrid.

HINTLIAN C B and HOTCHKISS J H (1986), 'The safety of modified atmosphere packaging: a review', *Food Technol*, 40(12), 70–76.

HOTCHKISS J H and LANGTON S W (1995), 'MAP of cooked meat and poultry products', in Farber J M and Dodds K L, *Principles of Modified-Atmosphere and Sous Vide Product Packaging,* Langcaster, Technomic Publishing Co. Inc., 137–152.

KADER A A, ZAGORY D and KERBEL E L (1989), 'Modified atmosphere packaging of fruits and vegetables', *CRC Crit Rev Food Sci Nut*, 28(1), 1–30.

LEISTNER L and GORRIS L G M (1995), 'Food preservation by hurdle technology', *Trends Food Sci Technol*, 6(2), 41–46.

LOPEZ M, LAVILLA T, GRAELL J, RECASENS I and VENDRELL M (1999), 'Effect of different CA conditions on aroma and quality of Golden Delicious apples', *J Food Qual*, 22(5), 583–597.

MOLLER J K S, JENSEN J S, OLSEN M B, SKIBSTED L H and BERTELSEN G (2000), 'Effect of residual oxygen on colour stability during chilled storage of sliced, pasteurized ham packaged in modified atmosphere', *Meat Sci*, 54(4), 799–405.

NGARMSAK T, OORAIKUL B and NGARMSAK M (2002), 'Minimal processing and modified atmosphere packaging of tropical fruits' Thai Patent Application No. 0203000422, submitted May 20, 2002.

O'CONNOR-SHAW R and REYES V (2000), 'Use of modified atmosphere packaging', in Robinson R, Batt C and Patel P (eds), *Encyclopedia of Food Microbiology*, Academic Press, San Diego.

OORAIKUL B (1988), 'Modified atmosphere packaging of selected bakery products as an alternative to low temperature preservation', Final Report, Engineering and Statistical Research Institute Report of Contract File #10SC.01916-3-EP16, Agriculture Canada, Ottawa, ON, 100 pp.

OORAIKUL B (1991), 'Modified atmosphere packaging of bakery products', in Ooraikul B and Stiles M E, *Modified Atmosphere Packaging of Foods*, London, Ellis Horwood, 49–117.

OORAIKUL B and STILES M E (1991), 'Introduction: review of the development of modified atmosphere packaging', in Ooraikul B and Stiles M E, *Modified Atmosphere Packaging of Foods*, London, Ellis Horwood, 1–17.

POWRIE W D, SKURA B J and WU C H (1987), 'Energy conservation by storage of muscle and plant products at latent zone and modulated subfreezing temperatures', Final Report, ERDAF File 0145B.01916-EP25, Agriculture Canada.

SCHILLINGER U, GEISEN R and HOLZAPFEL W H (1996), 'Potential of antagonistic microorganisms and bacteriocins for the biological preservation of foods', *Trends Food Sci Technol*, 7(5), 158–164.

SEILER D A L (1965), 'Factors influencing the mould free shelf life of cake with particular reference to the use of antimould agents', *Brit Baking Ind Res Assoc Report*, No 81.

SEILER D A L (1989), 'Modified atmosphere packaging of bakery products', in Brody A L, *Controlled/Modified Atmosphere/Vacuum Packaging of Foods*, Connecticut, Food & Nutrition Press, Inc, 119–134.

SKURA B J (1991), 'Modified atmosphere packaging of fish and fish products', in Ooraikul B and Stiles M E, *Modified Atmosphere Packaging of Foods*, London, Ellis Horwood, 148–168.

SMITH J P (1993), 'Bakery products', in Parry R T, *Principles and Applications of Modified Atmosphere Packaging of Food*, London, Blackie Academic & Professional, an imprint of Chapman & Hall, 134–169.

SMITH J P, JACKSON E D and OORAIKUL B (1983), 'Microbiological studies on gas packaged crumpets', *J Food Prot*, 46, 279–283.

SMITH J P, OORAIKUL B, KOERSEN W J, JACKSON E D and LAWRENCE R A (1986), 'Novel approach to oxygen control in modified atmosphere packaging of bakery products', *Food Microbiol*, 3, 315–320.

SMITH J P and SIMPSON B K (1995), 'Modified atmosphere packaging of bakery and pasta products', in Farber J M and Dodds K L, *Principles of Modified-Atmosphere and Sous Vide Product Packaging*, Langcaster, Technomic Publishing Co. Inc., 207–243.

SMITH J P, ABE Y and HOSHINO J (1995), 'Modified atmosphere packaging – present and future uses of gas absorbents and generators', in Farber J M and Dodds K L, *Principles of Modified-Atmosphere and Sous Vide Product Packaging*, Langcaster, Technomic Publishing Co. Inc., 287–325.

SPENCER, K (1999), 'Fresh-cut produce: applications of noble gases', in *Proceedings of the International Conference on Fresh-cut Produce*, Campden and Chorleywood Food Research Association, Chipping Campden.

STILES M E (1991), 'Modified atmosphere packaging of meat, poultry and their products', in Ooraikul B and Stiles M E, *Modified Atmosphere Packaging of Foods*, London, Ellis Horwood, 118–147.

THONGSOOK T, OORAIKUL B and SHUM M S (2001), 'Storage study of fresh Echinacea roots packaged in air, modified atmosphere, and vacuum', Unpublished data, Department of Agricultural, Food and Nutritional Science, University of Alberta, Canada.

VAROQUAUX P and WILEY R C (1994), 'Biological and biochemical changes in minimally processed refrigerated fruits and vegetables', in Wiley R C, *Minimally Processed Refrigerated Fruits & Vegetables*, New York, Chapman & Hall, 226–268.

VERMEIREN L, DEVLIEGHERE F, VAN BEEST M, DE KRUIJF N and DEBEVERE J (1999), 'Developments in the active packaging of foods', *Trends Food Sci Technol*, 10(3), 77–86.

WEATHERALL W E (1986), 'Studies on Starch in Crumpets', PhD thesis, Department of Food Science, University of Alberta, Canada.

YOUNG L L, REVIERE R D and COLE A B (1988), 'Fresh red meats: a place to apply modified atmospheres', *Food Technol*, 42(9), 65–69.

YUN S D and LEE S K (1999), 'MA storage of Korean fresh ginseng', *J Korean Soc Hort Sci*, 40(6). *http://www.ifis.org/hottopics/MAP2_abst.html*.

ZAGORY D (1997), 'Advance in modified atmosphere packaging (MAP) of fresh produce', *Perishables Handling Quarterly*, No 90, Special Issue: Modified Atmospheres, Postharvest Technology Research Information Centre, Department of Pomology, University of California.

ZENKLANG P (2001), 'Studies on Treatment of Black Rot and Golden Fruit Fly Problems on Thai Mangoes Using Disinfectants and $CO_2$', MSc. thesis, Department of Food Technology, Khon Kaen University, Thailand (Thai).

# 18

# Pulsed electric fields

L. Picart and J-C. Cheftel, Université des Sciences et Techniques du Languedoc, France

## 18.1 Introduction

The increasing consumer demand for fresh-like foods without excessive loss of flavours or nutrients during processing has resulted in the development of milder preservation and processing technologies. Among these novel processes the use of pulsed electric fields (PEF), a physical technology based on power electronics, permits operation at low or moderate temperature and therefore represents a promising non-thermal preservation alternative to heat pasteurisation. During the 1970s, PEF development branched into two different fields: (a) reversible electro-permeabilisation for DNA transfer into cells; (b) microbial inactivation and food preservation. Recent improvements in the field of electronics and energy control facilitate the development of more powerful and effective equipment, giving a new impetus to PEF technology.

Initial investigations on microbial inactivation induced by PEF and on PEF-processing of various fluid foods have been reviewed by several authors (Wouters and Smelt, 1997; de Jong and van Heesch, 1998; Barsotti and Cheftel, 1999; Jeyamkondan et al., 1999; Barbosa-Cánovas et al., 1999, 2000b, 2001; Ho and Mittal, 2000; Barbosa-Cánovas and Zhang, 2001; Dunn, 2001; Bendicho et al., 2002a; Góngora-Nieto et al., 2002a). The present chapter attempts, first, to summarise the basic physical and biological principles underlying this 'emerging technology'; then to report and comment on the main results from more than 100 research contributions published between 1999 and early 2003, dealing mainly with microbial inactivation and with effects on food constituents. Finally, we draw conclusions from these data in terms of advantages and limitations of PEF processing as a preservation technology, and of potential food applications.

## 18.2    Principles and technology

PEF processing for food preservation implies applying short electric pulses (usually 1–20 $\mu$s, but with a range of 50 ns to several milliseconds) with a high field strength (15–80 kV·cm$^{-1}$) to samples placed between two electrodes in a batch or continuous treatment chamber. To generate such a fast electrical discharge, different kinds of pulse-forming networks (PFN) are used. The main components of a PFN are:

1.  **Power supply.** A high voltage generator which supplies electrical energy ($W$) at the selected voltage ($U_0$) (up to about 40 kV);
2.  **One or several capacitor banks, inductors or/and resistors.** Capacitors store the electrical energy ($W$). These are connected in parallel to increase the amount of stored energy. The maximum voltage ($U_0$) across the capacitors equals that across the generator. Inductors temporarily store magnetic energy and thus delay the current rise. Resistors are mainly represented by the treatment chamber load and dissipate the electrical energy;
3.  **One or several switch(es) which deliver electrical energy ($W$) to the electrodes and the food sample.** Pulse duration ranges from less than a microsecond to several milliseconds. The switch must withstand the maximum voltage present across the capacitors, as well as the transfer of an electrical current with an intensity $I_{max}$ resulting primarily from the electrical resistivity of the food sample. The cost and service life should also be taken into account for the choice of this component. The different types of switches available for PEF technology are summarised by Barsotti *et al.* (1999). The ignitron appears to be poorly adapted to PEF systems. The major disadvantage of such spark gaps is their low service life. They depend on the dielectric breakdown of a gas surrounding two electrodes. This arc-over causes the formation of craters on the electrode surface, thus progressively decreasing the minimal voltage for gas electrical breakdown. The thyratron belongs to the gas discharge devices. It has a fairly long service life but consumes much energy. The solid-state semiconductor switches include: thyristors, gate turn-off thyristors (GTO), metal-oxide semiconductor field-effect transistors (MOSFET), insulated-gate bipolar transistors (IGBT), and more recently symmetrically gate-commutated thyristors (SGCT) or insulated-gate controlled transistors (IGCT). At the present time, this large group offers the best quality/price ratio with long service life and high electrical performances. These switches are often connected in parallel series in order to commute high voltages and currents.
4.  **One (or several) treatment chamber(s) with two electrodes between which the food sample either flows or is encased.** When the switch is closed, the capacitors discharge the stored energy into the treatment chamber and an electric pulse goes through the food sample. The rate of voltage increase across the electrodes depends on the rate of closure of the switch, on the electrical wiring and on the sample resistivity. When several treatment chambers are used, their electrical interconnection (parallel or

series) leads to some disturbances. It can be noted that the parallel interconnection remains easier to build than the series one. As the power delivered by the generator ($P = I \cdot U_0$) is limited, when the chambers are connected in parallel the global resistance of the PFN decreases and according to Ohm's law, the current through the system (which is a critical parameter for the components) increases. $U_0$ decreases (for constant $P$) resulting in a lower electric field value across the treatment chambers. When the chambers are connected in series, the voltage across each treatment chamber decreases. To obtain the same electric field it is necessary to increase the current and this is not safe for electrical components. As a result the applied electric field will be lowered.

5. **An oscilloscope to measure voltage across the electrodes and display pulse shape.** A low value resistance placed in series with the treatment chamber allows the oscilloscope to measure the current passing through the sample.

The simplest PFN is an RC circuit which is composed by a resistor (resistance R in $\Omega$) and a capacitor (capacitance C in Farads) connected in series (Fig 18.1a). This kind of PFN can generate exponential decay pulses, the voltage across the PEF chamber (R) as a function of time is then defined as:

$$u(t) = U_0 \cdot \exp(-t/\tau) \qquad\qquad 18.1$$

where $U_0$ (in V) is the voltage provided by the power supply, $t$ is the pulse duration time, $\tau = R \cdot C$, the time constant. It is difficult to avoid the presence of parasitic inductors due to electric wiring. The value of $L$ (inductance in Henry) should be minimised to avoid perturbation of the electrical signal.

However, in other types of PFN the properties of $L$ are used to generate different pulse wave shapes (square wave pulses, instant reversal pulses) (Fig. 18.1b). Indeed several capacitors and inductors may be associated within passive filter shapes which modify the initial electrical signal into different pulse wave shapes according to the relative electric values of each component. In the case of square wave pulses, the inductors delay the discharge of each capacitor in the treatment chamber and delay the current rise, as well as slow down the charging of capacitors in a prior step. However, if the impedance of the system is not the same as the impedance of the treatment chamber (mismatch) the shape of the pulse will be strongly distorted (for example for low resistive chambers). PFN generating square wave pulses are more complex and expensive than those used for exponential decay pulses (de Haan and Willcock, 2002).

### 18.2.1    Pulse waveforms
There are several types of pulse shapes, depending on the type of PFN: exponential decay or square wave pulses, both either monopolar or bipolar; oscillatory pulses; instant reversal pulses (Fig. 18.1). Exponential decay pulses or square wave pulses are mostly used. An exponential decay pulse has a

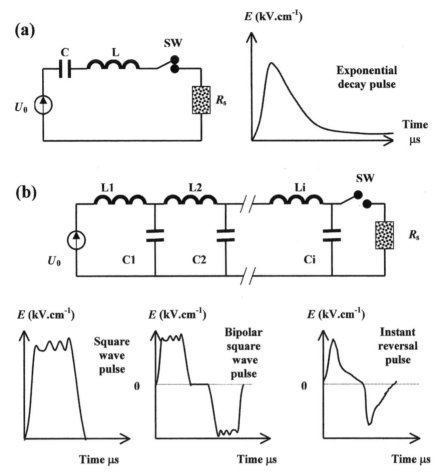

**Fig. 18.1**    Types of electrical pulses most used in PEF processing, and corresponding pulse-forming networks (PFN). $U_0$ is the charging voltage of the power supply, $R_s$ the treatment chamber resistance and SW the switch. (a) represents a simple RC circuit: C is the capacitor, and L the parasite inductor; (b) represents a more complex PFN: Ci are the capacitors and Li the inductors.

unidirectional voltage and current intensity which rise rapidly to maximum values and decay slowly to zero resulting in a long tailing with a low electric field but some resulting ohmic heating of the sample. Therefore the sample is not exposed to a constant electric field but to a spectrum of electric fields. For exponential decay pulses, the time constant, or effective pulse width ($\tau$, in s) is defined as the time interval between the peak voltage and the moment when the voltage has decreased to 37% of the peak voltage.

In contrast, square wave pulses maintain a constant peak voltage throughout most of pulse duration. $\tau$ is the time during which voltage is kept at a maximum value.

An instant reversal pulse corresponds to the application of a positive polarity spike pulse followed by a negative polarity spike pulse without relaxation time between pulses (in contrast to bipolar pulses). In this case, the pulse width corresponds to the whole duration of the pulse.

### 18.2.2    Treatment chambers

A treatment chamber usually consists of two electrodes held in position by an insulating material which also forms an enclosure containing the sample to be processed. The design of the treatment chamber is an important parameter for microbial inactivation and must conform to several specifications:

1. The treatment chamber should resist high current intensity.
2. The distribution of electric field in the treatment chamber should be as uniform as possible.
3. 'Dead zones' (absence of electric field or of sample circulation) should be avoided.
4. Dielectric breakdown (arcing) should be avoided since it would induce non-uniform processing and local overheating of the sample. It can be induced by local field enhancement on an electrode, electric tracking along an insulator surface and/or the presence of gas bubbles in samples.
5. The materials used should minimise electrochemical phenomena at the electrodes.

Various treatment chamber designs have been used for batch or continuous flow systems. They are thoroughly described by Barbosa-Cánovas et al. (2000b): parallel plate electrodes, coaxial cylinders and co-field arrangements are the most common configurations (Fig. 18.2). Parallel plate electrodes are commonly used in batch systems and give a quite uniform electric field distribution. In order to probe the electric field uniformity of a batch treatment chamber with circular parallel electrodes, Mañas-Perez et al. (2001) used an inoculated agar gel as solid treatment (and recovery) medium. The existence of a dead space (air bubble) in the treatment chamber was revealed. Moreover, it was observed that micro-organisms survived in the gel volume located exactly under this air bubble. Ravishankar et al. (2002) also used a gelled medium to investigate the electric field uniformity in their static treatment chamber. In a coaxial chamber, the product flows between two concentric cylindrical electrodes. Because of this radial geometry, the field strength across the inter-electrode gap is not uniform and decreases progressively from the inner to the outer electrode. For a given inter-electrode gap, the difference of electric field strength between the two electrodes can be lowered by increasing the radii. Moreover, the electric field distribution can be predicted and optimised during chamber design. In a co-field chamber, the product flows through a tube formed by two hollow cylindrical (= annular) electrodes interconnected by an insulating tube. The electric field distribution is not uniform but can also be predicted and improved (Lindgren et al., 2002). In contrast to coaxial chambers, co-field

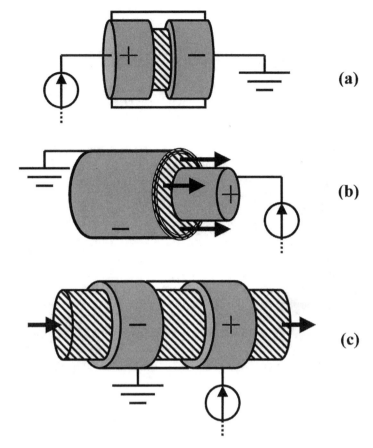

**Fig. 18.2**  Typical configurations of treatment chambers used in PEF processing: (a) batch treatment chamber with parallel plate circular electrodes; (b) coaxial continuous flow chamber, and (c) co-field continuous flow chamber. The electrodes are represented in grey, the food is hatched and the insulator white.

chambers have a low effective electrode area and thus present a high load resistance allowing the pulse generator to operate at lower currents. Although coaxial and co-field chambers do not give a constant electric field across the inter-electrode gap, in contrast to parallel systems, they are well suited to continuous flow, with advantageous fluid dynamics both for food processing and for cleaning in place.

Other types of continuous treatment chamber have been proposed, with partly insulated electrodes or ring/cylinder or coiled wire/cylinder arrangements (Sato *et al.*, 2001). These chambers enhance electric field and microbial inactivation, reducing the need for electric energy input. However, the uniformity of field and residence time and the risk of arcing and of product deposits remain to be assessed.

To improve the uniformity of continuous PEF treatments, several treatment chambers can be connected in series and associated to cooling sections so as to control process temperature. Several treatment chambers could also be placed in parallel to increase the flow throughput of a production line. Vernhes *et al.* (2002) studied the inactivation of amoebae (*Naegleria lovaniensis*) in water with two continuous chamber designs; with the electric field oriented in a perpendicular or parallel manner (co-field) to the flow direction. The flow was adjusted to deliver the same number of pulses (10 square wave pulses, $\tau = 10$ ms, $E = 0.25 - 1.6$ kV·cm$^{-1}$, $f = 1$ Hz) under laminar flow conditions (Reynolds number $< 2000$). The most efficient process was obtained when the field was parallel to the flow. It is suggested that the flexible amoebae cells are elongated in the direction of the flow. When the field orientation is parallel to the flow, this elongation increases the effective cell radius in the direction of the field and thus increases the sensitivity to PEF (see equation 18.12). However in the case of small rod-shaped cells (considered as non-flexible), turbulent flow through treatment chambers may be desirable because it enhances exposure on the whole surface of cells. From this standpoint, PEF processing of products with a low viscosity would be facilitated. The materials used for electrode construction will be discussed later (section 18.9), in connection with resistance to corrosion and electrochemical phenomena.

### 18.2.3    Calculation, monitoring and optimisation of treatment parameters

Among the main parameters which characterise a pulsed electric field treatment, 'system parameters' (independent variables) can be distinguished from 'process parameters' (depending variables). The 'system parameters' are: $U_0$ the voltage across the high voltage generator (in V); $C$ the capacity of the capacitor(s) (in F); $n$ the total number of pulses; $f$ the pulse repeat frequency (in Hz); the shape of the pulse; $d$ the inter-electrode gap (in m), $S$ the electrode surface in contact with the sample (in m$^2$); $\sigma_s$ the electrical conductivity of the sample (in S·m$^{-1}$); $T_{in}$ the inlet temperature of the sample (in °C); the flow rate of liquid sample (m$^3$·s$^{-1}$) in the case of continuous treatment. The 'process parameters' are calculated from the system parameters as follows.

If the sample, located between the two electrodes and in close contact with them, is homogeneous (constant value of the dielectric constant $\varepsilon'$ across the sample), the value of the electric field $E$ (in V·m$^{-1}$) is defined by:

$$E = U/d \tag{18.2}$$

$$\text{with } U = R \cdot I \tag{18.3}$$

where $U$ is the voltage (in V) across the electrodes, $R$ (in $\Omega$) is the sum of resistances of the electrical circuit and $I$ (in A) the current intensity through the electrodes. In practice, the resistance of electrical components is generally negligible relative to that of the sample ($R_s$, in $\Omega$) and thus Ohm's law (equation 3) can be written as:

$$U = R_s \cdot I \tag{18.4}$$

$$\text{with } R_s = \rho_s \cdot d \cdot S^{-1} = d \cdot (S \cdot \sigma_s)^{-1} \tag{18.5}$$

where $\rho_s$ is the electrical resistivity of the sample in ($\Omega \cdot$m). According to equations 2, 4 and 5 the electric field value depends directly on the electrical conductivity $\sigma_s$ of the sample (in S$\cdot$m$^{-1}$): the lower the conductivity, the higher the electric field. Thus to obtain the same value of $E$, a higher voltage $U_0$ must be applied for a high than for a low conductivity sample.

The electrical energy $W$ (in J) stored in the capacitor(s) is given by:

$$W = C \cdot U_0^2 / 2 \tag{18.6}$$

The energy density $W'$ (in J$\cdot$m$^{-3}$) dissipated in the food sample per pulse is equal to:

$$W' = (V^{-1}) \cdot \int u(t) \cdot i(t) \cdot \mathrm{dt} = (V^{-1}) \cdot \int (u^2(t) \cdot R_s^{-1}) \cdot \mathrm{dt} \tag{18.7}$$

where $u(t)$ and $i(t)$ are the instantaneous voltages across the electrodes and the instantaneous current crossing the sample, respectively, and $V$ is the volume of the treatment chamber (in m$^3$). The total cumulated treatment time $t_t$ (in s), and the total energy density dissipated in the sample $W_t$ (in J$\cdot$m$^{-3}$) are defined by:

$$t_t = n \cdot \tau \tag{18.8}$$

where $\tau$ is the time width of a single pulse (in s).

$$W_t = n \cdot W' \tag{18.9}$$

For an exponential decay pulse in a series-type circuit (resistances and capacitor(s) placed in series), the time constant $\tau$ (in s) is given by:

$$\tau = R \cdot C \sim R_s \cdot C \tag{18.10}$$

For a square wave pulse, the value of $\tau$ can be selected at will (in a restricted range which depends on the PFN) and therefore becomes an additional independent variable.

In adiabatic conditions, the temperature increase $\Delta T$ (in °C) after one pulse can be predicted from $W'$:

$$\Delta T = W' \cdot V \cdot m^{-1} \cdot c_p^{-1} \tag{18.11}$$

where $c_p$ is the specific heat capacity (in J$\cdot$kg$^{-1}\cdot$°C$^{-1}$) and $m$ the mass of sample ($m$ in kg) contained in volume $V$ ($m/V =$ density). The maximum sample temperature ($T_{max}$) reached during PEF processing is rarely reported because measurements in the treatment chamber are difficult (metal probes cannot be used, and optical fibre probes are easily destroyed by arcing). The final (batch processing) or outlet (continuous flow) temperature ($T_{out}$) is generally available.

Some investigators (Picart et al., 2002), using optical fibre thermometers were able to measure changes in sample (whole milk) temperature throughout the sequence of pulses (batch chamber, exponential decay pulses, 30 kV$\cdot$cm$^{-1}$,

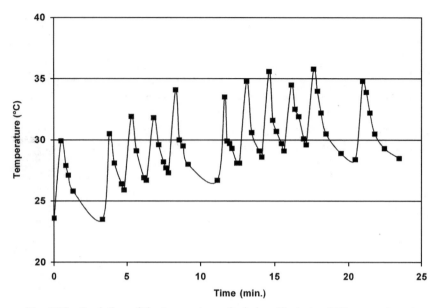

**Fig. 18.3**  Evolution of the temperature of whole milk during PEF processing at
$29\,\text{kV}\cdot\text{cm}^{-1}$. Energy density per pulse $= 2.6\,\text{J}\cdot\text{pulse}^{-1}$, $\tau = 0.84\,\mu\text{s}$, $f = 1\,\text{Hz}$. Room
temperature maintained at $21.5 \pm 1\,°\text{C}$. Temperature measured with an optical fibre probe
at the upper part of a batch vertical parallel plate treatment chamber (volume $= 5.6\,\text{ml}$).
Exponential decay pulses fired as 11 series of 32 pulses with 1–2 min. time intervals
between series.

1 Hz, series of 32 pulses, with 1 min. intervals between series) (Fig. 18.3). While
temperature increases result from dissipated electric energy, temperature
decreases are due to heat losses through the stainless steel electrodes. It should
be noted that the increase in sample temperature induces a marked increase in
sample conductivity and consequently a change in several process parameters.
Indeed, when $\sigma_s$ increases, $I$ increases but $U$ and therefore $E$ decrease, the
dissipated energy density $W'$ remaining unchanged. For example, at $20\,°\text{C}$, milk
(1.5% fat) and liquid whole egg have an electrical conductivity of $5.6\,\text{mS}\cdot\text{cm}^{-1}$,
orange juice 4.4, apple juice 2.8, and beer $2\,\text{mS}\cdot\text{cm}^{-1}$. At $60\,°\text{C}$ the same
products have electrical conductivities of 11, 8.5, 6 and $4\,\text{mS}\cdot\text{cm}^{-1}$, respectively
(Heinz *et al.*, 2002). In general, the electrical conductivity of foods increases
linearly with temperature.

A precise knowledge of the relationship between temperature and the
electrical conductivity of the sample can be used to calculate changes in sample
temperature during PEF processing from the oscilloscope recordings of $U$ and $I$
(equations 4 and 5) (Heinz *et al.*, 1999).

For an industrial PEF process, it would be necessary to monitor and control
sample temperature (using heat exchangers for cooling) to keep process
parameters fairly constant throughout the sequence of pulses, and to avoid
sample damage. Depending on the PEF microbial inactivation efficiency in the

temperature range 20–70 °C, and on the heat sensitivity of the samples, the PEF processing temperature could be selected to reduce cooling requirements and permit energy (heat) recovery. Computer modelling has been done of electric field distribution coupled to product flow and product temperature profile, in a co-field continuous flow treatment chamber (Fiala *et al.*, 2001). The predicted product temperatures downstream of the chamber were in good agreement with experimentally measured temperatures for a range of conditions (of pulse repeat frequency and of applied voltage). Temperature-dependent food properties, such as electrical conductivity (which affects electric field distribution), density, viscosity and thermal conductivity (which influence product flow and residence time) were considered. Results constitute a first step towards optimisation of the PEF treatment chamber for uniform electric field and residence time distribution, for minimal ohmic heating, absence of dielectric breakdown, etc.

Other investigators (Lindgren, 2001; Lindgren *et al.*, 2002) simulated the temperature increase in co-field continuous flow treatment chambers, taking into account flow velocity and distribution of electric field strength. Indeed, in a co-field chamber, the field strength is relatively weak in the centre of the pipe, where the residence time is the shortest. Four chamber models were used, differing by the length, internal diameter and angle of annular insulating section between pairs of electrodes. The radial distribution of the temperature increase was more homogeneous in the model where the insulator had a reduced diameter and intersected the electrodes with a 90 ° angle (without creating a notable recirculation effect). The maximum temperature increase was close to the wall, where the flow velocity is low. Cooling of the electrodes and insulator is therefore recommended to avoid hot spots. The minimum temperature increase (at the centre of the pipe) was 29 or 40% of the calculated average in the worst or the best, respectively, of the four models, indicating non-homogeneity of the PEF treatment, and the need to take this into account for safe processing. Microbial inactivation was experimentally evaluated using two of the treatment chamber designs. The result is consistent with the simulation and shows a small increase in inactivation and less needed energy input, giving less average temperature increase, for the chamber with a reduced diameter of the insulating spacer.

Recommendations for the installation of an efficient process monitoring system with accurate measurement of process parameters have been published by Góngora-Nieto *et al.* (2002b). The system permits real-time calculations of energy density and other relevant parameters and reports all measurements with their uncertainties. Adequate location probes, proper grounding, high signal to noise ratio have been considered. Implementation of industrial scale PEF metrology systems would be important tools for process and quality control, including HACCP.

For continuous PEF processing, the mean residence time $t_r$ of the liquid sample in the treatment chamber can be calculated as the ratio of sample volume in contact with the electrodes in the chamber over sample flow rate (for example for a sample flow rate of $500 \, l \cdot h^{-1}$ and for an effective volume of treatment chamber of 15 ml, $t_r \sim 0.1$ s). The number $n$ of pulses delivered to the sample in the chamber is then equal to the product $t_r \cdot f$.

For process control in the case of stable microbial inactivation, the field strength in the treatment chambers should be maintained constant by adjusting automatically the charging voltage of the storage capacitors. The energy density input should also be maintained constant by adjusting the pulse repeat frequency.

## 18.3   Mechanisms of microbial inactivation

Initial studies of microbial inactivation have been thoroughly reviewed (Wouters and Smelt, 1997; Barsotti and Cheftel, 1999; Jeyamkondam et al., 1999; Ho and Mittal, 2000; Barbosa-Cánovas et al., 1999, 2001; Dunn, 2001; Wouters et al., 2001a) and will not be detailed here. The processing conditions and results of recent investigations are summarised in Table 18.1. A comparison between the results of various groups of investigators is often challenging because equipment, processing and/or sample parameters differ from group to group and some critical parameters (especially maximum treatment temperature or dissipated energy density) are frequently not reported, and sometimes probably not precisely known.

A comprehensive knowledge of the mechanisms of inactivation would help establish optimal processing conditions to obtain safe and high-quality foods and permit the development of improved PEF equipments. However, these mechanisms are not yet fully elucidated. It is well known that a biological cell subjected to an electric field of sufficient strength undergoes reversible membrane permeabilisation. Recent investigations (Angersbach et al., 2000; Knorr et al., 2001) confirm a complex correlation between electric field strength and cell membrane permeabilisation. This phenomenon, known as 'electro-permeabilisation' (or electroporation) is commonly used for genetic transformation (transfer of exogenous nucleic acids into a cell). It can also facilitate an inverse transfer, namely the extraction of intracellular constituents (enzymes, metabolites).

A correlation between membrane electro-permeabilisation and microbial inactivation has also been established. Wouters et al. (2001b) studied PEF processing of Lactobacillus plantarum suspended in phosphate buffer, using propidium iodide (PI) uptake and analysis of single cells by flow cytometry. A correlation was observed between membrane permeabilisation and cell inactivation after treatment at 15 or 25 kV·cm$^{-1}$ (continuous flow chamber, square wave pulses), but not after thermal inactivation (3 min. at 45 to 95 °C). Indeed, cells were completely inactivated by heat before significant membrane permeabilisation occurred. This strongly suggests that the mechanisms involved in PEF inactivation somewhat differ from those of thermal inactivation. Unal et al. (2002), used a fast PI fluorescence staining technique to assess membrane damage of Lactobacillus leichmannii, Listeria monocytogenes and Escherichia *coli*, after treatment at 5–20 kV·cm$^{-1}$ (4 co-field flow treatment chambers, bipolar wave pulses). An increase in field strength increased the cell inactivation ratio and proportionally also increased the fluorescence intensity. The likelihood that microbial membranes are the primary target of high voltage electric pulses is in agreement with the high resistance of enzymes and other food constituents to PEF processing.

To explain the phenomenon of electroporation, Sale and Hamilton (1968) and Zimmerman (1986) developed the membrane 'dielectric rupture theory' based on physical principles and on the equivalent circuit model (a suspension of cells is modelled as resistors and capacitors, the cell membrane being assimilated to a dielectric capacitor). The theory assumes that the application of an external electric field leads to an increase in the transmembrane potential (TMP naturally present across the cell membrane) and to a reduction in membrane thickness. A viscoelastic restoring force opposes the electro-compression of the membrane. As the latter force increases more rapidly than the former, breakdown of the membrane occurs locally. The thickness of cell membranes being relatively constant from one organism to another (close to 7–10 nm), the breakdown TMP ranges from 0.7 to 2.2 V for spherical cells. When the strength of the external electric field and the pulse width increase, large irreversible pores are formed resulting in cell inactivation. The equation relating the TMP of spherical cells to the external electric field strength $E$ is given by:

$$\text{TMP} = 1.5 \cdot E \cdot f(\sigma) \cdot r \cdot \cos(\theta) \qquad\qquad 18.12$$

Where $\theta$ is the angle (in rad) between the field vector and the radius vector at the membrane point considered and $r$ the radius of the cell (in m). The factor $f(\sigma)$ is a function of the electrical conductivities of the suspending medium, cell cytoplasm and cell membrane, and of the ratio of membrane thickness over cell radius (Heinz *et al.*, 2002). From equation 12, it appears that large cells (e.g. yeasts, single cell parasites, cells from eucaryotes) require a smaller external electric field than bacteria for inactivation. This has been experimentally confirmed in several cases (see later sections). The different equations governing this electrochemical model are given by Barsotti and Cheftel (1999).

Schoenbach *et al.* (2000) explicated a dynamic model of pore formation; the critical voltage across the cell membrane must be applied for a time sufficient for the pores to expand to a critical diameter, and become irreversible. Whereas for pulses $> 1\ \mu$s this additional time is negligible, for sub-microsecond pulses it needs to be taken into account. Moreover, it was observed that applying nanosecond pulses (10–300 ns at electric fields higher than 50 and up to 300 kV·cm$^{-1}$) initiated cellular responses (in suspensions of human cells) distinctly different from responses to usual longer electroporation pulses; effects affected the cell interior rather than the plasmatic membrane, inducing apoptosis (Beebe *et al.*, 2002; Schoenbach *et al.*, 2002).

Other theories have been postulated in order to explain the phenomenon of electro-permeabilisation: conductive pores naturally present or formed by electroporation could generate localised ohmic heating (Bruhn *et al.*, 1998).

**Table 18.1** Microbial inactivation by pulsed electric fields (inoculated samples)

| Micro-organisms & reference | Medium | Treatment chamber & operating mode | Pulse characteristics | $E$ (kV·cm$^{-1}$) | $T_{max}$ (°C) | Inactivation ratio (log cycles) |
|---|---|---|---|---|---|---|
| *Enterobacter aerogenes* CECT 684 Selma et al., 2003 | Horchata pH 6.7, $\sigma = 2\,mS\cdot cm^{-1}$ | 4 continuous, co-field $n = 95$ pulses | Square, monopolar $\tau = 2\,\mu s$ | 30 | 30 | 1.1 |
| *Escherichia coli* O157:H7 *E. coli* 8739. Evrendilek et al., 1999 | Apple juice pH 7.0 | Continuous $n = 43$ pulses | Bipolar $\tau = 4\,\mu s, f = 1000\,Hz$ | 30 | <35 | 5 |
| *E. coli* ATCC 11 775 Dutreux et al., 2000a | Pasteurised skim milk pH 6.8, $\sigma = 4.8\,mS\cdot cm^{-1}$ | Continuous, coaxial $n = 63$ pulses | Exponential $\tau = 2.5\,\mu s, f = 3\,Hz$ | 41 | 37 | ~5 |
| | Na-phosphate buffer pH 6.8, $\sigma = 4.8\,mS\cdot cm^{-1}$ | | | | | ~5 |
| *E. coli* ATCC 26 McDonald et al., 2000 | Orange juice $\sigma = 4.2\,mS\cdot cm^{-1}$ | Continuous, coaxial $n = 6$ pulses per ml | Exponential $\tau = 2\,\mu s$ | 30 | 54 | 6 |
| *E. coli* ATCC 26 Aronsson et al., 2001 | Nutritive treatment medium, pH 5.0, $\sigma = 4\,mS\cdot cm^{-1}$ | 6 continuous, co-field $n = 40$ pulses | Square, monopolar $\tau = 2\,\mu s$ | 35 | 50 | 5 |
| *Pseudomonas aeruginosa* NCTC 8203 MacGregor et al., 2000 | 0.1% peptone water | Batch $n = 3000$ | Square, monopolar $\tau = 500\,ns, f = 10\,Hz$ | 30 | 25–30 | 3 |
| *Pseudomonas fluorescens* ATCC 17926 Fernandez-Molina et al., 2001 | Raw skim milk | Continuous, coaxial $n = 100$ pulses | Exponential $\tau = 2\,\mu s, f = 4\,Hz$ | 50 | 28 | 2.6 |

GRAM-

| Organism / Reference | Medium | Treatment system | Waveform / pulse | | | |
|---|---|---|---|---|---|---|
| *Pseudomonas fluorescens* Góngora-Nieto et al., 2001 | Liquid whole egg | Continuous, coaxial $n = 117$ pulses | Under-damped $\tau = 2\ \mu s$, $f = 3$ Hz | 48 | 32 | 0.82 for WSU-07 3.3 for ATCC 17400 |
| *Salmonella enteritidis* Jeantet et al., 1999 | Dia-ultrafiltered white egg pH 9.0, $\sigma = 4.8\ mS\cdot cm^{-1}$ | Continuous $n = 8$ pulses | Exponential $\tau = 9\ \mu s$, $f = 900$ Hz | | 30 | 3.5 |
| *Salmonella senftenberg* ATCC 43 845 Raso et al., 2000 | McIlvaine buffer pH 7, $\sigma = 2\ mS\cdot cm^{-1}$ | Batch, parallel $n = 50$ pulses | Square, monopolar $\tau = 2\ \mu s$, $f = 2$ Hz | 22 | NI | 1.5–2 |
| *Salmonella typhimurium* Liang et al., 2002 | Pasteurised orange juice pH 3.8 Freshly squeezed orange juice, pH 4.1 | Batch, parallel $n = 50$ pulses | Instant reversal $\tau = 2\ \mu s$ | 90 | 45 | 2.2 0.24 |
| GRAM+ | | | | | | |
| *Bacillus cereus* NCTC 11145 MacGregor et al., 2000 | 0.1% peptone water | Batch $n = 3000$ | Square, monopolar $\tau = 500$ ns, $f = 10$ Hz | 30 | 25–30 | 3.5 |
| *Bacillus cereus* IFR-NL94-25 vegetative cells Pol et al., 2001a | HEPES buffer, pH 7.0 | Batch parallel $n = 20$ | Square, monopolar $\tau = 2\ \mu s$, $f = 660$ Hz | 16.7 | 30 | ~1 |
| *Bacillus cereus* 11145 endospores Rowan et al., 2001 | 0.1% (w/v) peptone water | Batch $n = 2500$ | NI $\tau = 500$ ns, $f < 5$ Hz | 30 | 20 | 0.14 |
| *Bacillus subtilis* ATCC 9372 Pagán et al., 1998 | SMUF | Coaxial continuous $n = 5$ $n = 75$ | Square, monopolar $\tau = 2\ \mu s$, $f = 4.5$ Hz | 60 | 37 | 5-6 for vegetative cells O for spores |
| *Lactobacillus plantarum* Rodrigo et al., 2001 | Orange-carrot juice pH 4.2, $\sigma = 4.6\ mS\cdot cm^{-1}$ | Continuous, coaxial $t_t = 46\ \mu s$ | Exponential | 36 | NI | 2.5 |
| *Lactobacillus plantarum* Rodrigo et al., 2003 | 0.6% (w/v) peptone water $\sigma = 6\ mS\cdot cm^{-1}$ | 4 continuous, co-field $n = 64$ pulses | Square, bipolar $\tau = 2.5\ \mu s$ | 25 | 35 | 3.5 |

**Table 18.1** Continued

| Micro-organisms & reference | Medium | Treatment chamber & operating mode | Pulse characteristics | $E$ (kV·cm$^{-1}$) | $T_{max}$ (°C) | Inactivation ratio (log cycles) |
|---|---|---|---|---|---|---|
| *Leuconostoc mesenteroides* ATCC 8293 McDonald et al., 2000 | Orange juice $\sigma = 4.2$ mS·cm$^{-1}$ | Continuous, coaxial $n = 6$ pulses per ml | Exponential $\tau = 2\ \mu s$ | 30 | 54 | >3 |
| *Leuconostoc mesenteroides* ATCC 8293-1 Aronsson et al., 2001 | Nutritive treatment medium, pH 5.0, $\sigma = 4$ mS·cm$^{-1}$ | 6 continuous, co-field $n = 40$ pulses | Square, monopolar $\tau = 2\ \mu s$ | 35 | 50 | 0.5 |
| *Listeria innocua* ATCC 51 742 Dutreux et al., 2000a | Pasteurised skim milk pH 6.8, $\sigma = 4.8$ mS·cm$^{-1}$ | Continuous, coaxial $n = 63$ pulses | Exponential $\tau = 2.5\ \mu s\ f = 3$ Hz | 41 | 37 | 3.9 |
|  | Na-phosphate buffer, pH 6.8, $\sigma = 4.8$ mS·cm$^{-1}$ |  |  |  |  | 3.5 |
| *Listeria innocua* ATCC 33090 McDonald et al., 2000 | Orange juice $\sigma = 4.2$ mS·cm$^{-1}$ | Continuous, coaxial $n = 6$ pulses per ml | Exponential $\tau = 2\ \mu s$ | 30 | 54 | 5 |
| *Listeria innocua* ATCC 33090 Aronsson et al., 2001 | Nutritive treatment medium, pH 5.0, $\sigma = 4$ mS·cm$^{-1}$ | 6 continuous, co-field $n = 40$ pulses | Square monopolar $\tau = 2\ \mu s$ | 35 | 50 | 1 |
| *Listeria innocua* ATCC 51742 Fernandez-Molina et al., 2001 | Raw skim milk | Continuous, coaxial $n = 30$ pulses | Exponential $\tau = 2\ \mu s\ f = 4$ Hz | 50 | 28 | 2.7 |
| *Listeria monocytogenes* 11994 Rowan et al., 2001 | 0.1% (w/v) peptone water | Batch $n = 2500$ | NI $\tau = 500$ns $f < 5$ Hz | 30 | 20 50 | 2.6 4.1 |
| *Mycobacterium paratuberculosis* ATCC 19698 Rowan et al., 2001 | 0.1 % (w/v) peptone water or cow's milk | Batch $n = 2500$ | NI $\tau = 500$ ns, f $< 5$ Hz | 30 | 20 50 | 3.1 5.1 |
| *Micrococcus luteus* ATCC 9341a Dutreux et al., 2000b | Na-phosphate buffer pH 6.8, $\sigma = 4.8$ mS·cm$^{-1}$ | Continuous, coaxial $n = 50$ pulses | Exponential $\tau = 2\ \mu s, f = 3$ Hz | 32.5 | 20 | 2.4 |

| Organism / Reference | Medium | Treatment system | Pulse | | | |
|---|---|---|---|---|---|---|
| *Staphylococcus aureus* NCTC 4135 MacGregor et al., 2000 | 0.1% peptone water | Batch $n=3000$ | Square, monopolar $\tau=500$ ns, $f=10$ Hz | 30 | 25–30 | 2.8 |
| *Aspergillus niger* IMI 11414 MacGregor et al., 2000 | 0.1% (w/v) peptone water | Batch $n=3000$ | Square, monopolar $\tau=500$ ns, $f=10$ Hz | 30 | 25–30 | 0.5 for dormant spores 2.5 for germinated spores 4 |
| *Byssochlamys fulva* conidiospores ATCC 22967 Raso et al., 1998a | Tomato juice, pH 4.1, $\sigma=4.8$ mS·cm$^{-1}$ | Coaxial continuous $n=15$ | Exponential $\tau=2$ $\mu$s, $f=2$ Hz | 30 | 23 | |
| | Cranberry juice, pH 3.0, $\sigma=1.1$ mS·cm$^{-1}$ | Coaxial continuous $n=2$ | Exponential $\tau=3.3$ $\mu$s, $f=2$ Hz | 36.5 | 22 | 6 |
| *Neosartoria fischeri* ascospores ATCC 66781 Raso et al., 1998a | Fruit juices, pH 3–4.1, $\sigma=1$–4.8 mS·cm$^{-1}$ | Coaxial continuous $n=40$ | Exponential $\tau=2$–3.3 $\mu$s, $f=2$ Hz | 42–51 | 34 | <0.5 |
| *Saccharomyces cerevisiae* NCTC 10716 MacGregor et al., 2000 | 0.1% peptone water | Batch $n=3000$ | Square, monopolar $\tau=500$ ns, $f=10$ Hz | 30 | 25–30 | 3.5 |
| *Saccharomyces cerevisiae* ascospores McDonald et al., 2000 | Orange juice $\sigma=4.2$ mS·cm$^{-1}$ | Continuous, coaxial $n=6$ pulses per ml | Exponential $\tau=2$ $\mu$s | 30 | 54 | <1 |
| *Saccharomyces cerevisiae* CBS 7764 Aronsson et al., 2001 | Nutritive treatment medium, pH 5.0, $\sigma=4$ mS·cm$^{-1}$ | 6 continuous, co-field $n=40$ pulses | Square, monopolar $\tau=2$ $\mu$s | 35 | 50 | 6.5 |
| *Zygosaccharomyces bailii* ATCC 36947 Raso et al., 1998b | Fruit juices, pH 4.5, $\sigma=1$–3.6 mS·cm$^{-1}$ | Coaxial continuous $n=2$ | Exponential $\tau=2$–3.3 $\mu$s | 32–36 | 19–22 | ~4.5–5 for vegetative cells ~3.5–4 for ascospores |

Local and rapid heating (several degrees during microseconds to milliseconds) could induce thermal transitions in the membrane phospholipid bilayer from a rigid gel structure to a liquid crystalline structure, resulting in the displacement of membrane constituents and altered membrane properties. Transmembrane protein channels (naturally present or initiated by the external electric field) could be irreversibly denatured by heat and/or electrically induced changes in protein conformation (Jeyamkondan et al., 1999).

Microscopy observations of PEF-treated cells either with transmission or scanning electron microscopes (TEM or SEM) (Calderón-Miranda et al.,1999b; Dutreux et al., 2000b; Rowan et al., 2000; Jin et al., 2001) or with an atomic force microscope (Picart et al., 2002) generally reveal roughening, pinholes and craters at the cell wall surface, and profound effects on the intra-cellular structure and organisation of micro-organisms (such as cytoplasmic condensation and leakage of cytoplasmic material). Membrane breakdown, however, is not often observed. Aronsson et al. (2001) for example observed (TEM) PEF-processed Escherichia coli (40 pulses, $E = 30\,\text{kV·cm}^{-1}$), Listeria innocua (20 pulses, $E = 35\,\text{kV·cm}^{-1}$), Leuconostoc mesenteroides (20 pulses, $E = 35\,\text{kV·cm}^{-1}$) or Saccharomyces cerevisiae (20 pulses, $E = 35\,\text{kV·cm}^{-1}$) (in all cases 6 co-field flow treatment chambers, square wave pulses, $\tau = 4\,\mu s$). The corresponding inactivation ratios were 3.4 and 2.9 log cycles for L. innocua and L. mesenteroides, respectively, and a quasi-total inactivation was obtained for E. coli and S. cerevisiae. Detachment of the cell membrane from the cell wall and cytoplasmic condensation were observed for the three bacterial species, but consistent differences were not detected between control and PEF-treated S. cerevisiae. Harrison et al. (2001a) investigated the leakage of cellular material from Saccharomyces cerevisiae after PEF treatment (continuous coaxial treatment chamber, exponential decay pulses, $\tau = 4\,\mu s$, $E = 65\,\text{kV·cm}^{-1}$, $T_{inlet} = 22\,°C$). An increase in ATP, nucleic acid and protein leakage was observed when the number of pulses increased from 0 to 4. However, ATP leakage remained unchanged and nucleic acid or protein leakage decreased from 4 to 10 pulses. The disruption of subcellular organelles had been previously observed by TEM.

Investigations have also been carried out concerning the effects of PEF treatments on the sub-lethal injury of micro-organisms and the inactivation of metabolic enzymes. Simpson et al. (1999) studied cellular changes in aqueous suspensions of L. monocytogenes and Salmonella typhimurium subjected to PEF (batch treatment chamber, exponential decay pulses, $E = 10$, 15 or $20\,\text{kV·cm}^{-1}$). For both bacteria, an increased leakage of UV-absorbing material and a decreased ability to maintain a constant internal pH were observed when the electric field and the number of pulses (up to 10,000) increased. A lack of correlation was also observed between the inhibition of $H^+$-ATPase activity on the one hand, and PEF intensity, cell viability or cell-leakage on the other hand, suggesting that this enzyme was probably not a primary site of bacterial inactivation.

Sub-lethal injury was studied in order to determine whether microbial inactivation by PEF rests on an 'all or nothing' effect or mechanism. Sub-lethal damage was generally determined by measurement of growth on two different media, a selective and a non-selective one, and measured as the difference in counts. Some investigators did not detect any sub-lethal injury (Simpson *et al.*, 1999; Dutreux *et al.*, 2000a; Dutreux *et al.*, 2000b; Russell *et al.*, 2000) after PEF treatment, in contrast to others, who probed the same plus different micro-organisms (Wouters *et al.*, 1999; Unal *et al.*, 2001; Damar *et al.*, 2002, Picart *et al.*, 2002). Wouters (2001) studied the sub-lethal effects (continuous coaxial chamber, square wave pulses, $E = 20-25\,\text{kV·cm}^{-1}$, $\tau = 3.9\,\mu\text{s}, f = 3.5\,\text{Hz}$) in *L. innocua*, *L. plantarum* and *E. coli* (in phosphate buffer, pH 5.0) by plating treated bacteria in numeration media of different pHs (6.8, 5.4, 5.2 or 5.0). No sub-lethal injury was observed with the two latter micro-organisms, while sub-lethal injury of *L. innocua* increased when the number of pulses increased ($T_{\text{outlet}} = 54-59\,^\circ\text{C}$). Picart *et al.* (2002) also studied the sub-lethal effect of PEF processing on *L. innocua* (in phosphate buffer, pH 7.0) with quite different process parameters (batch chamber, exponential decay pulses, $E = 17-45\,\text{kV·cm}^{-1}$, $\tau \sim 1.45\,\mu\text{s}$, $f = 100\,\text{Hz}$, $T < 45\,^\circ\text{C}$) and observed the same trends as Wouters (2001). Selma *et al.* (2003) studied the growth characteristics of *Enterobacter aerogenes* in sterile horchata (a beverage made from plant tubers, pH 6.7, $\sigma = 2\,\text{mS·cm}^{-1}$) at different temperature (5, 8, 10, 12 and 16 °C) (4 coaxial treatment chambers in series, 25 to 95 square wave pulses, $E = 30\,\text{kV·cm}^{-1}$, $\tau = 2\,\mu\text{s}$, $T < 30\,^\circ\text{C}$). While the maximum specific growth rate was not affected by PEF, the lag time in PEF-treated cells was found to be significantly longer than in untreated cells. Lag time extension often indicates a repair and adaptation period and therefore revealed the presence of PEF-injured cells. It is difficult to explain why sub-lethal injury was induced in some cases only. Selective plating may not be an adequate investigation method.

Overall, the data reported in this section point to the lack of a 'unified mechanism' of electro-permeabilisation. This is not surprising when one considers that cell membranes (and cell walls) differ considerably between the different kingdoms (bacteria, yeasts, higher eucaryotes). The basic structure (lipid bilayers studded with more or less proteins) is the same, but the nature of the proteins, the presence and the composition of the cell wall, the presence of an outer cell membrane, vary widely, even between Gram+ (or Gram−) microbial species. Pore formation may have a similarly broad scope going from mere artefact to highly specific processes. It is difficult to differentiate between a pore and a channel molecule, a pore in the bilayer or one catalysed by proteins. The role of protein denaturation (e.g., by local heating) versus bilayer plasticity remains to be established in each case.

## 18.4    Critical factors determining microbial inactivation

Microbial inactivation by pulsed electric fields depends on many factors which can be classified as:

- treatment parameters
- microbial characteristics
- product parameters.

### 18.4.1    Treatment parameters

Electric field strength and total treatment time ($t_t$) or energy density input ($W_t$) are major parameters influencing microbial inactivation. It has been extensively demonstrated that increasing the electric field strength and/or the total pulse treatment time increased microbial inactivation (Sensoy *et al.*, 1997; Reina *et al.*, 1998; Wouters *et al.*, 1999; Barsotti, 2000; Raso *et al.*, 2000; Mañas-Perez *et al.*, 2001; Cserhalmi *et al.*, 2002; Picart *et al.*, 2002). However, to obtain a significant reduction in microbial counts, the electric field strength applied must exceed a critical value (Ec) (Fig. 18.4a). Ec ranges from 5 to 15 kV·cm$^{-1}$ depending on the micro-organism and the type of pulse and treatment chamber. Heinz *et al.* (1999) studied the PEF inactivation of *Bacillus subtilis* (in a pH 7.0 McIlvaine buffer)

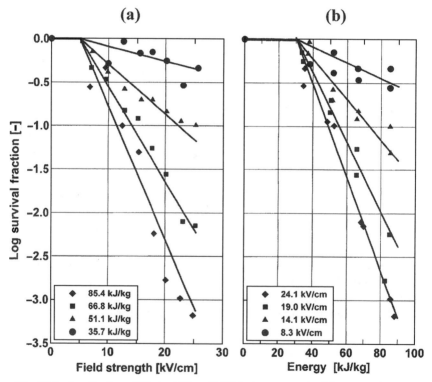

**Fig. 18.4**    Inactivation of *Escherichia coli* HB5α in response to PEF processing in a continuous flow system (Heinz *et al.*, 2002). Bacteria suspended in a Ringer solution. Solution inlet temperature of 42 °C. Treatment chamber with 2 parallel plate electrodes (2.5 mm gap). (a) Experimental design adjusted to study the effect of field strength at 4 values of energy density input. (b) Effect of energy density input at four different strengths.

(batch treatment chamber, 150 square wave pulses, $E = 2.5$ to $52.8\,kV\cdot cm^{-1}$, $T = 18\,°C$) under close to isothermal conditions. Applying 150 pulses with four different energy levels (0.4, 0.82, 1.22 or $1.68\,kJ\cdot kg^{-1}$ per pulse), it was found that a minimum energy input was also required to initiate microbial inactivation, independently of the critical electric field strength. At $20\,kV\cdot cm^{-1}$, no microbial inactivation was observed for a total energy input of $60\,J\cdot g^{-1}$, while inactivation ratios of 0.5, 0.9 and 1.1 log cycles were obtained for 123, 183 and $252\,J\cdot g^{-1}$. The same trend was observed for *E. coli* (Fig 18.4b). At field strength below $20\,kV\cdot cm^{-1}$, very high $W_t$ are needed for effective inactivation, with the risk of overheating and the additional need for cooling (Heinz *et al.* 2002). At higher field strengths, energy requirements are much reduced, but a practical higher limit of about $40\,kV\cdot cm^{-1}$ is respected in most PEF pilot systems to avoid dielectric breakdown of the food. Some data also suggest a maximum electric field strength above which the extent of inactivation does not further increase (Wouters *et al.*, 1999).

At $25–30\,kV\cdot cm^{-1}$ and for treatment temperatures of 20–40 °C, energy density inputs of $100–400\,J\cdot ml^{-1}$ give inactivation ratios of 2 to 6 log cycles for micro-organisms such as *E. coli*, *S. senftenberg*, *B. subtilis*, *L. plantarum*, *S. cerevisiae*. In the case of PEF-resistant strains of *Listeria*, $Wt \geq 1000\,J\cdot ml^{-1}$ (with cooling to maintain $T_{max}$ below 45 °C) were necessary for a 2 log cycle reduction (at pH 7), with square pulses (Alvarez *et al.*, 2002) or with exponential decay pulses (Picart *et al.*, 2002). It is of interest to note that Wouters *et al.* (1999) obtained more than 6 log cycle inactivation of *Listeria innocua* (at pH 5) with an energy density input of $80\,J\cdot ml^{-1}$ ($T_{in} = 20\,°C$, $47\,kV\cdot cm^{-1}$) or of $40\,J\cdot ml^{-1}$ ($T_{in} = 40\,°C$, $47\,kV\cdot cm^{-1}$). This suggests that a combination of moderate temperature (40–50 °C) to PEF decreases electrical energy requirements (probably due to phase transitions in the phospholipids of microbial membranes). According to Dunn (2001) and to Heinz *et al.* (2002), when energy density inputs are such as to raise temperature above 60–65 °C, microbial inactivation is indeed enhanced, thermal effects becoming prevalent (Fig. 18.5). Other investigations suggest a synergistic effect between PEF and these temperature levels (Wouters *et al.*, 1999; Aronsson and Rönner, 2001; Rowan *et al.*, 2001) (see section 18.5).

In spite of numerous studies, the exact correlations between electric field strength, energy density input (or total pulse treatment time) and microbial inactivation are not yet fully elucidated. It will however be necessary to optimise these parameters for industrial process applications, because they also determine energy consumption and cooling requirements. Wouters (2001) developed a new three-parameter inactivation model as a function of electric field strength, pulse length and number of pulses for continuous flow-through PEF processes. Based on this model the conditions for a PEF treatment were optimised with respect to the minimum energy required to obtain a certain level of inactivation. It was found that the most efficient way to improve the inactivation of *L. plantarum* was to increase the field strength up to $26\,kV\cdot cm^{-1}$, at the shortest pulse length investigated (0.85 $\mu$s), and then to test for the minimum required number of pulses.

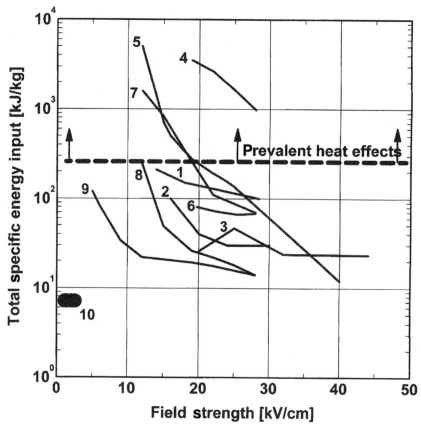

**Fig. 18.5** Approximation of major PEF parameters required to produce a 2 log cycle inactivation of given bacteria, yeasts, and plant cells (Heinz *et al.*, 2002). The numbered lines indicate that identical lethal effects are obtained at different settings of field strength and of energy density input, respectively. All details on medium composition and electrical conductivity, treatment temperature, pulse width and repeat frequency have been ignored. Gram-positive bacteria: (1) *B. subtilis* (vegetative), (2) *L. brevis*, (3) *L. plantarum*, (4) *L. monocytogenes*. Gram-negative bacteria: (5) *E. coli*, (6) *E. coli* (continuous PEF processing), (7) *S. senftenberg*, (8) *Y. enterocolitica*. Yeast: (9) *S. cerevisiae*. Plant cells: (10) potato tissue.

Pulse width and pulse shape also represent important parameters for microbial inactivation. For the same electric field strength and total pulse treatment time, 3–4 $\mu$s pulses appeared to be significantly more effective than 2 $\mu$s pulses for microbial inactivation (Aronsson *et al.*, 2001). Indeed reduction ratios of 3.6, 0.5, 0.3, or 4.6 log cycles were obtained with 2 $\mu$s pulses for *E. coli*, *L. innocua*, *L. mesentroides* or *S. cerevisiae*, respectively, while 5.4, 1.4, 1.6 or 6.3 log cycles were obtained with 4 $\mu$s pulses (6 co-field flow treatment chambers, square wave pulses, $t_t$=80 $\mu$s, $E = 30$ kV·cm$^{-1}$). The outlet temperature was kept below 50 °C. Some investigators observed that the advantage of longer pulses was cancelled at high field strengths (Wouters *et al.*, 1999), while others found no effect of pulse width on microbial inactivation (Raso *et al.*, 2000; Mañas-Perez *et al.*, 2001). These discrepancies may stem from the fact that the various groups of investigators used different types of pulses and of treatment chambers.

A comparison of the effects of electric pulses of different shapes has been presented by Wouters and Smelt (1997) and Barsotti and Cheftel (1999). In terms of microbial inactivation, square wave pulses are generally more efficient than exponential decay pulses (Jeyamkondan *et al.*, 1999). This is probably due to the fact that for identical maximum electric field and energy density input, a much larger proportion of the energy is dissipated at $E_{max}$ with a square wave pulse than with an exponential pulse. Oscillatory decay pulses have been reported as the least efficient, because cells are not continuously exposed to a high-value electric field, thereby probably preventing irreversible cell membrane breakdown over a large area (Barbosa-Cánovas *et al.*, 2000a). Bipolar pulses appear to be more efficient than monopolar pulses because they cause additional stress to the cell membrane. Bipolar pulses probably have the additional advantage of minimising electrolysis of liquid foods and solid deposits on electrode surfaces. The efficiency of instant reversal pulse is controversial, with high microbial inactivation reported in some cases and very low inactivation in others (Góngora-Nieto *et al.*, 2002a).

Few studies have been carried out concerning effects of pulse repeat frequency. Picart *et al.* (2002) observed that increasing this parameter from 1.1 to 100 Hz at $29 \, kV \cdot cm^{-1}$ (batch chamber, up to 400 exponential decay pulses, $\tau = 1 \, \mu s$) markedly increased the extent of inactivation of *Listeria innocua* in whole milk, but less so in skim milk. No influence of pulse frequency was observed on inactivation of the same organism in phosphate buffer or in liquid dairy cream (20% fat). However, in all cases, pulses were fired by series of 16 or 32 pulses (for $f = 100$ or 1.1 Hz, respectively), with 1 min intervals between series to permit heat removal and maintenance of sample temperature below 45 °C. Raso *et al.* (2000) did not detect any influence of pulse frequency on the PEF inactivation of *Salmonella senftenberg* suspended in a citrate-phosphate buffer (batch chamber, 50 square wave pulses, $\tau = 2 \, \mu s$, $22 \, kV \cdot cm^{-1}$). However, the range of pulse frequency studied was quite narrow (1–5 Hz). Conclusions concerning the effects of pulse repeat frequency are difficult at this stage. It has been suggested that a very short delay between each pulse prevents the cell membrane integrity from recovering (Aly *et al.*, 2001). It can be noted that some pulse-generating systems permit a pulse frequency of up to 1500 Hz (Yeom *et al.*, 1999). Another pulse related parameter which could influence microbial inactivation is the rate of voltage (and current) increase at the start of each individual pulse. The time to reach peak voltage is close to 100 nanoseconds for many pulse-generating systems, but effects of changes in this time interval are not known.

The effects of the temperature of PEF processing will be detailed in the section: 'Combinations with other preservation techniques'.

### 18.4.2    Microbial characteristics

It has been widely reported that vegetative cells of bacteria are more resistant to PEF than yeasts or moulds. Gram+ bacteria are generally more resistant than Gram− due to differences in cell wall membrane (see Table 18.1, Wouters *et al.*, 2001a; Heinz *et al.*, 2002). Aronsson *et al.* (2001) studied the PEF inactivation of different species of micro-organisms suspended in a nutritive treatment medium (6 tubular co-field flow chambers in series, 40 square wave pulses, $\tau = 2\,\mu s$, $35\,kV\cdot cm^{-1}$, $f = 250\,Hz$, $T < 50\,°C$) and observed 0.5, 1, 5 and 6.5 log cycle reduction for *Leuconostoc mesenteroides*, *L. innocua*, *E. coli* and *Saccharomyces cerevisiae*, respectively. It is interesting to note that Vernhes *et al.* (2002) obtained total eradication (5–6 log cycle reduction) of amoebae (*Naegleria lovaniensis*) in water using long pulses (10 square wave pulses, $\tau = 10\,ms$) at a low electric field strength ($2.5\,kV\cdot cm^{-1}$) (batch treatment chamber, $f = 1\,Hz$). The higher sensitivity of yeast cells or amoebae is partly explained by their larger size. Indeed, as predicted by equation 12, at a higher radius $r$, a lower external field strength $E$ is needed to reach the critical TMP. Heinz *et al.* (2002) reported the impact of cell size and geometry on the critical field strength and observed that a rod-shaped cell required at least a 5-fold higher field strength than a spherical cell with the same characteristics dimensions.

Wouters *et al.* (2001b) studied the permeabilisation of *Lactobacillus plantarum* (in a phosphate buffer, $\sigma = 15\,mS\cdot cm^{-1}$) after PEF treatment (continuous co-field chamber, $\tau = 2.3\,\mu s$, $25\,kV\cdot cm^{-1}$) using PI uptake and analysis of single cells by flow cytometry correlated to a specific software able to estimate individual cell size and shape in the bacterial population. Small cells appeared to be less vulnerable than large cells to membrane permeabilisation. Moreover, it was observed that the difference between the proportion of permeabilised cells in the small and large-cell populations disappeared gradually in the $15\,mS\cdot cm^{-1}$ buffer, and rapidly in the $4\,mS\cdot cm^{-1}$ buffer, when the total energy density input increased.

Bacterial spores generally resist electric pulse conditions which inactivate vegetative cells. A 0.6 log cycle reduction of spores of *Bacillus stearothermophilus* required 300 pulses of $2\,\mu s$ at $60\,kV\cdot cm^{-1}$ or 2000 pulses of 75 ns at $180\,kV\cdot cm^{-1}$ (Katsuki *et al.*, 2000). Moreover it was observed that there was no effect below $40\,kV\cdot cm^{-1}$. Cserhalmi *et al.* (2002) compared the PEF inactivation of spores and vegetative cells of *Bacillus cereus* (in 0.15% sterile NaCl solution) (6 continuous treatment chambers in series, 8.3 bipolar square wave pulses, $\tau = 2\,\mu s$, $25\,kV\cdot cm^{-1}$, $T < 30\,°C$). Reduction ratios of 1.4 and less than 0.5 log cycles were obtained for vegetative cells and spores, respectively. Combining electric fields with other physical or chemical treatments can however induce significant inactivation of bacterial spores (see section 18.5). The high resistance of spores to PEF is probably due to their small size, and to their dehydrated and mineralised state, with a thick cortex and coat layers which protect a conductive core (Barbosa-Cánovas *et al.*, 2001). In contrast, mould or yeast spores appear to be easily inactivated by PEF, but the number of studies is limited (see Table 18.1).

Khadre and Youssef (2002) found that human rotavirus was resistant to PEF treatment at 20 to 29 kV·cm$^{-1}$ (4 co-field flow chambers in series, ~48 bipolar wave pulses, $\tau = 3\,\mu s$, $f = 1000\,Hz$), while it was highly sensitive to ozone (25 $\mu g.ml^{-1}$) or to high hydrostatic pressure (300 MPa, 2 min., 25 °C). PEF sensitivity may differ between strains of the same microbial species. For example, Picart et al. (2002) found differences in the PEF inactivation of three strains of L. innocua isolated from foods (phosphate buffer, batch chamber, 100 exponential decay pulses, $\tau = 1.41\,\mu s$, 46 kV·cm$^{-1}$, $T < 45$ °C, $f = 1\,Hz$). Moreover, the resistance order of these three strains differed for PEF and for heat processing (10 min. at 60 °C).

It has been also frequently reported that cells in logarithmic growth phase are more sensitive to PEF than cells in stationary phase (Wouters et al., 1999; Alvarez et al., 2000, Wouters et al., 2001b; Alvarez et al., 2002). This is partly due to the weakening of the cell membrane during cell division. The effects of the initial microbial load on the inactivation ratio are variable (Wouters and Smelt, 1997; Barsotti and Cheftel, 1999). Alvarez et al. (2000) studied the PEF inactivation of Salmonella senftenberg (McIlvaine citrate-phosphate buffer, pH 7.0, batch chamber, 400 square wave pulses, $\tau = 2\,\mu s$, 22 kV·cm$^{-1}$, $f = 2\,Hz$, $T < 35$ °C) and observed the same inactivation ratio (2 log cycles) for different initial microbial loads ($3.10^9$, $3.10^7$ or $3.10^5$ cfu.ml$^{-1}$). In contrast, Damar et al. (2002) investigated E. coli inactivation (peptone solution, batch chamber, 10–30 bipolar exponential decay pulses, 20 kV·cm$^{-1}$, $T = 5$ °C) with initial cell concentrations between $10^3$ and $10^8$ cfu.ml$^{-1}$. Inactivation was inversely proportional to the initial cell concentration, the inactivation ratios for initial loads of $10^3$ or $10^8$ cfu.ml$^{-1}$ being 1.3 or 0.7 log cycles (for 30 pulses) and 1or 0.5 log cycles (for 10 pulses), respectively.

The temperature of prior microbial culture may affect PEF inactivation (Alvarez et al., 2002; Russell, 2002). Ohshima et al. (2002) observed that inactivation ratios of E. coli (distilled water, continuous treatment chamber, $f = 50\,Hz$, $T = 40$ °C, $W_t = 100$ J·ml$^{-1}$) reached 1.6 or 1.7 log cycles for a culture temperature of 20 or 42 °C, respectively, and 1 log cycle for a culture temperature of 30 or 37 °C. It was suggested that cultivation at 20 °C increased the unsatured fatty acid content and the fragility of E. coli membranes. The greater sensitivity observed after cultivation at 42 °C would be due to factors other than structural changes in cell membranes.

### 18.4.3  Product parameters

Electrical conductivity of the treated sample is one of the most important product parameters because it directly determines the resistance of the treatment chamber and thus electric field strength, pulse width and the increase in treatment temperature (section 18.2.3). At a constant energy density input and a constant field strength (23–28 kV·cm$^{-1}$), it was observed that an increase in the conductivity of the treatment medium (from 2.7 to 7.9 mS·cm$^{-1}$) decreased the inactivation of several micro-organisms (Wouters et al., 1999; Wouters, 2001).

The inactivation ratios of *L. innocua* (phosphate buffers, batch treatment chamber, exponential decay pulses, $E = 30\,\text{kV·cm}^{-1}$, $f = 100\,\text{Hz}$, $W_t = 600$ $\text{J·ml}^{-1}$) reached 0.75, 1 and 1.2 log cycles for buffer conductivities of 4.6 ($\tau = 0.9\,\mu s$), 3.1 ($\tau = 1.06\,\mu s$) and $2\,\text{mS·cm}^{-1}$ ($\tau = 1.6\,\mu s$), respectively (Picart, 2002, unpublished). It has also been reported that when the electric field strength, pulse length, number of pulses and energy density input were kept constant, the conductivity of the treatment medium did not influence PEF inactivation of *Salmonella senftenberg* (Alvarez *et al.*, 2000). However, the range of medium conductivity studied was quite narrow (2 and $3\,\text{mS·cm}^{-1}$). The influence of product temperature will be discussed in section 18.5 'Combinations with other preservation techniques'.

In the case of continuous PEF processing, changes in the physical properties of the sample (electrical conductivity, viscosity, density) due to temperature increase should be taken into account because of resulting changes in field strength and residence time in the treatment chamber(s) (Ruhlman *et al.*, 2001a; Heinz *et al.*, 2002). Product throughput and/or pulse repeat frequency must be adapted to keep sufficient total pulse treatment time and energy density input.

The influence of product pH on microbial inactivation by PEF is variable and appears to depend on the type of micro-organism and/or the treatment conditions (Wouters *et al.*, 2001a). Several investigators found that microbial inactivation increased when the product pH decreased (Wouters *et al.*, 1999; Aronsson and Rönner, 2001; Wouters *et al.*, 2001b). Alvarez *et al.* (2002) treated *Listeria monocytogenes* (in McIlvaine buffers) (batch parallel electrodes chamber, 400 square wave pulses, $\tau = 2\,\mu s$, $E = 25\,\text{kV·cm}^{-1}$, $T < 35\,°C$) and observed inactivation ratios of 1.48, 3.86 and 5.09 log cycles at pH 7.0, 5.4 and 3.8, respectively. In constrast, Alvarez *et al.* (2000) had found that *Salmonella senftenberg* was more resistant in McIlvaine buffer at pH 3.8 than at 7.0 ($E = 22\,\text{kV·cm}^{-1}$, others conditions identical). Acid products may also be more suitable for PEF preservation because the low pH may prevent sub-lethally damaged cells from recovery (Wouters *et al.*, 2001a).

Little information is available on the effect of the $A_w$ of the treatment medium on the microbial resistance to PEF, however, the few existing studies indicate that a reduction in $A_w$ increased microbial resistance, as expected (Alvarez *et al.* 2002). Aronsson and Rönner (2001) studied the inactivation (6 co-field treatment chambers in series, 20 square wave pulses, $\tau = 4\,\mu s$, $f = 250\,\text{Hz}$, $T = 30\,°C$) of *E. coli* ($E = 30\,\text{kV·cm}^{-1}$) and *S. cerevisiae* ($E = 25\,\text{kV·cm}^{-1}$) suspended in a nutritive treatment medium of different $A_w$. For *E. coli*, reduction ratios of 5.7 and 3.9 log cycles were obtained at $A_w$ values of 1 and 0.94, respectively (pH = 4.0). For *S. cerevisiae*, reduction ratios of 3.8 and 0.4 log cycles were obtained at $A_w$ values of 1 and 0.94, respectively (pH = 4.0). This trend was less pronounced at pH 7.0.

Ravishankar *et al.* (2002) investigated the inactivation of *Escherichia coli* O157:H7 in various gels (0.25% w/v gellan) (batch treatment chamber, 10 square wave pulses, $\tau = 3.25\,\mu s$, $E = 30\,\text{kV·cm}^{-1}$, $T = 35\,°C$). Inactivation

ratios of 3.5, 3 and 1.5 log cycles were obtained in a pH 6.5 gel (0.25% w/v), a
pH 3.5 gel (0.25% w/v) and a gel made from freshly squeezed apple juice (pH
3.5), respectively.

Mañas-Perez et al. (2001) studied the PEF inactivation of E. coli suspended
in different treatment media: phosphate buffer (pH 7.0, $\sigma = 2.2$ mS·cm$^{-1}$),
liquid dairy cream (33% fat, pH 6.8, $\sigma = 2.7$ mS·cm$^{-1}$), ovalbumin solution
(10% protein w/v, pH 6.7, $\sigma = 2.7$ mS·cm$^{-1}$), or a desalted suspension of fish
eggs (1–2 mm diameter, pH 6.8, $\sigma = 2.5$ mS·cm$^{-1}$), (batch treatment chamber,
exponential decay pulses, $\tau = 1.4-2\,\mu s$, $f = 1.1$ Hz, $E = 33$ kV·cm$^{-1}$,
$T < 30\,°C$). For a total treatment time of 90 $\mu s$, a reduction ratio of about 2
log cycles was obtained in all the media studied, suggesting that finely
emulsified lipids, soluble proteins or conductive food particulates (1–2 mm
diameter) did not protect against microbial inactivation. Moreover, the same
investigators processed ($\tau = 1.9\,\mu s$, $E = 33$ kV·cm$^{-1}$) agar gel discs (pH 7.0,
$\sigma = 2.3$ mS·cm$^{-1}$) inoculated with E. coli, and in which small cylindrical
particles of silicone (1.5 mm height, 5.6 or 3.3 mm diameter) had been
embedded. After firing 200 or 300 pulses, it was observed that the presence of
silicone particles markedly reduced microbial inactivation, since dense growth
was observed both above and under each particle. It was suggested that non-
conductive particles act as a barrier to the electric current and field strength.
Similar observations were made when an air bubble was entrapped at the top of
the agar gel disc. Dutreux et al. (2000b) observed a higher inactivation ratio for
E. coli attached to non-conductive polystyrene beads (2.97 $\mu m$ diameter) than
for free-living bacteria, while for L. innocua the same extent of inactivation was
obtained whether bacteria were attached or free (coaxial continuous treatment
chamber, 63 exponential decay pulse, $\tau = 2.5\,\mu s$, $E = 41$ kV·cm$^{-1}$, $f = 3$ Hz,
$T = 37\,°C$). Dunn (2001) also observed only minor differences between the
inactivation of E. coli suspended in a nutritive medium or entrapped in 2 mm
alginate beads (continuous flow, up to 100 J.ml$^{-1}$). The differences between
these results may be due to the fact that Mañas-Perez et al. (2001) used a static
chamber and a gelled medium preventing convective movements and treatment
uniformisation.

The protein content (between 5 and 20% of the total protein content of milk)
(Pol et al., 2001a) or fat content (of whole, 2% or skim milk) (Reina et al., 1998)
did not appear to influence microbial inactivation. Picart et al. (2002) studied the
inactivation of L. innocua suspended in three different media having the same
pH (6.6) and the same electrical conductivity ($\sigma = 5$ mS·cm$^{-1}$): commercial
UHT sterilised whole milk, commercial UHT sterilised skim milk and 40 mM
sodium phosphate buffer (batch chamber, 300 exponential decay pulses,
$E = 28-29$ kV·cm$^{-1}$, $\tau = 0.79-0.86\,\mu s$, $f = 1.1$ or 100 Hz, $T < 45\,°C$). For
a pulse repeat frequency of 1.1 Hz, the inactivation ratio of L. innocua was quite
similar when the bacteria were suspended in phosphate buffer or skim milk (~1
log cycle), and greater than in whole milk (~0.6 log cycle). In contrast, for a
pulse repeat frequency of 100 Hz, inactivation increased in the order: phosphate
buffer < skim milk < whole milk. The inactivation of L. innocua in liquid dairy

cream (20% fat, pH 6.7, $\sigma = 3.1\,\text{mS·cm}^{-1}$) ($E = 29$ or $38\,\text{kV·cm}^{-1}$, $\tau = 1\,\mu s$, $f = 1.1$ or $100\,\text{Hz}$) indicated no influence of the pulse repeat frequency. After a pulse treatment time of $250\,\mu s$, microbial inactivation reached a plateau close to 1 log cycle at $29\,\text{kV·cm}^{-1}$, and close to 2 log cycle at $38\,\text{kV·cm}^{-1}$, suggesting a protective effect of dairy cream.

### 18.4.4    Models describing microbial inactivation

Modelling PEF inactivation is difficult due to the large number of interacting parameters. Electric parameters clearly play a major role at low temperature, but interactions between higher temperatures and electric effects frequently occur (Smelt et al., 2002). Microbial inactivation as a function of electric field strength for a constant pulse treatment time, or as a function of pulse treatment time (or total dissipated energy density) for a constant electric field strength, generally follows a first order reaction (Reina et al., 1998; Fernandez-Molina et al., 2001, Picart et al., 2002). However, frequent tailing in inactivation curves has led investigators to define various other models. The main patterns used to characterise kinetic curves of microbial inactivation by PEF are as follows (some of them having been established for thermal inactivation):

Bigelow (1921) (first order kinetic model):

$$\log (N/N_0) = -t/D \qquad\qquad 18.13$$

where $N_0$ and $N$ are microbial counts before and after treatment (in $\text{cfu·ml}^{-1}$), respectively, $t$ is the pulse treatment time and $D$ is the decimal reduction time, mathematically, the inverse negative of the slope of the inactivation curve;

Weibull (1951):

$$\ln (N/N_0) = -(t/a)^b \qquad\qquad 18.14$$

where $a$ and $b$ are scale and shape factors, respectively. When b $< 1$ the survival curve is concave (it forms a tail), when $b > 1$ the survival curve is convex (it forms a shoulder) and when $b = 1$ the survival curve is a straight line on a ln scale (corresponding to Bigelow model).

Hülsheger et al. (1981) postulated several equations which relate the survival fraction to the electric field strength and/or to the pulse treatment time.

$$\ln (N/N_0) = -b_t \cdot \ln (t/t_c) \qquad\qquad 18.15$$

$$\ln (N/N_0) = -b_e \cdot (E - E_c) \qquad\qquad 18.16$$

$$N/N_0 = (t/t_c)^{[-(E-E_c)/k]} \qquad\qquad 18.17$$

(obtained by combination of equations 18.15 and 18.16).

where $b_t$ ($s^{-1}$) and $b_e$ ($\text{cm·kV}^{-1}$) are regression coefficients, $t$ the pulse treatment time, $E$ ($\text{kV·cm}^{-1}$) the applied electric field, $t_c$ the critical or threshold pulse treatment time (the longest treatment time for which the survival fractions equals 100%), $E_c$ the critical or threshold electric field and $k$ an empirical constant. Small values of $E_c$ or $t_c$ and high values of $b_e$ and $b_t$ indicate a high sensitivity of the micro-organism to PEF treatment (Barbosa-Cánovas et al., 2001).

Peleg (1995) and Sensoy et al. (1997) defined microbial inactivation curves as sigmoid as a function of time, and better described by Fermi's equation:

$$N/N_0 = 1/(1 + exp[(E - V_c)/k_e])$$    18.18

where $E$ is the applied electric field strength (kV·cm$^{-1}$), $V_c$ (kV·cm$^{-1}$) a critical value of $E$ where the survival level is 50%, and $k_e$ is a parameter that indicates the steepness of the survival curve around $V_c$. Smaller values of $k_e$ indicate high microbial sensitivity to PEF treatment. Both $V_c$ and $k_e$ are related to the number of pulses or to the pulse treatment time (Góngora-Nieto et al., 2002a).

Cole et al. (1993) described a log-logistic model:

$$Log(N/N_0) = Log\,(S_0) + (Log\,S_n - Log\,S_0)/[1 - exp(4 \cdot \Lambda \cdot$$
$$(t_s - Log\,t)/(Log\,S_n - Log\,S_0))]$$    18.19

where $S_0$ is the initial survival fraction at time zero, $S_n$ the final survival fraction, $\Lambda$ the maximum slope of the log of survival fraction curve, $t_s$ the log of the time at which the maximum slope is reached and $t$ the pulse treatment time. This model is an alternative to describe microbial inactivation kinetic curves when a distribution of resistance is assumed within the bacterial population. Other models (not described here) also include the effect of treatment temperature (based on Arrhenius relation) (Sensoy et al., 1997; Smelt et al., 2002).

Rodrigo et al. (2003) studied the inactivation of *Lactobacillus plantarum* (in peptone water) by PEF (4 co-field flow treatment chambers in series, square wave pulses, $\tau = 2.5\,\mu s$, $E$ up to 25 kV·cm$^{-1}$, $T < 35\,°C$) and compared three models (equations 18.13, 18.14 and 18.15) to predict PEF inactivation kinetics. The maximum reduction ratio obtained under these conditions was 3 log cycles, and it was observed that the Weibull distribution best fitted experimental data with $r^2$ closest to 1. Moreover, since the shape factor $b$ varied between 0.88 and 1.14 (close to 1) it was concluded that Bigelow model (with a $D$ value of 81 $\mu s$) and Weibull distribution function both described the experimental data. The same trend was observed by Rodrigo et al. (2001) when *L. plantarum* was PEF processed in an orange-carrot juice (continuous coaxial treatment chamber, exponential decay pulses, $E$ up to 35.9 kV·cm$^{-1}$, pulse treatment time up to 46.3 $\mu s$).

Raso et al. (2000) investigated *S. senftenberg* inactivation (batch treatment chamber, 500 square wave pulses, $\tau = 2\,\mu s$, $E = 12-28$ kV·cm$^{-1}$, $f = 1$ Hz) and obtained reduction ratios of 1 and 6 log cycles for $E = 12$ and 28 kV·cm$^{-1}$, respectively. Moreover the log-logistic model (eq. 18.19) was found to best fit experimental data with values of $r^2$ from 0.980 to 0.996, and with average values of Log $S_0$, Log $S_n$, and $\Lambda$ of 9.02, −5.75, and −4.19, respectively.

Damar et al. (2002) studied the inactivation of *S. aureus* and *E. coli* (cylindrical batch treatment chamber, 10 to 60 bipolar exponential decay pulses,

$E = 20\,\mathrm{kV\cdot cm^{-1}}$, $T = 5\,^{\circ}\mathrm{C}$) and observed maximum inactivation ratios of 1.9 and 1.2 for *E. coli* and *S. aureus*, respectively. The Hülsheger pattern (equation 18.16) was found to fit the experimental data with values of $r^2$ from 0.93 to 0.99 and an $E_c$ value close to $11-12\,\mathrm{kV\cdot cm^{-1}}$ for both bacteria. The constant $b_e$ was also modelled with a general equation ($b_e = a \cdot \exp\ (b.n)$ where $a$ and $b$ are constant and $n$ the number of pulses), the constant $b$ (pulse$^{-1}$) being found greater for *E. coli* (0.0026) than for *S. aureus* (0.0013), indicating a greater resistance of *S. aureus* to PEF processing.

This use of different models probably reflects the lack of a unified mechanism of microbial inactivation by PEF. It was therefore suggested to respect some guidelines (Góngora-Nieto *et al.*, 2002a): the use of specific target micro-organisms for products of interest; not to assume first-order kinetics; the use of sufficient microbial inoculation levels to avoid extrapolation; gathering enough data points (5–6 minimum) over a large range of inactivation cycles (6–7 log), etc.

## 18.5    Combinations with other preservation techniques

Various combinations of PEF with other anti-microbial processes or agents have been extensively investigated. Operating at higher product temperatures is the simplest combination treatment. Increasing the inlet sample temperature to moderate values (below 60 °C) immediately before PEF treatment markedly increases microbial inactivation. Aronsson and Rönner (2001) treated suspensions (in a pH 7.0 nutritive medium) of *E. coli* ($E = 30\,\mathrm{kV\cdot cm^{-1}}$, $W_t = 274\,\mathrm{J\cdot ml^{-1}}$) or of *S. cerevisiae* ($E = 25\,\mathrm{kV\cdot cm^{-1}}$, $W_t = 188\,\mathrm{J\cdot ml^{-1}}$) (6 co-field continuous treatment chambers in series, 20 square wave pulses, $\tau = 4\,\mu s$, $T_{max} < 50\,^{\circ}\mathrm{C}$) at different inlet temperatures. At 10 °C, a reduction of 0.9 log cycles was obtained for both micro-organisms, while for an inlet temperature of 30 °C reduction of 1.7 (*E. coli*) or 2.9 log cycles (*S. cerevisiae*) were obtained. Wouters *et al.* (1999) also observed a strong synergy between PEF treatment and heat for the inactivation of *L. innocua* suspended in a pH 5.0 phosphate buffer (coaxial continuous treatment chamber, square wave pulses, $\tau = 3.9\,\mu s$, $E = 47\,\mathrm{kV\cdot cm^{-1}}$, $T_{max} = 50\,^{\circ}\mathrm{C}$). For a total electrical energy density input of 40 J·ml$^{-1}$, inactivation ratios of 4.5 or 6 log cycles were obtained for inlet temperatures of 20 or 40 °C, respectively. It was assumed that at about 40 °C, the cell membrane switched from a rigid gel to a less ordered liquid-crystalline structure. The change in membrane fluidity could explain the increased sensitivity to PEF. Uemura and Isobe (2002) developed a new AC electric field system for continuous processing at moderate electric field ($E = 16\,\mathrm{kV\cdot cm^{-1}}$) and high temperature (up to 75 °C). The residence time in the PEF unit was less than 0.1 s and the treated product was immediately ($< 1$ s) cooled below 30 °C. Reduction ratios of 1.5 or 6 log cycles were obtained with *E. coli* (in 0.1 % saline water) at processing temperatures of 65 or 70 °C, respectively (four pairs of small titanium electrodes, $\sim$38 bipolar sinusoidal waves, $f = 20\,\mathrm{kHz}$, $T_{inlet} = 20\,^{\circ}\mathrm{C}$).

To obtain a 6 log cycle reduction of this strain by thermal inactivation at 75 °C without PEF, the minimal treatment time required was 300 s. Uemura and Isobe (2003) placed this PEF unit in a glass vessel under a pressure of 3 bars ($N_2$ gas) allowing process temperatures as high as 120 °C, with residence times as low as 0.1 s. This led to a 4 log cycle reduction of spores of *B. subtilis* in orange juice ($E = 16.3\,\text{kV·cm}^{-1}$). The loss in vitamin C was about 10%.

Combinations of PEF and moderate temperatures (60–75 °C) for short periods are also useful for enzyme inactivation (see section 18.6). They generally reduce the need for electrical energy and treatment time, thus demonstrating synergistic effects. However, it remains necessary to demonstrate first, that they do not alter the sensorial characteristics of heat-sensitive food fluids and secondly, that similar characteristics cannot be obtained (at lower cost) by UHT processing.

Heinz and Knorr (2000) studied the simultaneous effect of high pressure (200 MPa, less than 1 min.) and PEF (batch treatment chamber, 100 square wave pulses, $W = 0.5 - 2.1\,\text{J·g}^{-1}$, $E = 2.5 - 52.8\,\text{kV·cm}^{-1}$, $T_{max} < 30\,°\text{C}$) on vegetative cells of *B. subtilis* (in a pH 7.0 buffer). This combination did not increase microbial inactivation, as compared to PEF treatment at atmospheric pressure. However, a synergistic effect was observed when the cells were maintained at 200 MPa for 10 min. before PEF treatment. The same study indicated that the presence of 5% (v/v) ethanol in the bacterial suspension increased PEF-induced inactivation, provided the pH of the suspension was also decreased to 5.5. At pH 7 the presence of ethanol increased microbial resistance to PEF.

Additive and/or synergistic effects between PEF processing and the presence of nisin for microbial inactivation (vegetative cells) were demonstrated by several investigators. Dutreux *et al.*, 2000a studied the effects of combined exposure of *Micrococcus luteus* (in a pH 6.8 phosphate buffer) to nisin ($100\,\text{IU·ml}^{-1}$ at 20 °C for 2 h) and PEF (coaxial continuous treatment chamber, 50 pulses, $\tau = 2\,\mu\text{s}$, $E = 32.5\,\text{kV·cm}^{-1}$, $T < 17\,°\text{C}$). Viable counts were reduced by 1.4 or 2.4 log cycles by nisin or PEF alone, respectively. PEF treatment followed by nisin addition caused a reduction of 5.2 log cycles in comparison with a 4.9 log cycle reduction obtained with exposure to nisin followed by PEF. Calderón-Miranda *et al.* (1999a,c) observed a synergistic effect of PEF and nisin (10 or $100\,\text{IU·ml}^{-1}$) for the inactivation of *Listeria innocua* in skim milk or in liquid whole egg (continuous coaxial treatment chamber, 32 exponential decay pulses, $\tau = 2\,\mu\text{s}$, $E = 50\,\text{kV·cm}^{-1}$, $T = 36\,°\text{C}$). No difference was found in *L. innocua* inactivation when nisin was added before (to the treatment medium) or after (to the plating agar) PEF treatment. In contrast Góngora-Nieto *et al.* (2001), found that the combination of PEF treatment (continuous coaxial treatment chamber, 117 under-damped pulses, $E = 48\,\text{kV·cm}^{-1}$, $\tau = 2\,\mu\text{s}$, $T < 32\,°\text{C}$) and up to $1000\,\text{IU·ml}^{-1}$ of nisin (added just before PEF treatment) revealed no significant synergistic effect on the inactivation of *Pseudomonas fluorescens* in liquid whole egg.

Iu *et al.* (2001) added nisin (2% w/v) or cinnamon (2% w/v) to fresh apple cider (pH 4.0) inoculated with *E. coli* O157:H7 immediately before PEF treatment (batch treatment chamber, 10 instant reversal pulses, $\tau = 2\,\mu\text{s}$,

$E = 80\,\text{kV·cm}^{-1}$, $T = 42\,^{\circ}\text{C}$) . Inactivation ratios of 5.2, 4.63 or 2 log cycles were observed for PEF treatment alone, nisin alone or cinnamon alone, respectively. In contrast, ratios of more than 8 log cycles or 6.23 log cycles were obtained when PEF was carried out on cider containing nisin or cinnamon, respectively. Pol *et al.* (2001a) observed a synergistic effect between PEF (continuous co-linear treatment chamber, 30 pulses, $\tau = 2\,\mu\text{s}$, $E = 20\,\text{kV·cm}^{-1}$, $T < 25\,^{\circ}\text{C}$) and the presence of carvacrol (0.4 mM) for the inactivation of vegetative cells of *Bacillus cereus* in milk (but not in HEPES buffer). PEF treatment was applied 1.5 min after the addition of antimicrobial agents to the cell suspension and during a time span of 10 min. Moreover, carvacrol (1.2 mM) was able to enhance the synergy obtained between nisin (0.08 $\mu\text{g.ml}^{-1}$) and PEF treatment in milk (and also in HEPES buffer, with 0.04 $\mu\text{g.ml}^{-1}$ of nisin and 0.5 mM of carvacrol). PEF with or without nisin did not cause any inactivation of spores of *Bacillus cereus* (Pol *et al.*, 2001b).

Smith *et al.* (2002) investigated the inactivation of the endogenous flora (total plate count) of raw skim milk by pulsed electric field alone (batch treatment chamber, 50 instant reversal pulses, $\tau = 2\,\mu\text{s}$, $E = 80\,\text{kV·cm}^{-1}$, $T = 52\,^{\circ}\text{C}$) or combined with the antimicrobial agents nisin and lysozyme, added separately (100 IU·ml$^{-1}$ of nisin or 4250 IU·ml$^{-1}$ of lysozyme) or together ('NL mix', 38 IU·ml$^{-1}$ of nisin and 1638 IU·ml$^{-1}$ of lysozyme). When used alone, antimicrobials were held in raw skim milk at 52 °C for 30 min. before plating for microbial enumeration. When used in combination, antimicrobials were added to raw skim milk prior to heat treatment (up to 52 °C) or prior to the PEF treatment. PEF processing alone resulted in a 1.3 log cycle reduction. Nisin, lysozyme or the NL mix slowly reduced the microbial population with a maximum reduction of 1.2 log cycles. Synergistic effects took place since inactivation ratios of 5.72, 3.19 or 7.04 were observed for PEF + nisin, PEF + lysozyme or PEF + NL mix, respectively.

Liang *et al.* (2002) investigated the inactivation of *Salmonella typhimurium* in pasteurised orange juice by pulsed electric field alone (batch treatment chamber, 30 instant reversal pulses, $\tau = 2\,\mu\text{s}$, $E = 90\,\text{kV·cm}^{-1}$, $T = 45\,^{\circ}\text{C}$) or combined with the same antimicrobial agents, added separately (100 IU·ml$^{-1}$ of nisin or 2400 IU·ml$^{-1}$ of lysozyme) or together (27.5 IU·ml$^{-1}$ of nisin and 690 IU·ml$^{-1}$ of lysozyme). When used alone, antimicrobials were held in the juice (pH 3.8) for 1 hour at $\sim 0\,^{\circ}\text{C}$. When used in combination, antimicrobials were added to preheated orange juice just before the PEF treatment. PEF treatment alone resulted in a 1.5 log cycle reduction. Nisin, lysozyme or the NL mix reduced the microbial population by about 1.6 log cycles. Additive or synergistic effects occurred since inactivation ratios of 3, 2.5 or 4.3 were observed for PEF + nisin, PEF + lysozyme or PEF + NL mix, respectively.

Pol *et al.*, 2000; Terebiznik *et al.*, 2000; Hodgins *et al.*, 2002; Terebiznik *et al.*, 2002; Ulmer *et al.*, 2002 also observed additive or synergistic effect between nisin and PEF processing.

Ulmer *et al.*, 2002 studied the combined effect of PEF (continuous treatment chamber, $E = 31.6\,\text{kV·cm}^{-1}$, $W_t = 70\,\text{J·g}^{-1}$, $T < 31\,^{\circ}\text{C}$) and hop extract

(100 p.p.m.) for the inactivation of *Lactobacillus plantarum* in a model beer (pH 3.6). The presence of hop extract during PEF treatment increased bacterial inactivation by 1.6 log cycles, as compared to inactivation in the model beer without antimicrobial. Moreover, the addition of hop extract resulted in an additional 2 log cycles of sub-lethally injured cells after PEF treatment but did not induce either an additional measurable loss of metabolic activity nor an additional loss of membrane integrity of *L. plantarum*.

The mechanisms involved in additive or synergistic effects between PEF and antimicrobials have not been investigated. It would be interesting to study whether the exposure to antimicrobials sensitises bacterial membranes to PEF or vice versa.

Jin *et al.* (2001) studied the effect of a prior addition of l-alanine (0.01% w/v) to the treatment medium (0.02% NaCl) for the PEF inactivation of spores of *Bacillus subtilis* (2 tubular treatment chambers in series, 300 bipolar wave pulses, $\tau = 6\,\mu s$, $E = 30\,kV \cdot cm^{-1}$, $f = 1000\,Hz$, $T = 36\,^{\circ}C$). It is reported that in this study alanine did not cause spore germination. Reductions of 1.4 or 0.5 log cycles were obtained for PEF with or without alanine, respectively.

Unal *et al.* (2001) studied the inactivation of *E. coli* O157:H7, *Lactobacillus leichmanii* and *Listeria monocytogenes* suspended in 0.1% NaCl by exposure to ozone followed by PEF processing (4 co-field flow chambers in series, bipolar wave pulses, $\tau = 3\,\mu s$, $f = 1000\,Hz$, $T_{max} < 35\,^{\circ}C$). The lethality of PEF treatment was synergistically enhanced by ozone treatment for *L. leichmanii* ($20\,kV \cdot cm^{-1}$, $146\,\mu s$, 0.75 or $1.0\,\mu g.ml^{-1}$ of ozone), *E. coli* ($15\,kV \cdot cm^{-1}$, $146\,\mu s$, $0.75\,\mu g.ml^{-1}$ of ozone) and *L. monocytogenes* ($15\,kV \cdot cm^{-1}$, $146\,\mu s$, 0.5 or $0.25\,\mu g.ml^{-1}$ of ozone).

In the case of additives such as ozone, additional studies would be necessary to check residual concentrations and possible reactions with food constituents. It is likely that combinations of PEF and chemical additives would not facilitate compliance with 'novel foods' regulations.

It can be concluded that PEF processing, alone or in association with other hurdles constitutes an effective preservation technique. Data concerning the PEF inactivation of the endogenous flora of some fluids foods and their resulting storage life are summarised in Table 18.2, however, the numerous investigations reported in the preceding sections reveal a high degree of variability. This can be partly accounted for by a variable sensitivity to PEF of given micro-organisms, depending on growth conditions or on characteristics of the treated samples (pH, $a_w$, electrical conductivity, etc). The non-uniformity of electric field strength, flow velocity, residence time and/or of the temperature increase in continuous treatment chambers are probably responsible for a large part of this variability. As a result, microbial inactivation ratios are decreased together with energy efficiency, thus requiring more intense treatments to ensure safety margins.

**Table 18.2** Microbial inactivation by pulsed electric fields (endogenous flora of fluid foods)

| Medium, initial counts & reference | Treatment chamber & operating mode | Pulse characteristics | $E$ (kV·cm$^{-1}$) | $T_{max}$ (°C) | Inactivation ratio (log cycles) | Storage life (days) |
|---|---|---|---|---|---|---|
| Fresh apple juice cider, pH 3.7 $N_0 \sim 10^5$ CFU·ml$^{-1}$ for bacteria $N_0 \sim 10^3$ CFU·ml$^{-1}$ for moulds + yeasts Evrendilek et al., 2000 | 12 continuous, co-field $n \sim 50$ | Square, monopolar $\tau = 1.92\ \mu s$, $f = 952$ Hz | 35 | 30 | 2.6 for total aerobic plate 1 for yeasts + moulds | 22 at 4 °C |
| Apple cider, pH 4.0, $N_0 = 10^{2.5}$ CFU·ml$^{-1}$ for bacteria $N_0 \sim 10^4$ CFU·ml$^{-1}$ for moulds + yeasts Iu et al., 2001 | Batch, parallel $n = 10$ | Instant reversal $\tau = 2\ \mu s$, $f = 600$ Hz | 80 | 42 | 1.8 for lactic acid bacteria 1.2 for coliforms 0.7 for yeasts + moulds | NI |
| Cranberry juice $N_0 = 10^{4.8}$ CFU·ml$^{-1}$ for bacteria $N_0 \sim 10^{4.5}$ CFU·ml$^{-1}$ for moulds + yeasts Jin and Zhang, 1999 | 4 continuous, co-field $n = 75$ | Square, monopolar $\tau = 2\ \mu s$, $f = 1000$ Hz | 40 | 25 | ~5 total aerobic plate, yeast + mould counts | 14 at 4 °C |
| Orange juice $N_0 = 5400$ CFU·ml$^{-1}$ for bacteria $N_0 \sim 2800$ CFU·ml$^{-1}$ for moulds + yeasts Jia et al., 1999 | 4 continuous, co-field $n = 120$ | Square, monopolar $\tau = 2\ \mu s$, $f = 1000$ Hz | 30 | 25 | 2.3–2.4 total aerobic plate, yeast + mould counts | 42 at 4 °C |

| | | | | | | |
|---|---|---|---|---|---|---|
| Orange juice $N_0 = 10^7$ CFU·ml$^{-1}$ Yeom et al., 2000a | 6 continuous, co-field $n = 42$ | Square, monopolar $\tau = 1.4\ \mu s$, $f = 600$ Hz | 35 | 60 | 7 total aerobic plate, yeast + mould counts | 112 at 4, 22 or 37°C |
| Orange juice $N_0 = 10^{2.34}$ CFU·ml$^{-1}$ Ayhan et al., 2002 | 6 continuous, co-field $t_t = 59\ \mu s$ | NI | 35 | NI | ~ 2.4 total aerobic plate counts | 112 at 4 or 22°C |
| Raw milk $N_0 = 15$ CFU·ml$^{-1}$ for coliform bacteria $N_0 = 250$ CFU·ml$^{-1}$ for aerobic mesophilic bacteria Sepúlveda-Ahumada et al., 2000 | Continuous, coaxial $n = 30$ pulses | Exponential $f = 3.3$ Hz | 35 | 30 | 1.18 for coliform bacteria 0.2 for aerobic mesophilic bacteria | NI |
| Raw skim milk pH 6.7 $N_0 = 10^7$ CFU·ml$^{-1}$ Smith et al., 2002 | Batch, parallel $n = 50$ | Instant reversal $\tau = 2\ \mu s$, $f = 600$ Hz | 80 | 52 | 1.3 total aerobic plate counts | NI |

NI : Not indicated

## 18.6    Effects on enzymes

Initial studies on enzyme inactivation have been reviewed by Barsotti and Cheftel (1999), Yeom and Zhang (2001), Van Loey *et al.* (2002) and Bendicho *et al.* (2002a), and will not be detailed here. It is clear that enzymes (and food proteins) are much more resistant to PEF than vegetative microbial cells. However, a striking observation is that some investigators did not observe notable enzyme inactivation by PEF, while others, probing the same or other enzymes, often reported 30 to 95% inactivation (Table 18.3). The reasons for these discrepancies are not entirely elucidated, but cannot come from non-uniform electric field or residence time in the treatment chamber(s), as observed for microbial inactivation, where much higher inactivation ratios are expected. Some enzymes may be more sensitive than others to electric fields because of a higher content of $\alpha$-helices and marked dipolar conformation. Differences in electric field strength and in the density of dissipated electrical energy probably account for most of the mentioned discrepancies between investigations, even when care is taken to maintain sample temperatures below thermal inactivation levels. The data examined in the following pages appear to indicate that PEF inactivation of many enzymes would require costly amounts of electrical plus cooling energy.

Among the group of investigators who did not observe notable enzyme inactivation, Van Loey *et al.* (2002) used monopolar square wave pulses ($n = 1$ to 1000, $\tau = 1$ to $40\,\mu s$, $f = 1$ or $100\,Hz$) at $E = 10 - 32\,kV{\cdot}cm^{-1}$ in batch treatment chambers, with two types of electrode geometry and material. Various enzymes were tested in distilled water, buffer solutions and fluid foods ($\sigma = 0.01$ to $6\,mS{\cdot}cm^{-1}$), since enzymes tend to be most resistant to inactivation when processed in a food or in the presence of their substrates. Sample temperature was monitored with an optical fibre system. Under the experimental conditions tested, the inactivation of soybean lipoxygenase (LOX), mushroom or apple polyphenol oxidase (PPO), tomato or orange pectin methylesterase (PME) or horseradish peroxidase (POD) in distilled water or in pH 7 buffers did not exceed 15%. Changing the PPO or POD concentration (from 1 to 5 mg·ml$^{-1}$) or the LOX concentration (up to $15\,mg{\cdot}ml^{-1}$), or changing the medium conductivity from 1 to 4 mS·cm$^{-1}$ (and consequently the energy density per pulse from 0.4 to $4\,J{\cdot}ml^{-1}$) (with $n = 100$ to 400) did not increase inactivation. In pH 4 solutions, PPO and PME remained stable to electric pulses, while a 60% inactivation of POD was obtained. In apple juice, PPO activity increased after PEF (at $31\,kV{\cdot}cm^{-1}$), probably because of enzyme release from initially intact fruit cells present in the juice. A similar observation was made with PME and orange juice (at $35\,kV{\cdot}cm^{-1}$). Lipoxygenase in green pea juice was not inactivated (at $20\,kV{\cdot}cm^{-1}$). Alkaline phosphatase in raw milk was not inactivated (at $20\,kV{\cdot}cm^{-1}$) unless enough electric pulses were fired to increase milk temperature to 70 °C. Lactoperoxidase in raw milk was not inactivated (at $19\,kV{\cdot}cm^{-1}$) even with a high energy density input of $500\,J{\cdot}g^{-1}$.

Other investigators used a wide range of pulse types, treatment chambers and operating conditions. Giner *et al.* (2000, 2001, 2002) studied the effects of high-voltage electric pulses on a pectin methylesterase (PME) extract from tomato and on polyphenol oxidase (PPO) extracts from apple, pear and peach (see Table 18.3). In the case of peach PPO, the following conditions were used in a Bio-Rad Gene Pulser: batch chamber with parallel Al electrodes, up to 400 exponential decay pulses, mono- or bipolar, $\tau = 20$ or $80\,\mu s$, $E = 2$ to $24\,kV\cdot cm^{-1}$, $T_{max} = 25\,°C$, energy density inputs per pulse $= 2$ to $111\,J\cdot ml^{-1}$. The treatment chamber was cooled with ice for 1 min. every 5 pulses for heat removal, some experiments lasting up to 80 min., with a very low pulse repeat frequency. Indeed, 100 pulses at $111\,J\cdot (ml\cdot pulse)^{-1}$ supply a very large amount of heat. A first order kinetics of enzyme inactivation was observed:

$$RA = RA_0 \cdot e^{-(k_1\cdot t)} \qquad\qquad 18.20$$

where $RA = \%$ residual enzyme activity and $t = n\cdot\tau$. In the case of peach PPO for example, the first order constant of inactivation $k_1$ varied from 9 (at $E = 3\,kV\cdot cm^{-1}$) to $234\,\mu s^{-1}$ (at $24\,kV\cdot cm^{-1}$). It was possible to express $k_1$ as a function of the electric field strength $E$:

$$k_1 = k_{01} \cdot e^{-(\omega\cdot E)} \qquad\qquad 18.21$$

where $k_{01}$ and $\omega$ are constants, and to express RA as a function of the total energy density $W_t$ supplied:

$$RA = RA_0 \cdot e^{-(K\cdot Wt)} \qquad\qquad 18.22$$

the following values were given for $k_{01}$ (19 for monopolar pulses and $11\,\mu s^{-1}$ for bipolar pulses), for $\omega$ ($0.1\,cm\cdot kV^{-1}$ for mono or bipolar pulses) and for $K$ (0.019 for monopolar and $0.04\,m^3\cdot GJ^{-1}$ for bipolar pulses). Bipolar pulses (obtained by inverting electrical contacts in the treatment chamber) were more effective than monopolar pulses. This modelling can be used for predicting the degree of enzyme inactivation from process conditions. The values of total energy density dissipated also facilitate comparisons between different electric pulse studies, including those done with different pulse generating machines. Since $W_t$ values of $30\,kJ\cdot ml^{-1}$ were found necessary to obtain 70% inactivation of peach extract PPO, or 80–85% inactivation of tomato extract PME, it is clear that these enzymes are greatly more resistant to electric pulses than micro-organisms, and that no economic process could be devised to inactivate such enzymes by pulsed electric fields. Indeed 30 kJ·ml$^{-1}$ represent over 70 times the energy needed for thermal pasteurisation (and blanching), and correspond to a $\Delta T$ of about 7100 °C. Even if sample temperature were permitted to increase to 40–70 °C rather than 25–35 °C, the cooling requirements would remain very costly. Since cooling is relatively slow, this also means that the very short electrical pulses would have to be fired progressively (using several treatment chambers in series), thus minimising the short time benefit of PEF processing. PPO in apple or pear extract was found to be somewhat less or more resistant to PEF, respectively, than that from peach extract. Enzyme resistance in fruit purées remains to be determined, and could be higher than in fruit extracts. A somewhat

**Table 18.3** Enzyme inactivation by pulsed electric fields

| Enzyme & reference | Medium | Treatment chamber & operating mode | Pulse characteristics | $E$ (kV·cm$^{-1}$) | Max. sample temperature (°C) | Extent of inactivation (%) & energy density (J/ml) |
|---|---|---|---|---|---|---|
| Polyphenol oxidases: Apple, peach, pear Giner et al., 2001, 2002. | Fruit enzyme extracts pH 6.5 or 4.5, 235 mS/cm | Batch | Exponential, mono or bipolar τ = 20–80 μs | 25 | 15–25 | 60–90%, with 30 000 J/ml |
| Apple, mushroom Van Loey et al., 2002 | Distilled water & pH 7 or pH 4 buffers (1–4 mS/ml) | Batch | Square, monopolar | 10–30 | 35 | ≤ 15% with various energy densities (up to 3 950 J/ml) & medium conductivities |
| Pectin methylesterases: Tomato, Giner et al., 2000 Orange, Yeom et al., 2002a | Fruit extract, 95 mS/cm Orange juice, pH 3.75 | As above. Continuous, co-field | As above. Square, bipolar, τ = 2 μs, 700 Hz | 24 30 35 25 | 25 50 63 65 | 80–90%, with 24 000 J/ml 40% 83% 90% |
| Tomato, orange Van Loey et al., 2002 | Distilled water & pH 7 buffer Orange juice | Batch | Square, monopolar τ = 5 & 40 μs | 30 | 35 | ≤10% Increased activity |
| Lipoxygenases: Soybean Green pea Van Loey et al., 2002 | Water & pH 7 buffer, 1.1 mS/cm. Green pea juice | Batch | Square, monopolar τ = 5 & 40 μs τ = 1 μs | 20 20 | 35 | ≤10% 0% |
| Peroxidase from Horseradish Van Loey et al., 2002 | pH 7 buffer pH 4 buffer | Batch | Square, monopolar | 30 | 35 | 15% (high energy density) 60% |

| Enzyme, Reference | Medium | Treatment | Pulse type | | | |
|---|---|---|---|---|---|---|
| Papain<br>Yeom et al., 1999 | Aqueous solution with & without reductants | Continuous, co-field | Square $\tau = 4\ \mu s$ | 50 | 35 | 45% |
| Lipase from *Pseudomonas fluorescens* (extracellular)<br>Bendicho et al., 2002c | SMUF, 5.2 mS/cm | Batch, parallel<br>Continuous, coaxial | Exponential<br>Exponential | 27<br>37 | 34<br>35 | 62% with 500 J/ml<br>13% with 425 J/ml |
| Extracellular protease from *Pseudomonas fluorescens*<br>Vega-Mercado et al., 2001a | Tryptic soy broth, Casein Tris buffer, Skim milk | Continuous, coaxial | Exponential<br>$\tau = 2\ \mu s$ | 18–32 | 24 | 0–80% depending on medium, with 400–1500 J/ml |
| Proteases from Novo (Alcalase, Protamex)<br>Palomeque et al., 2001 | Protein hydrolysate from faba bean (pH $\approx$ 7) | Continuous, coaxial | Exponential | 42–78 | 30 | 62–100% |
| Alkaline phosphatase (bovine)<br>Castro et al., 2001b<br><br>Van Loey et al., 2002 | <br>Milk<br>SMUF<br>Milk | Batch<br><br><br>Batch | Exponential<br>$\tau = 400\ \mu s$<br>$\tau = 780\ \mu s$<br>Square $\tau = 2\ \mu s$<br>Square $\tau = 40\ \mu s$ | 19<br>23<br>20<br>10 | 44<br><br>35<br>70 | 65% with $\approx$ 2000 J/ml<br>43%<br>0%<br>74% |
| Lactate dehydrogenase (bovine)<br>Barsotti et al., 2002 | Buffer, pH 7.2 | Batch, parallel | Exponential $\tau = 1\ \mu s$ | 32 | 35 | 0% with 580 J/ml |
| Lactoperoxidase (bovine)<br>Van Loey et al., 2000 | Milk | Batch | Square, monopolar $\tau = 5\ \mu s$ | 19 | 35 | 0% with 500 J/ml |

higher efficiency may, however, be expected at higher electric field values, and also using square wave pulses. It is also likely that pulse processing at 40–70 °C would induce synergistic effects on enzyme inactivation.

Yeom *et al.* (2002a) investigated the inactivation of pectin methylesterase (PME) in orange juice (pH 3.75). This alteration enzyme is more heat-resistant than the spoilage micro-organisms of orange juice, and thermal pasteurisation at 90 °C for 1 min. is specifically recommended for inactivation of PME as soon as possible after juice extraction. PEF processing was carried out in continuous mode (6 co-field flow, tubular treatment chambers placed in series; flow rate $= 1.1-1.5 \, \text{l·h}^{-1}$; residence time in the 6 chambers ~6 s; 84 or 125 bipolar square wave pulses, $\tau = 2 \, \mu s$; up to $35 \, \text{kV·cm}^{-1}$; $f = 700 \, \text{Hz}$) (time values in the text are given in milliseconds, but this must be a printing mistake since it is not possible to fire 2 millisecond pulses with a repeat frequency of 700 Hz). Sample temperature was partially adjusted by placing in a water bath the tubing connections between pairs of electrodes. Arcing occurred at a water bath temperature $> 30 \, °C$ when electric field strength exceeded $25 \, \text{kV·cm}^{-1}$. At $T_{\text{bath}} = 30 \, °C$, processing at 30 or $35 \, \text{kV·cm}^{-1}$ for $184 \, \mu s$ caused 40 or 83% enzyme inactivation, with a sample $T_{\text{outlet}}$ of 50 or 63 °C, respectively (treated samples being immediately cooled to 30 °C within 1 s). At $T_{\text{bath}} = 50 \, °C$, processing at $25 \, \text{kV·cm}^{-1}$ for $250 \, \mu s$ gave 90% enzyme inactivation, with $T_{\text{outlet}} = 65 \, °C$. Upon corresponding thermal processing at $T_{\text{bath}} = 30 \, °C$ and $T_{\text{outlet}} = 63 \, °C$, with the same residence times but without electric pulses, enzyme inactivation did not exceed 24%, demonstrating the additional effect of PEF. The electrical energy density dissipated is not indicated and cannot be calculated from the reported data. In previous studies (Yeom *et al.*, 2000a, 2000b), the following processing conditions (same treatment chambers, flow rate $= 98 \, \text{l·h}^{-1}$, system pressure $= 2.4-3.2$ bars, square wave monopolar pulses, $\tau = 1.4 \, \mu s$, $t_i = 59 \, \mu s$, $35 \, \text{kV·cm}^{-1}$, $f = 600 \, \text{Hz}$, $T_{\text{outlet}} = 60 \, °C$ maintained for 9 s before cooling) brought ~90% irreversible inactivation of PME in orange juice. At $25 \, \text{kV·cm}^{-1}$, the activation energy of PME inactivation (in orange juice) was calculated for the $T_{\text{bath}}$ interval 10–50 °C and found to be $36 \, \text{kJ·mol}^{-1}$ (Yeom *et al.*, 2002). When this value is compared to the activation energy ($10 \, \text{kJ.mol}^{-1}$) found for the PEF inactivation of *Salmonella dublin* in skim milk (Sensoy *et al.*, 1997), one can perhaps predict that increasing the PEF processing temperature of food fluids to ~70 °C would multiply the rate of enzyme inactivation by a larger factor than that of microbial inactivation. However, effects on food quality would have to be investigated, since such conditions would not correspond to 'non-thermal' or 'minimal' processing. Another important point in the case of fruit juices is whether the process aims at subsequent refrigerated or ambient temperature distribution.

Bendicho *et al.* (2002c) studied PEF inactivation of a heat-resistant lipase from *Pseudomonas fluorescens*, in a solution of simulated skim milk ultrafiltrate (SMUF, adjusted to $\sigma = 5.2 \, \text{mS·cm}^{-1}$). Thermal pasteurisation (75 °C, 15 s) only caused 5% inactivation of this lipase, while near complete inactivation required 30 min. at 75 °C or 5 min. at 90 °C. PEF treatment was carried out with exponential decay pulses (probably $\tau \sim 4 \, \mu s$), at a maximum sample temperature of 35 °C, either in a batch mode (parallel plate electrodes, $E = 16-27\,\text{kV·cm}^{-1}$), or in a continuous mode (coaxial electrodes, $E = 26-37\,\text{kV·cm}^{-1}$, with cooling before and after the chamber). In the batch mode, inactivation reached 62% after 80 pulses at $27\,\text{kV·cm}^{-1}$ (dissipated $W_t = 505\,\text{J·ml}^{-1}$). Inactivation followed first order kinetics (as a function of $n$) and increased markedly with an increase in electric field strength. In the continuous mode, inactivation also followed first order kinetics, and was found to be greater at a pulse repeat frequency of 3.5 Hz than at 2 Hz (a small difference in repeat frequency), but did not respond clearly to electric field strength. After 80 pulses at $37\,\text{kV·cm}^{-1}$ (dissipated $W_t = 424\,\text{J·ml}^{-1}$), lipase inactivation did not exceed 13%. It can be concluded that this heat-resistant lipase can be partly inactivated by PEF, but the lower efficiency of the continuous mode even at a higher field strength is difficult to explain (unless there was a large distribution of residence times and of field strengths in the treatment chamber). The dissipated electrical energy density required for 62% lipase inactivation in the batch mode is much less than that previously indicated for PPO (although PPO are not as heat-resistant), but still higher than that usually required for microbial inactivation. Since bacterial lipase from *Pseudomonas* spp often cause off-flavours in milk, its PEF inactivation should also be investigated in milk.

Castro *et al.* (2001b) reported on the PEF-inactivation of milk alkaline phosphatase ($1-2\,\text{mg·ml}^{-1}$) in SMUF or heat-pasteurised milk containing 0, 2 or 4% fat. The following conditions (batch Kodak GeneZapper with a $100\,\mu l$ BioRad cuvette, 70 exponential decay pulses, $\tau = 400\,\mu s$, $18.8\,\text{kV·cm}^{-1}$, $f = 0.07\,\text{Hz}$) induced 65% enzyme inactivation in skim milk and 59% in 2 or 4% fat milk. Seventy pulses ($\tau = 780\,\mu s$, $\sim 5.3\,\text{J·pulse}^{-1}$, $23\,\text{kV·cm}^{-1}$, $f = 0.07\,\text{Hz}$, $T_{max} = 44\,°C$) caused 33 to 43% inactivation of alkaline phosphatase dissolved in SMUF. Given a volume of enzyme solution in the cuvette of $100\,\mu l$, the dissipated energy density $W_t$ was $3700\,\text{J·ml}^{-1}$, a high value. Changes in the UV absorption spectrum of alkaline phosphatase and susceptibility to trypsin proteolysis after PEF processing indicated that electric pulses modified the secondary structure of the enzyme. Km measurements indicated that the affinity of the treated enzyme for the fluorophos substrate decreased. In a parallel study, Castro *et al.* (2001a) used polyacrylamide gel electrophoresis, and measurements of turbidity, light scattering, intrinsic tryptophan fluorescence, plus extrinsic fluorescence from 2 hydrophobic probes to assess changes taking place in the phosphatase molecule (a dimeric metalloenzyme of about 170 kDa) subjected to electric pulses as indicated above. Results indicate that the molecule was not hydrolysed but underwent the following changes in parallel to inactivation:

1. polarisation
2. partial unfolding with surface exposition of aliphatic hydrophobic groups
3. protein-protein aggregation, as a result of the previous steps.

In contrast, other groups of investigators observed high resistance of alkaline phosphatase activity to shorter and less energetic pulses. It is known that about

45% of the amino acids of native alkaline phosphatase are involved in $\alpha$-helices It would therefore be of interest to determine the proportions of the main secondary structures after PEF processing, and also after additional storage, since this enzyme is known to display partial regeneration after mild thermal treatment.

Yeom *et al.* (1999) studied the inactivation of a solution of papain (with initial activation of the SH group in the catalytic site) after firing 500 square wave pulses of $4\,\mu s$ each, with a repeat frequency of $1500\,Hz$, at $50\,kV\cdot cm^{-1}$ (continuous processing through 2 co-field tubular treatment chambers, with cooling, $T_{max} < 35\,°C$). The 45% irreversible inactivation observed immediately after PEF was due to the loss of $\alpha$-helix structure (as checked by circular dichroism), and not to oxidation of the cysteine residue at the active site. Papain inactivation increased upon further storage at $4\,°C$ for $24\,h$, even when a lower electric field strength ($20\,kV\cdot cm^{-1}$) was used. This may be due to a phenomenon of self-proteolysis induced by electric pulses.

For Vega-Mercado *et al.* (2001b), the response to continuous PEF processing of an extracellular protease from *Pseudomonas fluorescens* varied from 80% inactivation (in tryptic soy broth, 20 exp. decay pulses, $\tau = 2\,\mu s$, $f = 0.25\,Hz$, $18\,kV\cdot cm^{-1}$, $W_t = 406\,J\cdot ml^{-1}$, $T_{max} = 24\,°C$) to no inactivation (in a casein-Tris buffer, 16 pulses at $32\,kV\cdot cm^{-1}$, $W_t = 1444\,J\cdot ml^{-1}$ or 32 pulses at $23\,kV\cdot cm^{-1}$, $W_t = 1568\,J\cdot ml^{-1}$) or even to increased proteolytic activity (in skim milk, 16 pulses at $25\,kV\cdot cm^{-1}$, $W_t = 900\,J\cdot ml^{-1}$), depending on field strength, pulse repeat frequency and medium composition. The presence of a protein substrate (casein or casein micelles) protected the protease against inactivation, as frequently observed for thermal treatments of other proteases. Treating skim milk with PEF increased the susceptibility of the constituents proteins to the action of untreated protease. The present enzyme is a 40–50 kDa thiol protease containing $Zn^{2+}$. Another preparation of this protease was subjected to different conditions of batch PEF processing (in SMUF containing various $Ca^{2+}$ or EDTA concentrations, 20 exp. decay pulses, $\tau = 700\,\mu s$, $6.2\,kV\cdot cm^{-1}$, $T_{max} = 15-20\,°C$, $f = 0.1\,Hz$) (Vega-Mercado *et al.*, 2001a). The extent of inactivation (30%) did not depend on the calcium concentration (0 to 15 mM), while calcium partially protected the enzyme against thermal inactivation. Protease inactivation by PEF was enhanced when SMUF contained the metal chelatant EDTA.

PEF processing was also used to inactivate commercial proteases (Alcalase[TM] and Protamex[TM] from Novo) added to a suspension of faba bean protein concentrate to prepare a protein hydrolysate with appropriate solubility and water absorption characteristics (Palomeque *et al.*, 2001). The initial suspension (pH 7) contained 0.5% protein in water, a protease/protein ratio of 0.5% and was incubated at $60\,°C$ for 15 min. Proteolysis was then stopped either by heat ($92\,°C$, 5 min.), acidification (pH 4) or continuous PEF processing (coaxial flow chamber, 104 exp. decay pulses at $42\,kV\cdot cm^{-1}$, or 31 pulses at $78\,kV\cdot cm^{-1}$, $\tau = 2-4\,\mu s$, $f = 3\,Hz$, $T_{max} = 30\,°C$). Inactivation reached 62% (at $42\,kV\cdot cm^{-1}$) or 100% (at $78\,kV\cdot cm^{-1}$), versus about 60% after heating or acidification. There was no change in enzyme activity of the PEF-treated solutions after 48 h at 4 °C. The protein solubility index and the water absorption capacity of the PEF hydrolysate were higher than those of the hydrolysates stopped by heat or acidification.

For Bendicho *et al.* (2002a), a commercial protease from *Bacillus subtilis* suspended in SMUF or in skim milk was found to be quite PEF-resistant (0–15% inactivation) (up to 100 pulses at 16–25 kV·cm$^{-1}$, batch or continuous processing). Combining pulse processing with mild heat (63 °C) or acidification to pH 5 increased inactivation to 30–50%.

Beef heart lactate dehydrogenase, a tetrameric enzyme stabilised in part by electrostatic interactions, and quite sensitive to either freezing or high-pressure treatment, was not inactivated after processing an enzyme solution (in a pH 7.2 buffer, $\sigma = 3.7$ S·cm$^{-1}$) with 200 exponential decay pulses ($\tau \sim 1 \, \mu$s, $f = 1.1$ Hz, 31.6 kV·cm$^{-1}$, maximum sample temperature $< 35$ °C, dissipated $W_t = 580$ J·ml$^{-1}$) (Barsotti *et al.*, 2002). It is thus likely that the tetrameric structure was not dissociated by the high-voltage pulses. The fact that enzyme resistance to PEF and to other stresses are not necessarily correlated (e.g., for PEF-resistant fruit PPO and for heat-resistant bacterial lipase) probably indicates that PEF inactivation does not always depend on extensive unfolding of the secondary and/or tertiary structure of enzymes. Further investigations will be necessary to check whether changes in amino acid side chains or displacement of metal ions could also be involved in the mechanisms of partial enzyme inactivation by intense electric pulses.

Most results reported above indicate that non-thermal PEF processing cannot be used economically to ensure the enzymatic stability of foods without a need for subsequent refrigerated storage.

## 18.7    Effects on food proteins

There are less PEF studies dealing with food proteins than with food enzymes. However, all studies published at this date reveal very few, if any, protein conformational changes. Jeantet *et al.* (1999) subjected ultra-filtered plus dia-filtered egg white (1.5–1.8 mS·cm$^{-1}$, pH 7 to 9) to 2–8 exponential decay monopolar pulses in a batch cell under conditions which caused partial inactivation of *Salmonella* (20–35 kV·cm$^{-1}$, $f = 100 - 900$ Hz, $T_{initial} = 4$ to 30 °C). Surface hydrophobicity measurements with a fluorescent probe (ANS) did not indicate any increase after PEF processing, suggesting an absence of protein denaturation, in contrast to observations after heat treatment (55 °C for 15 min). Solutions of ovalbumin (2% w/v in a phosphate buffer, pH 7, 5 mS·cm$^{-1}$) were PEF-processed (batch mode, 200 exponential pulses, $\tau = 0.9 \, \mu$s, 31.5 kV·cm$^{-1}$, $f = 1$ Hz, $T_{max} \sim 40$ °C, $W_t = 460$ J·ml$^{-1}$) (Fernández-Diaz *et al.*, 2000). While the 4 sulfhydryl (SH) groups of native ovalbumin did not react with DTNB, they became reactive immediately after pulse processing, indicating either partial protein unfolding or enhanced SH ionisation into the more reactive S-form. The extent of SH reactivity increased with dissipated energy. However, SH reactivity was reversible and decreased markedly when pulse-processed ovalbumin was kept at 4 °C for more than 30 min. The fourth derivatives of UV spectra of ovalbumin were determined before and 15–30 min after pulse processing, to assess possible polarity and conformation changes in the environment of tyrosine and tryptophan. No differences were observed. Thermal gels prepared from fresh or dialysed egg white had markedly different mechanical and water retention characteristics. Pulse processing of dialysed egg white (200 pulses, $30 \, kV \cdot cm^{-1}$) only slightly reduced its gelling properties (Fernández-Diaz et al., 2000). Thus electric pulses known to induce significant microbial inactivation (2 to 5 log cycles for Escherichia coli NCTC 9001, Mañas-Perez et al., 2001) did not cause notable changes in the proteins investigated.

Beaten liquid whole eggs, containing 0.15% w/v citric acid, were processed (coaxial continuous treatment chamber, $0.5 \, l \cdot min^{-1}$, stepwise mode, up to 50 exponential decay pulses, $\tau = 2.4 \, \mu s$, $f = 3 \, Hz$, $48 \, kV \cdot cm^{-1}$, $T_{max} = 40 \, °C$), and the whole egg proteins analysed by polyacrylamide gel electrophoresis (without SDS) (Ma et al., 2001). No changes in PAGE patterns were observed.

Samples of cod muscle subjected to 7 pulses at electric fields from 11 to $18 \, kV \cdot cm^{-1}$ also revealed unchanged electrophoretic patterns of muscle proteins (Gudmundsson and Hafsteinsson, 2001). $\beta$-lactoglobulin solutions (2% w/w in phosphate buffers, pH 7, 1.4 to $3.6 \, mS \cdot cm^{-1}$) were subjected to 200 exponential pulses (batch mode, $\tau$ up to $1.3 \, \mu s$, $30 \, kV \cdot cm^{-1}$, $f = 1 \, Hz$, $T_{max} \sim 40 \, °C$). Fourth derivatives of the UV spectra of native and of pulse-processed $\beta$-lactoglobulin solutions were identical, in contrast to those of solutions heated from 70 to 90 °C for 15 min. (Barsotti et al., 2002), suggesting that PEF did not cause marked unfolding of the protein conformation. Experiments at higher protein concentration (8 and 12% w/v) were carried out to detect possible aggregation phenomena due to electric processing. Polyacrylamide gel electrophoresis (with or without SDS or MSH) indicated that no protein aggregates were formed, even after 500 pulses at $33 \, kV \cdot cm^{-1}$ ($T_{max} \sim 40 \, °C$, $W_t = 1350 \, J \cdot ml^{-1}$). The turbidity or the viscosity of a 17% w/v $\beta$-lactoglobulin solution also remained identical before and after PEF processing (Barsotti et al., 2002).

PEF processing of raw skim milk (previously kept at 60 °C for 30 min. to promote re-entry of $\beta$-casein into micelles) (batch parallel plate chamber, 160 exponential decay pulses at $f = 100 \, Hz$, or 320 pulses at $f = 1 \, Hz$, $29 \, kV \cdot cm^{-1}$, $T_{max} \sim 40 \, °C$) did not modify the size distribution of casein micelles, as determined by photon correlation spectroscopy (Thiebaud et al., non-published data). Pulses were fired by series of 16 or 32, with 1–2 min intervals between series, to permit heat removal through the metal electrodes, and prevent overheating. Similar processing of raw whole milk (batch chamber, 350 exponential pulses, $\tau = 0.81 \, \mu s$, $f = 1$ or $100 \, Hz$, $30 \, kV \cdot cm^{-1}$, $T_{max} \sim 40 \, °C$, $W_t = 812 \, J \cdot ml^{-1}$) hardly modified the subsequent coagulation of casein micelles with rennet, in terms of setting time or curd firmness, as determined by near infra-red transmittance (850 nm) in a Gelograph-NT apparatus (Picart et al., unpublished data). Electric pulse conditions used in these studies were found to cause microbial inactivation of *Listeria innocua* introduced in various dairy fluids (Picart *et al.*, 2002).

Cheddar cheeses prepared from raw milk processed either by electric pulses or by low or high thermal pasteurisation displayed differences in texture characteristics (Sepúlveda-Ahumada *et al.*, 2000), but more systematic investigations are needed before conclusions can be drawn on the coagulation and cheese-making ability of PEF-processed milk.

The marked resistance of heat-sensitive (and pressure-sensitive) proteins to PEF processing should probably be regarded as an indication that short length electric pulses fired at electric fields below $40 \, kV \cdot cm^{-1}$, energy density inputs below $400 \, J \cdot ml^{-1}$ and maximum sample temperatures of $40 \, ^{\circ}C$ can effectively inactivate micro-organisms (and damage microbial membranes) without much alteration of food constituents. These results also support the preceding statement that practical enzyme inactivation cannot be expected from non-thermal PEF processing. Conversely, it may be possible to use electric pulses to reduce the microbial load of enzyme solutions (or of foods to which enzymes have been added) without affecting enzymatic activity.

## 18.8    Effects on vitamins and other quality attributes of foods

Multivitamin model systems of skim milk and of simulated milk ultrafiltrate ($\sigma = 5.2 \, mS \cdot cm^{-1}$ in both cases) were prepared, containing $100 \, \mu g \cdot ml^{-1}$ of thiamine, riboflavin, ascorbic acid and tocopherol and $10 \, \mu g \cdot ml^{-1}$ of cholecalciferol (Bendicho *et al.*, 2002b). PEF processing was carried out at 20–25 or 50–55 °C, adjusting input voltage to obtain electric fields of 18, 23 or $27 \, kV \cdot cm^{-1}$ at both temperatures (batch chamber with stainless steel parallel plate electrodes, 10 to 118 exponential decay pulses, $\tau = 4 \, \mu s$). In parallel the vitamin-containing solutions were also subjected to thermal pasteurisation (75 °C, 15 s or 63 °C, 30 min). Ascorbic acid was the only vitamin which suffered some destruction. For PEF processing, losses increased with pulse treatment time, but less clearly with electric field strength, and were similar at 25 or 55 °C. Maximum losses of 39% in SMUF and of 28% in skim milk were observed, with an energy density input close to $500 \, J \cdot ml^{-1}$. Milk constituents therefore appear to exert some protective effect against ascorbic acid destruction by PEF. Upon thermal pasteurisation (75 °C, 15 s), losses were greater in milk (13%) than in SMUF (2%). It can be concluded that PEF processing conditions known to decrease significantly microbial counts in milk did not affect the milk content in several vitamins. It is possible that prior deaeration of milk could have reduced the loss in vitamin C.

The retention in vitamin C after PEF processing of orange juice has been studied by several investigators (Hodgins *et al.*, 2002). Losses ranged from 0.2 to 15%, probably depending on the number of pulses, type of pulses, process temperature, and level of dissolved oxygen in the juice. This loss is significantly less than that for thermal pasteurisation of orange juice (95 °C, 15 s). Ayhan *et al.* (2001) investigated vitamin C retention in orange juice processed in an integrated pilot plant PEF system, packaged in sanitised ($H_2O_2$) containers of different materials using a glovebox system, then stored at 4 °C for up to 16 weeks (Yeom *et al.*, 2000b). Residual hydrogen peroxide was < 0.1 ppm per bottle prior to filling, headspace was close to 1%. Vitamin C retention after 16 weeks was higher in glass (91%) or PET (78%) bottles than in $O_2$-permeable PE bottles.

In addition to vitamin content and enzyme activity, other quality attributes of fruit juices have been investigated after PEF processing, together with microbial inactivation, and compared to the effects of thermal pasteurisation. Initial experiments are detailed by Barbosa-Cánovas *et al.* (2000a). No difference in colour or anthocyanin content was observed for PEF-treated cranberry juice (Jin and Zhang, 1999). Anthocyanin loss during storage (4 °C, 14 days) was less than for heat-pasteurised juice. Multivariate analysis of the volatile components showed than PEF-treated cranberry juice had similar flavour or aroma profiles as the controls, while thermal treatments significantly altered the overall flavour profile. The colour of a filtered apple juice became significantly paler after PEF processing (Zárate-Rodriguez *et al.*, 2000).

Harrison *et al.* (2001b) clarified freshly processed apple juice by plate filtration, centrifugation or ultrafiltration, obtaining higher or lower microbial loads, respectively. The differently clarified juices were then subjected to PEF processing (coaxial treatment chamber, 0.5 l·min$^{-1}$, 6 exponential pulses per unit volume, $\tau = 4\,\mu s$, 65 kV·cm$^{-1}$, $T_{inlet} = 22\,°C$), stored at 23 or 4 °C for various periods of time, and analysed for microbial viability, volatile flavour profile and sensorial difference, acceptability or rating tests. Results indicate that the shelf life of raw apple juices was extended to one month (at 4 °C, not at 23 °C) while acceptability was maintained equal to that of freshly pressed juice, and better than that of commercial apple juices. Shelf life could be further extended if more pulses or higher electric fields were used. Analysis by gas chromatography suggests that few, if any, changes affected the volatile chemicals.

Jia *et al.* (1999) determined the loss of individual flavour volatiles in freshly squeezed orange juice subjected to PEF processing (4 stainless steel co-field tubular treatment chambers, flow rate = 2 ml·s$^{-1}$, with recirculation, square wave pulses, $\tau = 2\,\mu s$, 30 kV·cm$^{-1}$, $f = 1$ kHz, $T = 25\,°C$). The average losses of flavour compounds were 3 or 9% for PEF ($t_t = 240$ or $480\,\mu s$) and 22% for heat processing (90 °C, 60 s). However, the flavour loss in the PEF process was mostly due to vacuum degassing, which was necessary to remove small air bubbles from the juice (these bubbles produced arcing in the treatment chamber). In another study without degassing but under a pressure of 2.4 bar (Yeom *et al.*, 2000b) (6 co-field tubular treatment chambers, flow rate = 98 l·h$^{-1}$, square wave monopolar pulses, $\tau = 1.4\,\mu s$, $t_t = 59\,\mu s$, 35 kV·cm$^{-1}$, $f = 600$ Hz, $T_{max} = 60\,°C$ for 9 s, aseptic juice packaging in trilaminate plastic cups), no losses occurred in the following analysed volatiles, immediately after

PEF processing or thermal pasteurisation (95 °C, 30 s): $\alpha$-pinene, myrcene, octanal, limonene, decanal. Losses taking place during juice storage at 4 °C for up to 16 weeks were always less rapid for PEF- than for heat-treated juice. The browning index (measured at 420 nm on centrifuged juice) increased slower during chilled storage of the PEF-processed juice, while the whiteness and hue angle of that same juice decreased slower than for the heat-treated juice. These lesser changes can be attributed to a lower heat load during processing and therefore to a lesser induction of non-enzymatic browning reactions and ascorbic acid degradation. When storage was carried out at 22 °C, less differences were noted between PEF- and heat-treated juices. The pH and Brix values of both juices did not change during storage. The importance of appropriate package material for the storage of similarly PEF-processed orange juice was further studied (Ayhan et al., 2001). Glass or polyethylene terephthalate bottles improved the retention of flavour compounds, as compared to high or low density polyethylene bottles, probably because of less oxygen penetration and less flavour absorption. Differences in colour parameters were also apparent during storage at 22 but not at 4 °C. Microbial stability of the juices was observed for 16 weeks at both 4 and 22 °C, and hedonic scores were hardly modified during storage, except for low density PE bottles.

In another study of orange juice processing at 35 kV·cm$^{-1}$ for 59 $\mu$s in the integrated pilot plant scale PEF system (involving a sanitary fluid-handling system and a glove box packaging system into sterile bottles), Ayhan et al. (2002) indicated microbial stability of the juice during storage at 4 or 22 °C for 16 weeks. PEF processing induced a small increase in the hydrophobic hydrocarbons D-limonene, $\alpha$-pinene, myrcene and valencene, probably through release from orange pulp into the aqueous phase. The levels of octanal, decanal, linalool and ethyl butyrate were not modified. In contrast, during storage, these more polar compounds decreased significantly, while the hydrocarbons remained stable. These effects are similar to those known to occur in heat-pasteurised orange juice. They probably result from limited reactions of aldehydes with amino acids (non-enzymatic browning) and linalool, and from hydrolysis of ethyl butyrate. Indeed, sensorial evaluation indicated no significant changes in juice colour or flavour after 16 weeks at 4 °C.

In the case of dairy fluids, initial studies revealed no sensorial differences between heat-pasteurised and PEF-pasteurised milk (see Bendicho et al., 2002a). The size distribution of fat globules in heat-pasteurised milk (1.5 or 3.5% fat) was not modified after PEF processing (batch parallel plate chamber, 200 exponential pulses, $\tau = 0.8\ \mu$s, 29 kV·cm$^{-1}$, $f = 1$ Hz, 29 kV·cm$^{-1}$, $T_{max}$ $\sim$40 °C, $W_t = 400$ J·ml$^{-1}$), as checked by laser granulometry and photon microscopy (Barsotti et al., 2002). In the case of heat-pasteurised liquid dairy cream (35% fat, pH 6.7), PEF processing (same batch chamber, 200 exponential pulses, $\tau = 1.1\ \mu$s, $f = 1$ Hz, 32 kV·cm$^{-1}$, $T_{max}$ $\sim$40 °C, $W_t = 320$ J·ml$^{-1}$) tended to dissociate large fat globule aggregates without markedly changing the mean globule diameter or the interfacial surface (Barsotti et al., 2002). Model oil-in-water emulsions stabilised by $\beta$-lactoglobulin (30% peanut oil, 5% $\beta$-

lactoglobulin, pH adjusted to 6, 7.1 or 8) were processed in a similar manner, at $33-36 \, \text{kV·cm}^{-1}$, $W_t = 240-320 \, \text{J·ml}^{-1}$. The mean diameter ($D_{4,3}$, volume basis) decreased, as compared to controls. The proportion of large oil droplets ($10-15 \, \mu\text{m}$ in diameter) tended to decrease, and that of finer droplets ($0.5-7 \, \mu\text{m}$) to increase. Thus electric pulses appeared to slightly disperse large oil droplets into finer ones. However, these differences were significant only in the case of pH 6 emulsions (Barsotti *et al.*, 2002).

## 18.9   Strengths and weaknesses as a preservation technology

The main benefits of processing foods with short pulses of high electric fields are the very rapid inactivation of vegetative micro-organisms, including pathogenic and spoilage strains, at moderate temperatures (below 40 or 50 °C), and with small to moderate energy requirements ($50-400 \, \text{J·ml}^{-1}$). Food sanitation, reduction of the microbial load and extension of storage life can therefore be obtained without notable effects on food constituents or quality. There are, however, several limitations to the use of pulsed electric fields as a non-thermal technology for food preservation:

1. Only homogeneous fluid foods without gas bubbles or large particles can be effectively processed.
2. These fluid foods should be within a proper range of electrical conductivity and viscosity.
3. With high conductivity foods and/or energy inputs above $200 \, \text{J·ml}^{-1}$, product temperature will exceed 50 °C unless cooling systems are used.
4. Bacterial spores are not inactivated, thus PEF-treated non-acid foods necessitate refrigerated storage and distribution.
5. Since enzymes are only partly inactivated, most PEF-processed foods require refrigerated storage for shelf-life extension.
6. Care must be taken to ensure that all food elements receive sufficient pulse treatment since continuous processing implies a range of residence times in treatment chambers with zones of non-uniform electric field.
7. Detrimental chemical changes may take place if dielectric breakdown and electrochemical phenomena are not controlled.

Some of these limitations may be challenged by product formulation (less salt, less viscous, smaller particles), improved equipment design, or adequate processing conditions. For example, operation under pressure (a few bars) should facilitate gas solubilisation, eliminate gas bubbles and avoid dielectric breakdown (arcing). The use of short ($< 5 \, \mu\text{s}$) pulses and of proper electrodes markedly reduces the risk or extent of electrochemical reactions. Processing at higher temperatures (above 65 °C) or in combination with food additives may markedly enhance microbial (possibly even spore) and enzyme inactivation, and reduce the need for electrical energy, but probably with a resulting decrease in food quality and 'freshness' as compared to true non-thermal processing. There is no doubt that PEF processing achieves microbial inactivation using processing time/temperature conditions significantly less than those required for similar effects during thermal processing. In one case, PEF treatment has been carried out immediately after heat treatment to obtain microbial stability (tested after 17 weeks at 4, 22 or 37 °C) of a low acid product (chocolate milk beverage, pH 6.5, 15 Brix, 4.2 mS·cm$^{-1}$) (Evrendilek *et al.*, 2001). This required a holding period of 31.5 s at 112 °C followed by PEF treatment (6 co-field continuous tubular treatment chambers, 105 l·h$^{-1}$, mono-polar pseudo-square pulses, $\tau = 1.4\,\mu$s, $t_t = 45\,\mu$s, $f = 600$ Hz, 35 kV·cm$^{-1}$, $W_t = 250$ J·ml$^{-1}$, $T_{max} = 24$ °C). In this case, PEF processing was therefore used to achieve sterilisation with a very reduced overall heat load.

The extent of chemical changes occurring in food fluids subjected to high voltage electric pulses deserves further investigation, although available data indicate few changes affecting small molecules. Variable results in the case of biopolymers (variable enzyme inactivation, apparent stability in protein conformation) indicate that effects depend on several parameters, field strength, total pulse treatment time and dissipated energy density, type of pulse, maximum temperature, pH, in addition to the specific polymer resistance. Two phenomena can markedly enhance chemical changes: dielectric breakdown and electrochemical reactions.

### 18.9.1   Dielectric breakdown

This results from the local combination of an intense electric field and of neutral, dielectric (non-conductive) constituents or molecules, that are suddenly modified and become strongly conductive. When dielectric breakdown takes place within a biological structure, such as a cell membrane, the latter becomes much more permeable to current and to solutes. The behaviour of protein or polysaccharide macromolecules, or lipids, subjected to an intense electric field is not exactly known (Neumann, 1986). These molecules move slowly and are not directly responsible for current flow, however, they often carry electric charges; proteins and some polysaccharides possess a non-isotropic distribution of charged groups and behave as dipoles. In proteins, amino acid residues (peptide units) have a dipole moment of 3.46 debyes arising from the different polarities of NH and CO groups. In an α-helix, the n successive peptide units (3.6 per turn) are aligned in the same orientation, and therefore the α-helix has an overall moment of n · 3.46 D (negative at the carboxy end). Subjected to an electric field, non-charged lipids and other molecules may become induced dipoles. Under intense electric fields, forces exerted on dipoles cause molecule orientation (= polarisation) and deformation (such as unfolding of α-helices), possibly even breakdown of some covalent bonds. High pulse repeat frequency, high energy pulses and pulses with sharp rising or decreasing voltage may enhance deformation and unfolding, while slower pulses may permit molecule reorientation without rupture of protein-protein interactions. These phenomena should not modify significantly current flow, unless the above-mentioned macromolecules are present in biological membranes, and their modifications induce pores in the lipid bilayer or opening of protein channels. Such changes would then bring a fast flow of very mobile ions. The resulting current may cause local heating, thus enhancing modifications of macromolecules. Electric fields also induce the dissociation of weak acids and bases, and promotes the separation of ion pairs (Neumann, 1986). The presence of ions in relatively homogeneous media greatly increases current flow. Conductive media decrease the electric field across the electrodes, with a conversion of electrical energy into heat responding to Ohm's law:

$$\mathrm{d}W' = E^2 \cdot \sigma \cdot \mathrm{d}t \qquad\qquad 18.23$$

with $W$ as energy density (energy absorbed per unit volume).

Food samples with a heterogeneous structure or composition are prone to dielectric breakdown because the electric field within the food is less uniform, with local field enhancement. To reduce the risk of dielectric breakdown of the food matrix, the treatment chamber and electrodes should be designed to provide fields as uniform as possible. This requires electrodes with smooth surfaces and rounded or tapered edges, and also an inter-electrode gap d significantly smaller than the electrode diameter (for electrodes made of two flat parallel disks). The electric field distribution in coaxial and co-field flow electrodes is not uniform, but can be predicted and controlled during chamber design, as previously indicated. The triple contact point electrode/insulating material/fluid sample, and also electrode locations with protein or other solid deposits, may enhance dielectric breakdown and arcing.

Dielectric breakdown can also take place in some gases. A few electrons accelerated by the electric field collide with peripheral electrons from $O_2$ or $N_2$ and eject them, thus ionising these molecules. A multiplication process may occur and the resulting avalanche effect then induces intense current flow. Air ionisation takes place when the electric field exceeds $10\,\mathrm{kV\cdot cm^{-1}}$ (moist air) or $30\,\mathrm{kV\cdot cm^{-1}}$ (dry air). Ozone ($O_3$) is frequently produced. For dry air between two electrodes, the breakdown potential $\Delta V$ is proportional (over a large range) to the product $p \cdot d$, where $p$ is the gas pressure (related to gas density) and $d$ the thickness of the gas layer (in this case, also the inter-electrode distance). In practice, dielectric breakdown in liquid food samples is often caused by gas bubbles because the electric field is enhanced within these bubbles (Góngora-Nieto et al., 2003b). Simultaneously, the electric field decreases markedly in the liquid directly between the gas bubbles and the electrodes, preventing adequate microbial inactivation (Mañas-Perez et al., 2001). The size and position of gas bubbles, together with the inter-electrode distance, influence the electric field perturbation (Góngora-Nieto et al., 2003b). Prior de-aeration of liquid foods is useful, especially when these foods are subjected to turbulent flow in the continuous treatment chamber. For solid foods, slight compression between flat electrodes may be necessary to expel residual air. All facing electrode parts should be separated by the food or an insulating material, and never by air, however, some gas initially dissolved in the food may be evolved through electric pulses, especially if the sample temperature increases. Pulses may also induce the formation of hydrogen, chlorine or other gases at the electrodes through electrochemical reactions, for example: $2\,H^+ + 2\,e^- \rightarrow H_2$. The volume expansion of gas bubbles may generate an overpressure and explosive noise. Vaporisation of liquid water may also take place but requires a significant temperature increase. One way to prevent the formation or to suppress existing gas bubbles is to keep the food fluid under pressure ($\geq 4$ bars) (Góngora-Nieto et al., 2003b).

Depending on the magnitude of these phenomena, arc discharges may occur. Arcing usually generates UV radiation (spark), local overheating (with eventual electrode pitting) and free radicals plus reactive oxygen species ($\bullet OH$, $\bullet H$, superoxide anion radical $\bullet O_2^-$, singlet oxygen radical $\bullet O - O \bullet$, hydrated electron, $O_3$, $H_2O_2$). This may enhance microbial inactivation but would detrimentally affect food constituents (e.g., by oxidising lipids), and must therefore be avoided. However, arcing (and plasma formation in aerated liquid) can be used to oxidise or dehalogenate toxic molecules or inactivate micro-organisms in wastewater (Marsili et al., 2002). Pulsed high-current underwater discharges can even produce high-pressure (80–100 bar) shock waves able to inactivate bacterial suspensions enclosed in flexible packages (Zuckerman et al., 2002; Loske et al., 2002).

### 18.9.2   Electrochemical reactions (Oxidation/reduction)

These may take place at or very near both electrodes, especially when processing corrosive and/or highly conductive acid or NaCl-containing fluids. As indicated above, protons may be reduced at the cathode to form hydrogen, while chloride anions may be oxidised into chlorine and hypochlorite. Oxygen or oxidants present in the food fluid can react with hydrogen and enhance the rate of proton reduction. Electrode material (stainless steel) is often visibly oxidised at the anode, with the formation of a layer of metal oxide(s), and the possible release of metal cations into the food fluid. The oxidation of graphite electrodes releases $CO_2$. Current conduction through the bulk fluid medium depends mainly on ion migration, and much less on a flow of free electrons. The possible oxidation or electrolysis of food constituents during PEF processing has not been specifically investigated. In some cases, protein deposits have been observed on electrode surfaces. Metal ions or complex ions released from the anode could perhaps catalyse lipid or ascorbic acid oxidation during subsequent food storage, but their concentration would be too small to cause any toxicity (Lelieveld et al., 2001). Electrochemical phenomena are known to be minimal in the case of short (microsecond) low energy electrical pulses, especially of bipolar pulses. One of the reasons for this may be that initial pulse energy is consumed by orientation of water dipoles near the electrodes. This may retard or prevent the appearance of the full potential of the electric field near the electrodes, and therefore prevent some electrochemical reactions (Dunn, 2001). The pH of food fluids is generally unchanged after PEF processing, indicating minimal overall reduction of protons. However, platinum-coated titanium electrodes have been recommended to avoid surface corrosion (a surface layer of oxidised titanium would be chemically stable but poorly conductive). Other highly conductive metal oxides (e.g., from ruthenium) or polymer coatings could be used, provided that they are inert and food grade.

Thomson-CSF claims to have developed an electrode material which can withstand long pulse width (20 $\mu$s) and current densities up to 470 A·cm$^{-2}$ before the electrodes are damaged (Caplot and Cote, 1999). Graphite is more resistant than stainless steel. Small electrode surfaces (such as in co-field treatment chambers) limit current intensity and probably minimise electrochemical reactions. They may, however, increase the risk of arcing. It is suggested that any PEF operation where the food fluid is not de-aerated, is brought to $\geq 70$ °C and/or is subjected to a dissipated energy density above 400 J·ml$^{-1}$ should be carefully checked for possible chemical modifications.

Preliminary experiments to detect the possible formation of free radicals were carried out with a pasteurised fluid dairy cream (33% fat, pH 7, 2.6 mS·cm$^{-1}$ at 25 °C) subjected (or not) in a batch chamber to 200 exponential pulses ($\tau = 1.43\,\mu$s, $f = 1$ Hz, 33.2 kV·cm$^{-1}$, $T_{max} \sim 40$ °C, $W_t = 480$ J·ml$^{-1}$) (DiBin and Cheftel, unpublished results). Since oxygen reactive species are very short-lived, it is necessary to use a spin trap, to convert them into longer life free radicals, enabling detection by electron spin resonance (ESR). POBN (4 pyridyl-1-oxide-N-tert-butylnitrone) was selected as a spin trap because it has a fast reaction rate even though the conversion yield may be rather low and variable (as with other spin traps). In the presence of ethanol, hydroxyl radicals react with POBN to give the POBN-hydroxyethyl radical adduct (POBN-CH$\bullet$(OH)-CH$_3$) which is stable for long periods of time and therefore accumulates. This reaction is specific for hydroxyl radicals, and the adduct displays a characteristic ESR spectrum (3 doublets). The dairy cream was first made 75 mM in ethanol and 75 mM in POBN (0.46 g ethanol and 1.45 g POBN per 100 ml), then processed with electric pulses, and analysed by ESR within 20 min. of the last pulse. The spectrum of the adduct was detected (while absent in several control samples), but its concentration was small, probably in the range 1–10 $\mu$M. Assuming a conversion yield of 2% from hydroxyl radicals to the adduct, the initial concentration of hydroxyl radicals in the PEF-treated cream could be 50 to 500 $\mu$M. It is likely that such low concentrations can also be observed in some heat-processed or slightly oxidised food samples.

Another series of questions concern micro-organisms present in PEF-treated foods. Could repeated treatments induce the formation of PEF-resistant mutants, or could genes from pathogenic organisms be transferred to other surviving organisms as a result of electroporation? Specialists indicate that gene transfer experiments necessitate much higher microbial concentrations than those found in foods. For the same reason, it is unlikely that the release in foods of microbial proteins and enzymes from electroporated cells could enhance allergenicity or other undesirable effects (Lelieveld et al., 2001).

## 18.10   Applications

Equipment for the continuous processing of liquid foods at $35-45\,kV\cdot cm^{-1}$ with a flow rate of several thousands litres per hour were commercially available from PurePulse Technologies (a subsidiary of Maxwell Laboratories, San Diego, California) until this firm suspended operations. Other manufacturers are active (such as Thomson CSF, Enertronic-A2E Technologies and Europulse in France, Ohio State University and Diversified Technologies Inc. in the US), having provided laboratory or pilot plant equipment for food investigations. Patents dealing with PEF processing are mainly related to the design of treatment chambers. A list of recent patents is provided in Section 18.13.

The most studied food application of electric pulses concerns the 'pasteurisation' of orange and other fruit juices at a maximum temperature of $50\,°C$, aiming at a $\geq 5$ log cycle inactivation ratio of yeast ascospores (the most resistant yeast form). The feasibility of this process is well demonstrated at pilot plant scale (see Qiu et al., 1998, Barbosa-Cánovas et al., 2000a, Yeom et al., 2002b and previous sections). If it is assumed that inactivation of vegetative microbial cells requires an energy density input of about $200\,J\cdot ml^{-1}$ (48 calories per ml, i.e., less than for heat pasteurisation), then the temperature increase caused by electric pulses will be close to $40-45\,°C$. If the inlet temperature of the juice is close to $5\,°C$, the maximum temperature will not exceed $50\,°C$. Alternatively, electric pulses can be delivered in several treatment chambers placed in series, with coolers inserted between chambers. A maximum product temperature of $65\,°C$, maintained for less than $10\,s$, may be effective also for partial enzyme inactivation (pectin methylesterase, polyphenoloxidase). Investigations have demonstrated that PEF processing, combined with aseptic packaging, will extend the refrigerated ($4\,°C$) storage of such 'fresh' juices to four months. Industrial implementation is expected in the near future, in the USA and Europe, although high quality fruit juices preserved by mild thermal pasteurisation and chilled storage are already well established on the market.

In 1996, the US Food and Drug Administration has released a 'letter of no-objection' for liquid eggs treated with PEF. Fruit juices have the additional advantage for microbial safety and stability of being acid foods with a pH below 4.5. It is, however, likely that regulatory authorities will request further experimental data concerning the equivalency of this novel physical process to existing thermal processes in terms of food safety, especially for non-acid foods (Lelieveld et al., 2001; Góngora-Nieto et al., 2002a, Stewart et al., 2002). This encompasses microbial safety (kinetics of inactivation of most resistant pathogenic and spoilage micro-organisms; minimum lethal treatment conditions; accurate measurements and control of treatment parameters; assurance that the entire product receives at least the minimum required dose in the industrial scaled-up process) and the absence of newly formed toxic substances in processed foods. It will be necessary to demonstrate that electrochemical phenomena do not produce significant amounts of substances such as chlorine or hydrogen peroxide, nor induce the transfer into the food of undesirable

**Table 18.4**   Potential food sanitation and/or preservation by pulsed electric field processing

| Acid fluid foods | Non-acid fluid foods |
|---|---|
| Orange juice and other citrus juices | Raw whole milk |
| Apple juice (fresh or from concentrate) | Pasteurised milks |
| Tomato concentrate, ketchup | Liquid dairy creams |
| Fruit purées | Vegetable juices and purées; soups |
| Salsa sauce, mayonnaise | Guacamole |
| Spaghetti sauce (with meat pieces?) | Liquid whole egg |
| Liquid yoghurt (with fruit pieces?) | Liquid egg white |
| Jams | Sauces, spreads, fillings |
| Wines | Aqueous flavour and aromatic suspensions |
| Soft drinks | Vegetable protein or polysaccharide |
| Carbonated drinks, beer | preparations |
| (with processing under sufficient pressure) | Syrups; honey |
| | Oil-in-water emulsions |
| | Minced meat, fish mince, surimi? |
| | Aqueous solutions of bioactive food |
| | substances |
| | Enzyme preparations? |

constituents from the treatment chamber or the electrodes.

Various potential applications of pulsed electric fields to acid or non acid foods have been investigated or discussed (Table 18.4). Such processing could extend the refrigerated storage life of heat-pasteurised milk, or sanitise raw milk for the preparation of traditional cheeses from raw milk. The inactivation of *Listeria monocytogenes* and other pathogens would constitute a primary target in this last case, but inactivation of the endogenous flora may also change the sensorial characteristics of the final cheeses. In liquid egg products, dairy protein preparations and other food ingredients, electric pulses could also be applied with the aim of inactivating pathogens (*Salmonella, Listeria,* etc.) and reducing the microbial load without altering colour, flavour or texture (including solubility, viscosity, gelling, emulsifying or foaming ability). Beneficial or detrimental changes in the functional properties of some proteins are not excluded, however, since electric pulses may possibly cause slight changes in conformation or induce the rearrangement of disulfide bonds (in egg, dairy or vegetable proteins). In the case of egg white, prior dialysis (Fernández-Diaz *et al.*, 2000), or ultrafiltration plus diafiltration (Jeantet *et al.*, 1999) was necessary to reduce the electrical conductivity before PEF processing. Reformulation with a lower salt content has been suggested before processing salsa or cheese sauce (Ruhlman *et al.*, 2001b). Other investigators, however, were able to significantly inactivate *Staphylococcus* and *Micrococcus* strains in a smokehouse brine (26% sodium chloride, w/w, 300 $mS \cdot cm^{-1}$), using low energy (0.2–0.4 $J \cdot ml^{-1} \cdot pulse^{-1}$) instant reversal pulses, at 60 $kV \cdot cm^{-1}$ and $-8\,^{\circ}C$ (Ho and Mittal, 2001). Various sauces could be 'cold-pasteurised' by PEF processing, and experiments have been carried out to stabilise wines without the need for adding $SO_2$.

Only pumpable fluids can be processed in continuous flow. The influence of solid particles of various sizes and electrical conductivities on microbial inactivation should be further investigated (Dunn, 2001, and Mañas-Perez et al., 2001). It is unlikely that small solid foods (fruit pieces or gels; fish fillets; fish eggs; shellfish and shrimps; slices of meat and cured meats), could be efficiently subjected to electric pulses in batch or continuous treatment chambers for microbial inactivation. Such solid foods should be thin (because high electric fields necessitate small inter-electrode gaps), relatively homogeneous (for uniform processing), and have high moisture and low salt contents. It may be necessary to process such products in a liquid of appropriate resistivity, since a poor contact between food and electrodes, or the presence of air bubbles or of fat may cause arcing and dielectric breakdown. It is also likely that membrane electro-permeabilisation would detrimentally affect the water retention and texture of animal or plant tissues processed by electric pulses. Indeed Gudmundsson and Hafsteinsson (2001) reported detrimental effects on chicken and especially salmon muscle, even at electric fields below $2\,kV\cdot cm^{-1}$ (40–60 pulses, room temperature). Cell size decreased markedly (by 66% for salmon, 39% for chicken), while in the case of salmon, extensive cell separation and leakage of collagen into extracellular gaps also occurred. In contrast, lumpfish roe resisted PEF processing up to $12\,kV\cdot cm^{-1}$ (12 pulses), and its firmness was not affected. The total microbial counts (endogenous flora) were reduced by 1 log cycle. Mañas-Perez et al. (2001) obtained a $> 2.5$ log cycle inactivation ratio of Escherichia coli introduced in a suspension of lumpfish eggs (pH 6.8, $2.5\,mS\cdot cm^{-1}$, egg diameter $= 1-2\,mm$) with 80 exponential pulses at $33\,kV\cdot cm^{-1}$ ($\tau = 1.7\,\mu s$, $f = 1\,Hz$, $W_t = 190\,J\cdot ml^{-1}$, $T_{max} = 40\,°C$), without apparent damage to the eggs.

Small solid foods can be processed with the objective of improving extraction or penetration of solutes. Permeabilisation of the cell membranes of plant tissues (apple, carrot, sugar beet, potato, etc.) by electric pulses of relatively low field strength $(0.1-5\,kV\cdot cm^{-1})$ indeed increases the juice yield, and decreases the need for cellulases and pectinases, while apparently improving the quality of the juices or extracts. The electrical cell permeabilisation in fruit or vegetable pieces and slices (paprika, pepper, carrot, mango, coconut, etc.) can also be used to accelerate subsequent compression dewatering, osmotic drying or air drying. Prior processing by electric pulses could improve the preparation of meat or yeast extracts, and the selective or quantitative extraction of pigments, flavours, antioxidants, sucrose, polysaccharides, enzymes, and of various biologically active substances from animal organs, plant tissues, cell cultures, algae, or micro-organisms. It may also be possible to accelerate the penetration of salts, sugars or other solutes in cell-based animal or vegetable foods. Such pre-treatments have been recently investigated (Knorr and Angersbach, 1998; Angersbach et al., 1999; Rastogi et al., 1999; Bazhal and Vorobiev, 2000; Bouzrara and Vorobiev, 2000, 2003; Bazhal et al., 2001; Knorr et al., 2001;

Ade-Omowaye *et al.*, 2001a, b, 2002; Lebovka *et al.*, 2000, 2001, 2002; Jemai and Vorobiev, 2002; Eshtiaghi and Knorr, 2002; Taiwo *et al.*, 2002a, b; Tedjo *et al.*, 2002; Teissié *et al.*, 2002; Fincan and Dejmek, 2002), but do not come directly under food preservation.

Among non-food biological applications of PEF, one can mention electrofusion of cells (used for the formation of plant hybrids) and electrotransformation (electrically mediated gene transfer, used at the bench level to obtain genetically modified organisms). Reversible electro-permeabilisation is also used for medical applications, e.g., for delivery of chemotherapeutic drugs into tumour cells, for gene therapy and for transdermal drug delivery. These effects require 10 $\mu$s to 1 ms pulses with electric fields of 1 to 10 kV·cm$^{-1}$ (Schoenbach *et al.*, 2002). According to these authors, high frequency pulses with $\tau$ values < 100 ns and electric fields > 50 kV·cm$^{-1}$, which have the potential to short out the cell membrane, and to permeabilise intracellular membranes, could dissipate high energy levels within subcellular organelles. This would affect various cellular metabolisms and possibly trigger apoptosis (programmed cell death). Intracellular electromanipulation may be used for cancer treatment.

Another non-food application of pulsed electric fields is the control of biofouling and disinfection of domestic, surface or waste waters (Abou-Ghazala and Schoenbach, 2000), including water in cooling towers downstream of power plants. Some of the targets are pathogenic micro-organisms (e.g., *Legionella*) and protozoa (amoeba, *Giarda* or *Cryptosporidium*). Low-field long-duration square wave repetitive pulses (20 times 10 ms at 0.5 kV·cm$^{-1}$) were found to be effective against *Legionella* in domestic water (< 1 mS·cm$^{-1}$) (Teissié *et al.*, 2002). For *Giardia* and *Cryptosporidium*, electrical pulses were selected which did not bring direct inactivation, but caused electro-permeabilisation, enhancing the penetration of external solutes (Cl$_2$, H$_2$O$_2$, or KMnO$_4$) and reducing the chemical doses necessary for cyst inactivation (Haas and Aturaliye, 1999a, b). In the case of amoeba, short pulses ($\mu$s) with a high field intensity (> 10 kV·cm$^{-1}$) were more cost-effective in obtaining inactivation in the absence of added chemicals (Vernhes *et al.*, 2002). Death was not due to irreversible electro-permeabilisation, and was maximum when the direction of the electric field was parallel to the direction of the liquid flow. Cell deformation in the direction of the flow may constitute a critical factor. An inactivation ratio of 2 log cycles was obtained for less than 1 MW when treating contaminated water at 1 m$^3$·s$^{-1}$.

The operating cost of an electric pulse process for the 'pasteurisation' of fluid foods has been evaluated to about US$0.2 per litre, probably including equipment depreciation (Góngora-Nieto *et al.*, 2002a). It is difficult at this stage to quote prices for industrial PEF processing lines. The reliability and the life-time of the electronic components used for pulsed electric field equipment should be considered. New solid-state switches should require less maintenance and renewal than previous components. Safety and measurement devices certainly constitute a notable part of capital investments. The need for pumps and aseptic packaging systems should also be taken into account. Energy costs can be reduced by using pulse types specially efficient for microbial inactivation (and causing little ohmic heating), and/or by combining several antimicrobial processes. It is likely that a combination of electric pulses and temperatures of 60–70 °C would reduce the need for high voltage (and capital-costly) pulses, while regenerative heat-exchange (to cool the outlet fluid while pre-heating the inlet fluid) would decrease both heating and cooling requirements. For a food fluid with a fixed electrical conductivity, and a specific PEF equipment and pulse type, once the pulse length and the electric field strength have been selected, it is recommended to determine the minimum energy density input (corresponding to the minimum number of pulses) necessary for a given microbial inactivation ratio, or for a given extension of shelf life. Thus, $1060 \, \mathrm{J \cdot ml^{-1}}$ (89 exponential decay pulses, $\tau = 1.84 \, \mu s$, $f = 3 \, \mathrm{Hz}$, 23–38 $\mathrm{kV \cdot cm^{-1}}$ profile in a coaxial chamber, $T_{max} = 35 \, ^\circ \mathrm{C}$, with 9-fold recirculation through the chamber) were found necessary to ensure sanitation and extend to 20 days the chilled shelf life of liquid whole egg (Góngora-Nieto *et al.*, 2003a). When 0.5% citric acid was added to the liquid whole egg before processing, 30 pulses corresponding to an electrical energy density input of $357 \, \mathrm{J \cdot ml^{-1}}$ gave a chilled shelf life of 22 days. On the basis of 0.06€ per kW·h, $357 \, \mathrm{kJ \cdot l^{-1}}$ corresponds to an energy cost of 0.6 $\mathrm{cent \cdot l^{-1}}$. Cooling requirements were estimated at a corresponding additional $357 \, \mathrm{J \cdot ml^{-1}}$.

The required energy density input for microbial inactivation is known to decrease when the pulse treatment is performed at higher field strengths (Heinz *et al.*, 2002). However high field strengths increase the risk of dielectric breakdown of the food matrix. They also require smaller inter-electrode gaps (leading to reduced flow rates for parallel plate or coaxial chambers), and/or costly higher voltage generators and switches. Thus, most PEF pilot plant units operate at a maximum field of $40 \, \mathrm{kV \cdot cm^{-1}}$.

The feasibility of partial or extended preservation of various liquid foods by PEF is well demonstrated. The food industry now has to establish whether increased safety, longer shelf life, improved flavour freshness and/or novelty can balance initial investments, process costs and regulatory hurdles.

## 18.11    Acknowledgements

We wish to thank Professor P. Merle, Université des Sciences et Techniques du Languedoc, Montpellier, and Professor J. Rosenbusch, University of Basel, for their help and advice. One of us (L.P.) benefits from a doctoral scholarship given by the Ministère de la Recherche et des Nouvelles Technologies, Paris.

## 18.12    References

ABOU-GHAZALA A and SCHOENBACH K H (2000), 'Biofouling prevention with pulsed electric fields', *IEEE Trans. Plasma Sci.*, 28, 115–121.

ADE-OMOWAYE B I O, ANGERSBACH A, TAIWO K A and KNORR K (2001a), 'Use of pulsed electric field pre-treatment to improve dehydration characteristics of plant based foods', *Trends Food Sci. Technol.*, 12, 285–295.

ADE-OMOWAYE B I O, RASTOGI N K, ANGERSBACH A and KNORR K (2001b), 'Effects of high hydrostatic pressure or high intensity electrical field pulse pre-treatment on dehydration characteristics of red paprika', *Innov. Food Sci. Emerg. Technol.*, 2, 1–7.

ADE-OMOWAYE B I O, RASTOGI N K, ANGERSBACH A and KNORR K (2002), 'Osmotic dehydration of bell peppers: influence of high intensity electric field pulses and elevated temperature treatment', *J. Food Eng.*, 54, 35–43.

ÁLVAREZ I, RASO J, PALOP A and SALA F J (2000), 'Influence of different factors on the inactivation of *Salmonella senftenberg* by pulsed electric fields', *Int. J. Food Microbiol.*, 55, 143–146.

ÁLVAREZ I, PAGAN R, RASO J and CONDON S (2002), 'Environmental factors influencing the inactivation of *Listeria monocytogenes* by pulsed electric fields', *Letters Appl. Microbiol.*, 35, 489–493.

ALY R E, JOSHI R P, STARK R H, SCHOENBACH K H and BEEBE S J (2001), 'Repair time of bacteria after pulsed electric field application', *IEEE Int. Conf. Plasma Sci.*, P2H09.

ANGERSBACH A, HEINZ V and KNORR D (1999), 'Electrophysiological model of intact and processed plant tissues: cell disintegration criteria', *Biotechnol. Progress*, 15, 753–762.

ANGERSBACH A, HEINZ V and KNORR D (2000), 'Effects of pulsed electric fields on cell membranes in real food systems', *Innov. Food Sci. Emerg. Technol.*, 1, 135–149.

ARONSSON K, LINDGREN M, JOHANSSON, B R and RÖNNER U (2001), 'Inactivation of microorganisms using pulsed electric fields: the influence of process parameters on *Escherichia coli*, *Listeria innocua*, *Leuconostoc mesenteroides* and *Saccharomyces cerevisiae*', *Innov. Food Sci. Emerg. Technol.*, 2, 41–54.

ARONSSON K and RÖNNER U (2001), 'Influence of pH, water activity and temperature on the inactivation of *Escherichia coli* and *Saccharomyces cerevisiae* by pulsed electric fields', *Innov. Food Sci. Emerg. Technol.*, 2, 105–112.

AYHAN Z, YEOM H W, ZHANG Q H and MIN D B (2001), 'Flavor, color and vitamin C retention of pulsed electric field processed orange juice in different packaging materials', *J. Agric. Food Chem.*, 49, 669–674.

AYHAN Z, ZHANG Q H and MIN D B (2002), 'Effects of pulsed electric field processing and storage on the quality and stability of single-strength orange juice', *J. Food Prot.*, 65, 1623–1627.

BARBOSA-CÁNOVAS G V and ZHANG Q H, eds (2001). *Pulsed Electric Fields in Food Processing: Fundamental Aspects and Applications*, Technomic Pub. Co., Lancaster (PA), USA.

BARBOSA-CÁNOVAS G V, GÓNGORA-NIETO M M, POTHAKAMURY U R and SWANSON B G (1999), *Preservation of Foods with Pulsed Electric Fields*, Academic Press, San Diego (CA), USA.

BARBOSA-CÁNOVAS G V, GÓNGORA-NIETO M M and SWANSON B G (2000a), 'Processing fruits and vegetables by pulsed electric field technology', in Barbosa-Cánovas G V, Góngora-Nieto M M, Swanson B G and Alzamora S M, eds, *Minimally Processed Fruits and Vegetables. Fundamental Aspects and Applications*, Aspen Pub. Inc., Gaithersburg (MD), USA, 223–235.

BARBOSA-CÁNOVAS G V, PIERSON M D, ZHANG Q H and SCHAFFNER D W (2000b), 'Pulsed

Electric Fields', *J. Food Sci.*, Supplement: Kinetics of Microbial Inactivation for Alternative Food Processing Technologies, 65–79.

BARBOSA-CÁNOVAS G V, GÓNGORA-NIETO M M and SWANSON B G (2001), 'Pulsed electric power in food preservation', *Int. Food Inform. System*, http://www.ifis.org/hottopics/pulsedpower.html.

BARSOTTI L (2000), 'Effets des champs électriques pulsés sur les caractéristiques biochimiques et physico-chimiques de constituants et structures protéiques alimentaires', Thesis, Université des Sciences et Techniques du Languedoc, Montpellier, France.

BARSOTTI L and CHEFTEL J C (1999), 'Food processing by pulsed electric fields. 2- Biological aspects', *Food Rev. Int.*, 15, 181–213.

BARSOTTI L, MERLE P and CHEFTEL J C (1999), 'Food processing by pulsed electric fields. 1– Physical aspects', *Food Rev. Int.*, 15, 163–180.

BARSOTTI L, DUMAY E, MU T H, FERNÁNDEZ-DIAZ M D and CHEFTEL J C (2002), 'Effects of high voltage electric pulses on protein-based food constituents and structures', *Trends Food Sci. Technol.*, 12, 136–144.

BAZHAL M I and VOROBIEV E (2000), 'Electric treatment of apple slices for intensifying juice pressing', *J. Sci. Food Agric.*, 80, 1668–1674.

BAZHAL M I, LEBOVKA N I and VOROBIEV E (2001), 'Pulsed electric field treatment of apple tissue during compression for juice extraction', *J. Food Eng.*, 50, 129–139.

BEEBE S J, FOX P M, REC L J, SOMERS K, STARK R H and SCHOENBACH K H (2002), 'Nanosecond pulsed electric field effects on cells and tissues: apoptosis induction and tumor growth inhibition', *IEEE Trans. Plasma Sci.*, 30, 286–292.

BENDICHO S, BARBOSA-CÁNOVAS G V and MARTÍN O (2002a), 'Milk processing by high intensity pulsed electric fields', *Trends Food Sci. Technol.*, 13, 195–204.

BENDICHO S, ESPACHS A, ARÁNTEGUI J and MARTÍN O (2002b), 'Effect of high intensity pulsed electric fields and heat treatments on vitamins of milk', *J. Dairy Res.*, 69, 113–123.

BENDICHO S, ESTELA C, GINER J, BARBOSA-CÁNOVAS G V and MARTÍN O (2002c), 'Effects of high intensity pulsed electric field and thermal treatments on a lipase from *Pseudomonas fluorescens*', *J. Dairy Sci.*, 85, 19–27.

BIGELOW W D (1921), 'The logarithmic nature of thermal death time curves', *J. Infect. Dis.*, 29, 528–536.

BOUZRARA H and VOROBIEV E (2000), 'Beet juice extraction by pressing and pulsed electric fields', *Int. Sugar J.*, 102, 194–200.

BOUZRARA H and VOROBIEV E (2003), 'Solid-liquid expression of cellular materials enhanced by pulsed electric field', *Chem. Eng. Process.*, 42, 249–257.

BRUHN R E, PEDROW P D, OLSEN R G, BARBOSA-CÁNOVAS G V and SWANSON B G (1998), 'Heat conduction in microbes exposed to pulsed electric fields', *IEEE Trans. Dielectrics Electrical Insulation*, 5, 878–885.

CALDERÓN-MIRANDA M L, BARBOSA-CÁNOVAS G V and SWANSON B G (1999a), 'Inactivation of *Listeria innocua* in skim milk by pulsed electric fields and nisin', *Int. J. Food Microbiol.*, 51, 19–30.

CALDERÓN-MIRANDA M L, BARBOSA-CÁNOVAS G V and SWANSON B G (1999b), 'Transmission electron microscopy of *Listeria innocua* treated by pulsed electric fields and nisin in skim milk', *Int. J. Food Microbiol.*, 51, 31–38.

CALDERÓN-MIRANDA M L, BARBOSA-CÁNOVAS G V and SWANSON B G (1999c), 'Inactivation of *Listeria innocua* in liquid whole egg by pulsed electric fields and nisin', *Int. J. Food Microbiol.*, 51, 7–17.

CAPLOT M and COTE G (1999), 'Les technologies nécessaires aux machines de traitement par champs électriques pulsés', in *Formation technologique en agro-alimentaire: la conservation de demain*, AGIR & NOVELECT, Bordeaux, France.

CASTRO A J, SWANSON B G, BARBOSA-CÁNOVAS G V and DUNKER A K (2001a), 'Pulsed electric field denaturation of bovine alkaline phosphatase', in Barbosa-Cánovas G V and Zhang Q H, eds, *Pulsed Electric Fields in Food Processing: Fundamental Aspects and Applications*, Technomic Pub. Co., Lancaster (PA), USA, 83–103.

CASTRO A J, SWANSON B G, BARBOSA-CÁNOVAS G V and ZHANG Q H (2001b), 'Pulsed electric field modification of milk alkaline phosphatase activity', in Barbosa-Cánovas G V and Zhang Q H, eds, *Pulsed Electric Fields in Food Processing: Fundamental Aspects and Applications*, Technomic Pub. Co., Lancaster (PA), USA, 65–82.

COLE M B, DAVIES K W, MUNRO G, HOLYOAK C D and KILSBY D C (1993), 'A vitalistic model to describe the thermal inactivation of *Listeria monocytogenes*', *J. Industrial Microbiol.*, 12, 232–239.

CSERHALMI Z, VIDÁCS I, BECZNER J and CZUKOR B (2002), 'Inactivation of *Saccharomyces cerevisiae* and *Bacillus cereus* by pulsed electric fields technology', *Innov. Food Sci. Emerg. Technol.*, 3, 41–45.

DAMAR S, BOZOĞLU F, HIZAL M and BAYINDIRLI A (2002), 'Inactivation and injury of *Escherichia coli* O157:H7 and *Staphylococcus aureus* by pulsed electric fields', *World J. Microbiol. Biotechnol.*, 18, 1–6.

DUNN J (2001), 'Pulsed electric field processing: an overview', in Barbosa-Cánovas G V and Zhang Q H, eds, *Pulsed Electric Fields in Food Processing: Fundamental Aspects and Applications*, Lancaster (PA), USA, Technomic Pub. Co., 1–30.

DUTREUX N, NOTERMANS S, GÓNGORA-NIETO M M, BARBOSA-CÁNOVAS G V and SWANSON B G (2000a), 'Effects of combined exposure of *Micrococcus luteus* to nisin and pulsed electric fields', *Int. J. Food Microbiol.*, 60, 147–152.

DUTREUX N, NOTERMANS S, WIJTZES T, GÓNGORA-NIETO M M, BARBOSA-CÁNOVAS G V and SWANSON, B G (2000b), 'Pulsed electric fields inactivation of attached and free-living *Escherichia coli* and *Listeria innocua* under several conditions', *Int. J. Food Microbiol.*, 54, 91–98.

ESHTIAGHI M N and KNORR D (2002), 'High electric field pulse pre-treatment: potential for sugar beet processing', *J. Food Eng.*, 52, 265–272.

EVRENDILEK G A, ZHANG Q H and RICHTER E R (1999), 'Inactivation of *Escherichia coli* O157:H7 and *Escherichia coli* 8739 in apple juice by pulsed electric fields', *J. Food Prot.*, 62, 793–796.

EVRENDILEK G A, JIN Z T, RUHLMAN K T, QIU X, ZHANG Q H and RICHTER E R (2000), 'Microbial safety and shelf-life of apple juice and cider processed by bench and pilot scale PEF systems', *Innov. Food Sci. Emerg. Technol.*, 1, 77–86.

EVRENDILEK G A, DANTZER W R, STREAKER C B, RATANATRIWONG P and ZHANG Q H (2001), 'Shelf-life evaluations of liquid foods treated by pilot plant pulsed electric field system', *J. Food Process. Preserv.*, 25, 283–297.

FERNÁNDEZ-DIAZ M D, BARSOTTI L, DUMAY E and CHEFTEL J C (2000), 'Effects of pulsed electric fields on ovalbumin solutions and on liquid egg white', *J. Agric. Food Chem.*, 48, 2332–2339.

FERNÁNDEZ-MOLINA J J, BARKSTROM E, TORSTENSSON P, BARBOSA-CÁNOVAS G V and SWANSON B G (2001), 'Inactivation of *Listeria innocua* and *Pseudomonas fluorescens* in skim milk treated with pulsed electric fields', in Barbosa-Cánovas G V and Zhang Q H, eds, *Pulsed Electric Fields in Food Processing: Fundamental Aspects and Applications*, Technomic Pub. Co., Lancaster (PA), USA, 149–166.

FIALA A, WOUTERS P C, VAN DEN BOSCH E and CREYGHTON, Y L M (2001), 'Coupled electrical-fluid model of pulsed electric field treatment in a model food system', *Innov. Food Sci. Technol.*, 2, 229–238.

FINCAN M and DEJMEK P (2002), '*In situ* visualization of the effect of a pulsed electric field on plant tissue', *J. Food Eng.*, 55, 223–230.

GINER J, GIMENO V, ESPACHS A, ELEZ P, BARBOSA-CÁNOVAS G V and MARTÍN O (2000), 'Inhibition of tomato pectin methylesterase by pulsed electric fields', *Innov. Food Sci. Emerg. Technol.*, 1, 57–67.

GINER J, GIMENO V, BARBOSA-CÁNOVAS G V and MARTÍN O (2001), 'Effects of pulsed electric field processing on apple and pear polyphenoloxidases', *Food Sci. Technol. Int.*, 7, 339–345.

GINER J, ORTEGA M, MESEGUÉ M, GIMENO V, BARBOSA-CÁNOVAS G V and MARTÍN O (2002), 'Inactivation of peach polyphenoloxidase by exposure to pulsed electric fields', *J. Food Sci.*, 67, 1467–1472.

GÓNGORA-NIETO M M, SEIGNOUR L, RIQUET P, DAVIDSON P M, BARBOSA-CÁNOVAS G V and SWANSON B G (2001), 'Nonthermal inactivation of *Pseudomonas fluorescens* in liquid whole egg', in Barbosa-Cánovas G V and Zhang Q H, eds, *Pulsed Electric Fields in Food Processing: Fundamental Aspects and Applications*, Lancaster (PA), USA, Technomic Pub. Co., 193–211.

GÓNGORA-NIETO M M, SEPÚLVEDA D R, PEDROW P, BARBOSA-CÁNOVAS G V and SWANSON B G (2002a), 'Food processing by pulsed electric fields: treatment delivery, inactivation level, and regulatory aspects', *Lebensm. Wiss. Technol.*, 35, 375–388.

GÓNGORA-NIETO M M, YOUNCE F, HYDE G M, PEDROW P D, SWANSON B G and BARBOSA-CÁNOVAS G V (2002b), 'Metrology system for pulsed electric fields processing', *Innov. Food Sci. Emerg. Technol.*, 3, 337–348.

GÓNGORA-NIETO M M, PEDROW P D, SWANSON B G and BARBOSA-CÁNOVAS G V (2003a), 'Energy analysis of liquid whole egg pasteurized by pulsed electric fields', *J. Food Eng.*, 57, 209–216.

GÓNGORA-NIETO M M, PEDROW P D, SWANSON B G and BARBOSA-CÁNOVAS G V (2003b), 'Impact of air bubbles in a dielectric liquid when subjected to high field strengths', *Innov. Food Sci. Emerg. Technol.*, 4, 57–67.

GUDMUNDSSON M and HAFSTEINSSON H (2001), 'Effect of electric field pulses on microstructure of muscle foods and roes', *Trends Food Sci. Technol.*, 12, 122–128.

DE HAAN S W H and WILLCOCK P R (2002), 'Comparison of the energy performance of pulse generation circuits for PEF', *Innov. Food Sci. Emerg. Technol.*, 3, 349–356.

HAAS C N and ATURALIYE D (1999a), 'Semi-quantitative characterisation of electroporation-assisted disinfection processes for inactivation of *Giardia* and *Cryptosporidium*', *J. Appl. Microbiol.*, 86, 899–905.

HAAS C N and ATURALIYE D (1999b), 'Kinetics of electroporation-assisted chlorination of *Giardia muris*', *Water Res.*, 33, 1761–1766.

HARRISON S L, BARBOSA-CÁNOVAS G V and SWANSON B G (2001a), 'Pulsed electric field and high hydrostatic pressure induced leakage of cellular material from *Saccharomyces cerevisiae*', in Barbosa-Cánovas G V and Zhang Q H, eds, *Pulsed Electric Fields in Food Processing: Fundamental Aspects and Applications*, Lancaster (PA), USA, Technomic Pub. Co., 183–191.

HARRISON S L, CHANG F J, BOYLSTON T, BARBOSA-CÁNOVAS G V and SWANSON B G (2001b), 'Shelf stability, sensory analysis, and volatile flavor profile of raw apple juice after pulsed electric field, high hydrostatic pressure, or heat exchanger processing', in Barbosa-Cánovas G V and Zhang Q H, eds, *Pulsed Electric Fields in Food*

*Processing: Fundamental Aspects and Applications*, Lancaster (PA), USA, Technomic Pub. Co., 241–257.

HEINZ V and KNORR D (2000), 'Effect of pH, ethanol addition and high hydrostatic pressure on the inactivation of *Bacillus subtilis* by pulsed electric fields', *Innov. Food Sci. Emerg. Technol.*, 1, 151–159.

HEINZ V, PHILLIPS S T, ZENKER M and KNORR D (1999), 'Inactivation of *Bacillus subtilis* by high intensity pulsed electric fields under close to isothermal conditions', *Food Biotechnol.*, 13, 155–168.

HEINZ V, ÁLVAREZ I, ANGERSBACH A and KNORR D (2002), 'Preservation of liquid foods by high intensity pulsed electric fields – basic concepts for process design', *Trends Food Sci. Technol.*, 12, 103–111.

HO S Y and MITTAL G S (2000), 'High voltage pulsed electrical field for liquid food pasteurization', *Food Rev. Int.*, 16, 395-434.

HO S Y and MITTAL G S (2001), 'Non-thermal inactivation in waste brine using high-voltage low-energy electrical pulses', *Innov. Food Sci. Emerg. Technol.*, 2, 251–259.

HODGINS A M, MITTAL G S and GRIFFITHS M W (2002), 'Pasteurisation of fresh orange juice using low-energy pulsed electrical field', *J. Food Sci.*, 67, 2294–2299.

HÜLSHEGER H, POTEL J and NIEMANN E G (1981), 'Killing of bacteria with electric pulses of high field strength', *Radiation Environ. Biophys.*, 20, 53–65.

IU J, MITTAL G S and GRIFFITHS M W (2001), 'Reduction in levels of *Escherichia coli* O157:H7 in apple cider by pulsed electric fields', *J. Food Prot.*, 64, 964–969.

JEANTET R, BARON F, NAU F, ROIGNANT M and BRULÉ G (1999), 'High intensity pulsed electric fields applied to egg white: effect on *Salmonella enteritidis* inactivation and protein denaturation', *J. Food Prot.*, 62, 1381–1386.

JEMAI A B and VOROBIEV E (2002), 'Effect of moderate electric field pulses on the diffusion coefficient of soluble substances from apple slices', *Int. J. Food Sci. Technol.*, 37, 73–86.

JEYAMKONDAN S, JAYAS D S and HOLLEY R A (1999), 'Pulsed electric field processing of foods: a review', *J. Food Prot.*, 62, 1088–1096.

JIA M, ZHANG Q H and MIN D B (1999), 'Pulsed electric field processing effects on flavor compounds and microorganisms of orange juice', *Food Chem.*, 65, 445–451.

JIN Z T, SU Y, TUHELA L, ZHANG Q H, SASTRY S K and YOUSEF A E (2001), 'Inactivation of *Bacillus subtilis* spores using high voltage pulsed electric fields', in Barbosa-Cánovas G V and Zhang Q H, eds, *Pulsed Electric Fields in Food Processing: Fundamental Aspects and Applications*, Lancaster (PA), USA, Technomic Pub. Co., 167–181.

JIN Z T and ZHANG Q H (1999), Pulsed electric field inactivation of micro-organisms and preservation of quality of cranberry juice', *J. Food Process. Preserv.*, 23, 481–497.

DE JONG P and VAN HEESCH E J M (1998), 'Review: effect of pulsed electric fields on the quality of food products', *Milchwissenschaft*, 53, 4–8.

KATSUKI S, MAJIMA T, NAGATA K, LISITYN A, AKIYAMA H, FURUTA M, HAYASHI T, TAKAHASHI K and WIRKNER S (2000), 'Inactivation of *Bacillus stearothermophilus* by pulsed electric field', *IEEE Trans. Plasma Sci.*, 28, 155–160.

KHADRE M A and YOUSEF A E (2002), 'Susceptibility of human rotavirus to ozone, high pressure, and pulsed electric field', *J. Food Prot.*, 65, 1441–1446.

KNORR D and ANGERSBACH A (1998), 'Impact of high intensity electric field pulse on plant membrane permeabilisation', *Trends Food Sci. Technol.*, 9, 185–191.

KNORR D, ANGERSBACH A, ESHTIAGHI M N, HEINZ V and LEE D U (2001), 'Processing concepts based on high intensity electric field pulses', *Trends Food Sci. Technol.*, 12, 129–135.

LEBOVKA N I, BAZHAL M I and VOROBIEV E (2000), 'Simulation and experimental investigation of food material breakage using pulsed electric field treatment', *J. Food Eng.*, 44, 213–223.

LEBOVKA N I, BAZHAL M I and VOROBIEV E (2001), 'Pulsed electric field breakage of cellular tissues: visualisation of percolative properties', *Innov. Food Sci. Emerg. Technol.*, 2, 113–125.

LEBOVKA N I, BAZHAL M I and VOROBIEV E (2002), 'Estimation of characteristic damage time of food materials in pulsed-electric fields', *J. Food Eng.*, 54, 337–346.

LELIEVELD H L M, WOUTERS P C and LEÓN A E (2001), 'Pulsed electric field treatment of food and product safety assurance', in Barbosa-Cánovas G V and Zhang Q H, eds, *Pulsed Electric Fields in Food Processing: Fundamental Aspects and Applications*, Lancaster (PA), USA, Technomic Pub. Co., 259–263.

LIANG Z, MITTAL G S and GRIFFITHS M W (2002), 'Inactivation of *Salmonella typhimurium* in orange juice containing antimicrobial agents by pulsed electric field', *J. Food Prot.*, 65, 1081–1087.

LINDGREN M (2001), 'Pulsed electric field food treatment and low frequency bioelectromagnetics', Thesis, Chalmers University of Technology, Göteborg, Sweden.

LINDGREN M, ARONSSON K, GALT S and OHLSSON T (2002), 'Simulation of the temperature increase in pulsed electric field continuous flow treatment chambers', *Innov. Food Sci. Emerg. Technol.*, 3, 233–245.

LOSKE A M, ALVAREZ U M, HERNÁNDEZ-GALICIA C, CASTAÑO-TOSTADO E and PRIETO F E (2002), 'Bactericidal effect of underwater shock waves on *Escherichia coli* ATCC 10536 suspensions', *Innov. Food Sci. Emerg. Technol.*, 3, 321–327.

MA L, CHANG F J, GÓNGORA-NIETO M M, BARBOSA-CÁNOVAS G V and SWANSON B G (2001), 'Comparison study of pulsed electric fields, high hydrostatic pressure, and thermal processing on the electrophoretic patterns of liquid whole eggs', in Barbosa-Cánovas G V and Zhang Q H, eds, *Pulsed Electric Fields in Food Processing: Fundamental Aspects and Applications*, Lancaster (PA), USA, Technomic Pub. Co., 225–239.

MCDONALD C J, LLOYD S W, VITALE M A, PETERSSON K and INNINGS F (2000), 'Effects of pulsed electric fields on microorganisms in orange juice using electric field strengths 30 and 50 kV/cm', *J. Food Sci.*, 65, 984–989.

MACGREGOR S J, FARISH O, FOURACRE R, ROWAN N J and ANDERSON J G (2000), 'Inactivation of pathogenic and spoilage microorganisms in a test liquid using pulsed electric fields', *IEEE Trans. Plasma Sci.*, 28, 144–149.

MAÑAS-PEREZ P, BARSOTTI L and CHEFTEL J C (2001), 'Microbial inactivation by pulsed electric fields in a batch treatment chamber: effects of some electrical parameters and food constituents', *Innov. Food Sci. Emerg. Technol.*, 2, 239–249.

MARSILI L, ESPIE S, ANDERSON J G and MACGREGOR, S J (2002), 'Plasma inactivation of food-related microorganisms in liquids', *Radiation Phys. Chem.*, 65, 507–513.

NEUMANN E (1986), 'Chemical electric field effects in biological macromolecules', *Prog. Biophys. Molec. Biol.*, 47, 197–231.

OHSHIMA T, OKUYAMA K and SATO M (2002), 'Effect of culture temperature on high-voltage pulse sterilisation of *Escherichia coli*', *J. Electrostatics*, 55, 227–235.

PAGÁN R, ESPLUGAS S, GÓNGORA-NIETO M M, BARBOSA-CÁNOVAS G V and SWANSON B G (1998), 'Inactivation of *Bacillus subtilis* spores using high intensity pulsed electric fields in combination with other food conservation technologies', *Food Sci. Technol. Int.*, 4, 33–44.

PALOMEQUE L A, GÓNGORA-NIETO M M, BERMÚDEZ A S, BARBOSA-CÁNOVAS G V and SWANSON B G (2001), 'Nonthermal inactivation of endoproteases by pulsed electric field technology', in Barbosa-Cánovas G V and Zhang Q H, eds, *Pulsed Electric Fields in Food Processing: Fundamental Aspects and Applications*, Technomic Pub. Co., Lancaster (PA), USA, 135–147.

PELEG M (1995), 'A model of microbial survival after exposure to pulsed electric fields', *J. Sci. Food Agric.*, 67, 93–99.

PICART L, DUMAY E and CHEFTEL J C (2002), 'Inactivation of *Listeria innocua* in dairy fluids by pulsed electric fields: influence of electric parameters and food composition', *Innov. Food Sci. Emerg. Technol.*, 3, 357–369.

POL I E, MASTWIJK H C, BARTELS P V and SMID E J (2000), 'Pulsed-electric field treatment enhances the bactericidal action of nisin against *Bacillus cereus*', *Appl. Environ. Microbiol.*, 66, 428–430.

POL I E, MASTWIJK H C, SLUMP R A, POPA M E and SMID E J (2001a), 'Influence of food matrix on inactivation of *Bacillus cereus* by combinations of nisin, pulsed electric field treatment, and carvacrol', *J. Food Prot.*, 64, 1012–1018.

POL I E, VAN ARENDONK W G C, MASTWIJK H C, KROMMER J, SMID E J and MOEZELAAR R (2001b), 'Sensitivities of germinating spores and carvacrol-adapted vegetative cells and spores of *Bacillus cereus* to nisin and pulsed-electric-field treatment', *Appl. Environ. Microbiol.*, 67, 1693–1699.

QIU X, SHARMA S, TUHELA L, JIA M and ZHANG Q H (1998), 'An integrated PEF pilot plant for continuous nonthermal pasteurization of fresh orange juice', *Trans. ASAE*, 41, 1069–1074.

RASO J, CALDERÓN M L, GÓNGORA M, BARBOSA-CÁNOVAS G V and SWANSON B G (1998a), 'Inactivation of mold ascospores and conidiospores suspended in fruit juices by pulsed electric fields', *Lebensm. Wiss. Technol.*, 3, 668–672.

RASO J, CALDERÓN M L, GÓNGORA M, BARBOSA-CÁNOVAS G V and SWANSON B G (1998b), 'Inactivation of *Zygosaccharomyces bailii* in fruit juices by heat, high hydrostatic pressure and pulsed electric fields', *J. Food Sci.*, 63, 1042–1044.

RASO J, ÁLVAREZ I, CONDÓN S and SALA TREPAT F J (2000), 'Predicting inactivation of *Salmonella senftenberg* by pulsed electric fields', *Innov. Food Sci. Emerg. Technol.*, 1, 21–29.

RASTOGI N K, ESHTIAGHI M N and KNORR D (1999), 'Accelerated mass transfer during osmotic dehydration of high intensity electrical field pulse pretreated carrots', *J. Food Sci.*, 64, 1020–1023.

RAVISHANKAR S, FLEISCHMAN G J and BALASUBRAMANIAM V M (2002), 'The inactivation of *Escherichia coli* O157:H7 during pulsed electric field (PEF) treatment in a static chamber', *Food Microbiol.*, 19, 351–361.

REINA L D, JIN Z T, ZHANG Q H and YOUSEF A E (1998), 'Inactivation of *Listeria monocytogenes* in milk by pulsed electric field', *J. Food Prot.*, 61, 1203–1206.

RODRIGO D, MARTÍNEZ A, HARTE F, BARBOSA-CÁNOVAS G V and RODRIGO M (2001), 'Study of inactivation of *Lactobacillus plantarum* in orange-carrot juice by means of pulsed electric fields: comparison of inactivation kinetics models', *J. Food Prot.*, 64, 259–263.

RODRIGO D, RUÍZ P, BARBOSA-CÁNOVAS G V, MARTÍNEZ A and RODRIGO M (2003), 'Kinetic model for the inactivation of *Lactobacillus plantarum* by pulsed electric fields', *Int. J. Food Microbiol.*, 81, 223–229.

ROWAN N J, MACGREGOR S J, ANDERSON J G, FOURACRE R A and FARISH O (2000), 'Pulsed electric field inactivation of diarrhoeagenic *Bacillus cereus* through irreversible electroporation', *Letters Appl. Microbiol.*, 31, 110–114.

ROWAN N J, MACGREGOR S J, ANDERSON J G, CAMERON D and FARISH O (2001), 'Inactivation of *Mycobacterium paratuberculosis* by pulsed electric fields', *Appl. Environ. Microbiol.*, 67, 2833–2836.

RUHLMAN K T, JIN Z T and ZHANG Q H (2001a), 'Physical properties of liquid foods for pulsed electric field treatment', in Barbosa-Cánovas G V and Zhang Q H, eds, *Pulsed Electric Fields in Food Processing: Fundamental Aspects and Applications*, Technomic Pub. Co., Lancaster (PA), USA, 45–56.

RUHLMAN K T, JIN Z T, ZHANG Q H, CHISM G W and HARPER W J (2001b), 'Reformulation of a cheese sauce and salsa to be processed using pulsed electric fields', in Barbosa-Cánovas G V and Zhang Q H, eds, *Pulsed Electric Fields in Food Processing: Fundamental Aspects and Applications*, Technomic Pub. Co., Lancaster (PA), USA, 213–223.

RUSSELL N J (2002), 'Bacterial membranes: the effects of chill storage and food processing. An overview', *Int. J. Food Microbiol.*, 79, 27–34.

RUSSELL N J, COLLEY M, SIMPSON R K, TRIVETT A J and EVANS R I (2000), 'Mechanism of action of pulsed high electric field (PHEF) on the membranes of food-poisoning bacteria is an "all-or-nothing" effect', *Int. J. Food Microbiol.*, 55, 133–136.

SALE A J H and HAMILTON W A (1968), 'Effects of high electric fields on micro-organisms. III. Lysis of erythrocytes and protoplasts', *Biochim. Biophys. Acta*, 163, 37–43.

SATO M, ISHIDA N M, SUGIARTO A T, OHSHIMA T and TANIGUCHI H (2001) 'High-efficiency sterilizer by high-voltage pulse using concentrated-field electrode system', *IEEE Trans. Ind. Appl.*, 37, 1646–1650.

SCHOENBACH K H, JOSHI R P, STARK R H, DOBBS F C and BEEBE S J (2000), 'Bacterial decontamination of liquids with pulsed electric fields', *IEEE Trans. Dielectrics Electrical Insulation,* 7, 637–645.

SCHOENBACH K H, KATSUKI S, STARK R H, BUESCHER E S and BEEBE S J (2002), 'Bioelectrics – new applications for pulsed power technology', *IEEE Trans. Plasma Sci.*, 30, 293–300.

SELMA M V, FERNÁNDEZ P S, VALERO M and SALMERÓN M C (2003), 'Control of *Enterobacter aerogenes* by high-intensity, pulsed electric fields in horchata, a Spanish low-acid vegetable beverage', *Food Microbiol.*, 20, 105–110.

SENSOY I, ZHANG Q H and SASTRY S K (1997), 'Inactivation kinetics of *Salmonella dublin* by pulsed electric field', *J. Food Process Eng.*, 20, 367–381.

SEPÚLVEDA-AHUMADA D R, ORTEGA-RIVAS E and BARBOSA-CÁNOVAS G V (2000), 'Quality aspects of cheddar cheese obtained with milk pasteurised by pulsed electric fields', *Trans. IChemE*, 78, part C, 65–71.

SIMPSON R K, WHITTINGTON R, EARNSHAW R and RUSSELL N J (1999), 'Pulsed high electric field causes "all or nothing" membrane damage in *Listeria monocytogenes* and *Salmonella typhimurium*, but membrane H$^+$- ATPase is not a primary target', *Int. J. Food Microbiol.*, 48, 1–10.

SMELT J P P M, HELLEMONS J C, WOUTERS P C and VAN GERWEN S J C (2002), 'Physiological and mathematical aspects in setting criteria for decontamination of foods by physical means', *Int. J. Food Microbiol.*, 78, 57–77.

SMITH K, MITTAL G S and GRIFFITHS M W (2002), 'Pasteurization of milk using pulsed electrical field and antimicrobials', *J. Food Sci.*, 67, 2304–2308.

STEWART C M, TOMPKIN R B and COLE M B (2002), 'Food safety: new concept for the new millennium', *Innov. Food Sci. Emerg. Technol.*, 3, 105–112.

TAIWO K A, ANGERSBACH A and KNORR D (2002a), 'Influence of high intensity electric field pulses and osmotic dehydration on the rehydration characteristics of apple slices at different temperatures', *J. Food Eng.*, 52, 185–192.

TAIWO K A, ANGERSBACH A and KNORR D (2002b), 'Rehydration studies on pretreated and osmotically dehydrated apple slices', *J. Food Sci.*, 67, 842–847.

TEDJO W, TAIWO K A, ESHTIAGHI M N and KNORR D (2002), 'Comparison of pretreatment methods on water and solid diffusion kinetics of osmotically dehydrated mangoes', *J. Food Eng.*, 53, 133–142.

TEISSIÉ J, EYNARD N, VERNHES M C, BÉNICHOU A, GANEVA V, GALUTZOV B and CABANES P A (2002), 'Recent biotechnological developments of electropulsation. A prospective review', *Bioelectrochem.*, 55, 107–112.

TEREBIZNIK M R, JAGUS R J, CERRUTTI P, DE HUERGO M S and PILOSOF A M R (2000), 'Combined effect of nisin and pulsed electric fields on the inactivation of *Escherichia coli*', *J. Food Prot.*, 63, 741–746.

TEREBIZNIK M R, JAGUS R J, CERRUTTI P, DE HUERGO M S and PILOSOF A M R (2002), 'Inactivation of *Escherichia coli* by a combination of nisin, pulsed electric fields, and water activity reduction by sodium chloride', *J. Food Prot.*, 65, 1253–1258.

UEMURA K and ISOBE S (2002), 'Developing a new apparatus for inactivating *Escherichia coli* in saline water with high electric field AC', *J. Food Eng.*, 53, 203–207.

UEMURA K and ISOBE S (2003), 'Developing a new apparatus for inactivating *Bacillus subtilis* in orange juice with high electric field AC under pressurized conditions', *J. Food Eng.*, 56, 325–329.

ULMER H M, HEINZ V, GÄNZLE M G, KNORR D and VOGEL R F (2002), 'Effects of pulsed electric fields on inactivation and metabolic activity of *Lactobacillus plantarum* in model beer', *J. Appl. Microbiol.*, 93, 326–335.

UNAL R, KIM J G and YOUSEF A E (2001), 'Inactivation of *Escherichia coli* O157:H7, *Listeria monocytogenes*, and *Lactobacillus leichmannii* by combinations of ozone and pulsed electric field', *J. Food Prot.*, 64, 777–782.

UNAL R, YOUSEF A E and DUNNE C P (2002), 'Spectrofluorimetric assessment of bacterial cell membrane damage by pulsed electric field', *Innov. Food Sci. Emerg. Technol.*, 3, 247–254.

VAN LOEY A, VERACHTERT B and HENDRICKX M (2002), 'Effects of high electric field pulses on enzymes', *Innov. Food Sci. Emerg. Technol.*, 12, 94–102.

VEGA-MERCADO H, POWERS J R, BARBOSA-CÁNOVAS G V and SWANSON B G (2001a), 'Effect of added calcium and EDTA on the inactivation of a protease from *Pseudomonas fluorescens* M3/6 when exposed to pulsed electric fields', in Barbosa-Cánovas G V and Zhang Q H, eds, *Pulsed Electric Fields in Food Processing: Fundamental Aspects and Applications*, Technomic Pub. Co., Lancaster (PA), USA, 121–134.

VEGA-MERCADO H, POWERS J R, MARTÍN-BELLOSO O, LUEDECKE L, BARBOSA-CÁNOVAS G V and SWANSON B G (2001b), 'Changes in susceptibility of proteins to proteolysis and the inactivation of an extracellular protease from *Pseudomonas fluorescens* M3/6 when exposed to pulsed electric fields', in Barbosa-Cánovas G V and Zhang Q H, eds, *Pulsed Electric Fields in Food Processing: Fundamental Aspects and Applications*, Technomic Pub. Co., Lancaster (PA), USA, 105–120.

VERNHES M C, BENICHOU A, PERNIN P, CABANES P A and TEISSIÉ J (2002), 'Elimination of free-living amoebae in fresh water with pulsed electric fields', *Water Res.*, 36, 3429–3438.

WEIBULL W (1951), 'A statistical distribution function of wide applicability', *J. Appl.*

*Mech*, 51, 293–297.

WOUTERS P C (2001), 'Pulsed electric field inactivation of microorganisms', Thesis, Technical University of Berlin, Germany.

WOUTERS P C and SMELT J P P M (1997), 'Inactivation of micro-organisms with pulsed electric fields: potential for food preservation', *Food Biotechnol.*, 11, 193–229.

WOUTERS P C, DUTREUX N, SMELT J P P M and LELIEVELD H L M (1999), 'Effects of pulsed electric fields on inactivation kinetics of *Listeria innocua*', *Appl. Environ. Microbiol.*, 65, 5364–5371.

WOUTERS P C, ÁLVAREZ I and RASO J (2001a), 'Critical factors determining inactivation kinetics by pulsed electric field food processing', *Trends Food Sci. Technol.*, 12, 112–121.

WOUTERS P C, BOS A P and UECKERT J (2001b), 'Membrane permeabilization in relation to inactivation kinetics of *Lactobacillus* species due to pulsed electric fields', *Appl. Environ. Microbiol.*, 67, 3092–3101.

YEOM H W, STREAKER C B, ZHANG Q H and MIN D B (2000a), 'Effects of pulsed electric fields on the activities of microorganisms and pectin methyl esterase in orange juice', *J. Food Sci.*, 65, 1359–1363.

YEOM H W, STREAKER C B, ZHANG Q H and MIN D B (2000b), 'Effects of pulsed electric fields on the quality of orange juice and comparison with heat pasteurization', *J. Agric. Food Chem.*, 48, 4597–4605.

YEOM H W and ZHANG Q H (2001), 'Enzymatic inactivation by pulsed electric fields: a review', in Barbosa-Cánovas G V and Zhang Q H, eds, *Pulsed Electric Fields in Food Processing: Fundamental Aspects and Applications*, Technomic Pub. Co., Lancaster (PA), USA, 57–63.

YEOM H W, ZHANG Q H and DUNNE C P (1999), 'Inactivation of papain by pulsed electric fields in a continuous system', *Food Chem.*, 67, 53–59.

YEOM H W, ZHANG Q H and CHISM G W (2002a), 'Inactivation of pectin methyl esterase in orange juice by pulsed electric fields', *J. Food Sci.*, 67, 2154–2159.

YEOM H W, MCCANN K T, STREAKER C B and ZHANG Q H (2002b), 'Pulsed electric field processing of high acid liquid foods: a review', *Adv. in Food and Nutr. Res.*, 44, 132.

ZÁRATE-RODRÍGUEZ E, ORTEGA-RIVAS E and BARBOSA-CÁNOVAS G V (2000), 'Quality changes in apple juice as related to nonthermal processing', *J. Food Quality*, 23, 337–349.

ZIMMERMAN, U. (1986), 'Electrical breakdown, electropermeabilization and electrofusion', *Rev. Physiol. Biochem. Pharmacol.*, 105, 176–256.

ZUCKERMAN H, KRASIK Y E and FELSTEINER J (2002), 'Inactivation of microorganisms using pulsed high-current underwater discharges', *Innov. Food Sci. Emerg. Technol.*, 3, 329–336.

## 18.13   Patents

US 4,695,472. Filed in 1985. US 4,838,154. Filed in 1987. Methods and apparatus for extending the shelf life of fluid food products. Dunn, Pearlman. Maxwell Laboratories.

WO 90/15547. Priority: 1989. US 5,048,404. Filed in 1990. US 5,235,905. Filed in 1992. High pulsed voltage systems for extending the shelf life of pumpable food products. Bushnell, Dunn, Clark, Pearlman. Foodco. Corp.

US 5,393,541. Filed in 1994. Prevention of electrode fouling in high electric field systems for killing microorganisms in food products. Bushnell, Clark, Dunn, Lloyd. Foodco Corp.

US 5,447,733. Filed in 1994. Prevention of electrochemical and electrophoretic effects in high-strength-electric-field pumpable-food-product treatment systems. Bushnell, Clark, Dunn, Lloyd. PurePulse Technologies.

US 5,514,391. Filed in 1995. Process for reducing levels of microorganisms in pumpable food products using a high pulsed voltage system. Bushnell, Clark, Dunn, Lloyd. PurePulse Technologies.

US 6,027,754. Filed in 1998. Uniform product flow in a high-electric-field treatment cell. Bushnell, Lloyd. PurePulse Technologies.

US 6,110,423. Filed in 1998. WO 99/39752. Priority: 1998. High-strength electric field pumpable food product treatment in a serial electrode treatment cell. Bushnell, Dunn, Clark, Lloyd. PurePulse Technologies.

US 5,549,041. Filed in 1995. Batch mode food treatment using pulsed electric field. Zhang, Qin, Barbosa-Cánovas, Swanson, Pedrow. Washington State University Research Foundation.

US 5,690,978. Filed in 1996. WO 98/14074. Priority: 1996. High voltage pulsed electric field treatment chambers for the preservation of liquid food products. Yin, Zhang, Sastry. Ohio State University, The Ohio State Research Foundation.

US 5,776,529. Filed in 1997. US 6,019,031. Filed in 1998. Continuous flow electrical treatment of flowable food products. Qin, Barbosa-Cánovas, Swanson, Pedrow, Olsen, Zhang. Washington State University Research Foundation.

WO 99/49561. Priority: 1998. A high voltage pulse generator. Zhang, Qiu. The Ohio State Research Foundation.

US 6,214,297 B1. Filed in 1999. High voltage pulse generator. Zhang, Qiu. The Ohio State University.

WO 00/15054. Apparatus and process for preserving foods. Lelieveld. Unilever PLC. Priority: 1998.

US 6,231,908 B1. Filed in 1999. Method and apparatus for preserving food products. Lelieveld, Volanschi. Lipton, Division of Conopco.

US 6,086,932. Filed in 1998. High electric pasteurization. Gupta.

US 6,083,544. Filed in 1998. Process for the use of pulsed electric fields coupled with rotational retorting in processing meals ready to eat. Addeo.

FR 2 779 741. Filed in 1998. WO 99/64634. Procédé de traitement des betteraves sucrières. Method for treating sugar beet. Eshtiaghi, Knorr. Eridania Beghin Say.

WO 00/56179. Priority: 1999. Method for treating products by high voltage pulses. De Winter, Mastwijk, Bartels. ATO-DLO.

US 6,138,555. Filed in 1999. Food processing device and electric system for the processing device, and high voltage-weak pulse electric current impresser for food. Hata. Kowa Business Planning of America & Hata & Mitsubishi International Corp.

FR 2 805 199. Filed in 2000. Procédé d'extraction de liquide d'un matériau cellulaire, et dispositifs de mise en œuvre dudit procédé. Vorobiev, André, Bouzrara, Bazhal. Association Gradient & Fonderies et Ateliers L. Choquenet.

US 2002/0155611 A1. WO 00/63355. Priority: 1999. Method for treatment of an aqueous flux by electropulsation of a field parallel to the flow, pulsation chamber and use thereof. Vernhes, Cabannes, Teissié. Electricité de France & Centre National de la Recherche Scientifique.

FR 2 792 308. Filed in 1999. WO 00/62821. Priority: 1999. Method for eliminating protozoas, especially free-living amoebae from a colonized aqueous flux. Method for treating an aqueous flux by electropulsation and use thereof in the elimination of protozoas. Vernhes, Cabannes, Teissié. Electricité de France & Centre National de la Recherche Scientifique.

US 2002/0172616 A1. WO 00/62822. Priority: 1999. Method for eliminating Legionella from a colonised aqueous flow by electropulsing. A method for treating an aqueous flow by electropulsing, and its application to eliminating Legionella. Eynard, Cabannes, Teissié. Electricité de France & Centre National de la Recherche Scientifique.

FR 2 815 640. Filed in 2000. WO 02/33065 A2. Priority: 2000. Method for producing proteins by electroporation. Teissié, Ganeva, Galutzov. Centre National de la Recherche Scientifique.

US 6,326,177 B1. Filed in 2000. Method and apparatus for intracellular electro-manipulation. Schoenbach, Beebe, Buescher. Eastern Virginia Medical School & Old Dominion University.

US 2001/0017082 A1. Filed in 2001; US 2002/0170439 A1. Filed in 2002; US 6,393,975 B2. Filed in 2001; EP 1 123 662 A1. Filed in 2001. Treatment apparatus and method for preserving pumpable food products in a pulsed electric field. Morshuis, van den Boesch, De Haan, Ferreira. Stork Foods and Dairy Systems.

US 2002/0036175 A1. Filed in 2001. Method and apparatus for the molecular destruction of waste-activated sludge using high electrical voltage. Held, Chauhan.

# 19

# High hydrostatic pressure technology in food preservation

**Indrawati, A. Van Loey, C. Smout and M. Hendrickx, Katholieke Universiteit Leuven, Belgium**

## 19.1 Introduction

In the context of food preservation, conventional thermal food processes are mostly used in the food industry. Recently, technologies have been developed to optimise the process (i.e., reducing the severity of the thermal processes leading to better food quality retention). Consumer requirements indicate the desire for high quality foods in the sense of more convenient, fresher, less heavily processed (e.g., processed with less heat), more natural, healthier and with less preservatives than foods that have previously been available. To respond to this situation, new and improved physical process techniques are being developed, for example, high hydrostatic pressure (HP) technology has the potential to produce foods that meet many of these consumer demands. This technique allows inactivating enzymes and microorganisms (vegetative cells) and at the same time offers advantages in minimal deleterious effects on food quality, e.g., colour, flavour, nutritional value.

High pressure technology is unlikely to replace conventional thermal processing because the latter is a well-established and relatively cheap food preservation method. Currently, the reported cost range of high pressure processes is 0.1–0.2€ per litre whereas the cost for thermal treatment may be as low as 0.02–0.04€ per litre (Grant *et al.*, 2000). However, the technology offers commercially feasible alternatives for conventional heating in the case of novel food products with improved functional properties that cannot be attained by conventional heating. The range of HP applications in food preservation includes pasteurisation of fruit and vegetable products (Parish, 1997; Yen and Lin, 1996), tenderisation of meat products (Elgasim and Kennick, 1980; Ohmori *et al.*, 1991; Cheftel and Culioli, 1997), texturisation of fish proteins, applications in the dairy industry (Messens *et al.*, 1997) and high pressure freezing/thawing (Kalichevsky *et al.*, 1995).

A number of commercial high pressure food products are currently available in Japan, Europe and the United States. A Japanese company, Meidi-Ya, introduced the first commercial pressure treated fruit-based jam on the market in April 1990, followed in 1991 by a wide variety of pressure-processed fruit yoghurts, fruit jellies, fruit sauces, savoury rice products, dessert and salad dressings (Mertens and Deplace, 1993). In Europe, fruit juice was the first commercially available high pressure product in France followed by a pressurised delicatessen style ham in Spain and pressurised orange juice in the United Kingdom. In the United States, high pressure treated guacamole has been launched in the commercial market. In addition, pressure treated oysters and hummus are commercially available. A list of pressurised food products that are or have been available in Japan, Europe and the United States in the last decade is summarised in Table 19.1.

## 19.2   Principles and technologies

The high pressure technique is essentially additive-free, mostly non-thermal or involves reduced heat treatments. Based on the Pascal or isostatic principle, the hydrostatic pressure at a given point is the same in all directions and pressure is transmitted uniformly and immediately through the pressure transferring medium. Thus, the effects of pressure are independent on product size and geometry (Knorr, 1993). It is often stated that HP processing is a uniform way of processing foods. However, care should be taken with this statement: although the uniformity of pressure indeed results in a great advantage as compared to thermal treatment, this new technique cannot avoid the classical limitation of heat transfer. In fact, heat transfer limitation can become important during pressurisation and decompression, since an increase or a decrease of pressure is associated with a proportional temperature change of the vessel contents due to adiabatic heating or cooling.

The effectiveness of a high pressure treatment is influenced by various intrinsic and extrinsic factors. Treatment time, pressurisation/decompression rate, temperature and the number of pulses are critical to the effectiveness of the process (Knorr, 2001). Moreover, factors which include the effect of pressure on water, adiabatic heating and heat dissipation, food composition and the physiological states of microorganisms to be inactivated must be taken into account when optimising pressure treatments for the production of safe, high quality foods (Smelt *et al.*, 2002).

The difference between reaction affected by pressure (activation volume) and temperature (activation energy) leads to the possibility of retaining food quality attributes such as vitamins (Van den Broeck, *et al.*, 1998), pigments (Van Loey *et al.*, 1998) and flavour components, while inactivating microorganisms and food quality related enzymes and changing the structure of the food system and

**Table 19.1** Commercial pressurised food products in Japan, Europe and the United States in the last decade (after Cheftel, 1997)

| Product | Country | Company | P/T/time combination | Role of HP |
|---|---|---|---|---|
| **Plant based products** | | | | |
| Fruit based products (pH < 4.5); jams (apple, kiwi, strawberry); jellies; purées; yoghurts | Japan | Meidi-ya | 400 MPa, 10–30 min, 20 °C | Pasteurisation, improved gelation, faster sugar penetration; limiting residual pectinmethylesterase activity |
| Grapefruit juice | Japan | Pokka Corp. (stopped in the last couple of years) | 200 MPa, 10–15 min, 5 °C | Reduced bitterness |
| Mandarin juice (winter season only) (only ≈ 20% of HP juice in final juice mix) | Japan | Wakayama Food Ind. | 300–400 MPa, 2–3 min, 20 °C | Reduced odour of dimethyl sulfide; reduced thermal degradation of methyl methionine sulfoxide; replace first thermal pasteurisation (after juice extraction) final pasteurisation before packing: 90 °C, 3 min. |
| Sugar impregnated tropical fruits (kept at −18 °C without freezing) for sorbet and ice cream | Japan | Nisshin fine foods | 50–200 MPa | Faster sugar penetration and water removal |
| Ice nucleating bacteria (for fruit juice) | Japan | QP corp | / | Inactivation of Xanthomonas, no loss of ice nucleating properties |
| 'Raw' sake (rice wine) | Japan | Chiyonosono | / | Yeast inactivation, fermentation stopped without heating |
| Japanese mandarin juice | Japan | Ehime co. | / | Cold pasteurisation |
| Moci rice cake, Yomogi fresh aromatic herbs, hypoallergenic precooked rice, convenience packs of boiled rice | Japan | Echigo seika | 400–600 MPa, 10 min, 45 or 70 °C | Microbial reduction, fresh flavour and taste, enhances rice porosity and salt extraction of allergenic proteins |

| Product | Country | Company | Conditions | Effect |
|---|---|---|---|---|
| Fruit juice | Japan | Takansi | / | Cold pasteurisation |
| Squeezed orange juice | Japan | Pon (test market in 2000) | / | / |
|  | United Kingdom | Orchard House Foods Ltd. | 500 MPa, room temperature | Inactivation of micro flora (especially yeast) and enzyme, keeping natural taste |
| Fruit juice (orange, grape fruit, citrus, mixed fruit juice) | France | Pampryl | 400 MPa, room temperature | Inactivation of micro flora (up to $10^6$ CFU/g), partial inactivation of pectinmethylesterase |
| Acidified avocado spread paste (Guacamole, chipotle sauce, salsa and pieces) | United States | Avomex | 700 MPa, 10–15 min, 20 °C | Microorganism inactivation, polyphenoloxidase inactivation, chilled process |
| Hummus | United States | Hannah International Foods | / | / |
| **Meat and fish based products** | | | | |
| Raw pork ham | Japan | Fuji chiku mutterham | 250 MPa, 3 hours, 20 °C | Faster maturation (reduced from 2 weeks to 3 hours); faster tenderisation by internal proteases, improved water retention and shelf life |
| Deli-style processed meats (cured-cooked and raw-cooked ham) | Spain | Espuna | 400–500 MPa, few min., 20 °C | / |
| 'Shiokara' and raw scallops | Japan | Kibun (stopped in 1995) | / | Microbial sanitation, tenderisation, control of autolysis by endogenous proteases |
| Fish sausages, terrines and 'pudding' | Japan | Yaizu fisheries (test market only) | 400 MPa | Gelation, microbial sanitation, good texture of raw HP gel |
| Oysters | United States | Motivatit, Nisbet Oyster Co, Joey Oyster | 300–400 MPa, room temperature, 10 minutes | Microorganism inactivation, keeping raw taste and flavour, no change in shape and size |

/: no detailed information is available.

functionality of food proteins (Hoover *et al.*, 1989; Knorr, 1995a; Barbosa-Cánovas *et al.*, 1997; Messens *et al.*, 1997; Hendrickx *et al.*, 1998). A number of key effects of high pressure on food components have been demonstrated including

- microorganism inactivation
- modification of biopolymers including enzyme activation and inactivation, protein denaturation and gel formation
- quality retention (e.g., colour, flavour, nutrition value)
- modification of physicochemical properties of water (Cheftel, 1991; Knorr, 1993).

### 19.2.1   General description of HP equipment for food industry

The main components of an HP system are a pressure vessel, a pressure generation system, a temperature control device and a materials handling system (Mertens, 1995). Most pressure vessels are made from a high tensile steel alloy 'monoblocs' (forged from a single piece of material), which can withstand pressures of 400–600 MPa. For higher pressures, pre-stressed multi-layer or wire-wound vessels are used. In operation, after all air has been removed, a pressure-transmitting medium (either water or oil) is pumped from a reservoir into the pressure vessel using a pressure intensifier until the desired pressure is reached. Temperature control in commercial operations can be achieved by pumping a heating/cooling medium through a jacket that surrounds the pressure vessel. This is satisfactory in most applications as a constant temperature is required but if it is necessary to change the temperature regularly, an internal heat exchanger is fitted.

There are two methods of processing foods in high pressure vessels: in-container processing and bulk processing. Since foods reduce in volume at the very high pressures used during processing, there is considerable stress and distortion to the package and the seal when in-container processing is used, making packaging selection an important issue in using this method. Materials handling for in-container processing is achieved using equipment similar to that used to load/unload batch retorts. Bulk handling of liquids is simpler, requiring only pumps, pipes and valves. High pressure equipment with pressure levels up to 900 MPa and temperatures in the range of 5 to 90 °C (on average) for times up to 30 minutes or longer are now available to the food industry (Linton and Patterson, 2000). Hoogland *et al.* (2001) have described the development of a new generation of HP processing equipment. By using composite materials instead of steel, the cost of the pressure vessel is reduced. The use of internal pressure intensifiers, pressurised by external pumps, further reduces cost. With new systems such as this cycle times are being reduced to 2–5 minutes.

Examples of semi-continuous systems have been developed by, for example, the companies Alstom and Flow Pressure Systems. In the Flow Pressure semi-continuous system, the liquid to be processed is pumped into one or more isolators (pressure vessels in which a separator partitions the food liquid from the ultra-high pressure (UHP) water source). After pressure treatment, the liquid is pumped into a holding tank and aseptic filling station. In the Alstom system, the pressure chamber is filled with the liquid to be treated and compressed directly by a mobile piston (pushed by pressurised water). After a predetermined holding time, pressure is released and the liquid pumped by the piston to a holding vessel. Several pressure chambers can be served in parallel by the same main pressure generator, so that a continuous downstream flow can be maintained. Since the pressure chamber is completely filled with product, the capacity per cycle is considerably increased and cycle time is reduced by about 30% (Träff, 1998).

## 19.3   Effects of high pressure on microorganisms

The effect of combined high pressure and temperature on microorganisms (vegetative cells) has been investigated extensively (Sonoike et al., 1992; Hashizume et al., 1995; Knorr, 1995b; Heinz and Knorr, 1996; Hauben, 1998; Reyns et al., 2000; Linton and Patterson, 2000; Lado and Yousef, 2002). The pressure and temperature resistance of microorganisms may be due to the intrinsic stability of macromolecules (ribonucleic acid/RNA; ribosomes, nucleic acids, enzymes, the cell protein, the cell membrane and in some cases the cell wall) (Yuste et al., 2001a; Smelt et al., 2002). The effect of high pressure on bacterial survival is influenced by a number of interacting factors such as pressure level and duration of the treatment, temperature, bacteria species and the bacterial development phase (Patterson et al., 1995; Smelt et al., 2002).

Vegetative forms of prokaryotes such as yeasts and moulds are most pressure sensitive and inactivated by pressures between 200 and 300 MPa. In general, gram-positive bacteria (Listeria monocytogenes, Staphylococcus aureus) are more resistant to pressure than gram-negative (Pseudomonas, Salmonella spp, Yersinia enterocolitica, Vibrio parahaemolyticus) but large differences can exist between strains within the same species (Smelt, 1998). Moreover, cocci are more resistant than rods because of fewer morphological changes under pressure. Cultures in the exponential growth phase have been shown to be far more sensitive than cultures in the logarithmic growth or stationary phase (Hoover et al., 1989). However, exposing any surviving fraction of vegetative cells to repeated pressure cycles can also increase their pressure resistance (Hauben, 1998; Alpas et al., 1999; Benito et al., 1999).

In contrast, spores at ambient temperature can resist pressures up to 1000 MPa. However, pressure treatments combined with temperatures of about 70 °C are necessary to obtain a significant level of inactivation. It has also been shown that lower pressures (250 MPa) associated with mild temperatures (40 °C) can inactivate spores in a two stage process, pressure first inducing germination and then inactivating the baro-sensitive germinated spores. Pulsed or oscillating pressurisation at high and low pressure is also more effective in spore inactivation than continuous pressure (Heinz and Knorr, 2002). Rapid decompression increases the impact force on the spore coat much more than the preceding compression and makes possible sterilisation at lower pressures (Yuste et al., 2001a). The success of this approach depends on conditions such as pressure intensity and duration of the process together with other factors such as temperature and the number of pulses (Yuste et al., 2001b). Tailing phenomena for germination and inactivation curves can also occur for 'super dormant' spores after long exposure times.

To deal with these problems a combination of pressure with temperatures of 60 °C and higher is required for extensive inactivation of spores. The lower the pressure applied, the higher the required temperature to induce a required level of inactivation (Sale et al., 1970; Heinz, 1997; Wuytack, 1999). At temperatures below 60 °C in combination with a pressure of about 400 MPa, for example, maximal three log-cycle reductions were obtained for Clostridium sporogenes and Bacillus coagulans spores (Roberts and Hoover, 1996; Mills et al., 1998). To achieve sterility with minimal impact on nutritional value, flavour, texture and colour, high pressure processing using multiple high pressure pulses and achieving an end temperature above 105 °C under pressure for a short time has been proposed (Meyer et al., 2000; Krebbers et al., 2001). In general, full sterilisation of food products is not possible with high pressure at levels below 500 MPa. Most industrial applications operate at a ceiling of 400 to 500 MPa maximum, and products require chilled storage to maximise shelf life.

## 19.4    Effects of high pressure on quality-related enzymes

In literature, contradictory results have been found since pressure stability of enzymes is strongly dependent on several intrinsic (e.g., enzyme type, enzyme origin, medium composition) and extrinsic (e.g., temperature, pressure cycle, treatment time) factors.

In cruciferae, myrosinase (MYR) (EC 3.2.3.1) is important to catalyse the hydrolysis of glucosinolates, a group of sulphur-containing pseudo-glycosides. Products formed from hydrolysis of indole glucosinolates attract special attention because of their anticarcinogenic function and have undesirable effects because of their pungency, bitterness and toxic or goitrogenic activity (Dunford and Temelli, 1996; Wathelet et al., 1996). At 20 °C, the inactivation occurred in the pressure range of 200 to 500 MPa and can be described by a consecutive step model. At 35 °C, thermal inactivation was retarded at pressure lower than 350 MPa (Ludikhuyze et al., 1999). In the presence of its substrate (sinigrin), MYR activity was enhanced by applying pressure up to 100 MPa in the temperature range of 20 to 40 °C (Ludikhuyze et al., 2000a).

Lipoxygenase (LOX) (EC 1.13.1.13) is present in plant tissues, especially in legumes. Its enzymatic reaction results in some undesirable effects (e.g., destruction of essential fatty acids, off flavours development and colour degradation). LOX was irreversibly inactivated by HP at low/subzero

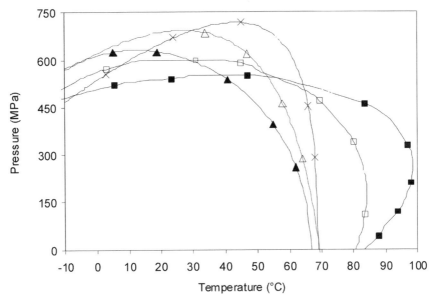

**Fig. 19.1**    Effect of different food matrixes on LOX inactivation. Pressure temperature combinations resulting in the same inactivation rate constant ($k = 0.1535\,\mathrm{min}^{-1}$) for different sources of LOX, i.e., purified soybean in borate buffer (pH 9) (x), in green bean juice (GBJ, [△]); green beans *in situ* (GBI, [▲]); in green pea juice (GPJ, [□]) and green peas *in situ* (GPI, [■]).

temperatures (Indrawati *et al.*, 1998) and at elevated temperatures (Heinisch *et al.*, 1995; Ludikhuyze *et al.*, 1998a; 1998b; Indrawati, 2000). The pressure inactivation could be described by first order reaction kinetics. At room temperature, LOX inactivation occurred between 400 and 600 MPa. The level of pressure and temperature needed for LOX inactivation is dependent on the food matrix (Fig. 19.1). The highest pressure stability of LOX in legumes (i.e., soybean, green peas and green beans) occurred at room temperature (Indrawati, 2000).

Pectinases including pectinmethylesterase (PME) and polygalacturonase (PG) are responsible for cloud destabilisation in juices and texture changes in tissue systems. PME (EC 3.1.1.11) catalyses the de-methylation of carboxylate groups on pectic substances resulting in an improved ideal substrate for PG (EC. 3.2.1.15). PG cleaves the $\alpha$-$(1 \rightarrow 4)$-glycosidic bonds in the D-galacturonan moiety of pectic substances. Threshold pressures for inactivation of PME from different sources have been reported to vary from 150 to 1200 MPa depending on its origin and the medium in which inactivation was performed. Complete kinetic characterisation of PME inactivation in orange juice across a broad range of pressures and temperatures showed a slight antagonistic effect of low pressure and high temperature (Van den Broeck, 2000). Inactivation occurs faster in an acid medium and is protected by an increased amount of soluble solids (Ogawa *et al.*, 1990). Most studies report only partial inactivation of PME due to the presence of isozymes with different pressure resistance but it depends on the enzyme origin. As compared to orange PME, tomato PME was found to be much more pressure resistant with a strongly antagonistic effect of high temperature and pressure (Crelier *et al.*, 1995; Van den Broeck *et al.*, 2000a). PG inactivation in tomato juice occurred in the temperature range of 20 to 55 °C combined with pressures between 200 and 550 MPa (Fachin *et al.*, 2000).

Alkaline phosphatase (ALP, EC. 3.1.3.1.) is a phosphomonoesterase that catalyses the hydrolysis of phosphoric monoesters at alkaline pH. This enzyme is widely used as an indicator for thermal pasteurisation of milk. Seyderhelm *et al.* (1996) found 90% ALP inactivation in Tris buffer at 600 MPa and 55 °C for 30 min. ALP inactivation followed first order reaction kinetics (Mussa and Ramaswamy, 1997; Ludikhuyze *et al.*, 2000b). In milk, lower pressure stability was found by Mussa and Ramaswamy (1997). They reported that the D values at 200 MPa and 400 MPa (presumably at room temperature) were 1039 min. and 301 min. respectively and an activation volume of $-14.1 \, cm^3/mole$ at room temperature was found. Ludikhuyze *et al.* (2000b) found an antagonistic effect of pressure lower than 300 MPa on ALP inactivation in a temperature range of 55 to 63 °C. At 25 °C, ALP inactivation occurred at relatively high pressure levels (625–725 MPa).

Polyphenoloxidase (PPO) (EC 1.14.18.1) is one of the main causes of quality deterioration (enzymatic browning and concomitant changes in appearance and organoleptic properties) during post-harvest handling, storage and processing. Pressures need to induce substantial inactivation of PPO vary between 200 and 1000 MPa, depending on the enzyme origin and microenvironmental conditions such as medium composition or pH (Weemaes, 1998; Lopez-Malo *et al.*, 1999). Whilst PPO in some fruits such as apple and grape is sensitive to pressure, PPO in others, such as pear and plum, is resistant to pressure inactivation.

Palou *et al.* (2000) have analysed the effects of continuous and oscillatory high pressure treatment on guacamole. Significantly less ($p < 0.05$) residual PPO activity was obtained by increasing the process time and number of pressurisation-decompression cycles. The lowest residual PPO activity value (15%) was obtained after four high pressure cycles at 689 MPa with five minutes of holding time each (presumably at room temperature). Browning during storage was related mainly to changes in the hue attributed to a decrease in the green contribution to the colour. A shelf life of 20 days was achieved at $<15$ °C.

Peroxidase (POD) (EC 1.11.1.7) is generally considered to be the most heat stable vegetable enzyme and often used as an indicator for evaluating the efficiency of a blanching process. In literature, contradictory results about pressure stability of POD have been reported. Most cases found that POD was extremely pressure resistant (Quaglia *et al.*, 1996; Seyderhelm *et al.*, 1996; Crelier *et al.*, 1998; Lemos, 1998). In green beans, a pressure treatment of 900 MPa at room temperature had little effect, though elevated temperatures enhanced the inactivation effect at 600 MPa (Quaglia *et al.*, 1996). Cano *et al.* (1997), on the contrary reported POD in strawberry purée and orange juice to be inactivated at room temperature with pressures up to 300 and 400 MPa, respectively. At a higher temperature (45 °C), a decrease in activity was found for all pressures (50–400 MPa).

In milk, the pressure resistance of lactoperoxidase was strongly dependent on the medium used for inactivation. Seyderhelm and co-workers (1996) found that pressure treatment at 600 MPa and 25 °C for 2 min. resulted in 70% and 30% of lactoperoxidase in Tris buffer and milk respectively. However, Ludikhuyze *et al.* (2001) found no inactivation under the same condition and an antagonistic effect of pressure (100 and 700 MPa) on thermal inactivation was noticed at temperatures ranging from 69 to 75 °C.

It can be concluded that enzyme inactivation occurs at different pressure-temperature combinations depending on the type of enzyme, enzyme origin and the medium used for inactivation. It seems that enzymes are generally more resistant than vegetative cells with respect to pressure-temperature treatment. Hence, food quality related enzymes are more likely to become the critical issue in defining optimal pressure processes rather than vegetative microorganisms.

## 19.5   Effects of high pressure on nutritional value and colour quality

The effect of high pressure on vitamins has been investigated by a number of authors and shows that high pressure treatment has little effect on the vitamin contents of food products. Most authors have reported that the ascorbic acid content is not significantly affected by HP treatment, e.g., 82% ascorbic acid retention in fresh green peas after pressure at 900 MPa/20 °C for 5–10 min. (Quaglia *et al.*, 1996); no significant decrease of ascorbic acid content in egg yolk, guava purée and fruits (strawberry and kiwi) jam resulted after pressure preservation between 400 and 600 MPa for 10–30 min. at room temperature (Kimura *et al.*, 1994; Yen and Lin, 1996; Sancho *et al.*, 1999). However, at extreme conditions of high pressure (up to 850 MPa) combined with high temperature (up to 80 °C) for a long treatment time can cause a decrease in ascorbic acid (Van den Broeck *et al.*, 1998). The same finding was also reported for vitamin A and carotene (Butz and Tauscher, 1997; Tauscher, 1998; de Ancos *et al.*, 2000; Fernández-Garcia *et al.*, 2001) and vitamin B, E and K (Bognar *et al.*, 1993; Sancho *et al.*, 1999; Tauscher, 1999, Sierra *et al.*, 2000). As a consequence, high pressure is a feasible technology to maintain vitamin content in food products.

The most interesting effect of high pressure on lipids is the influence on solid-liquid lipid phase transition (Buccheim *et al.*, 1999). Unfortunately, HP treatment of some food products can cause lipid oxidation and hydrolysis, e.g., pressure induced lipid oxidation of extra virgin olive and seed oil (Severini *et al.*, 1997) and cod muscle (Angsupanich and Ledward, 1998); production of free fatty acids in red fish meat at 200 MPa and room temperature for 30 minutes (Wada, 1992; Wada and Ogawa, 1996); increasing lipid oxidation in pressurised (800 MPa/19 °C/20 min.) meat (Cheah and Ledward, 1995; 1997) and pressurised

(100–500 MPa/10 °C/10–30 min.) turkey meat (Dissing *et al.*, 1997). However, Krebbers and co-workers (2001) have reported that pulsed high pressure ($>= 700$ MPa) sterilisation (2 pulses of 1 minute holding time) at temperature ($>= 65$ °C) can retain the essential oil content in basil. The evidence of pressure induced lipid oxidation may limit the HP applications in meat and fish products unless an antioxidant or suitable product packaging is used.

High pressure preserves fresh colour of fruit and vegetables, e.g., pressure treated strawberry (Matser and Bartels, 1999), pressurised guava purée (600 MPa/25 °C/15 min.) (Yen and Lin, 1996), no chlorophyll degradation was found at pressure treatment up to 800 MPa combined with temperatures lower than 40 °C for 3 hours (Van Loey *et al.*, 1998; Weemaes *et al.*, 1999). Some authors (Johnston *et al.*, 1992; Mussa and Ramaswamy, 1997) reported a high retention of lightness (L value) colour of milk after HP treatment at 300 MPa for one hour. In meat products, high pressure treatment can cause meat discolouration such as a whitening effect in a pressure range of 200 to 350 MPa and a loss of red colour. It is dependent more on critical pressure thresholds than processing time (Nose *et al.*, 1994; Carlez *et al.*, 1995; Cheftel and Culioli, 1997). HP processing of fresh red meat is a feasible alternative only when subsequent cooking is carried out. In contrast, HP processing is unlikely to cause serious colour problems of cured meat and white meats.

## 19.6    Effects of high pressure on water-ice transition of foods

Most high pressure effects previously discussed are obtained under conditions where the product does not undergo a phase transition. However, by taking advantages of the effect on the solid liquid phase transition of water (Bridgman, 1912) (Fig. 19.2), some potential applications in food processing (in P/T area of ghij, Fig. 19.2) such as pressure assisted freezing (pathway abef), pressure shift freezing (pathway acdf), pressure assisted thawing (pathway feba), pressure induced thawing (pathway fdca), non-frozen storage under pressure at subzero temperature (pathway acd) and formation of different ice polymorphs can be offered while keeping other food quality properties (Kalichevsky *et al.*, 1995). The terminology used for those different processes, i.e., (a) pressure-assisted refers to the phase transition occurred under constant pressure; (b) pressure shift means that a phase transition caused by a pressure change and (c) pressure induced means a phase transition initiated with pressure change continued at constant pressure was first introduced by Knorr and co-workers (1998).

Pressure shift freezing occurs because of the pressure-induced melting point depression which enables water in the liquid phase to be supercooled up to −22 °C at 207.5 MPa, resulting in rapid and uniform nucleation and growth of ice crystals upon pressure release producing smaller ice crystals rather than a stress-inducing ice front moving through the sample. Additional cooling of the sample is needed to enable complete freezing of the sample because of the large heat of fusion of ice formation. An additional advantage of pressure-assisted and

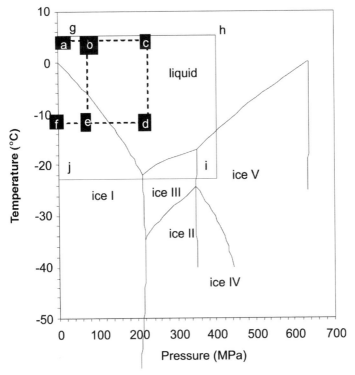

**Fig. 19.2**  Water phase diagram showing feasibility of HP technology in food applications (ghij): pressure shift freezing (pathway acdf), pressure assisted freezing (pathway abef) and thawing (pathway feba), pressure induced thawing (pathway fdca) and non-frozen storage under pressure (pathway acd).

shift freezing is the increased freezing rate as compared to a conventional freezing process at ambient pressure (Denys *et al.*, 1997).

In an analogous way, pressure induced thawing involves pressurising a frozen sample up to the liquid area of the phase diagram, thus increasing the thawing rate if the appropriate heat of fusion is provided (Deuchi and Hayashi, 1992; Kalichevsky *et al.*, 1995). The use of HP on water offers the possibility to obtain other ice polymorphs instead of ice I (the type we are familiar with), e.g., ice II, III, IV, V, etc., which all have a smaller volume as compared to the liquid state (Bridgman, 1912; Kalichevsky *et al*, 1995). Other ice polymorphs can be obtained by direct pressurisation at subzero temperature (e.g., pathway ji, Fig. 19.2) (Takahashi, 1992; Hashizume *et al.*, 1995; Fuchigami *et al.*, 1996) or alternatively by pressurising a liquid sample above 200 MPa and subsequently cooling the sample (e.g., pathway ghi, Fig. 19.2) however ice I will be formed after decompression.

So far, the effects of high pressure combined with subzero temperature on food products have been studied and it showed some stimulating results with regard to food quality retention. The effect of pressure shift freezing on various food products has been investigated, e.g., (a) in meat and fish based products; uniform nucleation during pressure shift freezing of pork muscle (Martino *et al.*, 1998), (b) in plant based products; an homogeneous structure of pressure assisted frozen tofu (similar to that of the untreated product) (Kanda and Aoki, 1993), uniform nucleation during pressure shift freezing of eggplants (Otero *et al.*, 1998), an improvement in the texture and histological structure of frozen vegetables, i.e., carrots and cabbage (Fuchigami *et al.*, 1996; 1998). The effect of pressure induced thawing on food products has been studied more intensively than pressure shift freezing. Qualitative studies on various food products showed that pressure induced thawing could reduce the time needed to thaw the product completely (Takai *et al.*, 1991; Makita, 1992; Pothakamury *et al.*, 1995; Zhao *et al.*, 1996; 1998; Chevalier *et al.*, 1999) and better quality products could be obtained as compared to conventional thawing methods.

In meat and fish based products, some negative effects including discolouration and whitening of the meat and fish (caused by protein denaturation) occurred depending on the pressure level applied (Makita, 1992; Murakami *et al.*, 1992; Pothakamury *et al.*, 1995) However at low pressure, thawing at 50 MPa and −20 °C resulted in no change in original colour and with low drip, e.g., frozen beef (Deuchi and Hayashi, 1991, 1992), tuna back muscle (Murakami *et al.*, 1992), carp meat (Yoshioka *et al.*, 1996) and frozen beef (Zhao, *et al.*, 1998). In plant based products, pressure-assisted thawing of strawberry as a pre-treatment of thermal processing resulted in an increase in sugar absorption (Eshtiaghi and Knorr, 1996). Non-frozen storage of meat and fruit while keeping its original flavour and texture was studied by Deuchi and Hayashi (1992). Moreover pressure treatment at subzero temperatures induces gel formation, e.g., sardined washed mince (Pérez-Mateos and Montero, 1997), ovalbumin, egg yolk and soy protein (Dumoulin *et al.*, 1998).

## 19.7   Future trends

High pressure technology combined with subzero and elevated temperatures offers diverse applications in food preservation in order to obtain higher food quality retention and new food functionality as compared to conventional thermal treatment. However, high pressure as a novel unit operation should be able to guarantee increased overall quality, i.e. to increase functional properties within the constraints of microbial and toxicological safety. In the current situation, pulsed high pressure treatments combined with high temperature for short times have been proposed for food sterilisation because of its effective microbial spore inactivation. However, the stability of nutrients (e.g., vitamins) and possibly chemical compounds is limited under such extreme pressure temperature conditions. More research is needed on these aspects under high pressure sterilisation conditions; both mechanistic and kinetic information will be indispensable in the future.

## 19.8   Sources of further information and advice

European Commission (EC)-funded projects of FAIR-CT96-1113 (High pressure treatment of liquid foods and derived products) and FAIR-CT93-1175 (Combined high pressure thermal treatment of foods: a kinetic approach to safety and quality evaluation) has been completely reported in the book entitled *Ultra High Pressure Treatment of Foods* (Hendrickx, MEG and Knorr, D (eds)), 2002, Kluwer Academic/Plenum Publishers, New York, USA). List of academic and non-academic research centres (1991–2001) in Japan, Europe and the United States actively involved in high pressure research in the field of bioscience, food science and chemistry can be found in 'High pressure processing' (Indrawati *et al.*, 2001 in Henry, CJK and Chapman C (ed.), *The nutrition handbook for food processors,* Woodhead Publishing, Cambridge, England, pp. 433–461). Annual meetings of high pressure research in Japan, Europe and the United States can be obtained from professional organisations such as the European High Pressure Research Group (http://www.ehprg.org), Institute of Food Technologist (IFT) Non Thermal Division (http://www.ift.org/divisions/nonthermal/), UK High pressure club for food processing and the Japanese Research Group of High Pressure.

## 19.9   Acknowledgements

The authors would like thank the Fund for Scientific Research – Flanders (FWO) for financial support.

## 19.10   References

ALPAS H, KALCHAYANAND N, BOZOGLU F, SIKES A, DUNNE P and RAY B (1999), 'Variation in resistance to hydrostatic pressure among strains of food-borne pathogens', *Appl Environ Microbiol,* 65(9), 4248–51.

ANGSUPANICH K and LEDWARD D A (1998), 'Effects of high pressure on lipid oxidation in fish', in Isaacs N S (ed.), *High pressure food science, bioscience and chemistry*, The Royal Society of Chemistry, Cambridge, pp. 284–287.

BARBOSA-CÁNOVAS G V, POTHAKAMURY U R, PALOU E and SWANSON B G (1997), 'High pressure food processing', in Barbosa-Cánovas G V, Pothakamury U R, Palou E and Swanson B G (eds), *Nonthermal preservation of foods*, Marcel Dekker Inc., New York, pp. 9–52.

BENITO A, VENTOURA G, CASADEI M, ROBINSON T and MACKEY B (1999), 'Variation in resistance of natural isolates of *Escherichia coli* O157 to high hydrostatic pressure, mild heat, and other stresses', *Appl Environ Microbiol,* 65(4), 1564–9.

BOGNÀR A, BUTZ P, KOWALSKI E, LUDWIG H and TAUSCHER B (1993), 'Stability of thiamine in pressurized model solution and pork', in Schlemmer U (ed.), *Bioavailability '93 part II – Nutritional, chemical and food processing implications of nutrient availability*, Bundesforschungsanstalt für Ernährung, Karlsruhe, pp. 352–356.

BRIDGMAN P W (1912), 'Water, in liquid and five solid forms, under pressure'. *Proc Am Acad Arts Sci*, 47(13), 123–330.

BUCHHEIM W, FREDE E, WOLF M and BALDENEGGER P (1999), 'Solidification and melting of some edible fats and model lipid systems under pressure', in Ludwig H (ed.), *Advances in high pressure bioscience and biotechnology*, Springer, Heidelberg, pp. 153–156.

BUTZ P and TAUSCHER B (1997), 'Food chemistry under high hydrostatic pressure', in Isaacs N S (ed.), *High pressure food science, bioscience and chemistry*, The Royal Society of Chemistry, Cambridge, pp. 133–144.

CANO M P, HERNANDEZ A and DE ANCOS (1997), 'High pressure and temperature effects on enzyme inactivation in strawberry and orange products', *J Food Sci,* 62, 85–88.

CARLEZ A, VECIANA-NOGUES T and CHEFTEL J C (1995), 'Changes in colour and myoglobin of minced beef meat due to high pressure processing', *Lebensm Wiss u Technol*, 28, 528–538.

CHEAH P B and LEDWARD D A (1995), 'High pressure effects on lipid oxidation', *J Am Oil Chem Soc*, 72(9), 1059–1063.

CHEAH P B and LEDWARD D A (1997), 'Catalytic mechanism of lipid oxidation following high pressure treatment in pork fat and meat', *J Food Sci*, 62(6), 1135–1138; 1141.

CHEFTEL J C (1991), 'Applications des hautes pressions en technologies alimentaire', *Ind Aliment Agric*, 108, 141–153.

CHEFTEL J R (1997), 'Commercial pressurized foods in Japan'. In Isaacs, N.S. (ed.), *High pressure food science, bioscience and chemistry*, The Royal Society of Chemistry, Cambridge, pp. 506–507.

CHEFTEL J R and CULIOLI J (1997), 'Effect of high pressure on meat: a review', *Meat Sci,* 46(3), 211–236.

CHEVALIER D, LE BAIL A, CHOUROT J M and CHANTREAU P (1999), 'High pressure thawing of fish (whiting): Influence of the process parameters on drip losses', *Lebensm Wiss u Technol*, 32, 25–31.

CRELIER S, TÂCHÉ M-C, RENKEN A and RAETZ E (1995), 'High pressure for the inactivation of enzymes in food products', *Poster presentation at the 9th World Congress on Food Science and Technology*, July 31–August 4, Budapest, Hungary.

CRELIER S, ROBERT M C and JUILLERAT M A (1998), 'Effect of a high pressure treatment on the texture and enzyme activities of selected vegetables', *Poster presentation at International Conference on High Pressure Bioscience and Biotechnology*, August 30–Sept 3, Heidelberg, Germany.

DE ANCOS B, GONZALEZ E and PILAR CANO M (2000), 'Effect of high pressure treatment on the carotenoid composition and the radical scavenging activity of persimmon fruit purees', *J Agric Food Chem*, 48, 3542–3548.

DENYS S, VAN LOEY A, DE CORDT S, HENDRICKX M and TOBBACK P (1997), 'Modelling heat transfer during high pressure freezing and thawing', *Biotechnol Prog*, 13(4), 416–423.

DEUCHI T and HAYASHI R (1991), 'Pressure application to thawing of frozen foods and to food preservation under subzero temperature', in R Hayashi (ed.), *High pressure science for food*, Kypto, San-Ei Suppan, pp. 101–110.

DEUCHI T and HAYASHI R (1992), 'High pressure treatments at subzero temperature: application to preservation, rapid freezing and rapid thawing of foods', in Balny, C., Hayashi, R., Heremans, K., Masson, P. (eds), *High pressure and biotechnology*, Colloque INSERM 224, John Libbey Eurotext Ltd., France, pp. 353–355.

DISSING J, BRUUN-JENSEN L and SKIBSTED L H (1997), 'Effect of high-pressure treatment on lipid oxidation in turkey thigh muscle during chill storage', *Z Lebensm Unters Forsch A*, 205, 11–13.

DUMOULIN M, OZAWA S and HAYASHI R (1998), 'Textural properties of pressure-induced gels of food proteins obtained under different temperatures including subzero', *J Food Sci*, 63(1), 92–95.

DUNFORD N T and TEMELLI F (1996), 'Effect of supercritical $CO_2$ on myrosinase activity and glucosinolate degradation of canola', *J. Agric Food Chem*, 44, 2372–2376.

ELGASIM E A and KENNICK W H (1980), 'Effect of pressurization of pre-rigor beef muscles on protein quality', *J Food Sci*, 45, 1122–4.

ESHTIAGHI M N and KNORR D (1996), 'High hydrostatic pressure thawing for the processing of fruit preparations from frozen strawberries', *Food Biotecnol*, 10(2), 143–148.

FACHIN D, VAN LOEY A M, LY NGUYEN B, VERLENT I, INDRAWATI and HENDRICKX M (2002), 'Comparative study of the inactivation kinetics of pectinmethylesterase in tomato juice and purified form', *Biotechnol Prog*, 18, 739–744.

FERNÁNDEZ GARCIA A, BUTZ P, BOGNÀR A and TAUSCHER B (2001), 'Antioxidative capacity, nutrient content and sensory quality of orange juice and an orange-lemon-carrot juice product after high pressure treatment and storage in different packaging', *Eur Food Res Technol*, 213, 290–296.

FUCHIGAMI M, KATO N and TERAMOTO A (1996), 'Effect of pressure-shift freezing on texture, pectic composition and histological structure of carrots', in Hayashi, R. and Balny, C., (eds), *Progress in biotechnology 13 high pressure bioscience and biotechnology*, Elsevier Science, Amsterdam, pp. 379–385.

FUCHIGAMI M, KATO N and TERAMOTO A (1998), 'High-pressure-freezing effects on textural quality of chinese cabbage', *J Food Sci*, 63(1), 122–125.

GRANT S, PATTERSON M and LEDWARD D A (2000), 'Food processing gets freshly squeezed', *Chemistry and Industry*, 24 January 2000, 55–58.

HASHIZUME C, KIMURA K and HAYASHI R (1995), 'Kinetic analysis of yeast inactivation by high pressure treatment at low temperatures', *Biosci Biotech Biochem*, 59, 1455–8.

HAUBEN K (1998), *High hydrostatic pressure as a hurdle in food preservation: inactivation and sublethal injury of Escherichia coli*, PhD dissertation no. 375, Katholieke Universiteit Leuven, Belgium.

HEINISCH O, KOWALSKI E, GOOSSENS K, FRANK J, HEREMANS K, LUDWIG H and TAUSCHER B (1995), 'Pressure effects on the stability of lipoxygenase: Fourier transform-infrared spectroscopy (FT-IR) and enzyme activity studies', *Z Lebensm Unters Forsch*, 201, 562–5.

HEINZ V (1997), *Wirkung hoher hydrostatischer Drücke auf das Absterbe- und Kiemungsverhalten sporenbildender Bakterien, am Beispiel von Bacillus subtilis*, ATCC 9372, PhD dissertation, Technische Universität, Berlin.

HEINZ V and KNORR D (1996), 'High pressure inactivation kinetics of *Bacillus subtilis* cells by a three-state-model considering distributed resistance mechanisms', *Food Biotechnol*, 10, 149–61.

HEINZ V and KNORR D (2002), 'Effects of high pressure on spores' in Hendrickx, M. and Knorr, D. (eds), *Ultra high pressure treatments of foods*, Kluwer Academic/Plenum Publishers, New York, United States, pp. 77–113.

HENDRICKX M, LUDIKHUYZE L, VAN DEN BROECK I and WEEMAES C (1998), 'Effects of high pressure on enzymes related to food quality', *Trends Food Sci Technol*, 9, 197–203.

HOOGLAND H, DE HEIJ W and VAN SCHEPDATE L (2001), 'High pressure sterilisation: novel technology, new products, new opportunities', *New Food*, 1 (4), pp. 21–26.

HOOVER D G, METRICK C, PAPINEAU A M, FARKAS D F and KNORR D (1989), 'Biological effects of high hydrostatic pressure on food micro-organisms', *Food Technol*, 43, 99–107.

INDRAWATI (2000), '*Lipoxygenase inactivation by high pressure treatment at subzero and elevated temperatures: a kinetic study*', PhD dissertation no. 444, Katholieke Universiteit Leuven, Belgium.

INDRAWATI, VAN LOEY A, DENYS S and HENDRICKX M (1998), 'Enzyme sensitivity towards high pressure at low temperature', *Food Biotechnol*, 12 (3): 263–277.

JOHNSTON D E, AUSTIN B A and MURPHY R J (1992), 'Effects of high hydrostatic pressure on milk', *Milchwissenschaft*, 44(12), 760–763.

KALICHEVSKY M T, KNORR D and LILLFORD P J (1995), 'Potential food applications of high pressure effects on ice-water transitions', *Trends Food Sci Technol*, 6, 253–259.

KANDA Y and AOKI M (1993), 'Development of pressure-shift freezing. Part I. Observation of ice crystals of frozen tofu', in Hayashi, R (ed.), *High pressure bioscience and food science*, Sai-Ei Suppan Co., Kyoto, Japan, pp 27–33.

KIMURA K, IDA M, YOSHIDA Y, OHKI K, FUKUMOTO T and SAKUI N (1994), 'Comparison of keeping quality between pressure-processed and heat-processed jam: changes in flavour components, hue and nutritional elements during storage', *Biosci Biotechnol Biochem*, 58, 1386–1391.

KNORR D (1993), 'Effects of high-hydrostatic-pressure processes on food safety and quality', *Trends Food Sci Technol*, 4, 370–375.

KNORR D (1995a), 'Hydrostatic pressure treatment of food microbiology', in Gould G W (ed.), *New Methods of Food Preservation*, Glasgow, Blackie Academic and Professional, pp. 159–175.

KNORR D (1995b), 'High pressure effects on plant derived foods', in *High Pressure Processing of Foods*, Ledward D A, Johnston D E, Earnshaw R G and Hasting A P M (eds), Nottingham University Press, Loughborough, pp. 123–135.

KNORR D (2001), 'High pressure processing for preservation, modification and transformation of foods', oral presentation in XXXIX *European High Pressure Research Group Meeting*, Santander (Spain), 16–19 September 2001.

KNORR D, SCHLUETER O and HEINZ V (1998), 'Impact of high hydrostatic pressure on phase transition of foods', *Food Technol*, 52, 42–45.

KREBBERS B, MATSER A, KOETS M, BARTELS P and VAN DEN BERG R (2001), 'High pressure-temperature processing as an alternative for preserving basil', poster presentation in XXXIX *European High Pressure Research Group Meeting*, Santander (Spain), 16–19 September 2001.

LADO B H and YOUSEF A E (2002), 'Alternative food-preservation technologies: efficacy and mechanisms', *Microbes Infect*, 4(4), 433–440.

LEMOS M A C L (1998), *Kinetic studies on the thermal inactivation of horseradish peroxidase under extreme conditions: Application to the development of measuring systems of process impact on food quality and safety*, PhD dissertation, Escola Superior De Biotechnologica, Departemento de Estudos Graduados, Porto, Portugal.

LINTON M and PATTERSON M F (2000), 'High pressure processing of foods for microbiological safety and quality (a short review)', *Acta Microbiol Immunol Hung*, 47(2–3), 175–182.

LOPEZ-MALO A, PALOU E, BARBOSA-CÁNOVAS G V, WELTI-CHANES J and SWANSON B G (1998), 'Polyphenoloxidase activity and color changes during storage of high hydrostatic pressure treated avocado purée', *Food Res Int*, 31(8), 549–56.

LUDIKHUYZE L, INDRAWATI, VAN DEN BROECK I, WEEMAES C and HENDRICKX M (1998a), 'Effect of combined pressure and temperature on soybean lipoxygenase: I. Influence of extrinsic and intrinsic factors on isobaricisothermal inactivation kinetics', *J Agric Food Chem,* 46, 4074–80.

LUDIKHUYZE L, INDRAWATI, VAN DEN BROECK I, WEEMAES C and HENDRICKX M (1998b), 'Effect of combined pressure and temperature on soybean lipoxygenase: II. Modeling inactivation kinetics under static and dynamic conditions', *J Agric Food Chem,* 46, 4081–6.

LUDIKHUYZE L, OOMS V, WEEMAES C and HENDRICKX M (1999), 'Kinetic study of the irreversible thermal and pressure inactivation of myrosinase from broccoli (*Brassica oleracea* L. cv. Italica)', *J Agric Food Chem,* 47, 1794–1800.

LUDIKHUYZE L, RODRIGO L and HENDRICKX M (2000a), 'The activity of myrosinase from broccoli (*Brassica oleracea* L. cv. Italica): Influence of intrinsic and extrinsic factors', *J Food Prot,* 63(3), 400–403.

LUDIKHUYZE L, CLAEYS W and HENDRICKX M (2000b), 'Combined pressure-temperature inactivation of alkaline phosphatase in bovine milk: a kinetic study', *J Food Sci,* 65, 155–160.

LUDIKHUYZE L, CLAEYS W and HENDRICKX M (2001), 'Effect of temperature and/or pressure on lactoperoxidase activity in bovine milk and acid whey', *J Dairy Res,* 68, 625–637.

MAKITA T (1992), 'Application of high pressure and thermophysical properties of water to biotechnology', *Fluid Phase Equilibria,* 76, 87–95.

MARTINO M N, OTERO L, SANZ P D and ZARITZKY N E (1998), 'Size and location of ice crystals in pork frozen by high pressure assisted freezing as compared to classical methods', *Meat Sci,* 50(3), 303–313.

MATSER A M and BARTELS P V (1999), 'Nieuwe eigenschappen met bekende ingrediënten, *VMT,* 13, 30–32.

MERTENS B (1995), 'Hydrostatic *pressure* treatment of food: equipment and processing' in Gould G W (ed.), *New Methods of Food Preservation,* London, Blackie Academic and Professional, pp. 135–58.

MERTENS B and DEPLACE G (1993), 'Engineering aspects of high pressure technology in the food industry', *Food Technol,* 47(6), 164–9.

MESSENS W, VAN CAMP J and HUYGEBAERT A (1997), 'The use of high pressure to modify the functionality of food proteins', *Trends Food Sci Technol,* 8, 107–12.

MEYER R S, COOPER K L, KNORR D and LELIEVELD H L M (2000), 'High-pressure sterilization of foods', *Food Technol,* 54(11), 67–72.

MILLS G, EARNSHAW R and PATTERSON M F (1998), 'Effects of high hydrostatic pressure on *Clostridium sporogenes* spores', *Lett Appl Microbiol,* 26, 227–30.

MURAKAMI T, KIMURA I, YAMAGISHI T, YAMASHITA M and SATAKE M (1992), 'Thawing of frozen fish by hydrostatic pressure' in Balny C, Hayashi R, Heremans K and Masson P (eds), *High Pressure and Biotechnology,* Colloque INSERM/ John Libbey Ltd, pp. 329–331.

MUSSA D M and RAMASWAMY H S (1997), 'Ultra high pressure pasteurisation of milk: kinetics of microbial destruction and changes in physico-chemical characteristics', *Food Sci Technol,* 30, 551–557.

NOSE M, IWAKI A and HATTORI M (1994), 'Development of processing system of meat and meat products by introduction of high pressure treatment', in Hayashi R, Kunugi S, Shimada S and Suzuki A (eds), *High Pressure Bioscience,* Kyoto, San-Ei Suppan, pp. 270–272.

OGAWA H, FUKUHISA K, KUBO Y and FUKUMOTO H (1990), 'Pressure inactivation of yeasts, moulds and pectinesterase in Satsuma mandarin juice: effects of juice concentration, pH and organic acids and comparison with heat sanitation', *Agric Biol Chem,* 54, 1219–25.

OHMORI T, SHIGEHISA T, TAJI S and HAYASHI R (1991), 'Effect of high pressure on the protease activities in meat', *Biol Chem,* 55(2), 357–61.

OTERO L, SOLAS M T and SANZ P D (1998), 'Contrasting effects of high-pressure-assisted freezing and conventional air-freezing on eggplant tissue microstructure', *Z Lebensm Unters Forsch,* 206, 338–342.

PALOU E, HERNANDEZ-SALGADO C, LOPEZ-MALO A, BARBOSA-CÁNOVAS G V, SWANSON B G and WELTI J (2000), 'High pressure-processed guacamole', *Innovative Food Sci Emerg Technol,* 1, 69–75.

PARISH M E (1997), 'High pressure effects on quality of chilled orange juice', in Heremans K (ed.), *High Pressure Research in the Biosciences and Biotechnology,* Leuven, Leuven University Press, pp. 443–446.

PATTERSON M F, QUINN M, SIMPSON R and GILMOUR A (1995), 'Effects of high pressure on vegetable pathogens', in Ledward D A, Earnshaw R G and Hasting A P M (eds), *High Pressure Processing of Foods,* Nottingham, Nottingham University Press, pp. 47–63.

PÉREZ-MATEOS M and MONTERO P (1997), 'High-pressure-induced gel of sardine (*Sardina pilchardus*) washed mince as affected by pressure-time-temperature', *J Food Sci,* 62(6), 1183–1188.

POTHAKAMURY U R, BARBOSA-CÁNOVAS G V, SWANSON B G and MEYER R S (1995), 'The pressure builds for better food processing', *Chem Eng Progr,* March, 45–53.

QUAGLIA G B, GRAVINA R, PAPERI R and PAOLETTI F (1996), 'Effect of high pressure treatments on peroxidase activity, ascorbic acid content and texture in green peas', *Lebensm Wiss u Technol,* 29, 552–555.

REYNS K M F A, SOONTJES C C F, CORNELIS K, WEEMAES C A, HENDRICKX M E and MICHIELS C W (2000), 'Kinetic analysis and modelling of combined high pressure-temperature inactivation of the yeast *Zygosaccharomyces Bailii*', *Int J Food Microbiol,* 56, 199–210.

ROBERTS C M and HOOVER D G (1996), 'Sensitivity of *Bacillus coagulans* spores to combinations of high hydrostatic pressure, heat, acidity and nisin', *J Appl Bacteriol,* 81, 363–8.

SALE A J H, GOULD G W and HAMILTON W A (1970), 'Inactivation of bacterial spores by hydrostatic pressure', *J Gen Microbiol,* 60, 323–334.

SANCHO F, LAMBERT Y, DEMAZEAU G, LARGETEAU A, BOUVIER J M and NARBONNE J F (1999), 'Effect of ultra-high hydrostatic pressure on hydrosoluble vitamins', *J Food Eng,* 39, 247–253.

SEVERINI C, ROMANI S, DALL'AGLIO G, ROVERE P, CONTE L AND LERICI C R (1997), 'High pressure effects on oxidation of extra virgin olive oils', *It J Food Sci,* 3(9), 183–191.

SEYDERHELM I, BOGUSLAWSKI S, MICHAELIS G and KNORR D (1996), 'Pressure induced inactivation of selected food enzymes', *J Food Sci,* 61, 308–310.

SIERRA I, VIDAL-VALVERDE C and LOPEZ-FANDINO R (2000), 'Effect of high pressure on the vitamin B1 and B6 content of milk', *Milchwissenschaft,* 55(7), 365–367.

SMELT J P P M (1998), 'Recent advances in the microbiology of high pressure processing', *Trends Food Sci Technol,* 9, 152–158.

SMELT J P, HELLEMONS J C and PATTERSON M (2002), 'Effects of high pressure on vegetative microorganisms' in Hendrickx, M. and Knorr, D. (eds), *Ultra high pressure treatments of foods*, Kluwer Academic/Plenum Publishers, New York, United States, pp. 55–76.

SONOIKE K, SETOYAMA T, KUMA Y and KOBAYASHI S (1992), 'Effects of pressure and temperature on the death rates of *Lactobacillus casei* and *Escherichia coli*', in Balny C, Hayashi R, Heremans K and Masson P (eds), *High Pressure and Biotechnology 224*, Montrouge, John Libbey Eurotext, pp. 297–301.

TAKAHASHI K (1992), 'Sterilization of microorganisms by hydrostatic pressure at low temperature' in Balny, C., Hayashi, R., Heremans, K., Masson, P. (eds), *High pressure and biotechnology,* Colloque INSERM 224, John Libbey Eurotext Ltd.: France, pp. 303–307.

TAKAI R, KOZHIMA T T and SUZUKI T (1991), 'Low temperature thawing by using high pressure', in *Les Actes du XVIIeme Congrés International du Froid, Montreal, Quebec.*, Int. Inst. of Refrigeration, Paris, pp. 1951–1955.

TAUSCHER B (1998), 'Effect of high pressure treatment to nutritive substances and natural pigments', in Autio K (ed.), *Fresh novel foods by high pressure*, Technical Research Centre of Finland, VTT Symposium 186, Espoo, Finland, pp. 83–95.

TAUSCHER B (1999), 'Chemical reactions of food components under high hydrostatic pressure', in Ludwig H (ed.), *Advances in high pressure bioscience and biotechnology*, Springer, Heidelberg, pp 363–366.

TRÄFF A (1998), 'A 600 MPa press for food processing', presentation at the Nordic Network Seminar on Non-thermal Processing Technologies, SIK, Göteborg, Sweden, 9 March.

VAN DEN BROECK I (2000), '*Kinetics of Temperature and Pressure Inactivation of Pectinesterase from Oranges and Tomatoes*', PhD dissertation no. 415, Katholieke Universiteit Leuven, Belgium.

VAN DEN BROECK I, LUDIKHUYZE L, WEEMAES C, VAN LOEY A and HENDRICKX M (1998), 'Kinetics for isobaric-isothermal degradation of L-ascorbic acid', *J Agric Food Chem*, 46, 2001–2006.

VAN DEN BROECK I, LUDIKHUYZE L R, VAN LOEY A M and HENDRICKX M E (2000), 'Effect of temperature and/or pressure on tomato pectinesterase activity', *J Agric Food Chem,* 48, 551–8.

VAN LOEY A, OOMS V, WEEMAES C, VAN DEN BROECK I, LUDIKHUYZE L, INDRAWATI, DENYS S and HENDRICKX M (1998), 'Thermal and pressure-temperature degradation of chlorophyll in broccoli (*Brassica oleracea* L. italica) juice: a kinetic study', *J Agric Food Chem*, 46(12), 2785–2792.

WADA S (1992), 'Quality and lipid change of sardine meat by high pressure treatment', in Balny C, Hayashi R, Heremans K and Masson P (eds), *High pressure and biotechnology 224*, John Libbey Eurotext, Ltd., Montrouge, pp. 235–238.

WADA S and OGAWA Y (1996), 'High pressure effects on lipid degradation: myoglobin change and water holding capacity', in Hayashi R and Balny C (eds), *High pressure bioscience and biotechnology*, Elsevier Science B.V., Amsterdam, pp. 351–356.

WATHELET J P, MABON N, FOUCART M and MARLIER M (1996), 'Influence du blanchiment sur la qualité du chou de Bruxelles (*Brassica oleracea* L cv. Gemmifera)', *Sci. Aliment.*, 116, 393–402.

WEEMAES C (1998), *Temperature and/or pressure inactivation of polyphenoloxidases for prevention of enzymatic browning in foods: a Kinetic Study*, PhD dissertation, Katholieke Universiteit Leuven, Belgium.

WEEMAES C, OOMS V, LUDIKHUYZE L, VAN DEN BROECK I, VAN LOEY A and HENDRICKX M
    (1999), 'Pressure-temperature degradation of green color in broccoli juice', *J Food
    Sci*, 64, 504–508.
WUYTACK E Y (1999), *Pressure-induced germination and inactivation of bacillus subtilis
    spores*, PhD dissertation, Katholieke Universiteit Leuven, Belgium.
YEN G C and LIN H T (1996), 'Comparison of high pressure treatment and thermal
    pasteurisation on the quality and shelf life of guava puree', *Int J Food Sci Technol*,
    31, 205–13.
YOSHIOKA K, KAGE Y and OMURA H (1992), 'Effect of high pressure on texture and
    ultrastructure of fish and chicken muscles and their gels', in Balny C, Hayashi R,
    Heremans K and Masson P (eds), *High Pressure and Biotechnology,* Colloque
    INSERM/John Libbey Ltd, pp. 325–327.
YUSTE J, CAPPELAS M, PLA R, FUNG D Y C and MOR-MUR M (2001a), 'High pressure
    processing for food safety and preservation: a review', *J Rapid Methods and
    Automation in Microbiology*, 9, 1–10.
YUSTE J, PLA R, CAPPELAS M, SENDRA E, BELTRAN E and MOR-MUR M (2001b), 'Oscillatory
    high pressure processing applied to mechanically recovered poultry meat for
    bacterial inactivation', *J Food Sci*, 66, 482–484.
ZHAO Y, FLORES R A and OLSON D G (1996), 'The action of high hydrostatic pressure on the
    thawing of frozen meat', poster presentation at the 1996 IFT Annual Meeting, New
    Orleans, USA.
ZHAO Y, FLORES R A and OLSON D G (1998), 'High hydrostatic pressure effects on rapid
    thawing of frozen beef', *J Food Sci*, 63, 272–275.

# Part IV

# Assessing preservation requirements

# 20

# Modelling food spoilage

J. Sutherland, University of North London, UK

## 20.1 Introduction: spoilage mechanisms

Spoilage of food is still a relatively poorly understood process and can involve many facets. It is an economically significant problem for food manufacturers, retailers and consumers. Consumers assess spoilage through visual and olfactory impressions, e.g., raw meat may be judged as spoiled when it has lost its characteristic bright red colour. The subjective nature of spoilage is exemplified by mould-ripened cheese, which is regarded as a delicacy by some consumers, but is repulsive to others and a further example is game, which after hanging has a characteristic odour, caused by the presence of sulphydryl compounds.

Food spoilage can occur as a consequence of intrinsic physical or chemical changes in the food, or as a consequence of the activities of micro-organisms as they multiply in the food, causing undesirable sensory changes. Microbial numbers *per se* are not always a guide to the extent of spoilage, but microbial activity is extremely important, e.g., micro-organisms produce enzymes such as lipases and proteases which cause breakdown of proteins and fats. This process releases organic compounds, which may or may not be volatile. Volatile compounds are generally responsible for the off-odours and flavours associated with spoiling foods and non-volatile metabolites can also contribute to off-flavours.

According to Gram and Huss (1996), manifestations of overt spoilage include:

- production of extra-cellular polysaccharides, causing the appearance of visible slime on the food
- gas production, e.g., carbon dioxide, with consequent splitting or cracking of the product and swelling of vacuum packs

- production of diffusible pigments, resulting in discolouration
- growth of moulds, yeast and bacteria to the extent that distinct colonies are visible on the spoiling food.

Raw perishable foods tend to contain a variety of micro-organisms, but according to the environmental conditions in the food, e.g., temperature of storage, pH value, water activity ($a_w$) and presence of preservatives, one particular organism or group of organisms generally becomes predominant during storage and is likely ultimately to spoil that food. The micro-organisms themselves can change the conditions in the food, e.g., by increasing the pH value due to their metabolic activities, creating a 'window of opportunity' for another organism to develop and become dominant, thus creating a spoilage succession. The mechanisms of spoilage successions and other factors that cause one group of micro-organisms to become dominant over others are not fully understood. It is known that onset of spoilage can be influenced by factors such as the condition of the substrate, e.g., raw meat of high pH value has a lower glucose content and onset of spoilage occurs at lower cell numbers than in meat of normal pH value and higher glucose content (Gill 1983). The spoilage microflora of high pH meat tends to be Enterobacteriaceae and *Shewanella putrefaciens* (Dainty 1996), while the predominant spoilage agents of meat of normal pH are generally pseudomonads. Furthermore, spoilage succession can be affected by the nature and duration of any processing applied to the product, the type of packaging, and even the geographical region in which harvesting, processing and manufacturing takes place.

## 20.2    Approaches to spoilage modelling

It has long been the aim of food microbiologists and chemists to identify a marker for spoilage, i.e., a chemical compound of microbiological origin which is easily detectable in the food, increases in quantity as deterioration progresses and, if present, is invariably a sign that spoilage of the food will occur. The marker should be an end-product of metabolism, since some metabolites can be further metabolised. Examples of possible markers include gluconic acid, lactic acid, acetic acid and ethanol (Skandamis and Nychas 2001). Predictive microbiologists have the ambition to quantify such compounds and measure increases in the food with time, so that a predictive model for food spoilage can be constructed. However, the reality is not straightforward. Skandamis and Nychas (2001) observed that methods to determine spoilage by chemical or biochemical techniques are generally not applicable in practice, probably because they can be so readily influenced by packaging methods or use of preservatives.

Prediction of spoilage is more complex than prediction of pathogen growth because, apart from the straightforward aspects of increase in microbial number, spoilage prediction should also include some measure of the activities of micro-organisms, resulting in a distinction between spoilage models and growth models for food spoilage micro-organisms. Dalgaard (1995) introduced the concept of specific spoilage organisms (SSO), where the organism responsible for spoilage of a product may be present in lower numbers than other organisms, but the more numerous organisms may have a less deleterious effect on the quality of the food. Spoilage of chilled vacuum- or modified-atmosphere packed cod had always been associated with high numbers of *Shewanella putrefaciens*, but Dalgaard (1995) identified *Photobacterium phosphoreum* as the actual spoilage agent, since despite being present in lower numbers, it produced more of the main spoilage metabolite, trimethylamine (TMA), than *Sh. putrefaciens*. Thus it is important not to assume that because an organism is present in high numbers, it will inevitably be the primary cause of spoilage of the particular food. The relationship between numbers and spoilage activity is not well defined, although Ellis *et al.* (2002) noted a correlation between overt spoilage of chicken meat at 20 °C and a total viable count (TVC) of $10^7$ cfu/g *Pseudomonas* spp. However, Braun and Sutherland (in press) observed (in microbiological media) that at temperatures of 2–6 °C, protease activity occurred and lipases were produced when pseudomonads achieved numbers of only $10^4 - 10^5$ cfu/ml.

The main aim of the European Union project FAIR CT-98 4083 (funded under Framework 5) was to develop generic spoilage models for perishable foods. The project was approached by categorising the main food spoilage micro-organisms into six groups of broadly similar organisms (pseudomonads, yeasts, Enterobacteriaceae, *Brochothrix thermosphacta*, lactic acid bacteria and bacilli). Each group was inoculated as a cocktail of component strains into liquid media with pH and $a_w$ values pre-adjusted to conditions representative of foods and stored at temperatures between 2 and 20 °C. At intervals during growth microbial numbers were estimated, enzyme production (lipases) and activity (proteases) were measured and organic metabolic compounds related to increases in numbers of micro-organisms were measured using gas chromatographic methods and Fourier transform infra-red (FTIR) spectrometry. Suitable data were modelled and the models verified and validated by inoculation of specific foods.

## 20.3    Developing spoilage models

The following points need consideration prior to and during development of models and decisions need to be based on what is required from the model.

### 20.3.1    Selection of strains of micro-organisms

The strains used to develop predictive models are of considerable importance. In some published models, only one strain of a specific micro-organism has been used, but in most cases, a cocktail of strains was used. Generally, the aim is to include at least one strain in the cocktail that is particularly resistant to each environmental condition under investigation, e.g., one strain that can grow well at low temperature, one that is more resistant than other strains to low pH value, etc. This will increase confidence in the ability of the model to predict with accuracy throughout the range of environmental scenarios. It is possible that interactions may occur between the different strains of micro-organisms used in the cocktail. This may be particularly likely with lactic acid bacteria, but mutual inhibition is also reported to occur among Gram-negative organisms (Gram and Melchiorsen 1996). Moreover, in real situations, perishable foods generally contain an indigenous or adventitious mixed microflora, which can affect the growth rate of the organism(s) of interest and consequently cause differences from predicted growth rates.

### 20.3.2   Experimental design

The experimental design can have an important effect on the predictive capability of the model ultimately produced. A number of predictive models have been based on the central composite design or some modification of it (Palumbo et al. 1992, Abdullah et al. 1994, Guerzoni et al. 1996, Cheroutre-Vialette and Lebert 2000). The central composite design assumes there will be constant variability of data above and below the central or optimum point. However, this is not necessarily the case with microbial growth in foods, since the further from optimum conditions for microbial growth in foods (or media), the greater the potential variability of the growth rates of micro-organisms growing in those conditions.

A more useful approach is an empirical experimental design, founded on the basis that the further the data produced is from optimum conditions, the greater will be the variability of the data. A good or robust model is one that has minimal variability. It is therefore advisable to concentrate data-gathering experiments in sub-optimal conditions, particularly in regions where variability of experimental results is likely to be greatest, notably near the growth/no growth interface. Some experiments should ideally be set up in the same conditions two or three times and all the growth data (not just the 'best') included in the curve-fitting and modelling processes. This will have the effect of smoothing the variability of the data and help to ensure that the model will provide reliable and realistic predictions in the sub-optimal conditions that generally prevail in refrigerated foods.

Figure 20.1 shows the experimental plan used for generation of microbiological data for Enterobacteriaceae in the FAIR CT98-4083 project. Each point in the three-dimensional matrix (i.e., the nominal variables space) of environmental conditions represents a combination of conditions at which data for a growth curve was prepared.

### 20.3.3   Generic versus specific models

Generic models are those that have been produced in microbiological media adjusted as required to represent a range of environmental conditions. However,

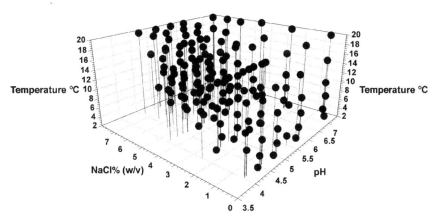

**Fig. 20.1**   Distribution of growth curves through the environmental conditions for
Enterobacteriaceae (FAIR CT98-4083).

specific models are those in which a particular food itself has been modified to
different specifications of pH, $a_w$ and/or preservative concentration and
incubated at a range of temperatures. Which is the better method has been a
matter for debate among predictive microbiologists. Supporters of the principle
of food inoculation believe that only by using the particular food of interest can
a valuable and applicable model be constructed, relevant to the specific
circumstances. However, this can result in a plethora of models of relatively, and
in some cases, extremely limited applicability. Furthermore, it is highly labour
intensive to prepare a range of models using this procedure. Nevertheless, a
number of models based on direct estimates of growth of micro-organisms
inoculated into foods have been published (Nicolai *et al.* 1993; Abdullah *et al.*
1994).

The alternative approach, preparation of generic models in microbiological
media, readily allows adjustments to encompass a variety of environmental
conditions. It is necessary to accept in these circumstances that the growth rate
of inoculated micro-organisms will almost invariably be more rapid than in any
food of similar environmental conditions, since there will be no constraints by
competition from indigenous organisms or the structure of the food itself.
Consequently, the main disadvantage of using media is that in some cases the
predictions from the model can be extremely conservative. It is therefore
advisable to verify and validate the applicability of generic models to foods of
particular interest.

### 20.3.4   Model verification and validation

In the project FAIR CT98-4083, the following procedures for verification and
validation of models were used. To verify models, the same cocktail of micro-
organisms which was used to construct the model was inoculated into specified

sterile foods, or foods which contained very low numbers of indigenous organisms, and incubated at a given temperature. As the organisms grew, they were enumerated and ancillary measurements made, including enzyme production or activity and increases with time of volatile and non-volatile metabolites. The growth curves produced in the food were compared with the original curves generated in media (under equivalent conditions) and/or with predictions from the model. This provides an indication of the intermediate error, attributable to the food itself, distinct from errors introduced by the presence of indigenous micro-organisms (Pin *et al.* 1999).

Figure 20.2 shows comparisons of predicted curves (thicker line) with observed growth curves (thinner line, fitted to data points) derived from inoculated commercially sterile foods. Figure 20.2a demonstrates predicted growth of pseudomonads in UHT cream at 4 °C, in which the prediction is very close to the observation. Figures 20.2b and 2c (Enterobacteriaceae in UHT cream at 4 °C and *Br. thermospacta* in irradiated raw minced beef at 6 °C, respectively) show more divergence between the predicted and actual growth curves but the prediction is slightly faster, indicating that it is 'fail-safe'. Generally, greater divergence between predicted and measured growth curves is encountered in more heterogeneous foods, e.g., meat (see also section 20.7.3), suggesting that the structure of the substrate itself is limiting growth, resulting in the 'intermediate error' of Pin *et al.* (1999).

Validation of models involved allowing foods to spoil 'naturally' (i.e., without inoculation) at given temperatures and estimating both the TVC and numbers of specific groups of spoilage micro-organisms, using selective media and also recording consequential increases in organic metabolites and enzyme synthesis or activity. This provided an indication of the overall error of the model, including the effects of the presence of other organisms and the food itself (Pin *et al.* 1999). Such experiments can have more chance of successfully validating models than use of data derived from the literature (see below), since all relevant environmental conditions (pH and $a_w$ values, temperature, concentration of preservatives, etc.) can be measured. However, success in validation using this procedure can be limited if the micro-organism in question is not present or not detected in the food.

Analysis of information available from existing publications can also be used to validate predictive models. Measured (observed) lag times, growth rates, generation times or times to a given increase in microbial number can be extracted from existing publications and compared with predictions from the model for the same growth conditions (Sutherland and Bayliss 1994, Miles *et al.* 1997, Neumeyer *et al.* 1997b). Performance of models can be judged using the bias and accuracy factors (Ross 1996, Baranyi *et al.*, 1999), which measure the discrepancy between predicted and observed values. However, so many disadvantages are associated with the use of public domain data (Sutherland and Bayliss 1994) that Neumeyer *et al.* (1997b) commented that 'it may be more appropriate to use [for validation] data that has been derived in controlled conditions rather than using literature data, where full details of the growth

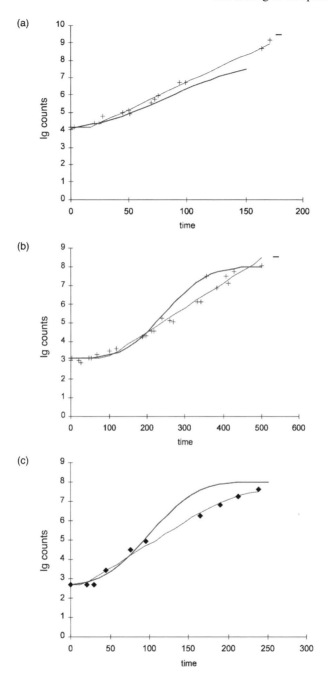

**Fig. 20.2** Comparison of predicted and observed growth curves in inoculated food studies. (a) UHT cream inoculated with $10^4$ cfu/ml pseudomonads incubated at 4 °C. (b) UHT cream inoculated with $10^3$ cfu/ml Enterobacteriaceae incubated at 4 °C. (c) Irradiated raw minced beef inoculated with $10^3$ cfu/g *Br. thermosphacta* incubated at 6 °C.

conditions may not be known, so that the model's performance is not unfairly prejudiced by comparisons to unrepresentative or poor quality data'.

## 20.4    Measurement techniques

Some techniques for data acquisition for predictive microbiology are well established but others are still at a developmental stage.

### 20.4.1    Enumeration of micro-organisms

Estimation of TVC of micro-organisms during growth in specific environmental conditions is still the most commonly employed technique for data generation and the procedures are detailed in many publications, e.g., Gibson *et al.* (1988), McClure *et al.* (1993), Pin and Baranyi (1998). The advantages of viable counting techniques are that they are rapid and easy to carry out, do not require expensive or specialist materials or equipment and the results are generally consistent and reliable. However, the procedure is highly labour intensive and there is inevitably at least a 24–48 hour delay before the results of sampling are available.

### 20.4.2    Optical density measurements

Initially, optical density (OD) data were difficult to model because of specific difficulties, which are fully documented by McMeekin *et al.* (1993). One of the main problems is that visible (measurable) turbidity is not observed until numbers of micro-organisms achieve $10^5 - 10^6$ cfu/ml, so the entire lag phase duration and early- to mid-exponential phase cannot be measured. However, modification of experimental procedures and mathematical developments in handling data derived from OD methods mean that the technique has become more useful. Detection times (i.e., the times taken for the optical density to achieve a measurable level from different inoculum concentrations) can be measured and used to estimate growth parameters (Hudson 1993), but the variance of the detection time increases as the inoculum size decreases. However, Baranyi and Pin (1999) used the 'physiological state theorem' of Baranyi (1998) to minimise this variability and reliably estimated bacterial growth parameters using OD techniques. Neumeyer *et al.* (1997a) used turbidimetric measurements, calibrated against viable counts, to determine generation times and construct a model for *Pseudomonas* spp.

### 20.4.3    Measurement of increases in metabolic compounds

In principle, the quantities of metabolites that cause off-odours and/or off-flavours (i.e., spoilage) produced by the activities of micro-organisms during growth, should be related directly to the number of organisms in the food or broth. It is a concern, however, that metabolic pathways of micro-organisms may alter under the influence of different environmental conditions and this possibility should be investigated by preliminary experiments before a major programme of data generation is commenced.

*Volatile metabolites*
Volatile compounds produced by micro-organisms during growth can be trapped and collected from the headspace above the substrate (microbiological media or food) in which the organism is growing. Guerzoni *et al.* (1990) used gas chromatographic techniques to measure volumes of carbon dioxide evolved during growth of *Saccharomyces cerevisiae* to predict shelf life of fruit-based products. This metabolite appears to correlate well with microbial growth under a wide range of environmental conditions and the technique was used in the FAIR CT98-4083 project to develop predictive models for food spoilage by *Brochothrix thermosphacta*, *Pseudomonas* and related genera and Enterobacteriaceae. The technique did not work well for a cocktail of yeast strains because biphasic curves were produced, probably because of differing rates of evolution of $CO_2$ by the different constituents of the cocktail. In the same project, accumulation of 3-methyl-butanol (3-MB) is being used as a measure of growth by *Br. thermosphacta* to model growth and spoilage by this organism.

Figure 20.3 shows predicted and observed values for TVC, percentage of $CO_2$ and logarithm of the peak area (LPA) of 3-MB (on the chromatogram) during growth of *Br. thermosphacta* at 10 °C, pH 6.0 and sodium chloride (NaCl) concentration 5.5%. The viable count data corresponds more closely to its prediction than the metabolites. The $CO_2$ data can be used to predict spoilage in terms of time to 'detectable $CO_2$ production', but should not be used to predict the $CO_2$ production rate. The volatile compound 3-MB is detected later during the phase of growth; the rate is 'modellable', but the concentration is low.

Metabolic data for predictive modelling is best generated using a large-capacity, fully automated gas chromatography system, where many samples can be retained for repeated sampling in a dedicated incubator assigned to a gas chromatograph with an automatic sampling facility, but such systems are, of course, expensive. Where a less or non-automated system is available, with a significant amount of manual input, the number of samples may be limited to only 10–12 per working day. In such circumstances, the need to take frequent samples when growth is rapid at or near optimal conditions, can be difficult to accommodate.

*Other metabolites*
While volatile metabolic compounds produced by micro-organisms can be extracted from the headspace above the medium (or food), non-volatile metabolic compounds need to be extracted from the substrate itself before quantification. Examples of these compounds include D- and L-lactic acid, acetic acid and ethanol, occurring as a consequence of the activities of homo-

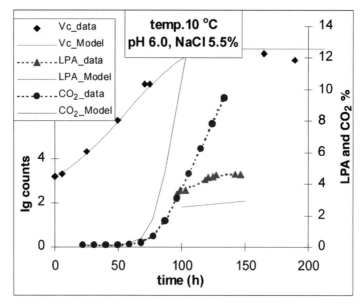

Vc_data: viable counts of *Br. thermosphacta* at 10 °C, pH 6.0 and NaCl 5.5%
Vc_model: predicted growth curve for *Br. thermosphacta*
LPA_data: logarithm of peak areas of 3-methyl butanol derived experimentally
LPA_model: LPA of 3-MB predicted by the model
$CO_2$ data: percentage of $CO_2$ in headspace derived experimentally
$CO_2$_model: percentage of $CO_2$ predicted by the model

**Fig. 20.3**    Demonstration of growth of *Brochothrix thermosphacta* with simultaneous
production of $CO_2$ and 3-methyl butanol (FAIR CT98-4083).

and hetero-fermentative lactic acid bacteria.

Fourier-Transform Infra-Red (FTIR) spectroscopy is a technique which is
able to carry out rapid, multi-component analyses of systems (Vannini *et al.*
1996) and record changes with time of functional groups on the basis of
absorbances of the spectrum of specific wavebands. This allows study of the
dynamics of microbial growth by tracing accumulation of metabolites and/or
depletion of substrate components. Ellis *et al.* (2002) used FTIR spectroscopy to
determine the progress of spoiling chicken meat at 20 °C. FTIR spectroscopy is
in use in the FAIR CT98-4083 project to generate data for construction of a
model for growth of lactic acid bacteria by measuring increases in lactic and
acetic acids and decrease in glucose content of the growth medium.

### 20.4.4    Impedance/conductance measurements
These methods use the principle of measuring changes in conductance or
impedance in a liquid medium during microbial growth as an indirect measure
of microbial number. The changes in impedance or conductance are caused by
breakdown of mainly uncharged or weakly charged substrates (proteins,

carbohydrates and lipids) into smaller, highly charged moieties (amino acids, organic acids) which increase conductivity of the medium. The attraction of impedance or conductance methods for data acquisition for predictive modelling is that they are less labour intensive than some other techniques and results can be obtained relatively rapidly. However, few publications are available on the use of this technique in predictive microbiology. This may be because the technique generally requires considerable development in terms of optimisation of specific media for individual micro-organisms (Szigeti and Farkas 2000). However, Borch and Wallentin (1993) and Wallentin Lindberg (1994) used conductance measurements to develop a model for *Yersinia enterocolitica*, while Deak and Beuchat (1994) used indirect conductance measurements for prediction of growth of food spoilage yeasts.

### 20.4.5   Luminescence techniques
*Luciferin/luciferase reaction*
In experiments using this reaction, a given volume of medium containing growing cells is removed at recorded times and the cells lysed to release ATP. The luciferin/luciferase reaction system is added to the lysed cell suspension and the following reactions take place:

$$Mg++$$

luciferin + luciferase + ATP  →  luciferin/luciferase/AMP + pyrophosphate
complex

luciferin/luciferase/AMP + $O_2$  →  oxyluciferin + luciferase + AMP + $CO_2$ + light
complex

The light thus released can be harnessed, measured and related to bacterial number by means of a calibration curve. Although it gives rapid results, this technique is not widely used to generate data for predictive microbiology, probably because of the expense of the equipment and pre-prepared consumables required. Furthermore, the success of the procedure can be compromised by interference from somatic and other environmental ATP and the sometimes unreliable results obtained when measuring bacterial numbers of less than $10^4$ cfu/ml.

*Lux genes*
A second technique employing bioluminescence involves incorporating lux genes into the genetic material of a micro-organism for which it is required to produce a model. The organism is inoculated into different environmental conditions and as it grows, light emission by viable cells can be measured. The light reduces in intensity as the organisms are subjected to increasingly inimical environmental conditions, as a consequence of impairment of cellular metabolism, thus affecting viability (Dodd *et al.* 1996). Again, the technique is not widely used in developing predictive models.

### 20.4.6   Measurement of enzyme synthesis and activity

Measurement of the amount of lipase produced and activity of proteases have been investigated as possible techniques to estimate shelf life (Braun *et al.* 1999) and generate data to model spoilage (Braun and Sutherland, in press). It was found that the amount or activity of the enzyme produced did not relate to the viable count of the micro-organism under investigation at low temperatures (2–6 °C) in particular, confirming that there may not be a direct relationship between microbial number and enzyme activity or amount of enzyme produced. Most enzyme synthesis took place during the stationary phase of growth. Since the curve of Baranyi *et al.* (1993) was developed to fit the exponential phase of microbial growth, difficulties were encountered in fitting it to the enzymatic data; consequently it was not possible to produce a satisfactory model for enzyme production or activity.

## 20.5   Constructing models

Construction of predictive models is generally a two-stage procedure, although Whiting and Buchanan (1993) included a third stage; the user interface, consisting of appropriate application tools and software packages.

### 20.5.1   First stage

This involves determination of growth responses to different environmental conditions and determining the parameters, e.g., growth rate (or maximum specific growth rate), maximum cellular number, lag time, or time to achieve a given quantity of a suitable metabolite, for each condition. In most cases, this involves fitting a curve to the data generated. The Gompertz curve, or some modification of it (e.g., Zwietering *et al.* 1990), is commonly used. However, the curve of Baranyi *et al.* (1993) fits a straight line to the exponential phase and is often considered more appropriate for growth of micro-organisms than the sigmoid shape of the Gompertz curve.

### 20.5.2   Second stage

This stage of model construction demonstrates the interdependence between the parameters derived from the first stage of modelling and the environmental conditions. The Arrhenius relationship, where the natural logarithm of the growth rate is inversely proportional to the absolute temperature, can be used and this relationship can be extended to include other factors such as pH and $a_w$. Belehradec or square root models are based on the linear relationship between the square root of the growth rate and the difference between the growth temperature and the theoretical minimum growth temperature. These models can also be expanded to include other factors.

Polynomial equations make no assumptions about relationships between growth controlling factors and growth rate, and the effect of several variables on growth rate is determined simultaneously. To avoid over-parameterisation, and in the interests of parsimony, non-significant coefficients can be identified by statistical testing and omitted (Pin and Baranyi 1998). These models can be improved by careful attention to experimental design; an empirical design where most data are generated around the 'edges' of the growth region gives more reliable predictions than the central composite design (see above).

It is important to recognise that the limits of the experimental conditions do not necessarily correspond to the limits of the model, unless every condition examined has resulted in a suitable growth curve. The limits of the model are encompassed by the strict interpolation region, or minimal convex polyhedron (Baranyi *et al.* 1996). The minimal convex polyhedron for Enterobacteriaceae in the FAIR CT980-4083 project is shown in Fig. 20.4 (compare with the nominal variables space; Fig. 20.1)

Recently, artificial neural networks (ANN) have been used in predictive microbiology (Geeraerd *et al.* 1998). These were developed from an attempt to apply the principles of the nervous system to data processing and decision-making. The advantages, described by Garcia-Gimeno *et al.* (2002) include lower standard errors of prediction compared with response surface models, ability to 'prune' the ANN, i.e., to remove unnecessary parameters (weights) during training of the network without losing capability and an ability to handle situations where parameters are not uniformly distributed. Neural networks can 'learn' from previous examples by iteration, without the need for first-hand knowledge of the relationships between variables (Cheroutre-Vialette and Lebert 2000).

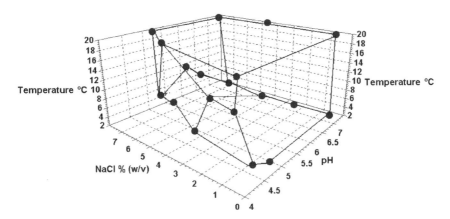

**Fig. 20.4**    The minimal convex polyhedron, or strict interpolation region, for Enterobacteriaceae (FAIR CT98-4083).

## 20.6   Applications of spoilage models

The ultimate test for predictive models is whether they can be used to predict reliable outcomes in real situations. Some of the main possibilities for use of models are discussed below, while McMeekin and Ross (1996) have published a more detailed commentary.

### 20.6.1   Product development and modification

There are considerable advantages in being able to predict the consequences, in terms of growth of specific micro-organisms, that cause deterioration of food (or foodborne disease) during the development process of a new food product or alternatively, during reformulation of an existing one. In former years, this has been achieved by costly and time-consuming shelf life testing and challenge testing with the organism of interest. Use of a predictive model incorporated in user-friendly software, which permits the operator to make changes to the environmental factors controlling microbial growth (e.g., temperature, pH, $a_w$, type and concentration of preservative) of relevant micro-organisms, allows identification of the likely spoilage status of different formulations of a particular food. Nevertheless, it is always advisable to check predictions with a limited amount of laboratory testing.

### 20.6.2   Process control and optimisation

Predictive models have a role to play in quality assurance, e.g., in the context of process control and determination of the optimum processing conditions for a food product. Use of a model to predict thermal death rates for relevant spoilage (and pathogenic) micro-organisms during heat processing of a food can allow adjustment of the process to ensure destruction of the organisms. Following heating, the cooling regime can be optimised to prevent, or at least limit, growth of organisms which may survive processing or which occur adventitiously on the processed product. This can be achieved by use of a model that predicts growth rates at a series of time-temperature programmes for a given spoilage organism.

   Use of predictive models means that decisions regarding product quality can be made with confidence, e.g., if there is a temporary failure of temperature control over a batch of a chilled product, it may need to be destroyed. However, provided that there is no danger of growth of food-borne pathogens, use of a model to predict 'worst possible scenarios' in terms of spoilage may mean that the product can be retrieved and damage limitation measures implemented, e.g., reduced shelf life.

### 20.6.3   Shelf life determination

Associated with product formulation is the use of predictive models to determine the likely shelf life of perishable foods. The importance of this is that it allows decisions on food quality and can thus provide commercial advantages, e.g., evaluation of the possibility of marketing a food on an international rather than countrywide basis. Examples of shelf life assessment using predictive models include the process risk model of Rasmussen *et al.* (2002) which used a predictive model for *Pseudomonas* growth (Neumeyer *et al.* 1997b) to determine the shelf life of Atlantic salmon fillets. Predictions of growth rates for *Pseudomonas* spp. and the TVC for the fish and slurry water revealed that the predicted shelf life of 6.5 days corresponded very closely with that observed (6.2 days) at 4 °C. Other examples of the use of models for predicting shelf life include the application of a shelf life decision system (SLDS) to predict the quality of marine fish (Koutsoumanis *et al.* 2002) and Sumner and Krist (2002) discussed the application of predictive models in the Australian meat industry. As well as having pathogenic properties, *Bacillus cereus* can cause spoilage of milk and Zwietering *et al.* (1996) used three different models and two literature sources to determine numbers of this micro-organism in pasteurised milk at the point of consumption and concluded that the models could give appropriate predictions. However, as in the case of product development and reformulation, these authors warn that models should not be relied on completely, but should be used as a tool to assist decision-making.

## 20.7    Limitations of models

'All models are wrong. The question is, how wrong do they have to be not to be useful?' (Box and Draper, 1987). This apposite quotation supports the comment that despite some problems, immense progress has been made in predictive microbiology during the last 20 years. As a science, it is still in its infancy and new developments are constantly taking place. The important point is that predicted response patterns are consonant with reality and the concept of predictive modelling should not be abandoned because of current limitations. Discussions of problems with predictive models are detailed by Knockel and Gould (1995), McMeekin *et al.* (1997) and ter Steeg and Ueckert (2002). The main difficulties are outlined below.

### 20.7.1    Lag phase predictions
It is acknowledged that growth models generally do not predict the lag phase duration of micro-organisms as efficiently as the growth rate. The growth rate of a particular micro-organism is an intrinsic feature of that organism, i.e., it depends only on the current environmental conditions, is not affected by the prior history of the cells and will always be the same for those conditions. However, the lag phase is dependent on the physiological state of the inoculum, which can be affected by many conditions and this can introduce considerable variation into the length of the lag phase (Robinson *et al.* 1998, 2001; Augustin

and Carlier 1999). The inoculum age (Pirt 1975) and size (Robinson *et al.* 2001) and the degree of injury, temperature, pH and $a_w$ (including the nature of the solute used to modify the $a_w$) can all affect the physiological condition of the inoculum (Robinson *et al.* 1998), and subsequently, the lag. These factors contrive to make the lag phase difficult to predict.

### 20.7.2    Changes in environmental conditions

In realistic conditions of food retailing, temperature variation can occur to a greater or lesser degree at many stages, including prior storage, distribution, at the point of sale in shops and after purchase by the consumer and there is concern that predictive models may not be able to provide satisfactory responses. Furthermore, the pH value of a product can change during manufacture and subsequent storage, e.g., during the fermentation process and $a_w$ can change in some circumstances, e.g., during drying of a product. In fermented meats such as salami, there is a pH decrease combined with a decrease in $a_w$ as the product ferments and dries. Moreover, the fermentation and drying processes are carried out at different temperatures. Products of this complexity present a considerable challenge in predictive microbiology.

Some attempts have been made to model the effects of temperature fluctuations on growth rates of micro-organisms, e.g., Baranyi *et al.* (1995) developed a model for *Br. thermosphacta* to predict growth at changing temperatures. This is made possible by the use of a factor ($\alpha_0$) which is a measure of the physiological condition of the organism (Baranyi and Roberts 1994). Specifically, the $\alpha_0$ value is a measure of the 'readiness to grow' of the cell, where a low value (e.g., 0.01) indicates that the cells will take some time to adjust to a new environment (i.e., are not 'ready to grow') but as the $\alpha_0$ value approaches 1, less adjustment will be needed and the lag phase will be correspondingly reduced. It was found that predictions of growth rate were well represented by observed data when temperature was decreased stepwise from 25 to 5 °C, but not when the decrease was from 25 to 3 °C (Baranyi *et al.* 1995) and it was hypothesised that at the lower temperature the physiological state of the cells was altered, possibly introducing additional lag.

### 20.7.3    Conservative nature of predictions

It is sometimes claimed that predictive models are excessively 'fail-safe', i.e., predictions of growth rate may be appreciably faster than the reality, providing a substantial, often unrealistic, margin of safety (Wilson *et al.* 2002). This is almost invariably the case when models are prepared in liquid medium such as nutrient broth, whereas in foods there are other unquantified inhibitory factors. A degree of over-prediction may be considered desirable, since it provides a margin of safety for the product. However, excessively 'fail-safe' predictions mean that product may be discarded when it is still acceptable, with consequent economic losses.

Some foods are uniformly liquid in structure, with possibly some suspended material e.g., fruit juice, but most are structured in some way, e.g., they may be gels, oil-in-water or water-in-oil emulsions, gelled emulsions, or they may have a solid surface (Wilson *et al.* 2002). All these types of structures support microbial growth, often in micro-environments within the major structure. Temperature is generally constant throughout a food stored in conditions of consistent temperature but pH value can vary, first as a consequence of the nature of the micro-environment and secondly, the pH of the micro-environment can be modulated by the metabolic activities of the organisms growing therein. A perceived limitation of models is that, if prepared in homogeneous systems, they may be considered not representative of conditions within the structure of a food. Attempts to explore micro-environments and the activities of micro-organisms within them, in order to improve modelling capability, were reported by Wilson *et al.* (2002).

Predictions from medium-based models have very occasionally been reported as 'fail-dangerous' (Walls *et al.* 1996). Nevertheless, successful uses of models in practice are reported (see above). There is currently no set of criteria which enables a model to be described as 'valid' (McMeekin and Ross 2002). However, verification and validation of models in suitable foods and objective measures of performance of models are of value in assessment of their usefulness, e.g., calculation of the bias and accuracy factors (Ross 1996, Baranyi *et al.* 1999).

## 20.8   Future trends

Developments in the next generation of predictive models will inevitably address the limitations described in section 20.7.

### 20.8.1   Lag phase investigations

Future trends in modelling are likely to be orientated towards lag and techniques for its control since, if the lag phase can be extended indefinitely, conventional spoilage will not take place. It is important, in the context of lag, to distinguish between repair of injured cells in the inoculum and the adaptation process that healthy cells undergo. It is likely that developments in single cell investigations using flow cytometry will be valuable for elucidation of the underlying mechanisms controlling growth of microbial populations, including injury repair and adaptation mechanisms (ter Steeg and Ueckert 2002). This will enhance understanding of the physiology of the lag phase and subsequently improve procedures for modelling it.

### 20.8.2   Growth/no-growth interface

The situation at the boundary between growth and non-growth has for some time been a source of interest to both microbiologists and mathematicians. The boundary occurs where one or more environmental factors become so extreme that microbial multiplication is inhibited to the point of cessation. Decline in microbial numbers, however, does not necessarily occur immediately; micro-organisms can survive for an extremely long time before undergoing a gradual decrease in number, suggesting that physiological modification or a degree of adaptation of the cells is taking place (McClure *et al.* 1996). Because of the problem of erratic growth, resulting in irregular growth curves, if indeed a growth curve can be prepared, existing interface models are mainly probability based (Ratkowsky and Ross (1995), Presser *et al.* (1998), Masana and Baranyi 2000). In the future, the growth/no-growth interface is likely to be investigated, by microbiologists interested in physiological changes affecting micro-organisms when stressed by inimical environmental conditions, and by mathematicians searching for methods of modelling data generated under these conditions.

### 20.8.3    Effects of competing micro-organisms

Most data from which predictive models have been prepared has been generated in axenic culture, usually in microbiological media. This isolationist approach may not be the most appropriate, since microbial growth can be modulated by the activities of other micro-organisms present. Pin and Baranyi (1998) attempted to quantify interactions between spoilage organisms by inoculating liquid medium with (a) one organism group alone ('type A' models) and (b) four groups of organisms together, using selective agars to identify and enumerate the individual groups of bacteria ('type B' models). The F test was used to determine whether there was a difference between the growth rate and lag time of a type A model and the appropriate group in the type B model. Group P (pseudomonads) were the organisms least affected by other groups, followed by Group B (*Br. thermosphacta*) then Group L (lactic acid bacteria) and the most affected group was Group E (Enterobacteriaceae). This has implications for predictions of growth of micro-organisms in food, where there is often an initial mixed microflora before one strain or group becomes dominant.

It is likely that future work in predictive microbiology will involve more investigation of interactions between micro-organisms, including consideration and evaluation of the concept of quorum-sensing.

### 20.8.4    Fermentation control

An area that has currently been little explored is the application of predictive microbiology to describe the functionality of beneficial micro-organisms in foods. Predictive growth models exist for lactic acid bacteria in the spoilage context (Wijtzes *et al.*, 2001) or are in preparation (FAIR CT98-4083) but some lactic acid bacteria are also beneficial food-grade strains which are added as starter cultures to milk, meat, vegetables and cereals for fermentation and preservation purposes. They produce metabolites, e.g., bacteriocins that are beneficial by virtue of controlling growth of undesirable organisms including food-borne pathogens, and exopolysaccharides, which can be used to improve the texture of foods such as fermented milks (De Vuyst and Degeest, 1999). Leroy *et al.* (2002) have developed models to predict exopolysaccharide yield by *Strepococcus thermophilis* and bacteriocin production by *Lactobacillus sakei* and models such as these will undoubtedly be developed and enhanced in the future.

## 20.9   Sources of further information and advice

A number of predictive models for spoilage micro-organisms and food-borne pathogens are available through the Internet. Some useful sites include:

The Seafood Spoilage Predictor [SSP] program, which contains predictive models for spoilage of fresh fish by *Photobacterium phosphoreum* and *Shewanella putrefaciens* (Dalgaard 1995; Dalgaard *et al.*, 2002) is available at http://www.dfu.min.dk/micro/ssp

Further information about Food Spoilage Predictor-FSP, which includes the *Pseudomonas* model of Neumeyer *et al.*, 1997b, can be found at http://www.hdl.com.au/html.body_fsp.htm

The Pathogen Modeling Program, for growth predictions for food-borne pathogens is available through a link at: http://www.arserrc.gov

Growth Predictor, which fits growth data with the curve of Baranyi *et al.* (1993) is accessible through the web-site of the UK Institute of Food Research at www.ifr.bbsrc.ac.uk

A significant amount of data and models from throughout the world will become available through the EU-funded 'COMBase' project. Further information is available at http://www.ifr.ac.uk/combase

It is anticipated that a website will be constructed to allow access to the spoilage models and data on enzymatic synthesis and activity being prepared in the FAIR CT98-4083, which should be accessible within the next year through the website of London Metropolitan University at http://www.londonmet.ac.uk

Other predictive microbiology services which are not available in the public domain include the 'Forecast' bureau service of Campden and Chorleywood Food Research Association, which offers growth predictions for spoilage organisms of chilled stored foods. Food MicroModel is an item of software available through the UK Food Standards Agency, which contains growth and thermal death models for food-borne pathogens, for the spoilage bacterium *Brochothrix thermosphacta* and yeasts *Zygosaccharomyces bailli* and *Saccharomyces cerevisiae*.

## 20.10   References

ABDULLAH B, GARDINI F, PAPARELLA A and GUERZONI M E (1994), 'Growth modelling of the predominant microbial groups on hamburgers in relation to the modulation of atmosphere condition, storage temperature and diameter of meat particle', *Meat Science* 38, 511–526.

AUGUSTIN J-C and CARLIER V (2000), 'Mathematical modelling of the growth rate and lag time for *Listeria monocytogenes*', *International Journal of Food Microbiology* 56, 29–51.

BARANYI J (1998), 'Comparison of stochastic and deterministic concepts of bacterial lag', *Journal of Theoretical Biology* 192, 403–408.

BARANYI J and PIN C (1999), 'Estimating bacterial growth parameters by means of detection times', *Applied and Environmental Microbiology* 65, 732–736.

BARANYI J and ROBERTS T A (1994), 'A dynamic approach to predicting bacterial growth in food', *International Journal of Food Microbiology* 23, 277–294.

BARANYI J, ROBERTS T A and MCCLURE P J (1993), 'A non-autonomous differential equation to model bacterial growth', *Food Microbiology* 10, 43–59.

BARANYI J, ROBINSON T P, KALOTI A and MACKEY B M (1995), 'Predicting growth of *Brochothrix thermosphacta* at changing temperature', *International Journal of Food Microbiology* 27, 61–75.

BARANYI J, ROSS T, MCMEEKIN T A and ROBERTS T A (1996), 'Effects of parameterization on the performance of empirical models used in "predictive microbiology"', *Food Microbiology* 13, 83–91.

BARANYI J, PIN C and ROSS T (1999), 'Validating and comparing predictive models', *International Journal of Food Microbiology* 48, 159–166.

BORCH E and WALLENTIN C (1993), 'Conductance measurements for predictive modelling', *Journal of Industrial Microbiology* 12, 286–290.

BOX G E P and DRAPER N R (1987), *Empirical model building and response surfaces*, New York, John Wiley and Sons.

BRAUN P and SUTHERLAND J P 'Predictive modelling of growth and enzyme production and activity by a cocktail of *Pseudomonas* spp., *Shewanella putrefaciens* and Acinetobacter sp.', *International Journal of Food Microbiology*. In press.

BRAUN P, FEHLHABER K, KLUG CH and KOPP K (1999), 'Investigations into the activity of enzymes produced by spoilage-causing bacteria: a possible basis for improved shelf-life estimation', *Food Microbiology* 16, 531–540.

CHEROUTRE-VIALETTE M and LEBERT A. (2000), 'Modelling the growth of *Listeria monocytogenes* in dynamic conditions', *International Journal of Food Microbiology* 55, 201–207.

DAINTY R H (1996), 'Chemical/biochemical detection of spoilage', *International Journal of Food Microbiology* 33, 19–33.

DALGAARD P (1995), 'Qualitative and quantitative characterisation of spoilage bacteria from packed fish', *International Journal of Food Microbiology* 26, 319–333.

DALGAARD P, BUCH P and SILBERG S (2002) 'Seafood Spoilage Predictor – development and distribution of a product specific application software', *International Journal of Food Microbiology* 73, 343–349.

DEAK T and BEUCHAT L R (1994), 'Use of indirect conductimetry to predict the growth of spoilage yeasts, with special consideration of *Zygosaccharomyces bailii*', *International Journal of Food Microbiology* 23, 405–417.

DE VUYST L and DEGEEST B (1999), 'Heteropolysaccharides form lactic acid bacteria', *FEMS Microbiology Reviews* 23, 153–177.

DODD C E R, ALDSWORTH T G and STEWART G S A B (1996), 'Bioluminescence as a reporter for modelling bacterial growth in complex systems', Power with Precision: Program and Abstracts of 2nd International Conference on Predictive Microbiology, 18–22 February 1996, Hobart, Tasmania. S7.3, pp. 37–38.

ELLIS D K, BRADHURST D, KELL D B, ROWLAND J J and GOODACRE R (2002), 'Rapid and quantitative detection of the microbial spoilage of meat by fourier transform infrared spectroscopy and machine learning', *Applied and Environmental Microbiology* 68, 2822–2828.

GARCIA-GIMENO R M, HERVAS-MARTINEZ C and DE SILONIZ M I (2002), 'Improving artificial neural networks with a pruning methodology and genetic algorithms for their application in microbial growth prediction in food', *International Journal of Food Microbiology* 72,19–30.

GEERAERD A H, HERREMANS C H, CENENS C and VAN IMPE J F (1998), 'Application of artificial neural networks as a non-linear modular modelling technique to describe bacterial growth in chilled food products', *International Journal of Food Microbiology* 44, 49–68.

GIBSON A M, BRATCHELL N and ROBERTS T A (1988), 'Predicting microbial growth: growth responses of salmonellae in a laboratory medium as affected by pH, sodium chloride and temperature', *International Journal of Food Microbiology* 6, 155–178.

GILL C O (1983), 'Meat spoilage and evaluation of the potential storage life of fresh meat', *Journal of Food Protection,* 46, 444–452.

GRAM L and HUSS H H (1996), 'Microbiological spoilage of fish and fish products', *International Journal of Food Microbiology* 33, 121–137.

GRAM L and MELCHIORSEN J (1996), 'Interaction between fish spoilage bacteria *Pseudomonas* sp. and *Shewanella putrefaciens* in fish extracts and on fish tissue', *Journal of Applied Bacteriology* 80, 589–595.

GUERZONI M E, GARDINI F and DUAN J (1990) 'Interactions between inhibition factors on microbial stability of fruit-based systems', *International Journal of Food Microbiology* 10, 1–18.

GUERZONI, M E, GIANOTTI A, CORBO M R and SINIGAGLIA (1996) 'Shelf life modelling for fresh cut vegetables', *Postharvest Biology and Technology* 9, 195–207.

HUDSON J A (1993) 'Construction and comparison of response surface kinetic models for the *Yersinia enterocolitica* type strain and a food isolate under aerobic conditions', *International Journal of Food Microbiology* 18, 201–209.

KNOCKEL S. and GOULD G. (1995), 'Preservation microbiology and safety: Quo vadis?', *Trends in Food Science and Technology* 6, 127–131.

KOUTSOUMANIS K, GIANNAKOUROU M C, TAOUKIS P S and NYCHAS G-J E (2002), 'Application of shelf life decision system (SLDS) to marine cultured fish quality', *International Journal of Food Microbiology* 73, 375–382.

LEBERT I, BEGOT C and LEBERT A (1998), 'Growth of *Pseudomonas fluorescens* and *Pseudomonas fragi* in a meat medium as affected by pH (5.8–7.0), water activity (0.97–1.00) and temperature (7–25 °C)', *International Journal of Food*

*Microbiology* 39, 53–60.

LEROY F, DEGEEST B and DEVUYST L (2002), 'A novel area of predictive modelling: describing the functionality of beneficial microorganisms in foods', *International Journal of Food Microbiology* 73, 251–259.

MCCLURE P J, BARANYI J, BOOGARD E, KELLY T M and ROBERTS T A (1993), 'A predictive model for the combined effect of pH, sodium chloride and storage temperature on the growth of *Brochothrix thermosphacta*', *International Journal of Food Microbiology* 19, 161–178.

MCCLURE P J, SUTHERLAND J P and BEAUMONT A L (1996), '*Escherichia coli* O157:H7: Preparation of a predictive model for survival', Power with Precision: Program and Abstracts of 2nd International Conference on Predictive Microbiology, 18–22 February 1996, Hobart, Tasmania. S5.5, p. 30.

MCMEEKIN T A and ROSS T (1996), 'Modelling Applications', *Journal of Food Protection*, Supplement 37–42.

MCMEEKIN T A and ROSS T (2002), 'Predictive microbiology: providing a knowledge-based framework for change management', *International Journal of Food Microbiology* 78, 133–153.

MCMEEKIN T A, OLLEY J N, ROSS T. and RATKOWSKY D A (1993), *Predictive Microbiology*, John Wiley and Sons Inc.

MCMEEKIN T A, BROWN J, KRIST K, MILES D, NEUMEYER K, NICHOLS D S, OLLEY J, PRESSER K, RATKOWSKY D A, ROSS T, SALTER M and SOONTRANON S (1997), 'Quantitative Microbiology: A basis for food safety', *Emerging Infectious Diseases* 3, 541–549.

MASANA M O and BARANYI J (2000), 'Growth/no growth interface of *Brochothrix thermosphacta* as a function of pH and water activity', *Food Microbiology* 17, 485–493.

MILES D W, ROSS T, OLLEY J and MCMEEKIN T A (1997), 'Development and evaluation of a predictive model for the effect of temperature and water activity on the growth rate of *Vibrio parahaemolyticus*', *International Journal of Food Microbiology* 38,133–142.

NEUMAYER K, ROSS T, THOMSON G and MCMEEKIN T A (1997a) 'Validation of a model describing the effects of temperature and water activity on the growth of pseudomonads', *International Journal of Food Microbiology* 38, 55–63.

NEUMAYER K, ROSS T and MCMEEKIN T A (1997b) 'Development of a predictive model to describe the effects of temperature and water activity on the growth of spoilage pseudomonads', *International Journal of Food Microbiology* 38, 45–54.

NICOLAI B M, VAN IMPE J F, VERLINDEN B, MARTENS T, VANDEWALLE J and DE BAERDEMAAKER J (1993), 'Predictive modelling of surface growth of lactic acid bacteria in vacuum-packed meat', *Food Microbiology* 10, 229–238.

PALUMBO S A, WILLIAMS A C, BUCHANAN R L and PHILLIPS J G (1992), 'Model for the anaerobic growth of *Aeromonas hydrophila* K144', *Journal of Food Protection* 55, 260–265.

PIN C and BARANYI J (1998), 'Predictive models as means to quantify the interactions of spoilage organisms', *International Journal of Food Microbiology* 41, 59–72.

PIN C, SUTHERLAND J P and BARANYI J (1999), 'Validating predictive models of food spoilage', *Journal of Applied Microbiology* 87, 491–499.

PIRT S J (1975), *Principles of microbe and cell cultivation*, London, Blackwell Scientific Publications, 1st Edition.

PRESSER K A, ROSS T. and RATKOWSKY D A (1998), 'Modelling the growth limits (growth/ no growth interface) of *Escherichia coli* as a function of temperature, pH, lactic acid concentration and water activity', *Applied and Environmental Microbiology* 64, 1773–1779.

RASMUSSEN S K J, ROSS T, OLLEY J and MCMEEKIN T (2002), 'A process risk model for the shelf life of Atlantic salmon fillets', *International Journal of Food Microbiology* 73, 47–60.

RATKOWSKY D A and ROSS T (1995), 'Modelling the bacterial growth/no growth interface', *Letters in Applied Microbiology* 20, 29–33.

ROBINSON T P, OCIO M J, KALOTI A and MACKEY B M (1998) 'The effect of the growth environment on the lag phase of *Listeria monocytogenes*', *International Journal of Food Microbiology* 44, 83–92.

ROBINSON T P, ABOABA O O, KALOTI A, OCIO M J, BARANYI J and MACKEY B M (2001) 'The effect of inoculum size on the lag phase of *Listeria monocytogenes*', *International Journal of Food Microbiology* 70, 163–173.

ROSS T (1996) 'Indices for performance evaluation of predictive models in food microbiology', *Journal of Applied Bacteriology* 81, 501–508.

SKANDAMIS P N and NYCHAS G-J E (2001) 'Effect of oregano essential oil on microbiological and physico-chemical attributes of minced meat stored in air and modified atmospheres', *Journal of Applied Microbiology* 91, 1011–1022.

SUMNER J and KRIST K (2002) 'The use of predictive microbiology by the Australian meat industry', *International Journal of Food Microbiology* 73, 363–366.

SUTHERLAND J P and BAYLISS A J (1994) 'Predictive modelling of *Yersinia enterocolitica*: the effects of temperature, pH and sodium chloride', *International Journal of Food Microbiology* 21, 197–215.

SZIGETI E and FARKAS J (2000) 'Use of impedimetry for data capture in predictive microbiology', Proceedings of the 3rd International Conference on Predictive Modelling in Foods, eds: J F M Van Impe and K Bernaerts, Leuven, Belgium, pp. 129–131.

TER STEEG P F and UECKERT J E (2002) 'Debating the biological reality of modelling preservation', *International Journal of Food Microbiology* 73, 409–414.

VANNINI L, LANCIOTTI R, GARDINI F and GUERZONI M E (1996) 'Evaluation of Fourier-transform infra red spectroscopy for data capture in predictive microbiology', *World Journal of Microbiology and Biotechnology* 12, 85–90.

WALLENTIN LINDBERG C (1994) 'Predictive microbiology applied to growth of *Yersinia enterocolitica* O:3 based on conductance measurements', Licenciate thesis, University of Lund, Sweden.

WALLS I, SCOTT V N and BERNARD D (1996) 'Validation of predictive mathematical models describing growth of *Staphylococcus aureus*', *Journal of Food Protection* 59, 11–15.

WHITING R C and BUCHANAN R L (1993) 'Predictive Modeling'. In: *Food Microbiology: Fundamentals and Frontiers* pp. 728–739, eds M.P. Doyle, L.R. Beuchat and T.J. Montville. American Society for Microbiology.

WIJTZES T, ROMBOUTS F M, KANT-MUERMANS M L T, VAN'T RIET K and ZWIETERING M (2001) 'Development and validation of a combined temperature, water activity, pH model for bacterial growth rate of *Lactobacillus curvatus*', *International Journal of Food Microbiology* 63, 57–64.

WILSON P D G, BROCKLEHURST T F, ARINO S, THUAULT D, JAKOBSEN M, LANGE M, FARKAS F, WIMPENNY J W T and VAN IMPE J F (2002) 'Modelling microbial growth in structured foods: towards a unified approach', *International Journal of Food Microbiology* 73, 275–289.

ZWIETERING M H, JONGENBURGER I, ROMBOUTS F M and VAN'T RIET K (1990) 'Modeling of the bacterial growth curve', *Applied and Environmental Microbiology* 56, 1875–1881.

ZWIETERING M H, DE WIT J C and NOTERMANS S (1996), 'Application of predictive microbiology to estimate the number of *Bacillus cereus* in pasteurised milk at the point of consumption', *International Journal of Food Microbiology* 30, 55–70.

# 21

# Modelling applied to foods: predictive microbiology for solid food systems

**E. J. Dens and J. F. Van Impe, Katholieke Universiteit Leuven, Belgium**

## 21.1  Introduction

For most models developed until now in the domain of predictive microbiology, the food is considered to be a perfectly mixed, homogeneous medium in which no concentration gradients exist. However, this is not true for most natural food systems. It is generally accepted that food structure has a large influence on the microbial evolution in a food product. In the last few years, an awareness of the need for models that are able to cope with the spatial aspects of microbial growth in structured foods has grown.

Wilson *et al.* (2002) subdivided the possible micro-architectures in a food into a number of categories. Generalizing, we discern four main categories:

1.  the **liquid**, aqueous phase, in which microorganisms grow planktonically
2.  **gelled** regions of the food, in which microorganisms are immobilized and constrained to grow as colonies
3.  the **surface** of vegetable or meat tissues which also typically results in the formation of colonies and
4.  **emulsions** in which the growth of microorganisms is mainly constricted by the availability of the aqueous phase.

In sections 21.2 to 21.5, we discuss the process of colony development, both for submerged colonies and for colonies growing on a surface. In sections 21.6 and 21.7), this knowledge is employed as a criterion to test the value of mathematical models available in literature to describe microbial growth in solid food systems. Conclusions are drawn in section 21.8 as well as future trends being outlined. In section 21.9 sources of further information can be found.

## 21.2   Microbial growth in solid food systems: colony dynamics

In the following sections, the process of colony development is discussed. First of all, a general introduction on colony dynamics is presented after which the direct consequences of diffusion limitation in solid media, namely, concentration gradients within and around the colony, are demonstrated. Then, the strategies bacterial cells exploit to optimize their growth performance are then discussed. This is denoted as the *microscopic viewpoint* or *cell bed*. Depending on these *cell level*, strategies, different growth distributions and colony morphologies may be observed. This is discussed and denoted as the *macroscopic viewpoint* or *colony level*. Finally, a conclusion on bacterial colony growth as a process of adaptive self-organization is discussed in section 21.6.

In or on solid foods, bacteria grow in the form of colonies, a phenomenon that has been noted by Mattila and Frost (1988), who inoculated chicken and pork/beef muscle surfaces with various food-borne bacterial pathogens. Also, Katsaras and Leistner (1991) observed microcolonies or *nests* in solid foods. A distinction must be made between colonies growing *on a food surface* and colonies growing *submerged* within a food matrix. Wimpenny *et al.* (1995b) note that the growth of bacteria causing spoilage or food poisoning is generally confined to the *surface* of foods on solid substrates, such as meat. If the food is mixed, however, as is the case for fermented sausages, and the food is then stored, the bacteria may grow *submerged* within the solid matrix. The same is true if a liquid food is coagulated, as is cheese, since the bacteria present become entrapped in the matrix which forms as the product solidifies. The difference between the two cases is schematically illustrated in Figure 21.1.

For the case of colony growth *on a surface*, Wimpenny (1992) schematically described colony evolution. The exponential increase in cells first produces a mono-layer on the surface and when cells near the center of the developing colony can no longer push aside their neighbours, they begin to pile on top of one another evolving into a three dimensional shape. In order to grow and divide, the individual cells require substrates – like, e.g., oxygen and carbon source(s) – and possibly produce metabolites, all depending on which kind of metabolic pathways they follow. The required substrates are taken up from the local environment surrounding the cells. As schematically illustrated in Fig. 21.1(a), oxygen diffuses from the gaseous phase downward into the colony and into the agar on which the colony grows, while glucose or another energy source is received from the medium below. The counter-diffusion and uptake of these elements causes concentration gradients to arise and results in certain regions in which the metabolism may be limited by oxygen availability while in others, the energy source can be lacking, or both. Four different zones can be distinguished. In Zone 1, both oxygen and nutrients are available so that aerobic growth on the available carbon source takes place. In Zone 2, the availability of oxygen is limited by diffusion. Anaerobic fermentation of the carbon source can occur,

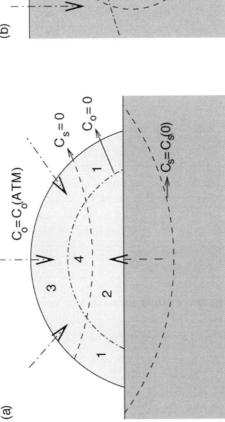

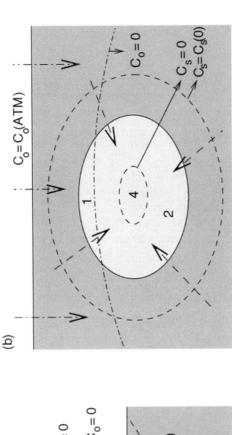

**Fig. 21.1** Schematic representation of a colony growing on a surface (a) and submerged colony growth (b). The agar medium contains a carbon source as a nutrient and is represented by the darker shade of gray while the colony itself is represented by the lighter shade of gray. The atmosphere is represented in white and has an oxygen concentration $C_0$ (*ATM*). The initial concentration of the carbon source in the agar medium is denoted by $C_s(0)$. The contours of equal nutrient and oxygen concentration are represented by the dashed and dash-dotted lines respectively. The directions of decreasing nutrient and oxygen concentration are indicated by the dashed and dash-dotted arrows respectively. Descriptions with respect to Zones 1 to 4 are given in the text.

leading to the production of acidic fermentation end-products. In Zone 3, oxygen is available in excess, but the availability of the carbon source is limited by diffusion. This situation only occurs for colony growth on a surface. Two cases are possible. Aerobic growth might occur at the point where oxygen diffusion downwards meets nutrient diffusion upwards, where the nature of these nutrients might be fermentation end-products produced in Zone 2, which can only be further metabolized by aerobic pathways. On the other hand, if sufficient amino acids are available in Zone 3, oxidative deamination of the amino acids might take place, releasing ammonia and thus leading to alkalinization. In Zone 4, neither oxygen, nor nutrients are available. Cells are dying due to starvation.

*Submerged* colony growth is schematically illustrated in Fig. 21.1(b). The development is essentially the same as for surface colonies, except that all nutrients must be provided from the surrounding food matrix. Therefore, the aerobic population is likely to become oxygen limited very quickly because oxygen solubility is very low. The actual growth rate of aerobic species (Zone 1) will be a function of the rate at which oxygen is transported by molecular diffusion through the matrix. When certain regions within the colony become anoxic (Zone 2), anaerobic bacteria will continue to grow fermentatively. When the colony continues to grow outwards, the inside of the colony will possibly become nutrient deprived as well (Zone 4). This causes cells in the center of the colony to die due to starvation (and inhibition). In contrast, cells at the colony periphery can still divide, maintaining colony expansion. This was observed by (Wimpenny *et al.*, 1995b). Note that Zone 3, which emerged at the top of surface colonies (and in which oxygen is available in excess while the carbon source is limited by diffusion) is not likely to occur in submerged colonies because of the low oxygen availability.

In either case, facultative anaerobes will show heterogeneous growth with cells at the perimeter of the colony using such oxygen as is available, while the remaining population grows fermentatively. As colonies grow larger, product accumulation will become a problem, especially if these are organic acids. In this case, pH changes will dominate the dynamics. In the following section, the available literature on experimental techniques to monitor these concentration gradients, and experimental evidence resulting from these observations is discussed.

## 21.3    Factors affecting microbial growth

### 21.3.1    Oxygen profiles

In 1977, Wimpenny and Lewis measured the ratio of the actual respiration rates of colonies on a solid surface to potential respiration rates of cells in liquid culture. Assuming this ratio to reflect the fraction of the colony having sufficient oxygen to respire aerobically, they estimated the depth to which oxygen penetrates into non-swarming bacterial colonies to be 31 $\mu$m for *Escherichia coli*, 41 $\mu$m for *Enterobacter cloacae* and 37 $\mu$m for *Bacillus cereus*. These results largely corresponded to an earlier calculation by Pirt (1967), based on the analysis of nutrient diffusion into a layer of cells with a diffusion coefficient for oxygen of $1.9 \times 10^{-5} \, cm^2/s$. The theory estimated that oxygen tension would be low at a depth of about 40 $\mu$m in an active colony of *E. coli* cells.

However, it has been pointed out by Wimpenny and Parr (1979) that one has to be careful transferring oxygen penetration values from one species of bacteria to another. They suggest that differences in oxygen penetration between colonies of different species can be related to a difference in height between the colonies. A higher colony may reflect the reduced metabolic rate of a given volume of colony material, perhaps because of the presence of inert substances such as bacterial polysaccharides. In this way, they interpret the high activity of enzymes characteristic of aerobically adapted cells up to a depth of 120 $\mu$m in colonies of *Enterobacter cloacae* (see also section 21.4). Wimpenny and Lewis (1977) have observations for *Staphylococcus albus* of only 9 $\mu$m oxygen penetration depth into the colonies. They interpret these results by a lower diffusion rate of oxygen through and between the tightly-packed spherical cells of this species than through the more loosely-packed cells of other species (like, e.g., *E. coli*).

More recently, micro-electrodes have been used to measure oxygen penetration into a colony. This technique was applied by Bungay *et al.* (1983) for *Pseudomonas ovalis* colonies and by Peters *et al.* (1987) for differently aged colonies of *Bacillus cereus*, *Escherichia coli* and *Staphylococcus albus*. They both observed a clear influence of the initial substrate concentration on the resulting oxygen profiles. Higher substrate concentration induces higher growth rate and, consequently, more oxygen is consumed. Older colonies show higher penetration depths for oxygen, because oxygen diffuses back into the colony which by then is probably nutrient limited.

Omar (1993) published a mini-review on oxygen diffusion through gels. This author concludes that both the particle size of the gel and the cell density in the gel beads has a great effect on the oxygen diffusivity. The higher the gel concentration the lower is the porosity of the gel and hence the diffusivity and uptake rate of oxygen. Therefore, they stress the importance of using an effectiveness factor in determining oxygen diffusivity.

Recently, Tammam *et al.* (2001) communicated that the measurement of oxygen gradients with the aid of micro-electrodes copes with some problems. Oxygen leakage around the electrode and poisoning of the tip (precipitation of hydroxides or organic matter) may lead to unreliable results. They suggest that a membrane inlet mass spectrometric measurement (MIMS) is more robust and allows for easier insertion into solid media. This makes it a *minimally invasive technique*. Another advantage of the MIMS probe is that it allows for simultaneous measurement of many gases. Tammam *et al.* (2001) used this technique to measure the $O_2$ and $CO_2$ gradients in and around agar grown cultures of *Lactobacillus paracasei* and in a developing Cheddar cheese ecosystem. The obtained profiles indicate that atmospheric oxygen concentrations prevail at the exposed surface while oxygen becomes undetectable at depths of 2.5–3 mm within the cheese and 5–6 mm in the agar model system. On the other hand, a 10-fold increase in $CO_2$ concentration takes place within the cheese over a six months maturation period, indicating that anaerobic production of $CO_2$ by lactobacilli in the cheese is prevalent. They suggest that the oxygen present at the surface may detrimentally affect the flavour development in the cheese and that these effects could be minimized by the use of packaging with lower oxygen permeability or by maturing the cheese in a modified atmosphere. They also suggest that their $CO_2$ measurements can be useful as a non-sensory indicator of the cheese maturation status.

### 21.3.2   pH gradients

For the determination of pH gradients within and around the colonies, micro-electrodes also may be used. Robinson et al. (1991) used this technique for the determination of pH profiles in and around colonies of *Bacillus cereus* growing on an agar surface. Walker et al. (1997) reported on similar measurements for *submerged* colonies of *Salmonella typhimurium*. Both teams observed a significant influence of the glucose concentration on the area of acidification. When a large amount of glucose is available, anaerobic fermentation leads to acidification, while the availability of amino acids may lead to alkalinization, due to the aerobic oxidation of the amino acids, releasing ammonia. The region of greatest acidification is the center of the colony, while the outer edge of the colony is found to be mostly alkaline.

The use of micro-electrodes is an invasive technique and colonies must be discarded after measurements have been taken. According to Malakar et al. (2000), the measurement itself might even influence the gradient. Therefore, they used *fluorescence ratio imaging* to study the formation of microgradients in immobilized bacterial colonies of *Lactobacillus curvatus*. This non-invasive technique is based on the fact that fluorescence (energy emitted as light), resulting from an excitation light energy, is environment dependent, and can thus be used as a probe of its immediate surroundings. A fluorescence microscope was used to capture the fluorescence intensity images, which were then processed with an image processing tool. The spatial resolution of the images was about 1.5 $\mu$m. This is about the scale of a bacterial cell, and therefore suitable for observing local effects in colonies. The pH gradients observed in these experiments were due to production of lactic acid by the *Lactobacillus* cells in the colony and due to the limited mass transfer.

For both the experiments of Malakar et al. (2000) and Walker et al. (1997), the colonies were grown within a model gel cassette system, designed at the Institute of Food Research (IFR) in Norwich, UK (Robins and Wilson, 1994). This model food system consists of a frame holding a layer of gel, formed between two PVC windows. The cassette is filled with a suspension of bacteria in a microbiological culture medium containing gelatine. When the gelatine solidifies, the bacteria are mainly immobilized. The Gel Cassette was developed at IFR as a model system to mimic the growth of bacteria in solid foods. The optical windows of the cassette make it amenable to microscopial examination. The importance of laboratory model systems has already been discussed by Wimpenny *et al.* (1995b) and Brocklehurst *et al.* (1997).

Ouvry *et al.* (2001) used a micro-electrode system in order to measure pH gradients developed during growth by *Escherichia coli* and *Lactobacillus plantarum* immobilized in gelled media used as a model food system. There is a clear difference in the observed gradients resulting from the homofermentative *L. plantarum* metabolism and the metabolism of *E. coli* which uses fermentation and/or respiration, depending on the available oxygen concentration. Not only the pH gradients developed by *E. coli* during growth were more spectacular, also the pH behavior of *E. coli* varies during growth. After seven hours of incubation, the acidification of the medium was much higher near the surface (where $O_2$ is available) than 4 mm below the surface. Once glucose was depleted, oxidative deamination of amino acids near the surface of the medium resulted in the production of $NH_3$ and a resulting alkalinization of the surface medium.

### 21.3.3  Substrate diffusion

Belova *et al.* (1996) monitored the cell mass dynamics and resulting distribution profiles of residual substrate in the agar layer beneath for the bacterial lawns formed by *Pseudomonas fluorescens* and *Alcaligenes* species. After one or two days, the concentration of pyruvate in the top layer adjacent to the bacterial lawn dropped below the level of detection, and, from this moment, the substrate was supplied to the lawn by diffusion from underlying agar layers. Diffusion of pyruvate in non-inoculated agar was found to follow Fick's equation with a diffusion coefficient of $1.17 \times 10-5 \, cm^2/s$. In order to determine the pyruvate concentration in a certain part of the agar medium, a segment of the medium was withdrawn and analyzed. They determined the content of pyruvate by an enzymatic method.

Stecchini *et al.* (1998) investigated the influence of the structural properties of the agar medium on the behavior of *Bacillus cereus* colonies. First of all, the diffusion coefficients of two compounds, namely, glucose and a protein (insulin-like growth factor) were determined from best-fit approximations of measured concentrations with the diffusion equation for a homogeneous medium (based on Fick's law). Labeled compounds were used to determine the concentration in the agar segments. The diffusion coefficient of glucose was $6.5 \times 10^{-6} \, cm^2/s$. The diffusion coefficient for the protein was $6.2 \times 10^{-6} \, cm^2/s$. Then, the architecture of the agar gel was modified by changing the agar content in the gel. Smaller colonies were observed as the agar content in the gel was larger. However, it was shown that the diffusivities of glucose and the protein were *not* affected by the gel architecture. This suggests that other factors, such as *mechanical* factors, may influence microbial growth in the agar systems used. In the agar concentration range tested, colony growth was affected by the reduction in the pore size and the increase in the bundle thickness of the gel, but not by the reduced diffusion of nutrients. These observations had already been suggested by Koch (1991) who described gels as being capable of appearing rigid, even though the content of solids is very small therefore diffusion is impeded very little. In general, the diffusion coefficient decreases as the molecular size of the diffusant increases. For high-molecular weight macromolecules, a marked effect of agar concentration in the gel on effective diffusivities has been found (Lebrun and Junter, 1993). The diffusivity of most low-molecular-weight solutes is essentially the same in water and in gels, irrespective of the agar concentration (Diaz *et al.*, 1993).

Westrin and Axelsson (1991) reviewed eleven experimental investigations of diffusion in gels containing immobilized cells. The experimental data, which quantitatively express the diffusion coefficient as a function of the cell concentration, are compared to a number of well-known equations developed for mass transfer in heterogeneous media. Based on this comparison, a procedure for the theoretical prediction of effective diffusion coefficients in cell-containing gels is proposed. As presumed, variations in diffusion coefficients with cell number density within a microcolony can be expected.

## 21.4   Microbial growth dynamics: cell level

As a consequence of the concentration gradients which arise due to diffusion limitation within and around the bacterial colonies, the individual bacterial cells may exploit different strategies in order to optimize their growth perform-ance. The three possible strategies discussed here are (i) biochemical differentiation, (ii) motility of the bacterial cells and (iii) communication between the cells.

### 21.4.1   Biochemical differentiation

Wimpenny and Parr (1979) have determined the activity of some enzymes that are proven to be active during growth with excess oxygen, to see whether bacteria have different enzyme activities, depending on their location within the colonies. This was done for different positions in large colonies of *Enterobacter cloacae*. The activity was found to be greatest in the top 120 $\mu$m of the colonies. Cells near the base of colonies had very low enzyme activities. These results would indicate that oxygen can diffuse at least 120 $\mu$m into colonies. For a discussion on this value with respect to other oxygen penetration measurements, see the paragraph on oxygen profiles in section 21.3.

Shapiro and Trubatch (1991) visualized *patterns* in the colonies of *Escherichia coli* by histochemical staining for differential biochemical activity and examination of colony surface structure by reflected light photography and scanning electron microscopy (SEM). Two types of differentiation were observed. The *concentric ring patterns* represent a group of phenotypically distinguishable bacteria which have many different ancestors but share a common position in the history of colony development. The *sectorial patterns* on the contrary are assumed to represent a phenotypically distinguishable group of bacteria descendent from a common ancestor. Higher magnification SEM analysis reveals further that distinct macroscopic zones can be resolved microscopically into zones consisting of distinct cell morphologies. This was also observed by Shapiro (1987). Shapiro and Trubatch (1991) regard bacterial organization as involving the operation of morphogenetic regulatory systems that are analogous to those controlling the development of complex multicellular structures in higher organisms. This must be distinguished from a much more causal response, that is the formation of periodic structures due to changes in the physicochemical environment. More research is needed to clarify this issue (Wimpenny, 1992).

Walker *et al.* (1998) compared the growth of *Salmonella enteritidis* and *Salmonella typhimurium* as submerged colonies in agarose gel and gelatin gel to planktonic growth in broth. Adenine nucleotide values and adenylate energy charge (AEC) were measured. The adenylate pool, including the adenine nucleotides, adenosine triphosphate (ATP), adenosine diphosphate (ADP) and adenosine monophosphate (AMP) can be used to quantify the physiological state of bacteria. They are frequently linked with metabolic processes involved in cell regulation and can give insight into the metabolic status of the cell. An important difference was that for the agarose and gelatin gelled cultures (growing in colonies), the percentage of adenosine triphosphate (ATP) in relation to the total adenylates showed random fluctuations, while for the broth cultures, the percentage ATP formed a smooth curve. This again demonstrates the higher physiological heterogeneity within colonies.

Also Stecchini *et al.* (2001) monitored a higher heterogeneity for *Bacillus cereus* cells when grown on an agar medium compared to growth in broth, and this with respect to both cell size and genomic content. Both properties are measured by means of a flow cytometer, in which the forward scatter (FS) parameter is used as a measure of cell size and an FL3 sensor is used to acquire red fluorescence which is related to DNA content of the cells.

## 21.4.2   Motility
Another strategy, on which bacterial cells may rely to optimize their growth performance is motility. When bacteria can move, they can try to find more favorable growth conditions or avoid unfavorable growth conditions. Different mechanisms of motility exist.

- The most common mechanism is called *swimming*. This is defined by Golding *et al.* (1998) as a surface translocation produced through the action of flagella. The cells are short (40 $\mu$m) and rod-like, have only a few flagella and move individually and at random. Microscopic observations reveal no organized flow-field pattern. These cells are only capable of swimming in semi-solid media, not of migrating over hard agar surfaces. Generally, they can produce a kind of surfactant (like, for example, *Bacillus subtilis* producing surfactin (Nakahara *et al.*, 1996)) to improve their motility. Ben-Jacob *et al.* (1992) also mention random walk-like movement within a well defined envelope that is formed by chemicals that are excreted by the bacteria and/or by fluid drawn by the bacteria from the agar.

- Another phenomenon of bacterial motility is *swarming*. According to the definition of Golding *et al.* (1998), swarming is also a surface translocation produced through the action of flagella, but unlike swimming, the movement is continuous and regularly follows the long axis of the cell (length and hyper-flagellation distinguish swarmer cells from swimmer cells). The cells are predominantly aggregated in bundles during their movement, and microscope observations reveal flow-field patterns highly organized in whirls and bands. The key aspect of swarming motility is its *collective nature*. More recently, Toguchi *et al.* (2000) and Gue *et al.* (2001) suggested also that the production of a *wetting agent*, or *surfactant* is indispensable for the swarming behavior. These surfactants are lipopolysaccharides (LPS) and/or exopolysaccharides (EPS).
- *Chemotaxis* is the movement of organisms towards or away from a chemical. For bacteria, chemotaxis is observed towards oxygen, minerals, organic nutrients. Bacteria sense the local concentration of a chemical via membrane receptors binding the chemical's molecules. Bacteria are too short to estimate spatial gradients of the chemical by simply comparing concentrations at different locations on their membrane. They deduce the spatial gradients by calculating temporal derivatives along their path. *Escherichia coli* can, for example, compare successive measurements over a time interval of 3 seconds (Wolfe and Berg, 1989). Berg and Brown (1972) showed that bacteria realize chemotactic response by modulating the periods between tumbling events. They decrease the probability of tumbling when moving in a preferred direction along the chemical gradient. This causes a bias in the random walk which results in a mean drift of the bacteria in the desired direction.

Wimpenny and Lewis (1977) monitored the differences in growth limitations and colony dimensions between colonies of swarming and non-swarming organisms. Growth limitation was estimated by the relation of *actual* respiration rates of colonies on a solid surface to *potential* respiration rates of cells in liquid culture. The dimensions of the colonies were measured with a transparent ruler under a microscope, viewing the colony through the agar of the inverted Petri dish. They observed little restriction of growth due to oxygen or nutrient limitation in young colonies of swarming organisms. This was because of the rapid spreading of the latter such that the cells can grow in regions containing excess nutrient and the colony remains sufficiently *flat* to allow oxygen penetration to all cells. The height of the colonies of the non-swarming organisms increased much more quickly, resulting in a much earlier limitation of oxygen and nutrient diffusion. All the non-swarmer organisms examined were facultative anaerobes such that, given sufficient nutrient, the centers of these colonies would grow anaerobically whilst the outer layers continue to grow at the faster aerobic rate.

Stecchini *et al.* (2001) observed the agar concentration to significantly influence the ability of the cells to move along the solid surface. They found the agar concentration to be inversely related to the quantity of *surface water* (the nominal water thickness reduces by approximately 30 times in the presence of 7% agar with respect to 1%, agar) and suggest that the motility of the cells would be related to the presence of a *liquid film* at the surface of the agar medium. Correspondingly, they observe thinner and larger colonies on low agar concentrations and thicker and smaller colonies on higher agar concentrations, reflected in the resulting *colony morphology*. This is discussed in more detail in section 21.5.

Also for *submerged* colonies, a clear difference in growth and morphology of the colonies of motile versus non-motile bacteria was observed by Wimpenny *et al.* (1995b) and Mitchell and Wimpenny (1997). They used light and electron microscopy (both scanning electron microscopy (SEM) and transmission electron microscopy (TEM)). At concentrations below 6.5 g/L, *motile* strains appeared to be able to move through the matrix, forming spherical colonies of a diffuse appearance. At higher agar concentrations, however, the same strains became immobilized and formed compact colonies, whose cells were tightly packed. The colony diameter of *non-motile* species was not affected by the agar strength. These strains formed small compact colonies in either case.

As a consequence of these different *motility mechanisms*, a number of pattern forming growth processes have already been observed. An example of *pattern* formation through the swarming process are the stable circular patterns formed by *Proteus* species as a result of alternating swarming and consolidation phases (Shapiro and Trubatch, 1991), which may be under catabolite repression control (Wimpenny, 1992). Also, chemotactic cells of *Escherichia coli* were observed to form concentric bands due to spatial gradients generated by diffusion limitation and metabolism (Adler, 1966). While the resulting patterns are similar, different mechanisms are at their origin.

### 21.4.3   Communication

Even in bacteria, development is frequently governed by intricate systems of intercellular communication (Kaiser and Losick, 1993). Information transfer between cells determines differentiation and morphogenesis in a wide variety of bacterial systems. Grossman and Losick (1988) report on spore formation of *Bacillus subtilis* as an example of differentiation that occurs in response to nutritional starvation. They present evidence that *B. subtilis* produces extracellular factors that are required for effective sporulation. These signals provide information about the cellular density and the state of the colony. *Myxococcus xanthus* (Kuspa *et al.*, 1992) employs similar signals during the process of the fruiting body formation.

Usually, chemotactic response implies a response to an *externally* produced field as in the case of chemotaxis towards nutrients (see previous paragraph). However, the chemotactic response can also relate to a field produced directly or indirectly by the bacterial cells themselves. Golding *et al.* (1998) refer to this case as *chemotactic signaling.* This process can, for example, help the organisms to avoid unfavorable conditions. Budrene and Berg (1991) and (1995) describe conditions under which cells of *Escherichia coli* aggregate in response to gradients of attractants which they excrete themselves. The result are colonies with *concentric ring patterns.* The attractant is a chemical sensed by the aspartate receptor and its excretion can be triggered by oxidative stress. As oxygen is limiting at high cell densities, aggregation of cells enables the cooperative degradation of toxic materials. The formation of these chemotactic cells of *E. coli* provides a striking example of biological self-organization by interacting microscopic elements.

## 21.5    Microbial growth dynamics: colony level

Depending on the *cell level* strategies the bacteria adopt to optimize their growth performance, different growth distributions within the colony and different colony morphologies may be observed. This is discussed in the current section with an emphasis on the experimental techniques which may be used to measure these aspects of colony evolution.

### 21.5.1    Growth distribution

Mckay *et al.* (1997) used computer-aided image analysis techniques to study specific growth rates in different regions of *Salmonella typhimurium* colonies. The image analysis program was developed by Wimpenny *et al.* (1995a) and captures transmission images of individual colonies and then converts the image data to optical density values, obtaining a 30 by 30 array of optical density data. This grid allows the calculation of the specific growth rate $\mu$ in different regions of the colony. From the obtained data it can be concluded that at the colony periphery, growth was approximately twice as fast as growth at the colony center. In the peripheral region, growth is unrestricted by the rate of nutrient diffusion while inwards from the peripheral region, growth is restricted by the rate of nutrient diffusion.

Likewise, Wentland *et al.* (1996) used image analysis techniques to visualize and quantify spatial variations in growth rate within *Klebsiella pneumoniae* colonies. However, instead of transmission images which are converted to optical density values, they used a cryoembedding technique to preserve the structure of the colonies for sectioning. The cross-sections were then stained with the fluorescent nucleic acid strain *acridine orange.* Subsequently, spatial patterns of fluorescent color and intensity with respect to depth in the colony were quantified using confocal microscopy and image analysis of the stained cross-sections. By means of this technique, they observed the cells of young colonies ($\sim$ 20 $\mu$m thick after 7–10 h) to be bright orange throughout, while older colonies ($>$ 200 $\mu$m after 24 h) were characterized by distinct bands of orange of 10–30 $\mu$m thick at the colony edges, near the air and the agar interface, and a dark green center. A high correlation between the average specific growth rate and the orange to green intensity ratio indicates that orange color corresponds to regions of rapid growth and green to regions of slow growth. This means that bacteria are growing rapidly near the air and agar interfaces and more slowly in the center of the colonies when thicker than about 30 $\mu$m. Reyrolle and Letellier (1979) studied the localization of bacterial multiplication sites within the colony using radioactive tracers. Hereto, they incorporated [$^3$H] leucine in bacteria of 18–48 h old colonies of five different bacteria and examined cut cross-sections with the aid of autoradiography.

Because of the existence of different microenvironments in solid foods, which can lead to differential growth and survival of the microorganisms, Stringer *et al.* (1995) emphasize the importance of the detection of microorganisms *in situ* in solid foods. Microbial detection in solid foods has long depended on methods that involve maceration of foods to produce a homogeneous suspension. This results in the loss of spatial information because it destroys the structural integrity of the foods. Stringer *et al.* give an overview of the possible techniques and conclude that cryosectioning allows a food to be examined with minimal distortion or loss of components. Subsequent staining can be used to visualize microbial cells and their background. Different microscopic staining methods are compared and, in addition, the use of antibody-linked probes is discussed.

### 21.5.2   Colony morphology

When the evolution of one single colony grown on an agar plate is monitored, some typical morphological changes can be observed. For colonies of *Aerobacter (Klebsiella) aerogenes*, Cooper *et al.* (1970) made colony drawings from the negatives of photographs with the aid of an enlarger magnifying 10 to 15 times. Initially, nutrient supply is sufficient for all the cells in the colony, resulting in a young circular colony. As the colony ages, the nutrient concentration in the agar beneath the colony is depleting, resulting in a competition for nutrients by the cells at the periphery of the evolving colony. Any *outgrowth* of cells in the colony perimeter will be advantageous with respect to the other cells in the colony. Therefore, such inequality in nutrient uptake will invoke an exaggerate *uneven frontal growth* of the bacterial colony resulting in a more and more irregular perimeter which is a characteristic of older colonies growing in nutrient limited conditions. Stirring the medium delays morphological changes, as does adding charcoal to agar gels to absorb toxic metabolites. It is possible to determine the coefficient of circularity of a colony by means of image analysis. This was done for colonies of *Escherichia coli* and clearly shows the increase in irregularity as a function of colony age (Wimpenny, 1992).

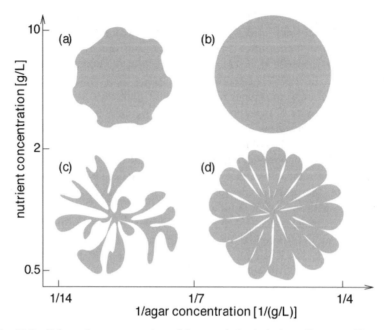

**Fig. 21.2** Schematic representation of the morphological phase diagram of bacterial colonies of *Bacillus subtilis* as a function of both the concentration of nutrients and the softness of the agar medium (adapted from Ohgiwari *et al.* (1992)).

For the different colony morphologies of *Bacillus subtilis*, not only the distinction between a circular and irregular perimeter in function of nutrient availability has been made. As a function of agar hardness (and mobility of the species), two additional colony morphologies have been observed. Fujikawa and Matsushita (1989) summarized the four different colony morphologies in a phase portrait which is schematically illustrated in Fig. 21.2. At high agar concentrations, motility of the organisms does not come into play, and depending on the nutrient concentration, a more or less circular colony (Eden-like growth, Fig. 21.2(a)) versus a colony with an irregular perimeter (DLA-like growth, Diffusion Limited Aggregation, Fig. 21.2(c)) can be observed (as was discussed in the previous paragraph). When colonies of motile organisms are observed on a surface with lower agar concentrations, the motility of the organisms will cause the colony to spread faster and more evenly. This can be illustrated by the difference between the Eden-like colony shape and the circular colony shape (Fig. 21.2(b)). The difference between the DLA-like colony shape and the DBM-like (Dense Branching Morphology) colony shape (Fig. 21.2(d)) illustrates the same effect.

The difference between these colony morphologies can be mathematically characterized by making use of *fractal dimensions*. The colonies were photographed through transmitted light and analyzed digitally through an image-scanner software to calculate the fractal dimension by means of the box-counting method (Matsuyama and Matsushita, 1993). The DLA-like colony morphology for example has a self-similar shape, with a fractal dimension of about 1.72. Because this value is consistent with colony shapes evolving from the Diffusion Limited Aggregation model (Witten and Sander, 1981), this morphology is called *DLA-like.* The Eden colony morphology itself is not a fractal, but its colony surface is known to be self-affine and to have interesting scaling properties. This morphology is named after the *Eden model* (Eden, 1960) which was designed to simulate cancer growth. The surface of the circular colony morphology has slightly different scaling properties, with a smaller roughness exponent, indicating a less rough interface.

The process of colony growth reflects an interplay between the *intrinsic factors* (products of the genetics of the individual cells) and *extrinsic factors* (the prevailing physicochemical environment in which the colony resides, like, substrate concentration or agar hardness) (Wimpenny, 1992). Key elements of the general underlying mechanisms of colony growth can be summarized as follows:

1. *Metabolism* of the organisms: what substances are used for energy supply and what metabolites are produced?
2. *Motility* of the bacteria: do the bacteria move, and how?
3. Mechanisms of *communication* between the cells.
4. *Environmental conditions:* the medium in which the organisms grow will determine the transport of the substrates, oxygen, metabolites through the medium.

The first three items reflect the intrinsic factors, or genotype of the organism, while the last item represents the extrinsic factors, like the environment in which the colony grows. In the next section, modeling methodologies to describe these mechanisms are reviewed, with respect to their ability to describe microbial growth within a food matrix.

## 21.6   Evaluating types of model

In the previous section, in which the dynamics of colony growth as a process of adaptive self-organization was discussed, some general underlying mechanisms of colony growth were summarized into four items. These items are used in the current section to evaluate the usefulness of the mathematical modeling methodologies available from literature to describe the evolution of microorganisms in a solid environment.

### 21.6.1   Partial differential equations: the continuous field approach
The traditional approach to describe the space-time evolution of a continuous system is the use of a coupled set of partial differential equations:

$$\frac{\partial N}{\partial t} = D_N(N,S,P)\,\nabla^2 N \quad + \quad f(N,S,P) \quad - \quad o(N,S,P)$$

$$\frac{\partial S}{\partial t} = D_S\nabla^2 S \qquad\qquad - \quad g(N,S,P)$$

$$\frac{\partial P}{\partial t} = D_P\nabla^2 P \qquad\qquad - \quad p(N,S,P) \qquad\qquad 21.1$$

$$\frac{\partial U}{\partial t} = \qquad\qquad\qquad\qquad\qquad + \quad o(N,S,P)$$

$$\underbrace{\qquad\qquad}_{\text{diffusion}} \qquad \underbrace{\qquad\qquad}_{\substack{\text{nutr. consumpt.}\\ \text{production}}} \quad \underbrace{\qquad\qquad}_{\substack{\text{active} \rightarrow\\ \text{inactive cells}}}$$

In these equations, $N$ is the concentration of biomass, $S$ represents the nutrient field, $P$ the concentration of secreted substances (these could be metabolic products, as well as lubrication fluid, as well as chemical fields for chemotactic communication) and $U$ the concentration of inactive cells.

In this approach, the four general mechanistic principles of colony growth as previously formulated can be incorporated in an elegant way.

- The reaction terms $f$ and $o$ constitute the *metabolism* of the cells. The function $f$ represents the growth rate of the microorganisms depending on the locally available biomass, nutrients and metabolites. The function $o$ represents the transition rate between growing cells and cells in the resting state ($U$). This transition may also depend on the locally available biomass, nutrient and/or metabolite concentrations.
- As was mentioned earlier, the *movement* of microorganisms can be governed by various mechanisms. In the population dynamics approach it is generally assumed that the motility of the organisms can be described by the diffusion equation. Diffusion coefficient $D_N$ can depend on biomass, nutrient and (most importantly) the secreted substance which could be a lubrication fluid, or a chemotactic substance.
- *Communication* between the cells might be accomplished by the dependence of the reaction terms and/or diffusion coefficient of the organisms $D_N$ on a substance secreted by the other cells. Assuming the diffusion to be linear or nonlinear strongly affects the growth patterns resulting from the numerical solution of the system.
- The *environmental conditions* (local nutrient and metabolite concentrations, secreted substances ...) are computed by the diffusion equations for $S$ and $P$.

A number of authors have used this approach to describe colony growth. An overview of some possible functional forms for $D_N$, $f$, $g$, $o$ and $p$ is given in Table 21.1. Some authors (e.g., Kawasaki *et al.* (1997) and Kitsunezaki (1997)) described density dependent cell movement in the form of a non-linear diffusion coefficient, possibly in combination with a transition from active to inactive

**Table 21.1** Functional forms for the diffusion coefficient of biomass $D_N$, the bacterial growth rate $f$, the nutrient consumption rate $g$, transformation between active and inactive cells $o$, and production rate of secreted substances $p$ as implemented in the partial differential equations (21.1). $\mu$ represents the specific growth rate, $\eta$ the specific consumption rate and $\kappa$ the rate of bacterial differentiation between the active and inactive state. $Y$ represents the growth yield and $K_S$ the half-saturation constant. For the other parameters, we refer to the referenced literature

| | $D_N(N,S,P)$ | $f(N,S,P)$ | $g(N,S,P)$ | $o(N,S,P)$ | $p(N,S,P)$ |
|---|---|---|---|---|---|
| Wakita et al. (1994) | ct. | $(\mu(S) - \theta N) \cdot N$ | $\eta \cdot S \cdot N$ | — | — |
| Kawasaki et al. (1997) | $\rho \cdot S \cdot N$ | $Y\eta \cdot \frac{S}{K_S+S} \cdot N$ | $\eta \cdot \frac{S}{K_S+S} \cdot N$ | | |
| Kitsunezaki et al. (1997) | $N^a, a > 1$ | $S \cdot N$ | $S \cdot N$ | $\kappa \cdot N$ | |
| Golding et al. (1998) | $P^{2a}, a > 0$ | $S \cdot N$ | $S \cdot N$ | $\kappa \cdot N$ | $k_p SN(P_{max} - P) - k_a P$ |
| Matsushita et al. (1998) | ct. | $Y \cdot S \cdot N$ | $S \cdot N$ | $S \cdot N^2$ | |

cells depending on the cell concentration. Golding *et al.* (1998) let the diffusion coefficient depend on a *lubrication fluid* secreted by the cells themselves. Other authors concentrated more specifically on modeling the chemotactic movement of bacteria. In order to describe this phenomenon, Segel and Jackson (1973) add a term of the form:

$$N \nabla^2 P \hspace{8cm} 21.2$$

to describe bacterial chemotaxis towards a secreted substance $P$ to the space-time description of the bacterial organisms in equation 21.1.

With this approach, many different colony morphologies, ranging from circular growth to fractal-like colony morphologies (see Fig. 21.2) can be simulated, depending on the parameter values used. However, different combinations in functional forms can result in similar (to the eye) colony morphologies. The fact that a comparison between experimental observations and model patterns cannot discriminate between the different mathematical expressions proposed (Golding *et al.*, 1998), implies that we cannot be certain whether the *true* biological features are included in the model. Clearly there is a difference between specifying a mathematical model which generates macroscopic structures that appear realistic, and building a model based on physiologically based assumptions (Kreft *et al.*, 1998). If the purpose of the model is predictive rather than descriptive (as in the domain of predictive microbiology), the first option must be avoided. Models that are fitted to empirical data are only valid in a well delineated set of environmental conditions, and the extrapolation of the fitting procedures becomes unreliable when it is extended into regions of the parameter space that are beyond the range of macroscopic tests (Barker and Grimson, 1993).

Another remark Grimson and Barker (1993) raised with respect to these models is that the diffusion coefficient of biomass $D_N$ is typically very small. They commented that for a small $D_N$ and a rather high growth rate $f$ in equations 21.1, the local biomass concentration is *not* constrained to the physically acceptable range up to a value consistent with a close-packed configuration of the cells. In such cases, the set of equations 21.1 is unable to provide an accurate description of the spatial dependence of microbial growth kinetics. Indeed, motility mechanisms such as swarming or chemotaxis, resulting in a higher diffusion coefficient for biomass, mostly appear on semi-solid agar surfaces on which the bacteria can more easily move than in/on solid foods. In those cases it might be appropriate to describe bacterial motility by the diffusion equation, since bacterial motility is often described as a *random walk* with possibly a *bias* in the direction of some secreted substances. However, Wimpenny (1992) also suggested that rather few examples of pattern formation (resulting from swarming or chemotaxis mechanisms, see section 21.4) can be found in a classical microbial ecosystem like, e.g., a natural food, suggesting a different motility mechanism. Grimson and Barker (1993) solved this problem by adding a *local growth limiting factor u(N)* to the local biomass growth rate $f$:

$$\frac{\partial N}{\partial t} = D_N \nabla^2 N + f(N, S) \cdot u(N) + \psi \cdot (\nabla N)^2 \qquad\qquad 21.3$$

This factor restrains the local growth of cell number to a maximum cell concentration $N_m$, corresponding to close-packing of the colony. If the colony is unable to add cells locally due to packing constraints ($u(N) \approx 0$) growth must occur by the nonlocal addition of cells on the periphery as a result of the expansion and reorganization of the colony. This effect is accounted for by the third term on the right-hand side of equation 21.3, which corresponds to nonlocal growth occurring at concentration gradients at the surface of the compact microcolony. Grimson and Barker (1993) simulated this model for the case of aerobic bacteria growing on the surface of a nutrient-rich growth medium under an oxygen-rich atmosphere. Initially, the total biomass in the biofilm can increase as a result of the local addition of biomass alone. However, once the biomass concentration at the centre of the biofilm approaches close packing, biomass is added to the biofilm by both local and non-local growth mechanisms. In steady-state regime, biofilm growth occurs solely by the non-local mechanism. In (Grimson and Barker, 1994) the resulting colony radius is compared to experimentally obtained data of colony radius against time for *Salmonella typhimurium* immobilized in a gelatin gel. A satisfying fit was obtained.

### 21.6.2   Rule based modeling: the discrete approach

Another way to model the displacement of microorganisms in a solid environment, is by making use of the rule based approach. This is illustrated by several authors.

Hills and Wright (1994) assumed the gel strength to be sufficient to prevent all individual bacterial motility. In addition, they invoke a *moving boundary mechanism* for colony expansion. Similar to the above-mentioned experiment, it can be concluded that, when the local cell number density at a certain discrete site exceeds the maximum cell number density, the excess population is divided equally among the neighboring sites. The cells that *spill-over* carry with them their own characteristics (e.g., cell mass). This approach was combined with partial differential equations describing the consumption/production and transport of oxygen, glucose and metabolites. The parameter values for the functional forms in these PDEs were obtained from batch experiments with *Listeria monocytogenes*. With these parameter values, the growth of an immobilized *Listeria monocytogenes* colony was simulated, obtaining a non-linear increase in colony radius with time, comparable to the simulation results of Grimson and Barker (1994). After some time, a stationary phase was reached by lack of oxygen. However, no experimental data of *Listeria monocytogenes* colony growth (and oxygen, nutrient and pH gradients in and around the colony) were available to compare the simulation results with.

Picioreanu *et al.* (1998) combined a *continuous field approach* (PDEs) for the reaction-diffusion of soluble components (e.g., substrates, like oxygen) and the growth of biomass with a *cellular automation algorithm* for the spreading and distribution of biomass in a colony.

> In a **cellular automaton (CA)**, space is explicitly discretized into a grid of sites. Each grid site has a specific *state* or *value*. The states change over discrete time steps, according to the *behavior* of the CA, i.e., the *rules* defining the behavior of a certain site in function of its neighboring sites. An additional restriction of CA is that the states must be discrete variables, for example a finite number of integers. This makes the CA discrete in space, time and states.

In the CA developed by Picioreanu *et al.* (1998), a site can be either *empty* or *occupied* with biomass, i.e., zero or one. When the local biomass concentration in a certain occupied site (calculated with the continuous field approach), exceeds its maximum level (i.e., close-packing of the cells), the biomass divides into two parts, one of which stays at the same site, whereas the second part is randomly placed in one of the neighboring sites. Therefore, a search for a free-space element is carried out among the nearest-neighbor elements. If no free site is available among the neighbors, the new biomass part will displace a neighbor biomass part chosen at random and this part will search again for a free-space neighbor. The model simulation results were only compared to *global* oxygen consumption rates. The calculated concentration profiles of oxygen and biomass in gel beads could therefore only be compared qualitatively.

Kreft *et al.* (1998) developed an individual based model for bacterial colony growth.

> In an **individual based concept (IbM)**, the rules constituting the model reflect the (presumed) behavior of individual cells, such as nutrient consumption, biomass growth, cell division, movement, differentiation, communication, . . . and their responses to external conditions.

Kreft *et al.* (1998) simulated the expansion of the growing colony by the individual cells which *push* each other aside in order to avoid overlap. This resulted in a colony somewhat lighter than close-packed. This rule could be adjusted to obtain denser colonies. They remark, however, that data on the volume fraction of a colony, to compare the simulation results with, are scarce.

Ben-Jacob *et al.* (1994) and Vicsek *et al.* (1995) concentrated more specifically on the description of the *swimming*, *swarming* and *chemotaxis* mechanisms as observed for organisms growing on semi-solid agar surfaces as discussed in section 21.4. Optical microscopy revealed that bacteria on a surface perform a random-walk movement within a well defined envelope which is formed presumably by chemicals excreted by the bacteria and/or by fluid drawn by the bacteria from the agar. The envelope propagates slowly as if by the action of effective internal pressure produced by the collective movement of the bacteria. Ben-Jacob *et al.* (1994) translated this knowledge into their model. The model incorporates *random walkers*, representing aggregates of bacteria and moving inside an envelope defined on a triangular lattice. When a walker hits the boundary of the envelope the step is not performed but a counter on the appropriate segment of the envelope is increased by one. When a segment counter reaches the threshold value, the envelope is shifted by one lattice step. The level of the threshold value represents the agar concentration, as more collisions are needed to push the envelope on a harder substrate. To incorporate the ability of *chemotactic communication* for the organisms, Ben-Jacob *et al.* let the walkers that had been exposed to a low level of nutrients produce a communication chemical. The movement of the active walkers was then changed from pure random walk (equal probability to move along any direction) to a random walk with a bias along the gradient of the communication field (high probability to move away from the signaling material). The effect of (i) nutrient concentration. (ii) agar hardness and (iii) the ability for chemotactic communication on the resulting colony morphologies was investigated. The phase portrait as presented in Fig. 21.2 could be reproduced by the model.

Vicsek *et al.* (1995) and Csahok and Vicsek (1995) modeled the collective biological motion of bacteria (like, e.g., swarming). In the model of Vicsek *et al.* (1995), the particles are driven by a constant absolute velocity, and at each time step they assume the average direction of motion of the particles in their neighborhood with some random perturbation added (noise). The particles can move in a continuous direction. Csahok and Vicsek (1995) translated this model into a *lattice gas CA* on a triangular lattice such that the direction of motion was confined to six.

> In a **lattice gas CA**, each particle has a certain (random) direction. At each time step, the particles jump across the lattice bonds to a neighboring site, predefined by their direction. In this way the fluctuating many-particle configurations of automaton particles resemble instantaneous configurations of molecules in a gas (Barker and Grimson, 1993).

In addition, Csahok and Vicsek introduced the influence of temperature on the behavior of the particles. Monte Carlo simulations were used to introduce the variability. As mentioned before, this kind of movement is rather unrealistic in natural food systems, in which the movement of microorganisms is generally severely restricted.

The previous examples illustrate the use of the rule based approach in modeling cell or biomass movement. It can be concluded that in this approach, a presumed mechanistic concept of biomass displacement, can readily be incorporated into the discrete model structure. This might be more appropriate when no continuous field equation is available to describe the phenomenon adequately. It must however be noted, that for none of the three examples, enough experimental evidence was available to validate the models (and thus the implemented mechanisms). This is an important shortcoming at this moment which will be further discussed in section 21.8 of this chapter.

Apart from modeling the movement of biomass and cell number on a CA, Barker and Grimson (1993) also describe the reaction-diffusion process of two diffusing components in combination with biomass growth as a CA algorithm. The diffusion of the two components (which could be identified with oxygen and glucose) is described as a *lattice gas* CA developed by Chopard and Droz (1991). In this way a *random walk* of the particles is simulated, which corresponds exactly to the description of a diffusion process. Chopard and Droz (1991) proved that for small diffusion coefficients (which is true for oxygen and glucose in a solid matrix), the macroscopic behavior of their CA obeys Fick's law with an exact relation between the diffusion coefficient D and (i) the rotation probabilities for the particles, (ii) the lattice spacing and (iii) the time constant. Implementation of this algorithm on special purpose machines (allowing for parallel computation) lead, according to Chopard and Droz, to the fastest way to simulate diffusion on a lattice. In general, because of the integer arithmetic and the use of lookup tables (i.e., lists defining all the possible states and behavior of any site in function of neighboring sites), CA are considered to have a numerical advantage over partial differential equations solvers. However, at the same time, the latter continue to undergo an evolution towards more and more efficient computations, which may cause these statements to no longer stand. Also, the required random number generation for probabilistic CA has a high computational demand, so that probabilistic CA are intrinsically slower than their deterministic counterparts (Hendry, 1995).

## 21.7   Selecting the right modelling approach

In the previous two sections, some literature examples are given of (i) partial differential equation models and (ii) rule based models to describe the evolution of microorganisms in solid environments. In both approaches, it is possible to introduce the basic mechanistic principles of colony growth in an elegant way. A point of concern is that the way microorganisms move in natural solid food systems differs considerably from the way they can move on *semi-solid* agar surfaces. In solid food systems, they are not able to move as freely, and therefore, the spreading of microbial colonies cannot be described by diffusion alone. This problem can be solved on a macroscopic level, i.e., through the partial differential equation approach as was proposed by Grimson and Barker (1993). Some other authors translated the presumed mechanisms of bacterial motility into a rule based model. The power and limitations of both approaches are summarized below.

### 21.7.1   Power and limitations of the continuous approach versus the rule based approach

An important advantage of the continuous partial differential equation models is that they are *analytic*. This means that tools from system analysis such as stability theory, bifurcation theory, and perturbation methods can be used to analyze the global behavior of the model, instead of having to simulate the behavior for a large number of different initial conditions. Also, the fact that PDE models are used in a large number of research areas, has stimulated the development of (i) user-friendly tools and (ii) more and more efficient solvers.

A limitation of the continuous field approach is that for some mechanisms, no continuous functions are available to accurately describe the problem. This is particularly true for systems of which the underlying mechanisms are not yet fully understood. In these cases, it might still be possible to choose a certain continuous equation that adequately describes the macroscopic behavior of the system under predefined environmental conditions. However, when the objective of the model is predictive rather than descriptive, a distinction must be made between mathematical models which generate macroscopic structures that appear realistic, and models based on physiologically based assumptions (Kreft *et al.*, 1998). The first option must be avoided since models that are fitted to empirical data are only valid in a well delineated set of environmental conditions, and the extrapolation of the fitting procedures becomes unreliable when it is extended into regions of the parameter space that are beyond the range of macroscopic tests (Barker and Grimson, 1993). In those cases, partial differential equations might be premature (Ermentrout and Edelstein-Keshet, 1993). Another factor is that for the continuous approach, the system under study (in our case the microorganisms) must be considered as a continuum. Therefore, this approach is only valid for a large number of organisms. This was illustrated by Giró *et al.* (1985) who used their individual based model to determine the limits where the macroscopic differential equation approach failed.

The rule based approach has the advantage that any mechanistic concept can be translated into discrete rules, also for a small number of organisms. Since a change in microscopic rules may lead to significantly different macroscopic behavior, it may be possible to rule out impossible mechanisms and to learn about the true mechanisms. This is not only true for the mechanisms of bacterial motility in solid environments (as illustrated in this chapter) but for any mechanism which is not fully understood, and/or for which no appropriate continuous function is available. Unfortunately, experimental evidence may often be lacking in order to discriminate between a number of different mechanistic concepts. This is the case for a number of concepts of colony spreading demonstrated in section 21.6.2. Also, these approaches cannot be discriminated from the continuous approach proposed by Grimson and Barker (1993) (section 21.6.1). When this problem occurs, it must be considered which kind of extra experimental evidence is needed to be able to distinguish between the remaining concepts.

A disadvantage of the rule based models is the fact that they are largely *non-analytic*. Only in very rare instances it has been possible to analytically prove the existence of some particular behavior for, e.g., a CA model. In general, the only available technique is to run the simulation which depends on the computational methodology and grid sensitivity in the case of the spatially explicit rule based models. In this respect, also the computational aspects of the rule based models must be addressed. As was already mentioned, CA are generally accepted to be computationally efficient. Moreover, their performance is not seriously restricted by geometrical or compositional complexity (Barker and Grimson, 1993). However, the use of special purpose parallel computers which seriously enhance the CA computations, is mostly not obvious. Also, the high number of random number generations required for probabilistic CAs increases the computational demand. On the other hand, the computational demand for individual based models may present a real problem. At each time step, the behavior of each individual must be computed separately. When exponential growth of microbial cells is simulated for example, the amount of cells will soon become too large and time and memory problems cannot be excluded. This problem is gradually disappearing as computing power is becoming cheaper and more widely available. Therefore, rule base models are becoming more and more popular.

Because of the above-mentioned disadvantages associated with the rule based modeling approach (e.g., non-analytic, high computational demand), it may be advisable to eventually translate these models into an analytic macroscopic model. The mechanistic concepts verified on a rule based level can then help in the construction of more mechanistically inspired continuous models, in order to be more generally valid. Note that this process is not always possible without introducing significant simplifications, which reduce the validity region of the resulting model.

### 21.7.2   Selecting an appropriate type of modeling approach

This choice is primarily determined by the properties of the system under study. As already mentioned in the previous paragraph, the number of microorganisms is an important factor with respect to the choice between a continuous and a discrete approach. For a small number of organisms, the population cannot be considered as a continuum and therefore, a rule based approach, considering the individual behavior of the organisms is recommended. Note that in the field of predictive microbiology, the initial amount of microorganisms in a food product can be quite small. Therefore, in these situations, the discrete approach may be valuable. An additional requirement in the domain of predictive microbiology is that the models must predict microbial evolution in a large number of different environmental conditions. In order for a model to be valid in a large number of different situations, it should incorporate as completely as possible the underlying mechanistic principles defining the system behavior. When no appropriate continuous function is available to describe the underlying mechanisms, the rule based approach can be of help. However, because of the computational and analytic problems related to rule based models, it must always be considered whether continuous models are available to do the same job. When, with the aid of the rule based modeling approach, new insight in the biological mechanisms behind the system behavior is obtained, this knowledge can serve as a guideline in the construction of new macroscopic models with more mechanistic background.

The choice for the type of rule based model (CA or IbM), depends on a number of aspects. Actually, there is an *overlap* between the two modeling approaches: a CA can be an IbM and vice versa. For example, in the lattice gas CA of Csahok and Vicsek (1995) describing collective biological motion, the interacting particles could be defined as individual bacterial cells. On the contrary, Barker and Grimson (1993) and Picioreanu *et al.* (1998) explicitly defined their CA-units as a certain amount of biomass, or a certain number of cells, and could therefore not be identified with individual organisms. The most important aspect of the CA models is their spatial explicity. Therefore, they are suitable for the description of mechanisms in which space is of major importance. An example is the bacterial motility on a surface. The dependence of the displacement of the CA units (can be identified with biomass units for example) can be described in function of the neighboring sites. IbM on the contrary must not be spatially explicit. They can also be used to model the behavior of individuals for which space has no specific meaning. The most important aspect of IbM is that they can describe the behavior of the individual organisms up to any level of detail. In addition, the fact that IbM can account for variability between the organisms, both in parameter values as well as in growth stage, is an interesting property for the description of some phenomena in the field of predictive microbiology.

## 21.8    Conclusions and future trends

In this chapter, the most important aspects of colony dynamics in solid food systems are highlighted and the modeling methodologies to describe these dynamics mathematically have been critically evaluated. Colony growth in/on solid media is the result of an interplay between *intrinsic* and *extrinsic* factors, and four general principles of colony growth have been extracted. Concerning the modeling methodologies, a distinction can be made between the *continuous approach* of the partial differential equations and the *discrete approach* of the rule based models. Literature examples are exhibited to illustrate the different strategies and the power and limitations of both modeling methodologies are emphasized. A main conclusion is that not enough experimental evidence is available to discriminate between the different models proposed in literature. This fact should not pose a problem when the level of accuracy obtained by the different approaches is sufficient for the model purpose. If this is the case, some more pragmatic (dis)-advantages of the different model structures, as discussed in section 21.7, should be taken into account. This would probably lead to the use of the macroscopic model of Barker and Grimson (1993) in combination with some extra partial differential equations for the description of the nutrient and metabolite field (as was proposed for example by Hills and Wright (1994)).

In general, when modeling a specific bacterial/food system, one must always start from the exact description of the system in terms of its extrinsic and intrinsic factors.

- Concerning *extrinsic factors*, the food in which the microorganisms will grow must be analyzed in detail. First of all, the initial conditions of available nutrients, oxygen, water activity and pH, and, even more importantly, the distribution of these properties within the food must be known. Cryosectioning of the food in combination with micro-electrode studies can be used for this purpose. Maybe the food is structured and different phases can be observed within the food matrix. This is for example the case for oil-in-water emulsions (e.g., mayonnaise), in which oil droplets are emulsified in the aqueous phase. It is normally assumed that the oil droplets can be treated as inert inclusions while microorganisms will grow in the aqueous phase (Robins and Wilson, 1994). The same goes for, e.g., lasagna, which is a combination of different types of food structures, each of which having a different influence on the microbial behavior and nutrient availability.

  Since it is a tedious job to determine all these aspects in a natural food system, the importance of a laboratory model food system has already been emphasized by Wimpenny *et al.* (1995b). These model systems could be agar gels in Petri dishes, an agar film coating a microscope slide, or the gel cassette systems developed at IFR (Brocklehurst *et al.*, 1997). They can be more rigorously controlled with respect to, e.g., initial conditions. Also, follow up of the microcolony growth is much more evident. The problem remains that, until now, the gap between model systems and real foods has not been bridged experimentally (Wimpenny *et al.*, 1995b). Motility of microorganisms in real food versus agar systems can differ considerably.

- Concerning *intrinsic factors*, the properties of the bacterial species of concern must be known. Therefore, the metabolism of the cells with respect to the environmental conditions in the food must be analyzed. The same goes for bacterial communication and motility. In section 21.2, some available techniques to analyze these properties were discussed. Enzyme and metabolite studies for the determination of the bacterial metabolism, and image analysis techniques to monitor colony spreading and growth distribution are two examples.

Based on the experimental evidence described above, a specific model structure can be selected. The data on the food structure and initial conditions will dictate the underlying spatial geometry to implement. As can be concluded, the amount of data that must be collected is considerable, which is probably the most important obstruction for the application of the available models to natural solid (and structured) food systems.

As emphasized already, one of the important obstructions to apply advanced modeling techniques to describe microbial evolution in complex (structured and/ or heterogeneous) food systems, is the laborous task of data gathering in order to quantify the food system in terms of its extrinsic (food properties) and intrinsic (distribution of the microorganisms within the food) factors. As Wimpenny *et al.* (1995b) states, the problem remains that the gap between model food systems (agar and gel systems) and real foods has not yet been bridged experimentally. According to the authors, this is one of the important steps to take in the future. This also involves the understanding of the way microorganisms move, or the way a colony spreads, in various food micro-environments.

Software packages to simulate microbial growth in static, homogeneous environments are already available. The potential of such software environments should be extended to also take food structure, and even microbial interactions as well as dynamic temperature environments into account. The user can then select the different micro-architectures present in a particular food product from an internal database and should also provide the relative volumes of the different micro-architectures. To each kind of micro-architecture, specific properties such as the diffusion coefficients of oxygen, nutrients and metabolites are related. Also the initial global concentrations of oxygen and relevant nutrients, within the different micro-architectures are necessary observations which should be provided by the user. These data constitute the extrinsic factors that make up the environment in which the microorganisms grow. The intrinsic factors consist of the different kinds of organisms that are likely to be present in the particular food micro-architectures, as well as their initial concentrations or amounts. These are again data that should be provided by the user. In a more ideal case, a database of different food types, such as cheeses, meat, yoghurt, juice, etc., is related to the software, and contains all necessary data concerning that food product. This can help the users since the amount of data that should be gathered can be consistently reduced. Depending on the temperature profile and external gas concentrations provided, the software simulates the evolution of microorganisms within the food product. Of course, the calculation of a certain risk factor on the results is indispensable in such applications.

An example of a software package that simulates colony growth in a heterogeneous environment is BacSim, and is commented on in the next section.

## 21.9   Sources of further information and advice

In this section, we discuss a software environment that was developed to simulate colony growth in a diffusion-limited environment. BacSim has been written by J. Kreft (http://www.theobio.uni-bonn.de/people/jan_kreft) at the *Cardiff School of Biosciences* at *Cardiff University* in Wales (UK). He is continuing this work now at the Group of Theoretical Biology of the University of Bonn (DE). The program is a spatially explicit individual-based model for bacterial colony/biofilm growth and is based on Gecko (http://www.gingerbooth.com/courseware/pages/demos.html gecko) which is an individual-based simulator for modeling ecosystem dynamics. Gecko is written by Ginger Booth, a programmer with the Center for Computational Ecology at Yale Institute for Biospheric Studies (New Haven, USA). BacSim and Gecko have recently been ported from the Objective-C programming language to Java. Both are object oriented programming languages.

The object oriented programming concept is particularly well suited for the programming of IbMs. Each individual bacterial cell can be defined as a new object of a general *Bacteria* class. A class is a template for multiple *objects* with similar features. It embodies all the features (state and behavior) of that particular set of objects. For example, for the class of the *Bacteria*, the potential regarding to the *state* and *behavior* of bacteria in general will be defined. A bacterium can, e.g., take up substrate, grow, reproduce, die, move. These actions constitute the behavior of all bacteria in general. The state of the individual bacteria will then be represented by their biomass, yield, growth rate, maintenance rate. To define an object's behavior, *methods* are created. Methods are functions defined inside classes that usually operate on instances of those classes. Methods do not always affect only a single object, objects communicate with each other using methods as well. In BacSim, for example, bacteria (objects of the *Bacteria* class) communicate with the diffusion lattice (object of the *Diffuse* class), to know the local substrate concentration. Vice versa, the diffusion lattice communicates with the bacteria to know the amount of substrate taken up by the bacteria.

An extra advantage of the software is that it is built in a modular way. This means that modules (or *classes*) can be added any time, which makes the software easily adaptable and extendable. This is necessary for a software which is continuously under development. At the moment, the authors are extending BacSim to simulate microbial lag behavior under dynamic temperature conditions. The source code for the program is available from the internet and the Java version of BacSim can be run as an applet within a web browser (http://www.theobio.uni-bonn.de/people/jan_kreft/bacsim.html). Screenshots and movies of colonies grown at various substrate concentrations can be found at http://www.theobio.uni-bonn.de/people/jan_kreft/colonies.html

## 21.10   References

ADLER, J. Chemotaxis in bacteria. *Science*, 153: 708–716, 1966.

BARKER, G. C. and M. J. GRIMSON. A cellular automaton model of microbial growth. *Binary*, 5: 132–37, 1993.

BELOVA, S. E., A. G. DOROFEEV and N. S. PANIKOV. Growth and substrate utilization by bacterial lawn on the agar surface: experiment and one-dimensional distributed model. *Microbiology*, 65(6): 690–694, 1996.

BEN-JACOB, E., H. SHMUELI, O. SHOCHET and A. TENENBAUM. Adaptive self-organization during growth of bacterial colonies. *Physica A*, 187: 378–424, 1992.

BEN-JACOB, E., O. SHOCHET, A. TENENBAUM, I. COHEN, A. CZIROK and T. VICSEK. Generic modelling of cooperative growth patterns in bacterial colonies. *Nature*, 368: 46–49, March 1994.

BERG, H. C. and D. A. BROWN. Chemotaxis in *Escherichia coli* analyzed by three-dimensional tracking. *Nature*, 239: 500–504, 1972.

BROCKLEHURST, T. F., G. A. MITCHELL and A. C. SMITH. A model experimental gel surface for the growth of bacteria on foods. *Food Microbiol.*, 14: 303–311, 1997.

BUDRENE, E. O. and H. C. BERG. Complex patterns formed by motile cells of *Escherichia coli*. *Nature*, 349: 630–633, 1991.

BUDRENE, E. O. and H. C. BERG. Dynamics of formation of symmetrical patterns by chemotactic bacteria. *Nature*, 376: 49–53, 1995.

BUNGAY, H. R., P. M. PETTIT and A. M. DRISLANE. Dissolved oxygen contours in *Pseudomonas ovalis* colonies. *ACS Sym. Ser.*, 207: 395–401, 1983.

CHOPARD, B. and M. DROZ. Cellular automata model for the diffusion equation. *J. Stat. Phys.*, 64(3/4): 859–892, 1991.

COOPER, A. L., A. C. R. DEAN and C. HINSHELWOOD. Morphological changes in growing colonies of *Aerobacter (Klebsiella) aerogenes*. *Proc. Roy. Soc. Lond. B*, 175: 95–105, 1970.

CSAHOK, Z. and T. VICSEK. Lattice-gas model for collective biological motion. *Phys. Rev. E*, 52(5): 5297–5303, 1995.

DIAZ, G., W. WOLF, A. E. KASTAROPOULOS and W. E. L. SPIESS. Diffusion of low-molecular-weight compounds in food model systems. *J. Food Process. Preserv.*, 17: 437–454, 1993.

EDEN, M. A two-dimensional growth process. In F. Neyman, editor, *Proceedings of Fourth Berkeley symposium on mathematics, statistics and probability*, volume 4, pages 223–239, Berkeley, 1960. University of California Press.

ERMENTROUT, G. B. and L. EDELSTEIN-KESHET. Cellular automata approaches to biological modeling. *J. theor. Biol.*, 160: 97–133, 1993.

FUJIKAWA, H. and M. MATSUSHITA. Fractal growth of *Bacillus subtilis* on agar plates. *J. Phys. Soc. Jpn.*, 58(11): 3875–3878, 1989.

GIRÓ, A., J. A. PADRÓ, J. VALLS and J. WAGENSBERG. Monte Carlo simulation of an ecosystem: a matching between two levels of observation. *Bull. Math. Biol.*, 47: 111–122. 1985.

GOLDING, I., Y. KOZLOVSKY, I. COHEN and E. BEN-JACOB. Studies of bacterial branching growth using reaction-diffusion models for colonial development. *Physica A*, 260: 510–554, 1998.

GRIMSON, M. J. and G. C. BARKER. A continuum model for the growth of bacterial colonies on a surface. *J. Phys. A: Math. Gen.*, 26: 5645–5654, 1993.

GRIMSON, M. J. and G. C. BARKER. Continuum model for the spatiotemporal growth of bacterial colonies. *Phys. Rev. E*, 49(2): 1680–1684, 1994.

GROSSMAN, A. D. and R. LOSICK. Extracellular control of spore formation in *Bacillus subtilis*. *Proc. Natl. Acad. Sci. USA*, 85: 4369–4373, 1988.

GUE, M., V. DUPONT, A. DUFOUR and O. SIRE. Bacterial swarming: a biochemical time-resolved ftir-atr study of *Proteus mirabilis* swarm-cell differentiation. *Biochemistry*, 40: 11938–11945, 2001.

HENDRY, R. J. *Spatial Modelling in Plant Ecology*. PhD thesis, University of Warwick, Department of Biological Sciences, Ecology and Epidemiology, Coventry, CV4 7AL, UK, 1995.

HILLS, B. P. and K. M. WRIGHT. A new model for bacterial growth in heterogeneous systems. *J. Theor. Biol.*, 168: 31–41, 1994.

KAISER, D. and R. LOSICK. How and why bacteria talk to each other. *Cell*, 73: 873–885. 1993.

KATSARAS, K. and L. LEISTNER. Distribution and development of bacterial colonies in fermented sausages. *Biofouling*, 5: 115–124, 1991.

KAWASAKI, K., A. MOCHIZUKI, M. MATSUSHITA, T. UMEDA and N. SHIGESADA. Modeling spatio-temporal patterns generated by *Bacillus subtilis*. *J. Thecor. Biol.*, 188: 177–185, 1997.

KITSUNEZAKI, S. Interface dynamics for bacterial colony formation. *J. Phys. Soc. Jpn.*, 66(5): 1544–1550, May 1997.

KOCH, A. L. Diffusion, the crucial process in many aspects of the biology of bacteria. *Adv. Microb. Ecol.*, 11: 37–70, 1991.

KREFT, J. U., G. BOOTH and J. W. T. WIMPENNY. BacSim, a simulator for individual-based modelling of bacterial colony growth. *Microbiology*, 144: 3275–3287, 1998.

KUSPA, A., L. PLAMANN and D. KAISER. A-signaling and the cell density requirement for *Myxococcus xanthus* development. *J. Bacteriol.*, 174(22): 7360–7369, 1992.

LEBRUN, L. and G. A. JUNTER. Diffusion of sucrose and dextran through agar gel membranes. *Enzyme Microb. Technol.*, 15: 1057–1062, 1993.

MALAKAR, P. K., T. F. BROCKLEHURST, A. R. MACKIE, P. D. G. WILSON, M. H. ZWIETERING and K. VAN 'T RIET. Microgradients in bacterial colonies: use of fluorescent ratio imaging, a non-invasive technique. *Int. J. Food Microbiol.*, 56: 71–80, 2000.

MATSUSHITA, M., J. WAKITA, H. ITOH, I. RAFOLS, T. MATSUYAMA, H. SAKUGUCHI and M. MIMURA. Interface growth and pattern formation in bacterial colonies. *Physica A*, 249: 517–524, 1998.

MATSUYAMA, T. and M. MATSUSHITA. Fractal morphogenesis by a bacterial cell population. *Crit. Rev. Microbiol.*, 19(2): 117–135, 1993.

MATTILA, T. and A. J. FROST. The growth of potential food poisoning organisms on chicken and pork muscle surfaces. *J. Appl. Bacteriol.*, 65: 455–461, 1988.

MCKAY, A. L., A. C. PETERS and J. W. T. WIMPENNY. Determining specific growth rates in different regions of *Salmonella typhimurium* colonies. *Lett. Appl. Microbiol.*, 24(1): 74–76, 1997.

MITCHELL, A. J. and J. W. T. WIMPENNY. The effects of agar concentration on the growth and morphology of submerged colonies of motile and non-motile bacteria. *J. Appl. Microbiol.*, 83: 76–84, 1997.

NAKAHARA, A., Y. SHIMADA, J. WAKITA, M. MATSUSHITA and T. MATSUYAMA. Morphological diversity of the colony produced by bacteria *Proteus mirabilis*. *J. Phys. Soc. Jpn.*, 65(8): 2700–2706, 1996.

OHGIWARI, M., M. MATSUSHITA and T. MATSUYAMA. Morphological changes in growth phenomena of bacterial colony patterns. *J. Phys. Soc. Jpn.*, 61(3): 816–822, March 1992.

OMAR, S. H. Oxygen diffusion through gels employed for immobilization. 2. In the presence of microorganisms. *Appl. Microbiol. Biotechnol.*, 40: 173–181, 1993.

OUVRY, A., R. CACHON and C. DIVIES. Application of microelectrode technique to measure pH and oxidoreduction potential gradients in gelled systems as model food. *Biotechnol. Lett.*, 23: 1373–1377, 2001.

PETERS, A. C., J. W. T. WIMPENNY and J. P. COOMBS. Oxygen profiles in, and in the agar beneath, colonies of *Bacillus cereus, Staphylococcus albus* and *Escherichia coli*. *J. Gen. Microbiol.*, 133: 1257–1263, 1987.

PICIOREANU, C., M. C. M. VAN LOOSDRECHT and J. J. HEIJNEN. A new combined differential-discrete cellular automaton approach for biofilm modeling: application for growth in gel beads. *Biotechnol. Bioeng.*, 57(6): 718–731, March 1998.

PIRT., S. J. A kinetic study of the mode of growth of surface colonies of bacteria and fungi. *J. Gen. Microbiol.*, 47: 181–197, 1967.

REYROLLE, J. and F. LETELLIER. Autoradiographic study of the localization and evolution of growth zones in bacterial colonies. *J. Gen. Microbiol.*, 111: 399–406, 1979.

ROBINS, M. M. and P. D. G. WILSON. Food structure and microbial growth. *Trends Food Sci. Technol.*, 5: 289–293, 1994.

ROBINSON, T. P., J. W. T. WIMPENNY and R. G. EARNSHAW. pH gradients through colonies of *Bacillus cereus* and the surrounding agar. *J. Gen. Microbiol.*, 137: 2885–2889, 1991.

SEGEL, L. A. and J. L. JACKSON. Theoretical analysis of chemotactic movement in bacteria. *J. Mechanochem. Cell Motility* 2: 25–34, 1973.

SHAPIRO, J. A. Organization of developing *Escherichia coli* colonies viewed by scanning electron microscopy. *J. Bacteriol.*, 169(1): 142–156, Jan. 1987.

SHAPIRO, J. A. and D. TRUBATCH. Sequential events in bacterial colony morphogenesis. *Physica D*, 49: 214–223, 1991.

STECCHINI, M. L., M. DEL TORRE, S. DONDA, E. MALTINI and S. PACOR. Influence of agar content on the growth parameters of *Bacillus cereus. Int. J. Food Microbiol.*, 64: 81–88, 2001.

STECCHINI, M. L., M. DEL TORRE, I. SARAIS, O. SARO, M. MESSINA and E. MALTINI. Influence of structural properties and kinetic constraints on *Bacillus cereus* growth. *Appl. Env. Microbiol.*, 64(3): 1075–1078, 1998.

STRINGER, S. C., C. E. R. DODD, M. R. A. MORGAN and W. M. WAITES. Detection of microorganisms *in situ* in solid foods. *Trends Food Sci. Technol.*, 6: 370–374, 1995.

TAMMAM, J. D., A. G. WILLIAMS, J. BANKS, G. COWIE and D. LLOYD. Membrane inlet mass spectrometric measurement of $O_2$ and $CO_2$ gradients in cultures of *Lactobacillus paracasei* and a developing Cheddar cheese ecosystem. *Int. J. Food Microbiol.*, 65: 11–22, 2001.

TOGUCHI, A., M. SIANO, M. BURKART and R. M. HARSHEY. Genetics of swarming motility in *Salmonella enterica* serovar typhimurium: critical role for lipopolysaccharide. *J. Bacteriol.*, 182(22): 6308–6321, 2000.

VICSEK, T., A. CZIROK, E. BEN-JACOB, I. COHEN and O. SHOCHET. Novel type of phase transition in a system of self-driven particles. *Phys. Rev. Lett.*, 75(6): 1226–1229, 1995.

WAKITA, J., K. KOMATSU, A. NAKAHARA, T. MATSUYAMA and M. MATSUSHITA. Experimental investigation of the validity of population dynamics approach to bacterial colony formation. *J. Phys. Soc. Jpn.*, 63(3): 1205–1211, March 1994.

WALKER, S. L., T. F. BROCKLEHURST and J. W. T. WIMPENNY. The effects of growth dynamics upon pH gradient formation within and around subsurface colonies *of Salmonella typhimurium. J. Appl. Microbiol.*, 82: 610–614, 1997.

WALKER, S. L., T. F. BROCKLEHURST and J. W. T. WIMPENNY. Adenylates and adenylate-energy charge in submerged and planktonic cultures of *Salmonella enteritidis* and *Salmonella typhimurium. Int. J. Food Microbiol.*, 44: 107–113, 1998.

WENTLAND, E. J., P. S. STEWART, C. T. HUANG and G. A. MCFETERS. Spatial variations in growth rate within *Klebsiella pneumoniae* colonies and biofilm. *Biotechnol. Prog.*, 12: 316–321, 1996.

WESTRIN, B. A. and A. AXELSSON. Diffusion in gels containing immobilized cells: a critical review. *Biotechnol. Bioeng.*, 38: 439–446, 1991.

WILSON, P. D. G., T. F. BROCKLEHURST, S. ARINO, D. THUAULT, M. JAKOBSEN, M. LANGE, J. FARKAS, J. W. T. WIMPENNY and J. F. VAN IMPE. Modelling microbial growth in structured foods: towards a unified approach. *Int. J. Food Microbiol.*, 73: 275–289, 2002.

WIMPENNY, J., T. WILKINSON and A. PETERS. Monitoring microbial colony growth using inage analysis techniques. *Binary*, 7: 14–18, 1995a.

WIMPENNY, J. W. T. Microbial systems, patterns in tune and space. *Adv. Microb. Ecol.*, 12:

469–522, 1992.

WIMPENNY, J. W. T., L. LEISTNER, L. V. THOMAS, A. J. MITCHELL, K. KATSARAS and P. PEETZ. Submerged bacterial colonies within food and model systems: their growth, distribution and interactions. *Int. J. Food Microbiol.*, 28: 299–315, 1995b.

WIMPENNY, J. W. T. and M. W. A. LEWIS. The growth and respiration of bacterial colonies. *J. Gen. Microbiol.*, 103: 9–18, 1977.

WIMPENNY, J. W. T. and J. A. PARR. Biochemical differentiation in large colonies *of Enterobacter cloacae. J. Gen. Microbiol.*, 114: 487–489, 1979.

WITTEN, T. A. and L. M. SANDER. Diffusion-limited aggregation, a kinetic critical phenomenon. *Phys. Rev. Lett.*, 47(19): 1400–1403, 1981.

WOLFE, A. J. and H. C. BERG. Migration of bacteria in semisolid agar. *Proc. Nat. Acad. Sci. USA*, 86: 6973–6977, 1989.

# 22

# Modelling applied to processes: the case of thermal preservation

**M. Peleg, University of Massachusetts, USA**

## 22.1   Introduction

Traditionally, microbial heat inactivation has been considered a process which follows a first order kinetics. Consequently, the heat resistance of microbial cells and spores has been expressed in terms of '$D$ values', the time needed to reduce their population by one log cycle (base ten) at a given temperature. The temperature dependence of $D$ has been assumed to obey a log linear relationship, which has produced the '$Z$ value', the temperature span needed to shorten $D$ by one log cycle (base ten). Or alternatively, the temperature dependence of the exponential inactivation rate, $k$, the reciprocal of $D$, has been assumed to obey the Arrhenius equation, originally developed for simple chemical reactions. Either way, the effectiveness of any given thermal preservation process has been evaluated in term of an '$F$ value'. It is a measure of the equivalence of the changing temperature integrated lethal effect, at the coldest point in the product, to an isothermal process at a reference temperature. Traditionally, for heat sterilization of low acid foods, it has been 121.1 °C (250 °F) with the inactivation target being *C. botulinum* spores. There are various numerical and graphical methods to incorporate these kinetic assumptions and considerations in the calculation of the theoretical efficacy of thermal processes. In the commercial sterilization operations, is a safety factor, which varies among products, also added to the calculation. Consequently, in most thermally preserved foods, the actual duration of the treatment usually exceeds the 'theoretical requirement' by a substantial margin.

In light of the impressive safety record of the canning industry, there has been little incentive to reexamine the traditional methods to calculate sterility. Yet, there are a few recognized problems with their theoretical foundations that may have safety implications in at least some heat treated foods. Or more specifically:

- There is growing evidence that the semi-logarithmic survival curves of many microorganisms and spores, including pathogens of food safety concern, are not linear as the first order kinetics implies. Thus, forcing a straight line through the curved experimental survival data to produce a '$D$ value' is not a permissible option. (In cases where the isothermal semi-logarithmic survival curve of the organism or spore has an upper concavity, or 'tailing', then forcing a straight line may result in under processing and hence, can at least potentially, increase the safety risk. On the other hand, if the semi-logarithmic survival curve has a downward concavity, then the result will be over processing to a level well beyond that which is required to guarantee product safety.)
- Even if microbial inactivation were a process, which followed a first order kinetics, the Arrhenius equation or log linear model to express the rate constant's temperature dependence would not be a good choice. The reason is that the logarithmic transformation of $k$ or $D$ and the assumption of a linear relationship between log $k$ or log $D$ and $1/T$ or $T$, respectively, gives an inappropriate weight to the low temperatures of the treatment at the expense of the high temperatures, where most of the inactivation actually takes place. As previously shown (Campanella and Peleg, 2001; Peleg et al., 2002) there is no reason to assume that there is a universal analogy between microbial mortality and simple chemical reactions that the use of the Arrhenius equation entails.
- The formula to calculate the '$F$ value' contains the reference temperature as a term. But since the '$F$ value' can be translated into a survival ratio, the latter will be independent of the reference temperature if, and only if, $D$ is well defined and has log linear temperature dependence.

The existence of these three problems is not a trivial matter and a rethinking of the whole issue of microbial survival during heat treatments is clearly warranted. One can also add, that the fundamentals of the current mathematical methods to estimate microbial survival in thermal processes were formulated in a time when the ability to perform complicated calculations was extremely limited. Hence, there was a premium on linear models whose parameters could be determined graphically or with the use of a mechanical desk calculator. With today's software and computation power, mathematical simplicity, although by no means undesirable, need not be the prime consideration as it has been in the past. As will be shown below, we can now formulate survival models that are based on realistic assumptions rather than on idealization and unproven analogies between microbial mortality and certain physical phenomena in the non-living realm.

The following discussion will focus on how microbial heat inactivation can be described, and even predicted, by mathematical models constructed almost exclusively on the basis of the targeted organism's or spores' experimentally observed inactivation patterns without the assumption that microbial inactivation is a process that follows a universal first order kinetics or any other preconceived kinetic model.

## 22.2   Understanding thermal inactivation

Survival curves, microbial included, depict the fraction of survivors as a function of time. Hence, each can be considered the cumulative form of a distribution of temporal mortality events. This has long been recognized and several authors have suggested a variety of distribution functions to describe them (e.g., Casolari, 1988, Little *et al.*, 1994; Stephens *et al.*, 1994; Anderson *et al.*, 1996; Linton *et al.*, 1996; Augustin *et al.*, 1998). If the thermal resistance of an organism or a spore is expressed as the time needed for its destruction or inactivation, then the survival curve's slope has rate units and hence the relationship between the survival curve's shape and the inactivation kinetics (Peleg and Penchina, 2000). Since different organisms and spores, in different media and at different temperatures can have different distributions of inactivation times, the shape of their isothermal survival curves can vary accordingly. Consequently, many microbial survival curves, when plotted on semi-logarithmic coordinates, have an upward or downward concavity. They can also have a sigmoid shape or exhibit a 'shoulder' or a 'tail'. The interpretation of the different shapes in terms of the mortality pattern has been discussed in a series of recent papers (Peleg and Penchina, 2000; Peleg, 2000, 2002, 2003). Suffice it to say that upward concavity is a manifestation of the rapid elimination of the weak members of the population leaving progressively sturdier survivors, while downward concavity is an indication that accumulated damage sensitizes the survivors. A true linear semi-logarithmic survival curve would indicate that all the population members have the same probability of being inactivated at any given time (the equivalent of a radioactive decay). The important point here is that any mathematical survival model should be derived from the actual shapes of the experimental isothermal semi-logarithmic survival curves, determined in the pertinent medium, and not from the assumption that all inactivation processes obey a single universal law. One must also take into consideration that the general shape of the isothermal semi-logarithmic survival curves of the same organism need not remain fixed. Thus, a concavity inversion as the treatment's temperature increases or decreases is by no means unusual.

The Weibull distribution function has been a successful model of many unrelated systems, where destruction and survival are involved (Van Boekel, 2002). One would therefore expect, that a ubiquitous mortality pattern would emerge if many organisms and spores had a Weibull, or 'Weibull like', distribution of heat resistances. Consequently, we have chosen this distribution as a model for much of this chapter's discussion. It can be shown that *C. botulinum* spores (in the range of 101 to 121 °C, and those of various bacilli, can indeed be considered as having a 'Weibull type' distribution of heat resistances

(Peleg and Penchina, 2000). Similarly, the heat inactivation of several food-borne pathogens, most notably that of *Salmonella,* can also be described as being governed by an underlying Weibull distribution of resistances (Peleg and Cole, 1998; Mattick *et al.,* 2001; Van Boekel, 2002). The proposed methodology to deal with such organisms, as it will become evident, can be extended to other survival patterns, which include 'tailing', 'shoulders' and concavity inversion, i.e., sigmoidal isothermal semi-logarithmic survival curves (Peleg and Penchina, 2000; Peleg, 2002; 2003). Needless to say, the same method also applies to organisms or spores whose semi-logarithmic survival curves are linear, which is just a special simple case of the Weibull distribution where the shape factor is equal to one (see below).

## 22.3   Modelling microbial death and survival

An isothermal survival pattern of a population governed by heat resistances having a Weibull distribution (Fig. 22.1) is characterized by:

$$\log_{10} S = -b(T)t^{n(T)} \qquad\qquad 22.1$$

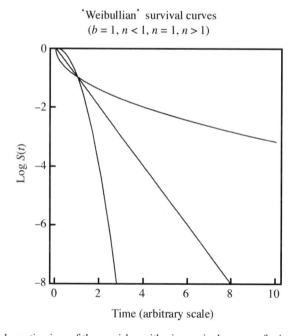

**Fig. 22.1**   Schematic view of the semi-logarithmic survival curves of microorganisms or spores whose heat resistances have a Weibull distribution with a shape factor, $n(T)$ in eqn 22.1, smaller, equal to and bigger than one.

where $S$ is the momentary survival ratio, $S = N(t)/N_0$ where $N(t)$ and $N_0$ are the momentary and initial number of viable cells or spores, respectively, and $b(T)$ and $n(T)$ temperature dependent coefficients representing the distribution's scale and shape factor respectively.

Consider the following assumptions (Peleg and Penchina, 2000):

- The microbial or sporal population is sufficiently large that eqn 22.1 can be used to describe the changes in its size at all temperatures and times in the pertinent range.
- The temperature dependence of the survival parameters, in our case, eqn 22.1 coefficients $b(T)$ and $n(T)$, can be described algebraically.
- The treatment's non-isothermal temperature 'profile', $T(t)$, can also be expressed algebraically.
- The momentary semi-logarithmic survival (or inactivation) rate, $d\log_{10}S/dt$, is the isothermal rate at the momentary temperature, $T(t)$, at a time, $t^*$, which corresponds to the momentary survival ratio, (Fig. 22.2).

According to eqn 22.1:

$$t^* = \left[\frac{-\log_{10}S(t)}{b(T)}\right]^{\frac{1}{n(T)}}$$  22.2

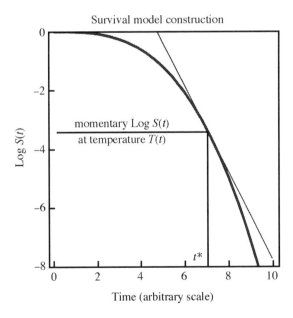

**Fig. 22.2**  Schematic view of the construction of the differential equation that describes a non-isothermal semi-logarithmic survival curve.

and

$$\frac{d\log_{10}S(t)}{dt} = -b(T)n(T)t^{*n(T)-1} \qquad 22.3$$

Combining eqns 22.2 and 22.3 yields the differential equation (Peleg and Penchina, 2000; Peleg et al., 2001):

$$\frac{d\log_{10}S(t)}{dt} = -b[T(t)]n[T(t)]\left\{\frac{-\log_{10}S}{b[T(t)]}\right\}^{\frac{n[T(t)]-1}{n[T(t)]}} \qquad 22.4$$

whose solution, $\log_{10}S(t)$, is the non-isothermal survival curve, which corresponds to the particular temperature profile, $T(t)$. In programs like Mathematica® (Wolfram Research, Champaign, IL), the one used to produce the plots shown in this chapter, defining the terms $b[T(t)]$ and $n(t) = n[T(t)]$ is a trivial matter. As will be seen below, the differential equation can be solved numerically to produce the survival curve, $\log_{10}S(t)$, even for very elaborate temperature profiles, which include heating and cooling, sudden interruptions and regular, irregular and even random temperature fluctuations.

### 22.3.1   Expressing $b(T)$

It is a well-known fact that microbial thermal inactivation starts in earnest only at a certain temperature. The same also applies to bacterial spores. Well below this temperature, there is hardly any mortality or inactivation (there might be even growth) and above it, the process accelerates. These features are implemented in the empirical log logistic model (Campanella and Peleg, 2001; Peleg et al., 2002):

$$b(T) = \log_e\{1 + \exp[k(T - T_c)]\} \qquad 22.5$$

where $k$ and $T_c$ are constants. The reader will notice that at $T << T_c, b(T) \approx 0$ and at $T >> T_c, b(T) = k(T - T_c)$, i.e., $b(T)$ increases linearly with temperature as shown in Fig. 22.3. The almost perfect fit of eqn 22.5 to the $b(T)$ vs. $t$ relationships of C. botulinum spores and Salmonella and Listeria cells has been reported by Peleg et al. (2002). If the observed increase of $b(T)$ is clearly non-linear, eqn 22.5 can be amended by adding an exponent to the right side, i.e.,

$$b(T) = \log_e[1 + \exp[k(T - T_c)]]^m \qquad 22.6$$

where $m$ is a constant ($m > 1$). Although neither eqn 22.5 nor 22.6 can be used for extrapolation, one can assume that the increase in $b(T)$ will be at least linear at temperatures slightly higher than those for which experimental data are available. Nevertheless, a scenario where there can be a certain degree of survival, irrespective of temperature, cannot be ruled out a priori. Hence extreme caution is needed even if eqn 22.5 is used only to estimate the borderline case by extrapolation.

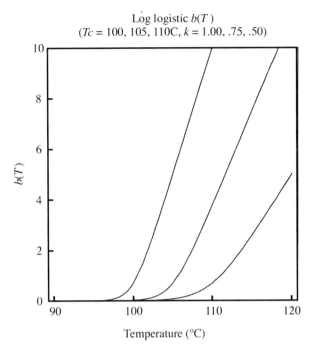

**Fig. 22.3**   The log logistic expression of the survival parameter $b(T)$ (in eqn 22.1). (Note that the same model would apply to $k(T)$ if an organism's semi-logarithmic survival curves happen to be linear.)

### 22.3.2   Expressing $n(T)$

While $b(T)$ in eqn 22.1 primarily accounts for the overall steepness of the survival ratio drop, $n(T)$ primarily expresses the semi-logarithmic survival curve's concavity direction and its degree of curvature. A power smaller than one, $n(T) < 1$, represents upward concavity ('tailing'), and bigger than one, $n(T) > 1$, downward concavity. When $n(T) = 1$, as already stated, the semi-logarithmic survival curve is linear. In contrast with $b(T)$, it is difficult to know, a priori, how $n(T)$ changes with temperature. At least in some cases, it can be assumed to be constant or practically constant at the pertinent lethal temperature range (e.g., Campanella and Peleg, 2001; Mattick *et al.*, 2001; Van Boekel, 2002), but this need not be the general rule.

## 22.4   Simulating thermal processes

Theoretically, the temperature at the coldest point in a processed can, or a glass container, can be calculated or be closely approximated, provided that the heat transfer mechanism and the thermal properties of the treated contents are known. The same applies to the mean temperature and residence times distribution of a fluid product passing through a heat exchanger, including a holding time tube, if

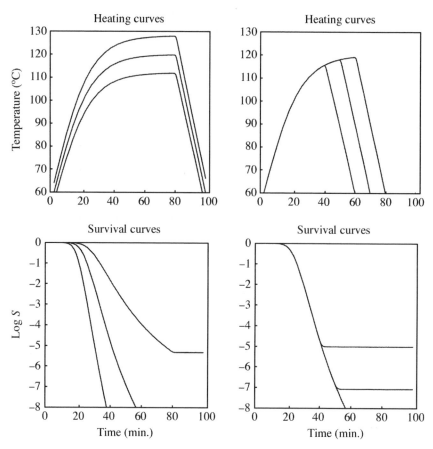

**Fig. 22.4**    Simulated sporal inactivation patterns in heat sterilization processes having different target temperatures (left) and durations (right).

the flow regime and the fluid's thermal and flow properties are known. In reality, most notably in foods treated in a sealed container, accurate calculation of the temperature profile can be complicated by inhomogeneities at various levels, within and outside the container. Consequently, the temperature profile at the coldest point is monitored at various locations in a retort, for example, using a set of thermocouples. Usually, the heating and cooling curve has the characteristic shape shown in Fig. 22.4 (Toledo, 1999). Such curves can be described by the empirical model (Campanella and Peleg, 2001):

$$T(t) = \frac{T_{asymp} - \log_e\{1 + \exp[k_1(t - t_{c1})]\}}{1 + \exp[k_2(t_{c2} - t)]} \qquad 22.7$$

or a similar model, where $T_{asymp}$ is the target or asymptotic temperature, 120 °C for example, and $k_1, k_2, t_{c1}$ and $t_{c2}$ are constants.

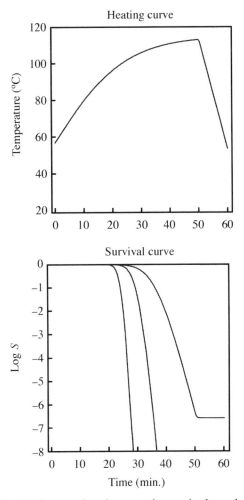

**Fig. 22.5** A simulated comparison between the non-isothermal semi-logarithmic survival curves of three hypothetical spores having the different heat resistances shown in Fig. 22.3 with $n(T) = 0.6$.

The realistic temperature profiles shown in Figs 22.4 and 22.5 were generated with eqn. 22.7 as a model. It is a combination of the logistic and log logistic equations and hence $T(t)$, when expressed in this way, is an ordinary algebraic continuous function. Thus, despite the discontinuous appearance of the temperature profile curve at the onset of cooling (Figs 22.4 and 22.5), the term $T(t)$ so defined can be used to express the changes in the survival parameters, $b[T(t)]$ and $n[T(t)]$ during the whole process cycle. These two terms, in turn, can be incorporated into the survival curve's differential equation (eqn 22.4), which will produce the corresponding survival curve. Despite its cumbersome mathematical structure, eqn 22.7 is a very convenient mathematical model for temperature profile simulations. Not only does it fit well (which would be expected from a model having five adjustable parameters) but it also enables easy control of the simulated temperature profile's shape. Or more specifically:

| Parameter | Increases | Decrease |
|---|---|---|
| $T_{asymp}$ | elevates the whole curve | lowers the whole curve |
| $k_1$ | increases the cooling rate | decreases the cooling rate |
| $t_{c1}$ | postpones the cooling | advances the cooling |
| $k_2$ | increases the heating rate | decreases the heating rate |
| $t_{c2}$ | increases the initial temperature (shifts the curve to the right) | decreases the initial temperature (shifts the curve to the left) |

If only the heating part of the profile is of interest to the analysis, then one can use the logistic component only, i.e.,

$$T(t) = \frac{T_{asymp}}{1 + \exp[k_2(t_{c2} - t)]} \qquad 22.8$$

Either way, in at least some cases, $t_{c2}$ can be dropped (i.e., $t_{c2} = 0$). This reduces the number of adjustable parameters without much effect on the fit.

The heating part of the curve can also be described by the three-parameter model:

$$T(t) = T_0 + \frac{t}{k_1' + \dfrac{t}{T_{asymp} - T_0}} \qquad 22.9$$

where $T_0$ is the initial temperature and $k_1'$ a constant, which can serve as a 'skeleton' for more elaborate profiles which contain oscillations.

'Regular' and 'irregular' temperature fluctuations can be simulated with a variety of models (Peleg, 2002), for example:

$$T(t) = T_0 + \frac{[1 + c_i \sum x_i \sin(\omega_i t)]t}{c_2 + \dfrac{t}{T_{asymp} - T_0}} \qquad 22.10$$

and

$$T(t) = T_0 + \sum \frac{c_3(c_4 + R_{ni})}{1 + \exp[(R_{nj} - t)(c_5 + R_{ni})]} \qquad 22.11$$

respectively. When eqn 22.10 is used as a model the oscillations' amplitude is controlled by $c_i$ and $x_i$ and their frequencies by $\omega_i$. In eqn 22.11, they are controlled not only by the fixed parameters $c_3, c_4$ and $c_5$ but also by two sets of random numbers: $R_{ni}(0 < R_{ni} < 1)$, which primarily controls the temperature's random 'increments' and $R_{nj}$, which primarily controls their frequency. (Each $R_{nj}$ is approximately the process duration divided by $i$, the number of random temperature 'increments'.) Although these models are far from being 'handy' they can still be used to examine the potential qualitative effect of process instabilities on the survival ratio – see below.

Steam interruption(s) and subsequent intermediate cooling can be simulated using models containing 'If' statements to separate the heating and cooling regimes before, during and after the steam supply had been interrupted and restored. A 'simplified' example is the model:

$$T(t) = \mathrm{If}[t \le t_{\mathrm{interrp}}, T(t), \ \mathrm{If}[t \le t_{\mathrm{interrpt}} + \Delta t, T(t_{\mathrm{interrp}})\mathrm{Decayterm}$$
$$(t - t_{\mathrm{interrp}}), T(t - t_{\mathrm{end\ of\ cooling}})]] \qquad\qquad 22.12$$

where $T(t)$ is the temperature rise equation of a non-interrupted cycle, e.g., eqns 22.7, 22.8, or 22.9, $t_{\mathrm{interrpt}}$ the time when the steam interruption started, $\Delta t$ the interruption duration, Decayterm ($t$-$t_{\mathrm{interup}}$) a decay function describing the temperature drop during the steam stoppage and $T_{\mathrm{end\,of\,cooling}}$ and $t_{\mathrm{end\,of\,cooling}}$ are the temperature and time when the steam supply was restored, respectively. The model is called 'simplified' because rarely, if ever, will the steam interruption and restoration be even approximately instantaneous, and because the heating curves before and after the interruption need not follow the same model. Nevertheless, such a model can capture the qualitative aspects of a steam stoppage and show how it can affect process efficacy. At least in principle, the simulations that it produces can be used to determine to what extent the safety of the product has been compromised and what kind of a 'remedial' treatment would be necessary. One should keep in mind though, that this sort of model would not account for possible sporal germination or microbial growth, which might be accompanied by toxin production, if the steam interruption is sufficiently long.

## 22.5   Using models to improve food safety and quality

The theoretical effect of the target temperature and the initiation of the cooling on the inactivation patterns of spores are in Fig. 22.4. They were generated using survival parameters similar to those of *C. botulinum* spores (Campanella and Peleg, 2001) derived from the published results of Anderson *et al.* (1996). These were obtained in a buffered solution rather than in a real food. One could therefore expect that in any given real food, the survival parameters, especially, $b(T)$, would be somewhat different. For the sake of this discussion, we will assume that the hypothetical food in question offers a certain degree of protection to the spores, which would be expressed by a simultaneous elevation of $T_c$ and the lowering of $k$ in eqn 22.5. We will therefore assign $T_c = 105\,^{\circ}\mathrm{C}$ instead of $102\,^{\circ}\mathrm{C}$ and $k = 0.25\,^{\circ}\mathrm{C}^{-1}$ instead of about $0.3\,^{\circ}\mathrm{C}^{-1}$. We shall also assume, for the sake of simplicity, that $n(T)$ is practically unchanged and remains constant, e.g., $n(T) \approx 0.3$. We can now generate survival curves with the new survival parameters and check whether any contemplated heating-cooling cycle produces a preset level of inactivation or not. Or similarly, one can generate a series of heating-cooling cycles in order to identify the conditions which will produce or surpass any given survival ratio deemed critical for microbial safety. Examples of such evaluations are shown in Fig. 22.4. In the simulations shown in the figure, and all subsequent simulations, the lowest marked survival ratio is $10^{-8}$. Eight orders of magnitude reduction seems to be the highest level that can be quantitatively determined by routine procedures in food microbiology laboratories. Hence, and unlike the traditional '12D reduction', it can be determined directly, without extrapolation. It is the author's opinion that a safety factor should be based on an actually observed survival ratio rather than on the extrapolation of the survival curve to survival levels where no experimental data are available.

### 22.5.1   Heat effects on different microorganisms

The emergence of new food-borne pathogens and discovery of heat resistant strains of old ones has recently become a food safety issue. The question that arises is whether existing thermal, or other preservation processes are sufficient for their inactivation and if not, how should the process be adjusted to cope with the new or potential danger. If survival parameters of a newly discovered pathogen can be expressed in a form suitable for the model, then one can assess the efficacy of a present or planned process by running a simulation with the corresponding temperature profile. This is demonstrated in Fig. 22.5 where simulated survival curves of a hypothetical heat sensitive and of a resistant strain are compared. Obviously, and as in any computer simulation of survival patterns, the result should be confirmed with experimental data. While these will provide the ultimate criterion of the product's safety, the simulation would still be a useful tool. They will enable rapid identification of processes, which are potentially safe or risky, thus narrowing the conditions range for the more time consuming and expensive experimental validation. Similar procedures can also be used to assess the potential effect of factors like pH, salt content, etc. If their effect can be expressed in terms of the survival parameters, e.g., $k$ and $T_c$ in eqn 22.5 and the magnitude of $n(T)$ in eqn 22.1, then simulations could be used to identify the range of potential treatment conditions that will produce a safe product that still satisfies organoleptic and other quality requirements.

### 22.5.2   Unstable processes

Let us examine a hypothetical erratic process where the heating was almost totally out of control. This could be a result of 'periodic' or 'random' variations in the steam supply. The temperature profiles, $T(t)$, in such processes can be described by models with fixed or random coefficients, of the kind given in eqns 22.10 and 22.11 for example (Peleg, 2002). Two exaggerated examples are shown in Fig. 22.6. The main purpose of the figure is to demonstrate that the complexity of the differential equation when such temperature profiles are introduced is not a hindrance to its numerical solution by Mathematica®. Therefore, at least in principle, survival curves of this kind can be generated and analyzed in order to evaluate the risk stemming from an irregular steam supply and determine if an additional treatment would be needed if it happens. The

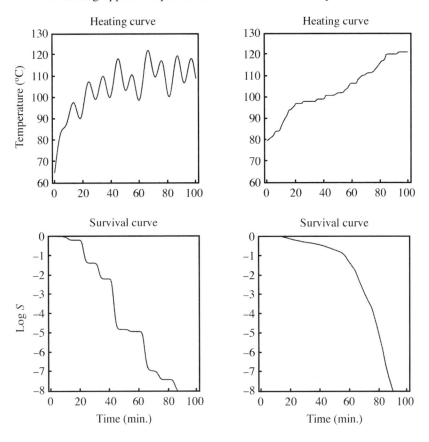

**Fig. 22.6** Simulated sporal inactivation patterns during two uncontrolled heating processes, with smooth (right) and random (left) temperature oscillations.

same procedure could also be used to determine the duration of the additional treatment once the need has been established.

### 22.5.3 Steam stoppage

The effect of an accidental steam shutdown in mid-process on the theoretical survival ratio can also be examined by the described procedure, at least in principle. This is demonstrated in Fig. 22.7, where the temperature profiles were generated using eqn 22.12 as the 'simplified' model. As before, the purpose is not to account for a specific event, but to show that the method works even when the temperature profile expression contains 'If' statements. Still, it is clearly evident that interrupted heating of same duration at different stages of the process can produce dramatically different effects on the residual survival ratio, and hence on the process safety. Again, a procedure of the kind that generated these demonstrations can be used to study the effect of steam interruptions on

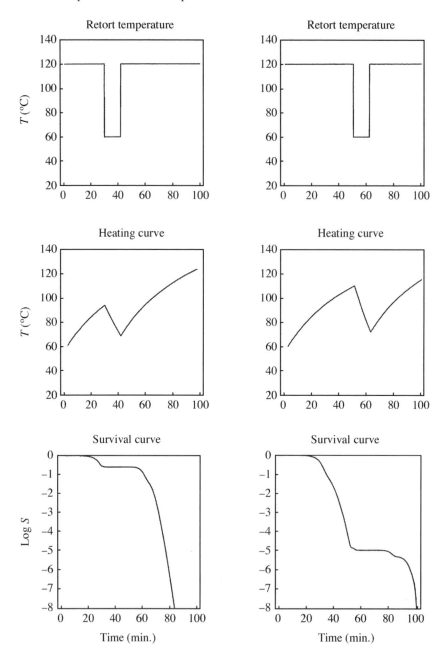

**Fig. 22.7**   Simulated steam interruptions of the same duration and their expected effect on the sporal inactivation pattern.

the final survival ratio in real food products and to determine how much additional treatment would be needed in order to guarantee their microbial safety.

## 22.6    Conclusions

The two main objectives of this chapter were to present an alternative interpretation of microbial inactivation kinetics and to demonstrate the capabilities of an unconventional mathematical procedure to assess the safety of thermal processes. No effort has been made to match accurately any particular thermal process or product in detail, or to obtain the accurate survival parameters of any particular organism, or spores, in a relevant food medium. At the time this chapter was written, the described method has been verified only for a limited number of profiles involving *Salmonella* and *Listeria*. Nevertheless, the method's development will continue and, hopefully, its usefulness could be demonstrated in a larger number of organisms and spores of food safety concern. In light of the growing evidence and recognition that microbial inactivation need not be, and in many cases is not, a process which follows a first order kinetics, governmental regulating agencies will have to face this reality and revise the procedures to assess the safety of thermal preservation processes. Moreover, the inadequacy of the current official methods to calculate sterility, which are based on forcing straight lines through curved data sets has become all too obvious. Therefore, there will be increasing pressure from the food industry and other quarters to develop alternative methods to calculate process safety based on more solid foundations than those now in use. With the computation power available today, such methods can be devised and easily implemented. As has been demonstrated in this chapter, and the publications on which it is based, the development of these methods will require a new critical view of the kinetics of microbial mortality and the abandonment of traditional concepts that have been around for many years.

Still unresolved is the pertinent medium issue. Currently, in order to obtain the 'isothermal' survival data, a microbial culture is heated and cooled in a capillary or narrow metal tube in order to shorten the come-up and cooling times as much as possible. Such experiments are very difficult if not impossible to perform with highly viscous foods or foods which contain particulates. Consequently, the 'isothermal' survival data, in many cases, are obtained by experiments performed with a surrogate medium and not with the actual food. The problem would be eliminated if the survival parameters could be determined directly by experiments performed under non-isothermal conditions, where good mixing of the treated sample is the only requirement.

It has been recently demonstrated that the calculation of the survival parameters from non-isothermal survival curves is theoretically possible. This has been demonstrated with *Salmonella* whose inactivation pattern in one non-isothermal heat treatment could be predicted from patterns observed in different non-isothermal treatments (Peleg and Normand, 2003; Peleg *et al.*, 2003). The method, however, still requires refinement and validation with other organisms and spores before it could be considered for general use. The described method should also be adapted for treatments where the temperature increase and decrease are accompanied by changes in other factors (e.g., moisture content, anti-microbial concentration, etc.), which can affect the inactivation rate. Although this has not yet been done, it seems that the mathematical tools already available will be sufficient for such applications as well.

## 22.7   References

ANDERSON, W.F., MCCLURE, P.J., BAIRD-PERKER, A.C. and COLE M.G. (1996) The application of a log-logistic model to describe the thermal inactivation of *C. botulinum* 213b at temperatures below 121.1 °C. *Applied Bacteriol.* **80**, 283–290.

AUGUSTIN, J.C., CARLIER, V. and ROZJIER, J. (1998) Mathematical modeling of the heat resistance of *L. monocytogenes*. *Applied Microbiol.* **84**, 185–191.

CAMPANELLA, O.H. and PELEG, M. (2001). Theoretical comparison of a new and the traditional method to calculate *C. botulinum* survival during thermal inactivation. *J. Sci. Foods Agric.* **81**, 1069–1076.

CASOLARI, A. (1988) Microbial death. In M.J. Bazin and J. I. Prosser, *Physiological models in microbiology* (pp. 1–44) Boca Raton, FL: CRC Press.

LINTON, R.H., CARTER, W.H., PIERSON, M.D., HACKEY, C.R. and EIFERT, J.D. (1996) Use of a Modified Gompertz equation to model non-linear survival curves of *Listeria monocytogenes*. Scott, A. *J. Food Protec.* **59**, 16–23.

LITTLE, C.L., ADAMS, M.R., ANDERSON, W.A. and COLE, M.B. (1994) Application of the Log-logistic model to describe the survival of *Yersinis enterocolitica* at sub-optimal pH and temperature. *Intnl. J. Food Microbiol.* **22**, 63–71.

MATTICK, K.L., LEGAN, J.D., HUMPHREY, T.J. AND PELEG, M. (2001) Calculating *Salmonella* inactivation in non-isothermal heat treatments from non-linear isothermal survival curves. *J. Food Protec.* **64**, 606–613.

PELEG, M. (2000) Microbial survival curves – The reality of flat shoulders and absolute thermal death times. *Food Res. Intnl.* **33**, 531–538.

PELEG, M. (2002) A model of survival curves having an 'activation shoulder'. *J. Food Sci.* **67**, 2438–2443.

PELEG, M. (2003) Calculation of the non-isothermal inactivation patterns of microbes having sigmoidal isothermal semi-logarithmic survival curves. *Crit. Rev. Food Sci. Nutr.* (in press).

PELEG, M. and COLE, M.B. (1998) Reinterpretation of microbial survival curves. *Crit. Rev. Food Sci.* **38**, 353–380.

PELEG, M. and NORMAND, M.D. (2003) Predicting microbial survival curves from non-isothermal inactivation data *Crit. Rev. Food Sci. Nutr.* (in press).

PELEG, M. and PENCHINA, C.M. (2000) Modeling microbial survival during exposure to a lethal agent with varying intensity. *Crit. Rev. Food Sci.* **40**, 159–172.

PELEG, M., PENCHINA, C.M. and COLE, M.B. (2001) Estimation of the survival curve of *Listeria monocytogenes* during non-isothermal heat treatments. *Food Res. Intnl.* 34, 383–388.

PELEG, M., ENGEL, R., GONZALEZ-MARTINEZ, C. and CORRADINI, M.G. (2002) Non-Arrhenius and non-WLF kinetics in food systems. *J. Sci. Food Agric.* **82**, 1346–1355.

PELEG, M., NORMAND, M.D. and CAMPANELLA, O.H. (2003) Estimating microbial survival parameters from survival curves obtained under varying conditions – The linear case. *Bull. Mathaemat. Biol.* **65**, 219–234.

STEPHENS, P.J., COLE, M.B. and JONES, M.V. (1994) Effect of heating rate on the thermal inactivation of *Listeria monocytogenes. J. Appl. Bacteriol.* 77, 702–710.

TOLEDO, R. (1999) *Fundamentals of food process engineering* (2nd edn). Aspen. Gaithersburg, MD. pp. 315–397.

VAN BOEKEL, M.A.J.S. (2002) On the use of the Weibull model to describe thermal inactivation of microbial vegetative cells. *Intnl. J. Food Microbiol.* **74**, 139–159.

# 23

# Food preservation and the development of microbial resistance

**S. Brul and F. M. Klis, University of Amsterdam, The Netherlands, D. Knorr, Berlin University of Technology, Germany, T. Abee, Wageningen University, The Netherlands and S. Notermans, TNO Nutrition and Food Research, The Netherlands**

## 23.1 Introduction

In this chapter we will discuss the origin of food preservation. We will take a historical perspective of the reasons why preservation is needed and will outline the current available techniques. We will then discuss food preservation in the context of food processing requirements and will touch a little on the concepts of microbial risk assessment as they are currently being laid down. We will go on highlighting novel developments in food preservation research, in particular the resistance of micro-organisms to (combined) food preservation treatments. Microbes react towards harmful environmental conditions by producing specialised stress metabolites and/or proteins. These cellular reactions eventually may lead to preservation stress resistance and hence survival of unwanted micro-organisms during food manufacturing and subsequently cause deterioration of the end-product in the food chain. In addition resistant microbes may change the microbial ecology of food manufacturing plants thereby influencing the prevailing $D$ and $z$ values used in the processing operations. Finally such resistant forms may also be the cause of extensive tailing of inactivation curves.

Genome-wide screens based on micro-array technology, proteomics, metabolomics and bioinformatics-assisted data analysis form a powerful tool for studying adaptation to stress conditions and will allow for a fundamental insight into microbial behaviour in food (related) systems. In addition, genomics-based studies of microbial behaviour in food will help to develop rapid detection methods of microbial spoilage and safety hazards in the food chain.

### 23.1.1  Unwanted micro-organisms in food manufacturing

Problems with food spoilage and food-borne diseases must have been a continuous preoccupation of early humans, once they began their hunting and food-gathering activities, and domestic production of food animals and crops. Although the exact timing is uncertain, organised food production probably started between 18,300 and 17,000 years ago, when barley production is said to have flourished in the Egyptian Nile Valley (Wendorf *et al.*, 1979). Some foods were treated with honey and later with olive oil (Toussaint-Samat, 1992). This led to the development of additional preservative measures, such as heating and salting. The situation changed after 1795, when the French government, driven by war, offered a substantial reward for anyone developing a new method of preserving food. It was Nicholas Appert, a Parisian confectioner, who accepted the challenge and developed a wide-mouth glass bottle that was filled with food, corked and heated in boiling water for about six hours. In 1810, Durand in England patented the use of tin cans for thermal processing of foods, but neither Appert nor Durand understood why thermally processed foods did not spoil (Hartman, 1997), despite the fact that in 1677 van Leeuwenhoek had discovered 'his little heat-sensitive animalcules' (Dobell, 1960).

It was Louis Pasteur who provided the scientific basis for heat preservation in the period 1854–1864. During this time, he showed that certain bacteria were either associated with food spoilage or caused specific diseases. Based on Pasteur's findings, commercial heat treatment of wine was first introduced in 1867 to destroy any undesirable micro-organisms, and the process was described as 'pasteurisation'. Another important development occurred in Germany, when Robert Koch introduced a method of growing micro-organisms in pure culture. Over the next 100 years or more, laboratory isolation and study of pure cultures of microbes has been the basis for developing scientifically based approaches for preservation of food.

Unfortunately, irrespective of the great advances made, the food and beverages industry still suffers from significant losses related to food poisoning and spoilage micro-organisms. A survey in the 1990s showed a high number of food safety incidents (Table 23.1 and discussed in Käferstein and Abdussalam, 1999). Presumably, an even larger number of food spoilage incidents where no direct food safety issue was recorded have taken place over the same timeframe. Although food safety was not compromised in these cases, the economical and ecological/environmental burden is considered to be substantial.

In 2000, figures from the United States Ministry of Agriculture (USDA) showed that shiga toxin producing *Escherichia coli* O157:H7 and non-O157:H7 *E. coli* causes > 2,000 registered cases of human infections with a total yearly cost of > $900 M (USDA homepage). The cost of food-related listeriosis doubled these figures. Very recently research in the USA has shown that in fact *Salmonella* and *Campylobacter* infections related to food occur even over five times more frequently than *E. coli* and over ten times more frequently than *Listeria* infections, particularly in infants (Vugia *et al.*, 2002). In other words, there is still a clear need to minimise the risk of food contamination both from a

**Table 23.1**  A survey of food-borne illness, hospitalisation and death in the United States (Mead *et al.* 1999)

| Health issues | Illness | Hospitalised | Deaths |
|---|---|---|---|
| Total illness/year | 173,000,000 | 774,000 | 6,800 |
| Food-borne illness/year | 76,000,000 | 325,000 | 5,000 |
| Food-borne illness caused by the known pathogens *Salmonella*, *Listeria* or *Toxoplasma* (and related) | 14,000,000 | 60,000 | 1,800 |

public health perspective and because of economic and ecological considerations caused by spoilage of food.

A few widely publicised cases of food poisoning due to contaminated hamburgers have led to political clamour for extending federal meat inspection to bacteriological contamination but not only would such an expansion be inordinately expensive, it would also be ineffective. No legislation or inspection procedure can prevent post-inspection undercooking (or other mishandling) of meat. A safe and dependable preventative measure against such food poisoning, however, has been available for at least 40 years: Gamma rays. But despite scientific approbation and widespread legal approval of such uses of radiation, an alarmist opposition hinders commercial acceptance. This example stresses the need to consider food preservation in the context of food processing and consumer perception as will be discussed in the next section.

### 23.1.2    Food preservation processes in a food processing context

Food processing serves a number of purposes. First of all it is key to the transformation of perishable foodstuffs into microbiologically stable and safe food products as has been discussed above. While this is clearly a prerequisite, processed foods are sold, particularly in the developed world, first and foremost on the basis of their organoleptic (i.e., taste and flavour) characteristics and their nutritional value; all well perceivable consumer benefits.

The former notions stress that a preservation method of choice always has to balance the quality against the stability constraints of a given product. To give an example, pasteurised milk tastes better and has a higher nutritional value than sterilised milk. However, since bacterial spore formers of the genus *Bacillus* show a higher than negligible risk of being present in raw milk and can survive preservation methods, pasteurised milk may be spoiled by germinating *Bacillus* spores (Zwietering *et al.*, 1996; Brown, 2000). Vegetative *B. cereus* cells actively grow in foods and may produce toxin (Agata *et al.*, 2002). The risk of having spores of *Bacilli* spoiling pasteurised milk by day seven after collecting the milk has been calculated and thus the time limit for consumption of pasteurised (often referred to as fresh) milk was set (see for further background reading Zwietering *et al.*, 1996). On the other hand, sterilised milk has, even at elevated (ambient) temperatures, a very long shelf life.

**Table 23.2**   Need for preservation and the techniques available for this

| Preservation targets | Preservation techniques |
|---|---|
| Micro-organisms | Drying |
| Insects | Heating |
| Enzymes | Cooling, freezing |
| Chemicals | Fermentation |
| Damage | Chemical preservation |
| Organoleptics | Mechanical (High pressure processing, US) |
| Freshness, | Physical means (PEF; irradiation, UV-light) |
| fit for consumption | |

Milk is one example of a simple straightforward liquid food. Nonetheless there are already locally major differences in preferences for either pasteurised or sterilised milk. The situation is often even more complex in the manufacturing of other processed foods such as for example mildly acid sauces. Often, a high-temperature processing step (typically 96–98 °C for up to ten minutes) combined with the mildly acidic conditions are sufficient to prevent outgrowth of pathogenic bacteria and common spoilage bacteria of the genus *Bacillus* (Ramaswamy *et al.*, 1997). However, consumers in the developed world more and more prefer less acid-processed food products, for instance, sauces containing fresh-like vegetable particles (recently discussed in Lado and Yousef, 2002). As a consequence, there has been a tremendous drive for research on new preservation systems based on a combination of physical treatments with the action of a natural preserving compound, often a regular food ingredient.

In summary, there always were and there still are many reasons why food needs to be preserved well. Preservation techniques available for practical use are, however, unfortunately still relatively limited. Table 23.2 summarises the reasons why we need to preserve foods and the currently available techniques for this. The next section will discuss these techniques in some detail and indicate some new developments.

## 23.2   Methods of food preservation

The five basic historical methods of food preservation still in use today comprise desiccation or drying, heating, freezing, fermentation, and chemical preservation (Grierson, 1997).

1. *Desiccation.* Desiccation (dehydration, or drying) prevents the rotting of meat, the germination of stored grains, and the sprouting of certain vegetables. It also inhibits the growth of micro-organisms, but some of these dormant micro-organisms can become dangerous with rehydration of the food. The Chinese and the Italians optimally started to use their noodles when, independently, they invented starchy dried foods with a very long shelf life.

2. *Heating.* Heat can increase shelf life by pasteurising or sterilising food. Meats can be spit-roasted or held over a fire on a pointed rod but our ancient ancestors could not adequately cook many plant foods until they developed pottery cooking vessels.

3. *Freezing.* Ancient peoples living in areas with cold winters would observe that frozen foods remained in good condition (at least to unsophisticated taste buds) almost indefinitely, whereupon humans developed rudimentary cold storage by cooling the recesses of caves and other shelters with ice and snow.

4. *Fermentation.* Fermentation is a gradual chemical change caused by the enzymes of some bacteria, moulds, and yeasts. Fermented beverages were ubiquitous in the earliest civilisations of Mesopotamia and Egypt. Not only did wine facilitate conviviality, it was usually more potable than the available water. Winemaking also served as a means of storing nutrients from grapes almost indefinitely. Similarly, Asian steppe dwellers turned mare's milk into koumiss, a fermented beverage that keeps much longer than unprocessed milk. Many cheeses with a long shelf life are produced by lactic-acid fermentation. One means of pickling, a very early form of food preservation, is to treat foods with vinegar, a liquid obtained by further fermenting alcoholic beverages.

5. *Chemical preservation.* Many people consider food additives a modern innovation, but humans have used preservatives for millennia. Today it is hard to understand how precious salt was in ancient times, when it was valued partly as an effective preservative. Salted herring were exported in large quantities from North Sea fishing communities and consumed throughout most parts of Middle Europe. Meat from slaughtered livestock was salted for consumption over the winter. Smoking is another ancient and common means of chemical food preservation. Smoked foods include bacon, kippered herring, and salmon. Classical smoking introduced antioxidants, butylated hydroxyanisole (BHA) and butyl gallate, for example, in large amounts. However, currently permitted levels of such antioxidants as additives are far below such levels. Spices are rich in antioxidants and even bactericides (substances that kill bacteria). The hot curries and chilli dishes popular in the tropics, where food safety is most difficult to achieve, tend to be high in such natural preservatives.

As with chemical preservation, many people consider freeze-drying, a combination of two of the time-tested methods described above, a modern innovation. But native South Americans living on the Altoplano, in the Andes, have subsisted on freeze-dried potatoes of a sort for thousands of years. The plateau dwellers carry the potatoes up into areas where the atmospheric pressure is very low, the sky is usually almost cloudless, and the night-time temperatures fall well below the freezing point of water. The natives slice and crush the potatoes and 'freeze-dry' the result by spreading it on rocks. In modern food-processing facilities, freeze-drying involves freezing foods hard and then drying the result in a vacuum.

In the course of time food preservation, especially using heat, has undergone many developments. The most important ones include controlling the risk of survival of pathogenic organisms by the use of mathematical models (McMeekin *et al.*, 1993 and Ross, 1999) and the introduction of flash-pasteurisation and heat processes also known as the high temperature-short time method (HTST) (Enright *et al.*, 1956, 1957). They are now widely used in the food industry, not only to preserve liquids from microbial spoilage but also to inhibit unwanted enzymatic activity in beverages such as orange juice. Nowadays the food processing industry is faced with an ever increasing demand for safe and minimally processed food with a high degree of wholesomeness and a fresh appearance. This has resulted in a number of non-thermal processing technologies (Gould 2000, 2001).

High hydrostatic pressure, which is applied for commercial food products at pressure levels up to 700 Mpa, has been proven to inactivate vegetative organisms (Smelt *et al.*, 2002b) as well as spores (Heinz and Knorr, 2002, Meyer *et al.*, 2000). Farkas and Hoover (2000) have identified critical process factors and future research needs. Key advantages of high pressure processing are the quality advantages achieved for various foods as evidenced by the commercial products which are mainly fruit juices, fruit preparations and selected meat products.

Ohmic heating (Joule heating, electrical resistance heating, electroconductive heating) is achieved by passing electric currents through food which is placed between electrodes. For inductive heating electric currents are induced within food material, due to oscillating electro-magnetic fields generated by electric coils. With both processes rapid – and in many cases uniform – heating of liquids and particulates can be achieved. Limited information is currently available regarding industrial applications of the processes. Sastry and Barach (2000) have presented critical process parameters and data on microbial inactivation. Microwave and radio frequency heating uses electromagnetic waves of given frequencies to generate heat. Due to difficulties in achieving uniformity of heating, industrial preservation processes have not yet been consistently successful. Datta and Davidson (2000) have summarised microbial aspects of these rapid heating processes.

High intensity pulsed electric fields involving the subjection of foods placed between electrodes to pulses of high voltage have been demonstrated to effectively and controllably permeabilise (reversible or irreversible) biological membranes (Anon, 2001). Pilot scale equipment is available in Europe as well as in the USA. The impact of pulsed electric fields on vegetative micro-organisms has recently been demonstrated by Wouters *et al.* (2001a, b), Heinz and Knorr (2001) and Barbosa-Carnovas *et al.* (2000). Ultra sound energy is generated by sound waves of 20 KHz and above. Ultrasound has a wide range of applications in medicine and biotechnology with limited applications regarding the inactivation of micro-organisms (Hoover, 2002). Selective inactivation of various micro-organisms has been accomplished recently and quality retention achieved due to removal of air from food systems by ultrasound treatment

(Zenker *et al.*, 2002). Finally, in many applications food manufacturers also make use of ultraviolet (UV) light to inactivate micro-organisms.

Examples of naturally occurring antimicrobial compounds include for instance the use of antimicrobial small organic biomolecules (flavours/fragrances), peptides from plant (crop) and microbial origin and microbial wall lytic enzymes (Brul and Coote, 1999; Cleveland *et al.*, 2001; Lewis, 2001; Lopez-Malo *et al.*, 2002). Some of the discussed non-thermal (or rather sometimes low thermal) techniques are already used commercially or are very close to commercial application. All the techniques discussed have their own specific applications. For example, the pulsed electric fields technique is suited only for pumpable liquid products. Ultraviolet light treatment is suited only for surface decontamination and for treatment of fluids with a high transparency. Natural antimicrobials often, but clearly not always (!), have a strong flavour or taste when applied in concentrations needed to be antimicrobial and thus have a limited scope in terms of product formulation. Alternatively, some natural antimicrobials constitute novel ingredients or have to be produced using modern genetic modification (gmo)-based biotechnology and as such have to pass the ever more severe legislation criteria. With respect to gmo technology it is furthermore needless to say that consumer attitudes towards this technology is, right or not, extremely suspicious currently discouraging the viability of this type of approach for the food industry.

Finally, combination preservation has often been proposed as the way forward, minimising adverse organopeltic effects of individual treatments while maximising their (combined) antimicrobial effect through synergistic action on the microbes. In order to apply combination preservation systems and to optimise the use of the currently available systems, a better understanding of the physiology and molecular cell biology of food spoilage micro-organisms is needed for a real breakthrough (Abee and Wouters, 1999; Brul *et al.* 2002a). Moreover, new techniques for a rapid and thorough assessment of the distribution of the various strain variations of harmful micro-organisms throughout the food chain need to be developed (see below; de Boer and Beumer, 1999; Ferretti *et al.*, 2001; Weimer and Mills, 2002; see also http://www.biochip-technologies.com/ of the Germany based company GeneScan). The following discussion provides a practical example of how ingredients containing herbs and spices might aid in the construction of a preservation system.

Byrne *et al.* (2002) tested the effects of commercial beefburger production and product formulation on the heat resistance of *Escherichia coli* O157:H7. In their experiments beef trimmings were inoculated with 6–7 log cfu of *E. coli* O157:H7, following which the trimmings were frozen and stored at $-18\,°C$ for one month. After that time the trimmings were tempered using a microwave in a temperature range from $-3\,°C$ to $2\,°C$. After mincing, 10-gram beefburger samples were formed either without addition of ingredients (Economy burgers) or with addition of ingredients (Quality burgers) including among others seasonings, spices, salt and soya concentrate. Thereafter the burgers were frozen to $-18\,°C$ and stored at $-18\,°C$. After a storage period of one month thermal inactivation studies were conducted at 55, 60 and $65\,°C$ and decimal reduction

**Table 23.3** Comparison of $D$-values for *Escherichia coli* O157:H7 in Quality and Economy beefburger formulations (Byrne *et al.*, 2002)

| Temperature °C | Quality formulation | | Economy formulation | |
|---|---|---|---|---|
| | Control | Frozen | Control | Frozen |
| 55 | 20.8 (1.0)* | 9.3 (1.0) | 41.1 (3.4) | 11.7 (1.7) |
| 60 | 2.7 (1.2) | 1.9 (0.3) | 4.2 (0.9) | 2.4 (0.5) |
| 65 | 0.6 (0.2) | 0.5 (0.1) | 0.7 (0.3) | 0.6 (0.1) |

\* $D$-value in min. (with standard deviation)

times in minutes were assessed. Freshly inoculated beefburgers not subjected to freezing and tempering steps were used as controls. The results are presented in Table 23.3. The results clearly demonstrate that the stresses caused by freezing (sublethal injury) and tempering did not evoke a protective effect against heat treatment. The stress caused by adding ingredients containing herbs and spices (natural antimicrobials) to the Economy formulated beefburgers clearly demonstrate an enhanced preservation effect. Both effects were very clear at the lowest heating temperature of 55 °C used and were not any more significant at a heating temperature of 65 °C. A protective effect was observed when the control samples of both formulation were compared with the heat resistance observed in brain heart infusion broth. In broth the $D$-value at 55 °C was 13.1 min. Finally, a relationship between $a_w$ and heat resistance has been reported in liquid systems by Kaur *et al.* (1998), who noted a decrease in the heat resistance of *E. coli* O157:H7 in salt and sucrose solutions.

It is here important to note that in the UK (ACMSF, 1995) and Ireland (FSAI,1999) it is recommended that minced beef and minced beef products, including beefburgers, should be heated to an internal temperature of 70 °C for 2 minutes or its equivalents (i.e., 75 °C for 30 seconds, 65 °C for 10 minutes and 60 °C for 45 minutes). These treatments are considered to be sufficient to give a 6 decimal reduction in numbers of *E. coli* O157:H7. At these temperatures the extra antimicrobial effects of the addition of ingredients to the product formulation on the survival of *E. coli* O157:H7 upon heat treatment is no longer significant.

## 23.3    Preservation techniques and food safety

Food preservation systems have to function in the context of the total food chain. In that respect it is crucial to apply the Hazard Analysis and Critical Control Points (HACCP) concept. This is a systematic approach to the identification, assessment and control of hazards in a particular food operation. It aims to identify problems before they occur and establish measures for their control at stages in production that are critical to ensuring the safety of food. Control is proactive, since remedial action is taken in advance of problems occurring. The

**Table 23.4**  The seven principles of the HACCP system (CAC Committee on Food Hygiene, 1997)

| Principle | Activity |
|---|---|
| 1. Conduct a hazard analysis | List all potential hazards associated with each step, conduct a hazard analysis, and consider any measures to control identified hazards |
| 2. Determine the Critical Control Points (CCPs) | Determine Critical Control Points (CCPs) |
| 3. Establish critical limit(s) | Establish critical limits for each CCP |
| 4. Establish a system to monitor control of the CCP | Establish a system of monitoring for each CCP |
| 5. Establish corrective actions | Establish the corrective action to be taken when monitoring indicates that a particular CCP is not under control |
| 6. Establish verification procedures | Establish procedures for verification to confirm that the HACCP system is working effectively |
| 7. Establish documentation and record keeping | Establish documentation concerning all procedures and records appropriate to these principles and their application |

full HACCP system, as described in Alinorm 97/13, is shown in Table 23.4. The document also gives guidelines for practical applications of the HACCP system.

Risk assessment and predictive modelling are increasingly used to establish critical limits for each Critical Control Point (CCP). For preservation processes so-called process criteria have to be established. For preservative agents that are added to food products, product (formulation) criteria have to be established. Meeting the criteria set needs to result in an acceptable safe product (Notermans *et al.*, 1995). An extensive discussion of HACCP falls outside the scope of this chapter. Examples of the use of predictive modelling and risk assessment in setting CCP levels may be found elsewhere in this book, in Zwietering *et al.* (1996) and Pflug and Gould (2000).

The food production chain starts with production of raw food materials including both arable farming products and products of animal origin A considerable number of studies have been documented and are still in progress on the mechanisms of infection of crops by, e.g., the fungal pathogen *Fusarium oxysporum*, reviewed in, e.g., Bacon *et al.* (2001). For original research papers see, e.g., Wang and Ng (2001); Straney *et al.* (2002). Equally, various studies on interactions between plants and pathogenic bacteria have been described (reviewed in, e.g., Boch and Bonas (2001), see for original research papers, e.g., Alamillo and Garcia-Olmedo (2001); Tang *et al.* (1999)).

A crucial determining factor for the manufacturer of processed foods is whether the effects of crop spoilage by micro-organisms are such that the final food safety and/or food quality are compromised. Doores (1983) provides an early view from the beverages industry while Doan and Davidson (2000) and Bullerman *et al.* (2002) provide more recent data. If so, a knowledge base of the physiological behaviour of the micro-organism, its occurrence and the plant's defence system needs to be firmly established and monitoring systems for the presence of the plant pathogen should be devised.

A second area of concern is where known human pathogenic micro-organisms may contaminate the food chain, survive and eventually cause food safety problems. This is particularly relevant for, for instance, *Salmonella* species and *Escherichia coli* strains such as O157:H7 (see, e.g., Ross and Shadbolt (2001) and for a recent case report Tessi *et al.* (2002)). For these types of micro-organisms low numbers have repeatedly been shown to cause severe health issues (Bäumler *et al.*, 2000). This holds in particular for the so-called fresh food chain where no processing occurs upon harvesting of the food products. It is, however, also relevant for very mildly processed foods such as certain dairy products and certain uncooked fermented meat products (Knudsen *et al.*, 2001; Ross and Shadbolt, 2001; Coia *et al.*, 2001). The current challenge is to assess at relevant points in the food chain the physiological characteristics of these micro-organisms, in particular their (preservation) stress resistance and to monitor their absolute numbers. Here there is a clear opportunity to use the novel genomics technologies in the development of biochip systems for rapid detection (see later in this chapter and Weimer and Mills, 2002).

In addition, the area of host-microbe interaction in food poisoning and microbial virulence deserves thorough attention. The study of the intestinal microbial ecology is a recognised crucial field of food science where medical microbiologists, nutritionists, microbial physiologists, and molecular biologists need to work in close collaboration. Only in this way can we hope to unravel the negative and positive host (intestine)-microbe interactions at the required level of detail (Dunne, 2001). The overall factors contributing to microbial virulence in relation to food-borne diseases are being studied in a few model systems, most noticeably in *Listeria monocytogenes*, *Salmonella typhimurium* DT104, and *Escherichia coli* O157:H7, infectious pathogens (Bearson *et al.*, 1996; Conte *et al.*, 2002; and a recently started project on *S. typhimurium* DT104 is discussed in Kieboom *et al.*, 2002). In order to understand and interfere with the unwanted growth of microbes in foods or their survival as a pathogen in the host, a detailed analysis of stress response and survival mechanisms is required. The challenge is to define the proper physiological markers that can be monitored at the DNA, transcript or protein levels and to translate this information to chip technology that is of practical use in the industry.

While safety issues are likely to boost research into biochip technologies for application during product/process development, the interest in similar (rapid detection) technologies to combat food spoilage problems and enhance food quality during food manufacturing is also expected to rise concurrently. Many predominantly spoilage problems with fungi or, for instance, spore-forming *Bacillus subtilis* strains put significant constraints on the quality characteristics that food processors can reach in their end-products (Cazemier *et al.*, 2001; Brul *et al.*, 2002b). Genomes of major spore-forming bacteria are on the verge of being, or just have been, completed. Updates of the state of various microbial genome projects over the world can be obtained at http://www.tigr.org/tdb/mdb/ mdbcomplete.html see also Lucchini *et al.* (2001). In conclusion, it is likely that individual food companies will want to see technology development for food safety and food spoilage micro-organisms go hand in hand.

Summarising, micro-organisms are extremely capable in adapting to many environmental circumstances. Through these adaptations they can become resistant to preservation processes. Such resistant species may cause many areas of concern to the food industry such as rapid spread through globalisation of the food supply chain, unwanted survival and growth in finished product, in particular mild products, and a change in the microbial ecology of raw materials used. Studies on the mechanisms behind and resulting model formation of microbial stress adaptation are now more than ever possible and should help to get a better grip on the above indicated issues. Such studies are discussed extensively in section 23.4.

## 23.4   Understanding microbial adaptation to stress

From the previous section it is clear that in order to ensure food safety and quality in an efficient way, measuring preservation stress response at the molecular level should facilitate the prediction of the behaviour of undesirable micro-organisms in the food chain (Abee and Wouters 1999; Verrips *et al.*, 2001; de Vos, 2001; Brul *et al.*, 2002a, b). Just recently the Institute for Food Technologists in the United States published an Expert Report on 'Emerging Microbiological Food Safety Issues: Implications for Control in the 21st Century' (www.ift.org/govrelations/microfs/). This report addresses amongst other things the tremendous impact that advances in applied genetics and molecular microbiology will have in this area for surveillance, regulatory thinking and policies to be set.

*S. cerevisiae* has long been and still is a model (eukaryote) of choice for cellular physiology studies. It was the first eukaryotic organism to be sequenced and analysed at the genome-wide level for its gene-expression under environmental changes, e.g., related to the shift from fermentative to respiratory metabolism during growth and to sporulation (De Risi *et al.*, 1997; Chu *et al.*, 1998). Subsequently, gene-expression of *Escherichia coli* was analysed during growth under optimal and stressed conditions. Transcription profiling showed that the general stress regulator protein, which is normally only induced upon reaching stationary growth-phase, is already induced in the logarithmic-phase of growth in cells stressed by low nutrient levels (Tao *et al.*, 1999). Recently, researchers have visualised gene-expression in *Bacillus subtilis* during early to mid-sporulation under conditions known to give rise to high thermal process resistant *Bacillus* endospores and during growth under anaerobic conditions, when stress responses of the bacteria are activated (Fawcett *et al.*, 2000; Ye *et al.*, 2000; Brul *et al.*, 2002b). The resulting gene-expression patterns specific for these developmental conditions should pave the way for the definition of (new) specific biomarkers indicating for instance the presence of high thermal resistant spore forming *Bacilli*.

Next to these valuable studies in model organisms, the advent of fast full genome sequencing has also made it possible to come to a comparison of the genomes of various strains (isolates) of non-pathogenic and pathogenic bacteria and fungi. In this way, the study of interspecies heterogeneity has become experimentally accessible. A comparison of sequenced genomes has shown for instance that there is substantial variation in genes present among pathogenic strains of *Escherichia coli* and *Staphylococcus aureus* as discussed in Fitzgerald and Musser (2001). In various isolates horizontal gene-transfer has been shown. Gene-based variation in physiology among strains of a given species has recently been illustrated as a key mechanism operative in soil where antibiotic resistance distribution was shown to be prominently mediated by horizontal gene transfer among a variety of micro-organisms as discussed in Nwosu (2001).

While current knowledge definitely explains part of the mode of action of antimicrobials, the power of the new genomics approaches in assessing gene transcript patterns has often not yet been applied in unravelling cellular responses to food related antimicrobial treatments. Micro-array based analyses are now starting to be used to assess the behaviour of micro-organisms in response to heat stress (Helmann *et al.*, 2001). Recently, such studies have also been initiated to analyse resistance development against sorbic acid and natural antimicrobials, as described later and in De Nobel *et al.* (2000); De Nobel *et al.* (2001) and Kurita *et al.* (2002).

### 23.4.1 The adaptation of spoilage and pathogenic micro-organisms to physico-chemical stresses

The physical stresses most often encountered in the food processing industry are heat, osmotic stress and acidification. It is remarkable that while we are working on many novel preservation technologies such as the application of high hydrostatic pressure, there are still many questions unanswered with respect to, for instance, heat stress adaptation and survival. Membrane adaptations in *Clostridium botulinum* cells resistant to heat have been reported but the mechanistic basis of these adaptations is not clear (Mazzotta and Montville, 1999). In *B. cereus* an extensive analysis of proteins involved in heat stress response has only recently been performed (Periago *et al.*, 2002).

Figure 23.1 shows our current level of understanding in this area with respect to activation and function of the so-called general stress response system in *B. subtilis*. This system is activated by a protein called sigma B, from which it takes its name, and protects the cells against a multitude of stresses (Völker *et al.*, 1999; Hecker and Völker, 2001). Further molecular studies meanwhile showed that next to this system also other, specific heat stress-protective systems play an important role in conferring the capability of surviving heat challenges upon *Bacillus subtilis* cells (see, e.g., Derre *et al.* (1999) and as discussed in Hecker and Völker (2001)).

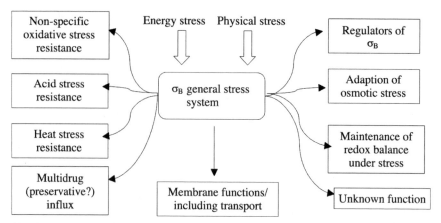

**Fig. 23.1**   A schematic impression of the role of the general stress system regulated by the transcription factor sigma B in the stress physiology of *Bacillus subtilis*. The activation of the multiple stress response reactions is depicted in the text boxes. Clearly there are ample chances for the occurrence of cross-stress resistance upon activation of the general stress system by one (preservation) stress treatment. More than 150 genes are involved in the indicated sigma B mediated reactions. Adapted from Hecker and Völker (2001) and Akbar *et al.* (2001).

While we now have some information on the output of stress reactions in *B. subtilis,* there are still many open issues relating to the initial signal perception. A recent paper by Akbar *et al.* (2001) describes the various components that are presumed to play a role in receiving an environmental signal and relaying it to the sigma B activation state. The role that non-proteinaceous small molecules play in signalling stress needs to be further integrated with the role of the signalling proteins themselves. This topic is discussed by, for instance, Diamant *et al.* (2001) with respect to the interaction between heat stress resistance and a cellular response to hyperosmotic stress in *Escherichia coli.* In addition, very recently Hohmann (2002) has extensively reviewed osmolarity signalling in bakers' yeast. For yeast it is clear that increased osmo-stress resistance may lead to a plethora of cross-resistance phenotypes. Cross-protection indicates the capacity of cells to gain resistance to the so-called hurdle approach, i.e., a combined preservation approach whereby various sub-lethal treatments are jointly or sequentially applied as hurdles for cellular survival while food organoleptic quality is preserved. The resulting insight should facilitate the choice of an effective combination of preservation stresses in the hurdle approach and thereby minimise concerns due to cross-resistance. This is especially relevant to the application of high pressure processing, the major currently studied and to some extent commercially used alternative to heat.

Mechanisms of microbial adaptation to high pressures are not well understood at all. Changes in the cell wall and membrane are known to take place upon pressure treatment of cells, as reviewed in Abee and Wouters (1999); see also Brul *et al.* (2000); Masschalck *et al.* (2001); Karatzas and Bennik

(2002). Reinforcement of these cellular structures might be involved in stress resistance to high pressure processing. The nature of the cell membrane is known to influence cell resistance to high-pressure preservation processes (reviewed in Smelt (1998) and Smelt *et al.* (2002a)).

Pressure resistant cells are known for their increased membrane fluidity and low diphosphatidylglycerol content (see, e.g., Russel *et al.* (1995); Fujii *et al.* (1996)). Bacterial spores are not only heat resistant, but also quite pressure resistant. The mechanistic basis for this is unclear; possibly, it is linked with the rigidity of the spore wall. It has been suggested that the presence of teichoic acid in the wall of vegetative Gram-positive microbes is linked to their increased high-pressure resistance compared to Gram-negative bacteria (discussed in Lado and Yousef, 2002). However, this still remains to be substantiated. The current indication that the level of expression of genes encoding small-acid-soluble-spore-proteins (Sasps) during sporulation is correlated to heat resistance also suggests that similar studies should be performed to help elucidate in more detail the mechanisms behind high pressure spore resistance (see Brul *et al.* (2002b) for a discussion of this topic).

In addition to high pressure, the use of pulsed-electric fields (PEF) is frequently discussed. The basis for PEF sensitivity or resistance has hardly been assessed. The generally accepted theory is that either membrane rupture due to high membrane potential takes place or that electroporation of protein channels and lipid domains is the cause of cell inactivation (Wouters *et al.*, 2001b and discussed in Lado and Yousef, 2002).

### 23.4.2   The adaptation of spoilage and pathogenic micro-organisms to biochemical stresses

In yeast, cellular changes as a function of stress adaptation to weak-organic acids have been described extensively. The notion that a proton-pumping ATP consuming protein plays a crucial role has been established for a long time. These studies received a strong impetus when the involvement of a multi-drug-resistance pump in resistance development against weak-organic acids was established (Piper *et al.*, 1998). Coote and collaborators provided compelling evidence in favour of these protein transporting preservatives, such as sorbic acid, benzoic acid, and acetic acid from the cytosol to the extracellular environment (Holyoak *et al.*, 1999). Micro-array and proteomics analysis of weak organic acid resistant *Saccharomyces cerevisiae* cells have been performed (De Nobel *et al.*, 2001). They point to additional important resistance mechanisms, and thus new preservation targets, such as the activation of heat-shock proteins and indications for the activation of oxidative stress response systems and the modulation of the cell wall integrity pathway in cells gaining resistance to sorbic acid. The latter pathway may mediate changes in cell wall and membrane structure that effectively lower the influx of sorbic acid upon stress adaptation of the cells. Upon inspection of the set of induced genes and proteins it is evident that events at the cellular plasma-membrane must be at the heart of the stress response against sorbic acid.

Recently it has been shown that a protein sensing the membrane's structural status (Wsc2p see, e.g., Klis *et al.*, 2002), regulates the membrane-localised proton pumping–ATPase protein (de la Fuente and Portillo, 2000). The latter is known to form a crucial part of the sorbic acid stress response output (see, e.g., Brul and Coote, 1999). From this and other data it may be inferred that membrane perturbation by sorbic acid may well be a signal that activates the cellular stress response against this compound (see the review by Piper *et al.*, 2001 and references therein for a recent update). Finally, Karl Kuchler and collaborators have recently further studied the regulatory mechanisms behind the signalling of weak-acid stress response in more detail (publication in press, personal communication). Finally, interestingly, the micro-array experiments by de Nobel *et al.* (2001) displayed an induction of genes involved in transposition movements through the genome. This corroborates the notion that under extreme stress conditions micro-organisms may use genome mutations as an ultimate way to survive.

While the quest for alternative heat treatments has been ongoing, replacement of preservatives by nature-derived alternatives has also been prominent on the research agenda. Currently, only nisin is in use as a natural antimicrobial in various applications (reviewed in Cleveland *et al.*, 2001). The efficacy of the compound varies significantly depending on application and strain. One series of studies has shown the crucial role that a particular lipid fraction seems to play in the sensitivity or resistance of bacteria with respect to nisin. Lipid II-enriched membranes bind nisin better, and cells containing high amounts of lipid II, such as certain *Micrococcus flavus* strains, are also highly sensitive to nisin (discussed in Breukink *et al.*, 1999). Noticeably, nisin exerts its antimicrobial action at a similar cellular site as the often last-resource antibiotic vancomycin. Indeed, Breukink *et al.* showed in 1999 that vancomycin blocks the activity of nisin against *M. flavus* cells. Since then it has been shown that nisin resistance can develop in various systems and may be quite independent of vancomycin resistance, presumably reflecting the peptide nature of the former antimicrobial (Mantovani and Russel, 2001).

In contrast, in some situations a co-resistance phenotype has been described. This holds in particular for ampicillin-resistant *Streptococcus pneumoniae* strains that showed, worryingly, a significant increased nisin and vancomycin resistance (Filipe *et al.*, 2002). Recent studies by the group of de Kruijff show clearly that often a higher level of cell wall structuring and cross-linking mediates nisin resistance (Ben de Kruijff, personal communication). Interestingly, the presence of specific cell wall proteins has been observed as a prime reason for the intrinsically high resistance of *Saccharomyces cerevisiae* against membrane active antimicrobial peptides and proteins (see, e.g., Yun *et al.*, 1997 and Dielbandhoesing *et al.*, 1998). Finally, acid-adapted *Listeria monocytogenes* displays enhanced tolerance against both nisin and lacticin 3147 which is presumably at least partially correlated with changes in the fatty acid composition of the bacterial membrane (van Schaik *et al.*, 1999).

The non-proteinaceous natural molecule carvacrol was studied extensively for its antimicrobial properties by Ultee *et al.* (1999, 2000). Changes in the membrane phospholipid fatty acid and head-group composition were proven to be crucial in increased resistance of *Bacillus cereus* against this compound. Other biochemical antimicrobials that are under study in the food industry include the antimicrobial saccharides pustulan and chitosan, and antimicrobial cell wall lytic enzyme systems. While chitosan has a membrane permeabilising effect (Helander *et al.*, 2001), chitosan fragments may, and pustulan fragments definitely, have a cell wall perturbing antimicrobial mode of action (Oomes *et al.*, 2001 unpublished observations; Bom *et al.*, 2001). Obviously, wall lytic enzymes have by virtue of their activity a wall perturbing mode of action as well (discussed in Brul and Coote, 1999; see also, e.g., Loeffler *et al.*, 2001). Resistance development against cell wall lytic enzymes has been studied extensively in yeast. De Nobel *et al.* (2000) showed that a *Saccharomyces cerevisiae* cell population resistant to wall lytic glucanase displayed cross-resistance in the form of increased thermotolerance.

### 23.4.3    Understanding the heterogeneity in stress resistance in microbial populations at the molecular level

Food spoilage organisms are confronted with various forms of stress. As discussed extensively, the environment may change in terms of water availability, acidity, temperature profile, presence of antimicrobial compounds (preservatives), absence of nutrients, etc. Similar to other biological systems, microbial populations of relevance to the food chain also generally respond non-homogeneously to stress conditions (Peleg and Cole, 1998). Differences may be due to cell age, state of the cell cycle, but also to stochastic variations in exact molecular cellular composition (discussed in Sumner and Avery, 2002). McAdams and Arkin (1997) analysed the distribution of transcription factors over cells in a given population. It was shown that the transcript concentration can frequently be low to very low (theoretically to significantly below one copy per cell). These observations imply that stochastic variations in the concentrations of transcription factors may contribute significantly to the observed heterogeneity in cellular response to (food preservation) stress.

The activity of particular stress response routes can nowadays be very well assessed through the use of reporter constructs. These are available as fluorescent reporters or as enzymatically active reporters. Hence, population heterogeneity in stress response can easily be measured and visualised. In yeast such studies showed that the population response to, for instance, heat stress is quite heterogeneous. Attfield *et al.* (2001) observed, while using Green Fluorescent Protein labelling, that heterogeneous induction of a heat shock protein took place in a population of yeast cells challenged with (sublethal) heat stress. Noticeably, the induction of the heat shock protein correlated with increased protection against heat induced loss of plasma-membrane integrity. What remains to be assessed is whether a deletion of the heat shock protein leads to significantly increased cell membrane damage and inactivation. In addition to increasing fundamental understanding of bacterial stress response and population dynamics, the mechanistic insight in microbial stress response will be used to identify new targets and set up new antimicrobial strategies tailored to food manufacturing. It will be crucial to link non-homogeneous inactivation kinetics to the cellular understanding of stress response in laboratory strains to the occurrence of molecular antimicrobial targets in populations of isolates obtained from spoiled foods.

## 23.5   Future trends

### 23.5.1   Predictive modelling of stress adaptation; what will be the future role of metabolomics, transcriptomics and proteomics in understanding microbial stress response?

To refresh the various definitions used in genomics studies, Fig. 23.2 summarises the main concepts. A prime area where genomics is expected to play a major role in food manufacturing is in guiding predictive modelling of the behaviour of the micro-organisms of concern by providing a molecular mechanistic basis (a molecular fingerprint) of the events that take place. This presumably will allow certain levels of extrapolation of results obtained with one set of environmental stress conditions to another set of environmental stresses.

As a result we should be able to predict which of the combined preservation treatments are best suited. We should thus be able to apply the hurdle principle in a more mechanistic knowledge-based manner which will lead to increased robustness of the predictive models used. Elucidation of this 'inside of the black

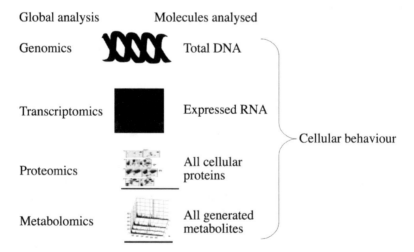

**Fig. 23.2**   A schematic view of the level at which the various genomics technologies operate and contribute to the understanding of cellular behaviour. Classical genomics is concerned with the sequencing and annotation of the full genome of a cell. Transcriptomics deals with the study of the global gene-expression using whole genome micro-arrays (Nouwens *et al.*, 2000; Lucchini *et al.*, 2001). Proteomics is the study of the full cellular complement of proteins using gelelectrophoresis and mass-spectrometry techniques while metabolomics is now emerging for the study of all generated cellular metabolites (see, e.g., Weimer and Mills, 2002 for discussions on applications in food science).

box' leads to a clear view of the way in which the cell restructures itself in response to the environmental stress imposed. That restructuring will involve extra work and thus requires energy investment, i.e., substrate consumption, as discussed by Ross (1999). This is regularly accompanied by a lag-time before growth resumes in the new stressful environment (see Mellefont and Ross, 2002; Mellefont *et al.*, 2002; and Mensonides *et al.*, 2002). In *Bacillus subtilis* we have recently studied the genome-wide response of cells towards environmental conditions in terms of forming high or low heat resistant spores (discussed in Brul *et al.*, 2002b). It was clear that during sporulation various genes were expressed preferentially in the test condition known to lead to the formation of heat resistant spores (Cazemier *et al.*, 2001). The data clearly corroborated a functional role for the small-acid-soluble-spore proteins (Sasps) in mediating spore heat resistance. This was further supported by independent experiments of Setlow and co-workers who used knock-outs of Sasps and assessed heat stress resistance in resulting spores (Setlow *et al.*, 2000).

   This type of transcript analysis data is being structured in large databases and serves as a reference guide for further study. Starting with rRNA gene-based data and Amplified Fragment Length Polymorphisms (AFLP), we are now at a stage where the molecular databases start actually to reflect the physiological parameters that we are most interested in, i.e., stress resistance or not. This was made possible through the advent of the indicated transcript profiling and the cDNA-AFLP as commercially developed by the Keygene company. The power of a full and relevant description of cellular response to environmental conditions lies in the combination of a transcriptome (completeness) and proteome/ metabolome (level of relevance) analysis (see, e.g., Nouwens *et al.*, 2000; Yoshida *et al.*, 2001 and De Nobel *et al.*, 2001; Oltvai and Barabási, 2002). It is evident that a full understanding of cellular (eco)physiology finally depends on a proper integration of the ecological information (which microbial species/strains are present), molecular data, the stress response options that microbial cells have, and the available substrate. Figure 23.3 schematically illustrates this concept.

   This integration of molecular microbiology and classical physiology into what is now often called functional genomics is we believe the major challenge and driving force for future research both in biology in general and in food preservation in particular. This view is shared with other leading food researchers as is reflected by the papers of Desiere *et al.* (2002) and Weimer and Mills (2002) in the context of the American Institute for Food Technologists.

### 23.5.2   Preservation process modelling prospectives

The understanding of cellular responses at the level of molecular events opens up the way to integrally assess microbial responses to environmental conditions beyond the level of growth-no growth or survival and death. If we succeed in translating results obtained in model systems to those relevant to actual food products, taking into account medium composition and strain variations this will allow for the development of mechanistic growth and inactivation models with a

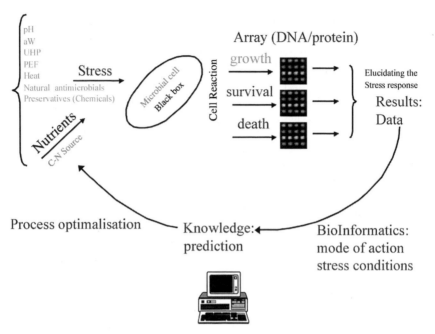

**Fig. 23.3** An overview of the iterative experimental and computational cycles that are operative in functional genomics research. The main challenge is to interpret the data coming from transcript and proteome analysis using biological knowledge and modern bioinformatics to handle such large data sets. The aim is to come to accurate predictions of the mode of action on micro-organisms of preservation processes in combination with product composition that can feed process optimisation both at the onset of the definition of new processes and at the optimisation of process routines.

predictive power also outside the measured data points. Lee *et al.* (2002) and Milo *et al.* (2002) give actual examples of current possibilities in this area for *Saccharomyces cerevisiae* and *Escherichia coli* respectively (see also Bammert and Fostel, 2000; Hughes *et al.*, 2000).

Models that will also look like chemical engineering tools are able to describe the flow of metabolites through cellular growth regulatory systems (see e.g., Teusink, 1999; Stephanopoulos and Kelleher, 2001). However, it should be realised that optimal use of the mechanistic knowledge of microbial death, survival and growth will be made only if this data can be put in the context of the physicochemical parameters that determine food taste, flavour and its nutritional value (Verrips *et al.*, 2001 see also Bruin, 2001). Figure 23.4 gives a schematic impression of an integrated process design concept.

The predictive models based on mechanistic insight will have to make use of the various levels of information and include physical parameters pertaining to the heat capacity and heat conductivity of compounds, heat transfer and mass transfer occurring during processing, and biochemical and nutritional parameters pertaining to the food. As alluded to at the beginning of this chapter, only through such structured multidimensional models will we reach an optimal

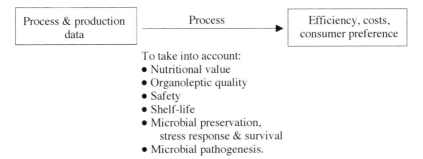

| Process & production data | → Process | Efficiency, costs, consumer preference |

To take into account:
● Nutritional value
● Organoleptic quality
● Safety
● Shelf-life
● Microbial preservation, stress response & survival
● Microbial pathogenesis.

**Fig. 23.4**  A schematic impression of the key events to be considered in food processing. Here physical, chemical and (micro)biological aspects of product processing need to be studied in an integrated manner to come to desired product attributes (adapted from Jongen, 2001).

balance between efficient product processing, product safety and product quality.

Finally, the current scientific developments also facilitate the construction of tools that allow for tracing and tracking of micro-organisms through the whole food chain based on their physiological and molecular ecological characteristics. Currently, projects have been and are being defined in order to obtain a transparent view of the food chain with respect to microbial food spoilage and resistance development against food preservation techniques. These projects are joint efforts by academia, research institutes and major multinational food processing companies including Nestlé and Unilever. It will be these public-private consortia that we expect to see moving forward with the right practical focus and the required speed whilst ensuring incorporation of state-of-the art new scientific and technological developments.

## 23.6    Sources of further information and advice

Most relevant literature data has been cited in the preceding paragraphs. Suffices here to state that food-related unwanted micro-organisms are being studied at many institutes and academic groups. A useful entry at the world-wide-web is http://www.ftns.wau.nl/id-array/index.htm . For further information the website of institutes such as the UK Institute for Food Research (IFR), the Institute Pasteur (IP), the Dutch Institute for Applied Food Research (TNO-Food), the Dutch National Institute for Health and Environment (RIVM), the Wageningen Centre for Food Sciences (WCFS), the Swammerdam Institute for Life Sciences (SILS), the Groningen Biomolecular and Biotechnology institute (GBB) are good reference points and can guide the interested reader further. While singling out individual groups would not do justice to the others it should be stressed that for further information on Gram-negatives the IFR is the best entry point, for information on Gram-positive pathogens the WCFS and for information on Gram-positive spoilage microbes and fungi including yeasts the SILS. Information of a general nature on this topic can be obtained at the website of the Federation of European Societies of Microbiology (FEMS) and the American Society for Microbiology (ASM).

The 2003 1st congress for European Microbiologists features many relevant topics such as the microbiological aspects of food safety, stress response of micro-organisms, emerging pathogens, and a specialised symposium on the genus *Bacillus* and its close relatives.

Finally, for a comprehensive overview of how the microbiological insights should fit in the day-to-day practice of food processing the websites of the European federation for food sciences and technology (Effost) and the USA Institute for Food Technologists (IFT) should be consulted.

## 23.7   Acknowledgements

Here we would like to thank those active in this area of research at the University of Amsterdam and Unilever who have contributed significantly to the shaping of our thoughts as described in this chapter. This holds in particular for Prof. dr. C.T. Verrips, former Chief Scientist at Unilever-Bestfoods, Dr. S. Bruin, former Leader of the Food Processing Group Unilever-Bestfoods, Dr. P.F. ter Steeg, Lead Scientist Food Microbiology Unilever-Bestfoods, Prof. dr. A.J. van Tunen, director of the Swammerdam Institute for Life Sciences, Prof. dr. F. Rombouts, emeritus professor of Food Microbiology Wageningen University, Prof. dr. K.J. Hellingwerf, professor of General Microbiology Swammerdam Institute for Life Sciences, Dr. L. Wesdorp, director Business Development Unilever-Bestfoods Food Research Centre and current leader of the Food Processing Group Unilever, Ing. H. Lelieveld, Senior Technologist Unilever-Bestfoods, Prof. dr. T. McMeekin, professor of Microbiology and director of the Centre for Food Safety and Quality at the University of Tasmania (Australia), and Mrs S. Oomes, Technical Assistant at Unilever-Bestfoods Food Research Center.

## 23.8   References

ABEE, T. and WOUTERS, J. A. (1999), 'Microbial stress response in minimal processing', *Int. J. Food Microbiol.* **50**, 65–91.

ACMSF (Advisory Committee on the Microbiological Safety of Food) (1995), 'Report on Verocytotoxin-producing *Escherichia coli*', HMSO, London.

AGATA, N., OHTA, M. and YOKOYAMA, K. (2002), 'Production of *Bacillus cereus* emetic toxin (cereulide) in various foods', *Int. J. Food Microbiol.* **73**, 23–27.

AKBAR, S., GAIDENKO, T.A., KANG, C.M., O'REILLY, M., DEVINE, K.M. and PRICE, C.W. (2001), 'New family of regulators in the environmental signalling pathway which activates the general stress transcription factor sigma (B) of *Bacillus subtilis*', *J. Bacteriol.* **183**, 1329–1338.

ALAMILLO, J. M. and GARCIA-OLMEDO, F. (2001), 'Effect of urate, a natural inhibitor of peroxynitrite-mediated toxicity, in the response of *Arabidopsis thaliana* to the bacterial pathogen *Pseudomonas syringae'*, *Phytochemistry* **57**, 1187–1195.

ANON, U. (2001), 'Special Issue: High intensity electric field pulses', *Trends Food Sci. & Technol.* **12**, 88–152.

ATTFIELD, P.V., CHOI, H.Y., VEAL, D.A. and BELL, P.J. (2001), 'Heterogeneity of stress gene expression and stress resistance among individual cells of *Saccharomyces cerevisiae'*, Mol. Microbiol. **40**, 1000–1009.

BACON, C.W., YATES, I.E., HINTON, D.M. and MEREDITH, F. (2001), 'Biological control of Fusarium moniliforme in maize', *Environ. Health Perspect.* **109** Suppl. 2, 325–332.

BAMMERT, G.F. and FOSTEL, J.M. (2000), 'Genome-wide expression patterns in *Saccharomyces cerevisiae*: comparison of drug treatments and genetic alterations affecting biosynthesis of ergosterol', *Antimicrob. Agents Chemother.* **44**, 1255–1265.

BARBOSA-CARNOVAS, G.V., PIERSON, M.D., ZHANG, Q.H. and SCHAFFNER, D.W. (2000), 'Pulsed electric fields', *J. Food Sci.*, Supplement **65**, 65–78.

BÄUMLER, A.J., HARGIS, B.M. and TSOLIS, R.M. (2000), 'Tracing the origins of *Salmonella* outbreaks', *Science* **287**, 50–52.

BEARSON, S.M., BENJAMIN, W.H.J.R., SWORDS, W.E. and FOSTER, J.W. (1996), 'Acid shock induction of RpoS is mediated by the mouse virulent gene mviA of *Salmonella typhimurium'*, *J. Bacteriol.* **178**, 2572–2579.

BOCH, J. and BONAS, U. (2001), 'Gram-negative plant pathogenic bacteria', *Contrib. Microbiol.* **8**, 186–196.

BOER, E. DE and BEUMER, R.R. (1999), 'Methodology for detection and typing of food borne microorganisms', *Int. J. Food Prot.* **62**, 1115–1122.

BOM, I.J., NOBEL, H., KLIS, F.M. and BRUL, S. (2001), 'A new strategy for inhibition of the spoilage yeast *Saccharomyces cerevisiae* and *Zygosaccharomyces bailii* based on combination of a membrane-active peptide with an oligosaccharide that leads to an impaired GPI-depend wall protein layer', *FEMS Yeast Res.* **1**, 187–194.

BREUKINK, E., WIEDEMANN, I., VAN KRAAIJ, C., KUIPERS, O.P., SAHL, H. and DE KRUIJFF, B. (1999), 'Use of the cell wall precursor lipid II by a pore-forming peptide antibiotic', *Science* **286**, 2361–2364.

BROWN, K.L. (2000), 'Control of bacterial spores', *Br.Med. Bull.* **56**, 158-171.

BRUIN, S. (2001), 'Food process engineering, the past 25 years and challenges ahead', Proceedings of the 2001 annual meeting of the Institute for Food Technologists.

BRUL, S. and COOTE, P. (1999), 'Preservative agents in foods', *Int. J. Food Microbiol.* **50**, 1–17.

BRUL, S., ROMMENS, A. and VERRIPS, C.T. (2000), 'Mechanistic studies on the inactivation of Saccharomyces cerevisiae by High Pressure', *Inn. Food Sci. Emerg. Technol.* **1**, 99–108.

BRUL, S., COOTE, P., OOMES, S.J.C.M., MENSONIDES, F.I.C., HELLINGWERF, K.J. and KLIS, F.M. (2002a), 'Physiological actions of preservative agents: prospective use of modern microbiological techniques in assessing microbial behaviour in food preservation', *Int. J. Food Microbiol.* **79**, 55–64.

BRUL, S., KLIS, F.M., OOMES, S.J.C.M., MONTIJN, R.C., SCHUREN, F.H.J., COOTE, P. and HELLINGWERF, K.J. (2002b), 'Genomics of survivors of food preservation processes for precision processing', *Trends Food Sci. Technol.* (in press).

BULLERMAN, L.B., RYU, D. and JACKSON, L.S. (2002), 'Stability of fumonisins in food processing', *Adv. Exp. Med. Biol.* **504**, 195–204.

BYRNE, C.M., BOLTON, D.J., SHERIDAN, J.J., BLAIR, I.S. and MCDOWELL, D.A. (2002), 'The effect of commercial production and product formulation stresses on the heat resistance of *Escherichia coli* O157:H7 (NTCC 12900) in beef burgers', *Int. J. Food Microbiology* **79**, 183–192.

CAC COMMITTEE ON FOOD HYGIENE (1997) 'Recommended international code of practice, general principles of food hygiene', CAC, *RCP* rev. 3, 1997, 1–30.

CAZEMIER, A.E., WAGENAARS, S. and TER STEEG, P.F. (2001), 'Effect of sporulation and recovery medium on the heat resistance and amount of injury of spoilage *Bacilli*', *J. Appl. Microbiol.* **90**, 761–770.

CHU, S., DE RISI, J., EISEN, M., MULHOLLAND, J., BOTSTEIN, D., BROWN, P.O. and HERSKOWITZ, I. (1998), 'The transcriptional program of sporulation in budding yeast', *Science* **282**, 699–705.

CLEVELAND, J., MONTVILLE, T.J., NES, I.F. and CHIKINDAS, M.L. (2001), 'Bacteriocins: safe, natural antimicrobials for food preservation', *Int. J. Food Microbiol.* **71**, 1–20.

COIA, J.E., JOHNSTON, Y., STEERS, N.J. and HANSON, M.F. (2001), 'A survey of the prevalence of Escherichia coli O157 in raw meats, raw cow's milk and raw-milk cheeses in southeast Scotland'. *Int. J. Food Microbiol.* **66**, 63–69.

CONTE, M.P., PETRONE, G., DI BIASE, A.M., LONGHI, C., PENTA, M., TINARI, A., SUPERTI, F., FABOZZI, G., VISCA, P. and SEGANTI, L. (2002), 'Effect of acid adaptation on the fate of *Listeria monocytogenes* in THP-1 human macrophages activated by gamma interferon', *Infect. Immun.* **70**, 4369–4378.

DATTA, A.K. and DAVIDSON, P.M. (2000), 'Microwave and radio frequency processing', *J. Food Sci.,* Supplement **65**, 32–46.

DE NOBEL, H., RUIZ, C., MARTIN, H., MORRIS, W., BRUL, S., MOLINA, M. and KLIS, F.M. (2000), 'Cell wall perturbation in yeast results in dual phosphorylation of the Slt2/Mpk1 MAP kinase and in an Slt2-mediated increase in FKS2-LacZ expression, glucanase resistance and thermotolerance', *Microbiology* **146**, 2121–2132.

DE NOBEL, H., LAWRIE, L., BRUL, S., KLIS, F., DAVIS, M., ALLOUSH, H. and COOTE, P. (2001), 'Parallel and comparative analysis of the proteome and transcriptome of weak-acid adapted *Saccharomyces cerevisiae* reveals a crucial function for the small heat-shock protein, Hsp26', *Yeast* **18**, 1413–1428.

DE RISI, J.L., IYER, V.R. and BROWN, P.O. (1997), 'Exploring the metabolic and genetic control of gene expression on a genomic scale', *Science* **278**, 680–686.

DERRE, I., RAPOPORT, G. and MSADEK, T. (1999), 'CtsR, a novel regulator of stress and heat shock response, controls *clp* and molecular chaperone gene expression in Gram-positive bacteria', *Mol. Microbiol.* **31**, 117–132.

DESIERE, F., GERMAN, B., WATZKE, H., PFEIFER, A. and SAGUY, S. (2002), 'Bioinformatics and data knowledge: the new frontiers for nutrition and foods', *Trends Food Sci. Technol.* **12**, 215–229.

DIAMANT, S., ELIAHU, N., ROSENTHAL, D. and GOLOUBINOFF, P. (2001), 'Chemical chaperones regulate molecular chaperones *in vitro* and in cells under combined salt and heat stresses', *J. Biol. Chem.* **276**, 39586–39591.

DIELBANDHOESING, S.K., ZHANG, H., CARO, L.H., VAN DER VAART, J.M., KLIS, F.M., VERRIPS, C.T. and BRUL, S. (1998), 'Specific cell wall proteins confer resistance to nisin upon yeast cells', *Appl. Env. Microb.* **64**, 4047–4052.

DOAN, C.H. and DAVIDSON, P.M. (2000), 'Microbiology of potatoes and potato products: a review', *J. Food Prot.* **63**, 668–683.

DOBELL, C. (1960), *Antony van Leeuwenhoek and his 'Little Animals.'*, New York, Dover Publications.

DOORES, S. (1983), 'The microbiology of apples and apple products', *Crit. Rev. Food Sci. Nutr.* **19**, 133–149.

DUNNE, C. (2001), 'Adaptation of bacteria to the intestinal niche: probiotics and gut disorder', *Inflamm. Bowel Dis.* **7**, 136–145.

ENRIGHT, J.B., SADLER W.W. and THOMAS, R.C. (1956), 'Observations on the thermal inactivation of the organism of Q fever in milk', *J Milk Food Technol*, **10**, 313–318.

ENRIGHT, J.B., SADLER, W.W. and THOMAS, R.C. (1957), *Thermal inactivation of Coxiella burnetii and its relation to pasteurisation of milk*, Public Health Service Publication No. 517. United States Government Printing Office, Washington, D C.

FARKAS, D.F. and HOOVER, D.G. (2000), 'High pressure processing', *J. Food Sci., Supplement*, **65**, 47–64.

FAWCETT, P., EICHENBERGER, P., LOSICK, R. and YOUNGMAN, P. (2000), 'Global gene expression profiles of *Bacillus subtilis* grown under anaerobic conditions', *J. Bacteriol.* **182**, 8063–8068.

FERRETTI, R., MANNAZZU, I., COCOLIN, L., COMI, G. and CLEMENTI, F. (2001), 'Twelve-hour PCR based method for detection of *Salmonella spp.* in food', *Appl. Env. Microbiol.* **67**, 977–978.

FILIPE, S.R., SEVERINA, E. and TOMASZ, A. (2002), 'The murMN operon: a functional link between antibiotic resistance and antibiotic tolerance in *Streptococcus pneumoniae*', *Proc. Natl. Acad. Sci.* **99**, 1550–1555.

FITZGERALD, J.R. and MUSSER, J.M. (2001), 'Evolutionary genomics of pathogenic bacteria', *Trends Microbiol.* **9**, 9–11.

FSAI (Food Safety Authority of Ireland) (1999), 'The prevention of *E. coli* O157:H7 infection: a shared responsibility', Food Safety Authority of Ireland, Dublin.

FUENTE, N. DE LA and PORTILLO, F. (2000), 'The cell wall integrity/remodelling MAPK cascade is involved in glucose activation of the yeast plasma membrane H(+) - ATPase. *Biochim. Biophys. Acta* **1509**, 189–194.

FUJII, S., IWAHASHI, H., OBUCHI, K., FUJII, T. and KOMATSU, Y. (1996), 'Characterization of a barotolerant mutant of the yeast Saccharomyces cerevisiae: importance of trehalose content and membrane fluidity', *FEMS Microbiol. Lett.* **141**, 97–101.

GOULD, G.W. (2000) Preservation: past, present and future. *Br. Med. Bull.* **56**, 84–96.

GOULD, G.W. (2001) New processing technologies: an overview. Symposium on 'nutritional effects of new processing technologies'. *Proc. Nutr. Soc.* **60**, 463–474.

GRIERSON, B. (1997), 'Food safety through the ages' *Priorities* **9**, 3 http://www.acsh.org/publications/priorities/0903/foodsafety.html

HARTMAN, P.A. (1997), 'The evolution of food microbiology', in Doyle M.P., Beuchat L.R. and Montville T.J. (eds), *Food microbiology: Fundamentals and frontiers*, Washington, ASM Press, pp. 3–13.

HECKER, M. and VÖLKER, U. (2001), 'General stress response of *Bacillus subtilis* and other bacteria', *Adv. Microb. Physiol.* **44**, 35–91.

HEINZ, V. and KNORR, D. (2001), 'Preservation of liquid foods by high intensity pulsed electric fields – basic concepts for process design', *Trends Food Sci. & Technol.* **12**, 103–111.

HEINZ, V. and KNORR, D. (2002), 'Effects of high pressure in spores', in: Hendrickx, M.E.G. and Knorr, D. (eds), *Ultra High Pressure Treatment of Foods*, Kluwer Academic, NY.

HELANDER, I.M., NURMIAHO-LASSILA, E.L., AHVENAINEN, R., RHOADES, J. and ROLLER, S. (2001), 'Chitosan disrupts the barrier properties of the outer membrane of gram-negative bacteria'. *Int. J. Food Microbiol.* **71**, 235–244.

HELMANN, J.D., WU, M.F., KOBEL, P.A., GAMO, F.J., WILSON, M., MORSHEDI, M.M., NAVRE, M. and PADDON, C. (2001), 'Global transcriptional response of *Bacillus subtilis* to heat shock', *J. Bacteriol.* **183**, 7318–7328.

HOHMANN, S. (2002), 'Osmotic stress signalling and osmoadaptation in yeasts', *Microbiol. Mol. Biol. Rev.* **66**, 300–372.

HOLYOAK, C.D., BRACEY, D., PIPER, P.W., KUCHLER, K. and COOTE, P.J. (1999), 'The *Saccharomyces cerevisiae* weak-acid-inducible ABC transporter Pdr12 transports fluorescein and preservative anions from the cytosol', *J. Bacteriol.* **181**, 4644–4652.

HOOVER, D.G. (2002), 'Ultrasound', *J. Food Sci. Supplement* **65**, 93–95.

HUGHES, T.R., MARTON, M.J., JONES, A.R., ROBERTS, C.J., STOUGHTON, R., ARMOUR, C.D., BENNETT, H.A., COFFEY, E., DAI, H., HE, Y.D., KIDD, M.J., KING, A.M., MEIJER, M.R., SLADE, D., LUM, P.Y., STEPANIANTS, S.B., SHOEMAKER, D.D., GACHOTTE, D., CHAKRABURTTY, K., SIMON, J., BARD, M. and FRIEND, S.H. (2000), 'Functional discovery via a compendium of expression profiles', Cell **102**, 109–126.

JONGEN, T. (2001), 'e-ntegrated design: where product, process and consumer come together', *Unilever Research Prize lecture 2000*, Vlaardingen, The Netherlands.

KÄFERSTEIN, F. and ABDUSSALAM, M. (1999), 'Food safety in the 21st century' *Bull World Health Organ.* **77**, 347–351.

KARATZAS, K.A. and BENNIK, M.H. (2002), 'Characterization of a Listeria monocytogenes Scott A isolate with high tolerance towards high hydrostatic pressure', *Appl. Env. Microbiol.* **68**, 3183–3189.

KAUR, J., LEDWARD, D.A., PARK, R.W.A. and ROBSON, R.L. (1998), 'Factors affecting the heat resistance of *Escherichia coli* O157:H7', *Lett. Appl. Microbiol.* **26**, 325–330.

KIEBOOM, J., ABEE, T., HERMANS, A., AARTS, H., BECK, P. and DE JONGE, R. (2002), 'Meer resistente/virulente pathogenen', *Voedingsmiddelen technologie* **11**, 29.

KLIS, F.M., MOL, P., HELLINGWERF, K. and BRUL, S. (2002), 'Dynamics of cell wall structure in *Saccharomyces cerevisiae*', *FEMS Microbiol. Rev.* **26**, 239–256.

KNUDSEN, D.M., YAMAMOTO, S.A. and HARRIS, L.J. (2001), 'Survival of *Salmonella spp.* and *Escherichia coli* O157:H7 on fresh and frozen strawberries', *J. Food Prot.* **64**, 1483–1488.

KURITA, S., KITAGAWA, E., KIM, C.H., MOMOSE, Y. and IWAHASHI, H. (2002),'Studies on the antimicrobial mechanism of capsaicin using yeast DNA microarray', *Biosci. Biotechnol. Biochem.* **66**, 532–536.

LADO, B.H. and YOUSEF, A.E. (2002), 'Alternative food-preservation technologies: efficacy and mechanisms', *Microbes and Infection* **4**, 433–440.

LEE, T.I., RINALDI, N.J., ROBERT, F., ODOM, D.T., BAR-JOSEPH, Z., BERBER, G.K., HANNET, N.M., HARBISON, C.T., THOMPSON, C.M., SIMON, I., ZEITLINGER, J., JENNINGS, E.G., MURRAY, H.L., GORDON, D.B., REN, B., WYRICK, J.J., TAGNE, J.-B., VOLKERT, T.L., FRAENKEL, E., GIFFORD, D.K. and YOUNG, R.A. (2002), ' Transcriptional regulatory networks in *Saccharomyces cerevisiae*', *Science* **298**, 799–804.

LEWIS, K. (2001), 'In search of natural substrates and inhibitors of MDR pumps', *J. Mol. Microbiol. Biotechnol.* **3**, 247–254.

LOEFFLER, J.M., NELSON, D. and FISCHETTI, V.A. (2001), 'Rapid killing of *Streptococcus pneumoniae* with a bacteriophage cell wall hydrolase', *Science* **294**, 2170–2172.

LOPEZ-MALO, A., ALZAMORA, S.M. and PALOU, E. (2002), '*Aspergillus flavus* dose-response curves to selected natural and synthetic antimicrobials', *Int. J. Food Microbiol.*, **73**, 213–218.

LUCCHINI, S., THOMPSON, A. and HINTON, J.C.D. (2001), 'Microarrays for Microbiologists', *Microbiology* **147**, 1403–1414.

MCADAMS, H.H. and ARKIN, A. (1997), 'Stochastic mechanisms of gene expression', *Proc. Natl. Acad. Sci. USA* **94**, 814–819.

MCMEEKIN, T.A., OLLEY, J., ROSS, T. and RATKOWSKY, D.A. (1993) *Predictive Microbiology: Theory and Application.* Wiley & Sons Inc., Somerset, UK.

MANTOVANI, H.C. and RUSSEL, J.B. (2001), 'Nisin resistance of *Streptococcus bovis*', *Appl.*

*Env. Microbiol.* **67**, 808–813.

MASSCHALCK, B., VAN HOUDT, R., VAN HAVER, E.G. and MICHIELS, C.W. (2001), 'Inactivation of gram-negative bacteria by lysozyme, denatured lysozyme and lysozyme derived peptides under high hydrostatic pressure', *Appl. Env. Microbiol.* **67**, 339–344.

MAZZOTTA, A.S. and MONTVILLE, T.J. (1999), 'Characterization of fatty acid composition, spore germination, and thermal resistance in a nisin-resistant mutant of *Clostridium botulinum* 169B and in the wild-type strain', *Appl. Env. Microbiol.* **65**, 659–664.

MEAD, P.S., SLUTSKER, L., DIETZ, V., MCCAIG, L., BRESEE, J.S., SHAPIRO, C., GRIFFIN, P.M. and TAUXE, R.V. (1999), 'Food-related illness and death in the United States', *Emerg. Infect. Dis.* **5**, 607–625.

MELLEFONT, L.A. and ROSS, T. (2002), 'The effect of abrupt shifts in temperature on the lag-phase duration of *Escherichia coli* and *Klebsiella oxytoca*', *Int. J. Food Microbiol.* (in press).

MELLEFONT, L.A., MCMEEKIN, T.A. and ROSS, T. (2002), 'The effect of abrupt osmotic shifts on the lag-phase duration of foodborne bacteria', *Int. J. Food Microbiol.* (in press).

MENSONIDES, F.I.C., SCHUURMANS, M.J., TEIXEIRA DE MATTOS, J., HELLINGWERF, K.J. and BRUL, S. (2002), 'The metabolic response of *Saccharomyces cerevisiae* to continuous heat stress', *Mol. Biol. Reports* **29**, 103–106.

MEYER, R., COOPER, K.L.L. and KNORR, D. (2000), 'High pressure sterilization of foods', *Food Technology* **54**, 67–72.

MILO, R., SHEN-ORR, S.,ITZKOVITZ, S., KASHTAN. N., CHLOVSKII, D. and ALON, U. (2002), 'Network motifs: simple building blocks of complex networks' *Science* **298**, 824–827.

NOTERMANS S., GALLHOFF G., ZWIETERING M.H. and MEAD G.C. (1995), 'Identification of critical control points in the HACCP system with a quantitative effect on the safety of food products', *Food Microbiology* **12**, 93–98.

NOUWENS, A.S., CORDWELL, S.J., LARSEN, M.R., MOLLOY, M.P., GILLINGS, M., WILCOX, M.D. and WALSH, B.J. (2000), 'Complementing genomics with proteomics: the membrane subproteome of *Pseudomonas aeruginosa* PAO1', *Electrophoresis* **21**, 3797–37809.

NWOSU, V.C. (2001), 'Antibiotic resistance with particular reference to soil microorganisms', *Res. Microbiol.* **152**, 421–430.

OLTVAI, Z.N. and BARABÁSI, A.-L. (2002), 'Life's complexity pyramid', *Science* **298**, 763–764.

OOMES, S.J.C.M., BRUL, S., ZAKRZEWSKA, A. and KLIS, F.M. (2001), 'Antimicrobial action of chitosan'. Unpublished data, *Unilever Research & Development, University of Amsterdam.*

PELEG, M. and COLE, M. (1998), 'Reinterpretation of microbial survival curves', *Crit. Rev. Food Sci. Nutr.* **38**, 353–380.

PERIAGO, P.M., VAN SCHAIK, W., ABEE, T. and WOUTERS, J.A. (2002), 'Identification of proteins involved in the heat stress response of *Bacillus cereus* ATCC 14579', *Appl. Env. Microbiol.* **68**, 3486–3495.

PFLUG I.J. and GOULD G.W. (2000), 'Heat treatment' in Lund B.M., Baird-Parker T.C.and Gould G.W., *The Microbiological Safety and Quality of Food.* Gaithersburg, Aspen Publishers, Inc, 37–63.

PIPER, P., MAHE, Y., THOMPSON, S., PANDJAITAN, R., HOLYOAK, C., EGNER, R., MUHLBAUER, M., COOTE, P. and KUCHLER, K. (1998), 'The pdr 12 ABC transporter is required for the development of weak organic acid resistance in yeast', *EMBO J.* **15**, 4257–4265.

PIPER, P., CALDERON, C.O., HATZIXANTHIS, K. and MOLLAPOUR, M. (2001), 'Weak acid adaptation the stress response that confers yeast with resistance to organic acid food preservatives', *Microbiology* **147**, 2635–2642.

RAMASWAMY, H.S., AWUAH, G.B. and SIMPSON, B.K. (1997), 'Heat transfer and lethality considerations in aseptic processing of liquid/particle mixture: a review', *Crit. Rev. Food Sci. Nutr.* **37**, 253–286.

ROSS, T. (1999), 'Predictive Microbiology for the Meat Industry', *Meat & Livestock Australia*, Meat & Livestock Australia, Sydney, Australia.

ROSS, T. and SHADBOLT, C.T. (2001), 'Predicting *Escherichia coli* inactivation in uncooked comminuted fermented meat products', *Meat and Livestock Australia* (publishers), Sydney, Australia.

RUSSEL, N.J., EVANS, R.I., TER STEEG, P.F., HELLEMONS, J., VERHEUL, A. and ABEE, T. (1995), 'Membranes as a target for stress adaptation', *Int. J. Food Microbiol.* **28**, 317–326.

SASTRY, S.K. and BARACH, J.T. (2000) 'Ohmic and inductive heating'. *J. Food Sci., Supplement,* **65** , 42–46.

SCHAIK, W. VAN, GAHAN, C.G. and HILL, C. (1999), 'Acid-adapted Listeria monocytogenes displays enhanced tolerance against the lantibiotics nisin and lacticin 3147', *J. Food Prot.* **62**, 536–539.

SETLOW, B., MCGINNIS, K.A., RAKOUSI, K. and SETLOW, P. (2000), 'Effects of major spore-specific DNA binding proteins on Bacillus subtilis sporulation and spore properties', *J. Bacteriol.* **182**, 6906–6912.

SMELT, J.P.P.M. (1998), 'Recent advances in the microbiology of high pressure processing', *Trends Food Sci. Technol.* **9**, 152–158.

SMELT, J.P.P.M., HELLEMONS J. and BRUL, S. (2002a), 'Physiological aspects of pressure decontamination in building inactivation models', *Trends in High pressure Bioscience & Biotechnology*, Hayashi, H. (ed.), Elsevier, New York, pp. 487–496.

SMELT, J.P.P.M., HELLEMONS, J.C. and PATTERSON, M. (2002b), 'Effects of high pressure on vegetative microorganisms', *Ultra High Pressure Treatment of Foods*, Hendrickx, M.E.G. and Knorr, D. (eds) Kluwer Academic, NY.

STEPHANOPOULOS, G. and KELLEHER, J. (2001), 'How to make a superior cell', *Science* **292**, 2024–2025.

STRANEY, D., KHAN, R., TAN, R. and BAGGA, S. (2002), 'Host recognition by pathogenic fungi through plant flavonoids', *Adv. Exp. Med. Biol.* **505**, 9–22.

SUMNER, E.R. and AVERY, S.V. (2002), 'Phenotypic heterogeneity: differential stress resistance among individual cells of the yeast *Saccharomyces cerevisiae*', *Microbiology* **148**, 345–351.

TANG, X., XIE, M., KIM, Y.J., ZHOU, J., KLESSIG, D.F. and MARTIN, G.B. (1999), 'Overexpression of Pto activates defense responses and confers broad resistance', *Plant Cell* **11**, 15–29.

TAO, H., BAUSCH, C., RICHMOND, C., BLATTNER, F.B. and CONWAY, T. (1999), 'Functional genomics: Expression analysis of *Escherichia coli* growing on minimal and rich media', *J. Bacteriol.* **181**, 6425–6440.

TESSI, M.A., ARINGOLI, E.E., PIROVANI, M.E., VINCENZINI, A.Z., SABBAG, N.G., COSTA, S.C., GARCIA, C.C., ZANNIER, M.S., SIULVA, E.R. and MOGUILEVSKY, M.A. (2002), 'Microbiological quality and safety of ready-to-eat cooked foods from a centralized school kitchen in Argentina', *J. Food Prot.* **65**, 636–642.

TEUSINK, B. (1999), 'Exposing a complex metabolic system glycolysis in *Saccharomyces cerevisiae*', PhD thesis, University of Amsterdam.

TOUSSAINT-SAMAT, M. (1992), *History of food*, Cambridge, Blackwell publishers.

ULTEE, A., KETS, E.P. and SMID, E.J. (1999), 'Mechanisms of action of carvacrol on the food-borne pathogen *Bacillus cereus*', *Appl. Env. Microbiol* **65**, 4606–4610.

ULTEE, A., KETS, E.P., ALBERDA, M., HOEKSTRA, F.A. and SMID, E.J. (2000), 'Adaptation of the food-borne pathogen *Bacillus cereus* to carvacrol', *Arch. Microbiol.* **174**, 233–238.

VERRIPS, C.T., WARMOESKERKEN, M.M.C.G. and POST, J.A. (2001), 'General introduction to the importance of genomics in food biotechnology and nutrition', *Curr. Opinion Biotechnol.* **12**, 483-487.

VÖLKER, U., MAUL, B. and HECKER, M. (1999), 'Expression of the sigma B-dependent general stress regulon confers multiple stress resistance in *Bacillus subtilis*', *J. Bacteriol.* **181**, 3942–3948.

VOS, W.M.-DE (2001), 'Advances in genomics for microbial food fermentations and safety', *Curr. Biotechnol Opin.* **12**, 493–498.

VUGIA, D., HADLER, J., BLAKE, P., BLYTHE, MORSE, D., CIESLAK, P., JONES, T., SHILLAM, P., CHEN, D.W., GARTHWRIGHT, B., CHARLES, L., MOLBAK, K., ANGULO, F., GRIFFIN, P. and TAUXE, R. (2002) 'Preliminary foodnet data on the incidence of foodborne illnesses – selected site, United States (2001)', *Morbidity and Mortality Weekly Report* **51**, 325–329.

WANG, H. and NG, T.B. (2001), 'Novel antifungal peptides from Ceylon spinach seeds', *Biochim. Biophys. Res. Commun.* **288**, 765–770.

WEIMER, B. and MILLS, D. (2002), 'Enhancing foods with functional genomics', *Food Technology* **56**, 184–189.

WENDORF, F.R., SCHILD, R., EL HADIDI, N., CLOSE, A.E., KOBUSIEWICZ, H., WIECKOWSKA, H., ISSAWI, B. and HAAS, H. (1979) 'Use of barley in the Egyptian late paleolithic', *Science* **205**, 1341–1348.

WOUTERS, P.C., ALVAREZ, I. and RASO, J. (2001a), 'Critical factors determining inactivation kinetics by pulsed electric food processing', *Trends Food Sci. & Technol.* **12**, 112–121.

WOUTERS, P.C., BOS, A.P. and UECKERT, J. (2001b), 'Membrane permeabilization in relation to inactivation kinetics of Lactobacillus species due to pulsed electric fields', *Appl. Env. Microbiol.* **67**, 3092–3101.

YE, R.W., TAO W., BEDZYK, L., YOUNG, T., CHEN, M. and LI, L. (2000), 'Global gene expression profiles of *Bacillus subtilis* grown under anaerobic conditions', *J. Bacteriol.* **182**, 4458–4465.

YOSHIDA., KOBAYASHI, K.I., MIWA, Y. C.-M., KANG, M., MATSUNAGA, H., YAMAGUCHI, H., TOJO, S., YAMAMOTO, M., NISHI, R., OGASAWARA, N., NAKAYAMA, T. and FUJITA, Y. (2001), 'Combined transcriptome and proteome analysis as a powerful approach to study genes under glucose repression in *Bacillus subtilis*', *Nucl. Acid Res.* **29**, 683–692.

YUN, D.J., ZHAO, Y., PARDO, J.M., NARASIMHAN, M.L., DAMSZ, B., LEE, H., ABAD, L.R.D., D'URZO, M.P., HASEGAWA, P.M. and BRESSAN, R.A. (1997), 'Stress proteins on the yeast cell surface determine resistance to osmotin, a plant antifungal protein', *Proc. Natl. Acad. Sci.* USA 94, 7082–7087.

ZENKER, M., HEINZ, V. and KNORR, D. (2002), 'Ultrasound-temperature combinations for inactivation of microbial loads'. Unpublished data, *Berlin University of Technology*, Berlin.

ZWIETERING, M.H., DE WIT, J.C. and NOTERMANS, S. (1996), 'Application of predictive microbiology to estimate the number of bacillus cereus in pasteurised milk at the point of consumption', *Int. J. Food Microbiol.* **30**, 55–70.

# 24

# Monitoring the effectiveness of food preservation

**P. Zeuthen, Consultant, Denmark and L. Bøgh-Sørensen, Danish Veterinary and Food Administration**

## 24.1 Introduction

Preservation techniques deal with how to produce foods with extended shelf life which are also safe to eat and meet consumer expectations of sensory quality. This book tries to give an account of how modern preservation techniques meet these objectives. However, no matter how suitable these techniques are, modern industrial production will not be successful if it is not monitored. Many factors are involved in ensuring safety and quality, such as the quality of raw materials, including their microbial suitability, and potable water for the production. In addition, a proper level of hygiene in production is implicitly required. The readers of this book are referred to the literature on these matters, e.g., Gould (1994) or CODEX Alimentarius (1996).

### 24.1.1 Legislation

Both at national and international levels legislation on safety is very extensive. Food safety regulations may be justified by the existence of a failure in the market for product safety attributes. Because consumers cannot ascertain the safety of many food products, they are unable to express preferences for greater safety in the marketplace. Furthermore, producers or retailers may be unable to ascertain or to certify safety because food-borne pathogens are living organisms that can enter the food at any point and may propagate over time. The lack – or high cost – of information about safety and the resulting consequences for public health is the fundamental justification for public intervention to improve food safety (Unnevehr and Jensen, 1999).

Within the European Union (EU) great efforts have been made by the European Commission (EC) to legislate on food safety and implement such legislation at national level. The EC has issued five horizontal Directives on processed foods: EC/79/112 on labelling, EC/89/109 on materials and articles in contact with food, EC/89/112 on additives, EC/89/107 on food for particular nutritional uses, and EC/89/397 on food control. Similarly the legislation covering primary production and products of animal origin is embodied in no less than 14 EC Directives. Apart from vertical Directives on specific foods of animal origin, the so-called Hygiene Directive (EC/93/43) covers general aspects of food hygiene as a horizontal Directive. The main focus of all these Directives is on food safety, whereas sensory qualities and other attributes of food products are only slightly covered. The reason for this is, of course, that the word 'quality' has so many meanings and is defined in so many ways that harmonisation is virtually impossible. For further information on the EC legislation reference is made to http://europa.eu.int/eur-lex/. Similarly, Codex Alimentarius (1996) has issued guidelines that, with some variations, are used both nationally and internationally.

## 24.2  HACCP and other monitoring systems

Since the HACCP (Hazard Analysis Critical Control Point) concept has become so widespread internationally and has gained so great acceptance as the best safety system available, it will be explained in more detail. HACCP is a systematic approach to the identification, assessment and control of hazards. The Pillsbury Company in the 1960s originally developed the HACCP procedure as a practical means of ensuring the safety of foodstuffs for space flights (APHA, 1971, Pillsbury Company, 1973). In their review of food safety Ropkins and Beck (2000) concluded that conventional end-point food testing could not effectively ensure food safety because:

- Significant proportions of a foodstuff have to be sub-sampled for analysis to ensure that it is representative.
- Food safety is only ensured with regards to tested hazards.
- Current food safety testing procedures are likely to be expensive, time-consuming, difficult to interpret, and destructive.
- Control of hazards is reactive.
- Responsibility for food safety is focused upon a relatively small component of the workforce responsible for quality assurance and control.
- Food safety is only assured at the point of testing.

The original Pillsbury HACCP procedure contained three essential components (Pillsbury Company, 1973):

1. The identification and assessment of all hazards associated with the final foodstuff.
2. The identification of the steps or stages within food production at which

these hazards may be controlled, reduced or elimininated, i.e., the Critical Control Points (CCPs).
3.  The implementation of monitoring procedures at these CCPs.

The generally accepted HACCP protocol today comprises seven principles:

1.  Assess the hazard, list the steps in the process where significant hazards can occur, and describe the prevention measures (sometimes referred to as 'a hazard analysis').
2.  Determine critical control points (CCPs) in the process.
3.  Establish critical limits for each CCP.
4.  Establish procedures to monitor each CCP.
5.  Establish corrective actions to be taken when monitoring indicates a deviation from the CCP limits.
6.  Establish record keeping for the HACCP system (described by Codex as 'procedures for verification to confirm that the HACCP system is working effectively').
7.  Establish documentation concerning all procedures and records appropriate to these principles and their application.

### 24.2.1  Dual purpose systems

Attempts have been made to modify or revise the basic HACCP system. In some places it has been amended to cover both safety and quality parameters. Many food scientists concerned with HACCP and food safety are opposed to this development as diluting the focus on safety (Jouve, 1997). However, several attempts have recently been made to integrate food safety with food quality features. Barendsz (1998) describes a Dutch study on merging the HACCP system with TQM (total quality management) systems including the ISO (International Standard Organisation) 9000 standard. A committee comprising seven Dutch certifying bodies agreed that 'for the time being, the HACCP and the ISO 9000 system certificates are to be regarded as separate entities'. Although one standard might emerge eventually, for the time being, companies must have the choice either to go for a HACCP certificate, an ISO certificate or both, but as separate systems.

Peters (1998) has described two Australian dual-purpose systems. Both are voluntary, third party certified standards focused on using the HACCP principles for both quality and food safety. The first system, SQF2000$^{TM}$ (Safe Quality Food), has six elements, and a total of 15 requirements. The other system, WVQMS (Woolworths Vendor Quality Management Standard$^{®}$) has nine requirements, including preparation of HACCP plans, document control, good manufacturing practices, cleaning procedures, pest control, training, calibration, product identification, and corrective actions. In addition to third party audit and certification requirements, the standard requires the HACCP plan component be independently verified. HACCP principles are also used to identify Quality Critical Points (QCPs) and Quality Points (QPs). Both standards originated in the control of horticultural products, but are being extended into other food and food processing areas. The WVQMS has also been extended into transport and distribution operations and various supermarket activities.

In a recent report Unnevehr and Jensen (1999) have summarised legislation and developments in this subject in the EU, the United States, Australia, New Zealand, and Canada, as well as in international trade through the Codex Alimentarius. The report points out that the basic idea of HACCP has been interpreted and implemented differently around the world. In addition, the report questions the cost-benefit from an economic point of view, but concludes that as long as the cost of directly monitoring microbial pathogens remains high, HACCP will continue to be the standard of choice because it focuses resources where they will have greatest effect in controlling hazards. Antle (1999) also discusses the benefits versus costs of food safety regulations. The paper gives an account of the use and limitations of currently available benefit and cost information for quantitative regulatory impact assessment (RIA) using the assessment of the mandatory HACCP and pathogen reduction regulation in the United States as an example. It concludes that there is a need for more research in the field for making better use of the limited and imperfect data that are available.

Perhaps one of the most interesting attempts to draw up a system that encompasses both safety and quality criteria is the document published by Codex Alimentarius (Codex, 2002). It is entitled 'Proposed draft code of practice for fish and fishery products' and is thus limited to those commodities. The code merges individual codes from a number of countries participating in Codex Alimentarius, and currently covers five out of ten proposed steps. The scope of the code applies to the growing, harvesting, handling, production, processing, storage, transportation and retail sale of fish and fishery products from both marine and freshwater sources which are intended for human consumption. It thus embraces a whole sector of commodities through the whole food chain. Since it is a Codex Alimentarius document it comprises the normal seven HACCP principles, but in order to include issues of quality it also introduces a concept called DAP (Defect Action Point) defined as 'a step at which control can be applied and a defect can be prevented, eliminated or reduced to acceptable level, or a fraud risk eliminated'. Since the code includes 'quality' the draft code also comprises a definition of shelf life: 'the period during which the product maintains its microbiological and chemical safety and sensory qualities at a specific storage temperature. It is based on identified hazards for the product, heat or other preservation treatments, packaging method and other hurdles or inhibiting factors that may be used'. The code uses the HACCP decision tree, but quality parameters are included as CCPs. It seems likely that codes of practice like this will be proposed for other commodity sectors in the future.

## 24.2.2   Automating monitoring and control systems

In the food industry, processes are especially difficult to automate and control owing to the variability in raw materials, and lack of means for real-time measuring and monitoring of key food process variables and food quality attributes. This control becomes particularly difficult when there are interactions between manipulated and controlled variables. Linko and Linko (1998) give an account of advanced control systems, which make use of a wide variety of methods from model-based predictive controllers to intelligent and 'software' sensors, neuro-fuzzy control and expert systems. The implementation of such systems will, however, take a number of years before they are being used widely and will probably only be used in large industrial facilities. Although the global food industry will be increasingly concentrated, many food products will in the future still be produced in small plants where the use of advanced control methods will be limited.

## 24.3    Instrumentation for monitoring the effectiveness of food preservation during processing

The management of a food plant is responsible for providing an effective system with adequate resources to ensure a safe production of food, and also responsible for knowing that the system remains effective through a process of audit and review. First and foremost this is done by establishing a HACCP system as described earlier, but adequate physical instrumentation and training of personnel is essential for implementation. Safety should be assured by good design and subsequent control during production, storage and distribution.

Quality monitoring of incoming raw materials may include traditional methods such as visual control, temperature measurement, and microbiological analysis, or more sophisticated methods such as biosensors, e.g., electronic noses (Kress-Rogers and Brimelow, 2001). However, indicators detecting the presence of pathogens and/or spoilage micro-organisms discussed in section 24.4 may also be used at the food processing plant. Biosensors designed to measure other quality parameters, e.g., pesticide residues, can also be used in order to check the suitability of raw materials (Tothill, 2003).

The effectiveness of food preservation techniques depends on the ability to monitor key safety parameters such as critical control points (CCPs) within HACCP systems. A similar systematic approach may be used to ensure essential quality, composition and labelling requirements or standards. As mentioned in 24.2.1 this approach is referred to as 'Defect Action Point (DAP) Analysis'. Monitoring may be continuous, or the frequency of measuring must be sufficient to guarantee that the CCP (or the DAP) is under control.

Examples of instrumentation for different preservation techniques will be discussed below. It is a general requirement, included in HACCP, TCM (Total Control Management) and similar systems, that instruments used in food control and especially in monitoring of a CCP give accurate and reproducible results. Moreover, such instruments must be serviced, tested, and calibrated at appropriate intervals. Their design must make it easy to read measurements and to provide a clear signal, e.g., sound or light, if the preservation process is out of control. A lot of research work has been done in recent years in order to develop on-line or at-line methods, preferably non-destructive and non-invasive, for monitoring food quality and manufacturing processes (Tothill, 2003).

### 24.3.1    Thermometers

Temperature is very often the most important parameter in food preservation. This is especially the case in heat preservation (see Chapters 9 and 10), where the heating process must result in a certain temperature for a certain time in the centre (the coldest point) of the product. The thermal process for each product (in each container) must be specified, including information on heating-up time, cooking time and temperature, cooling rate and time, etc. This is established by means of a heat penetration test, in which the temperature at the centre of the product is monitored during thermal processing in order to calculate the sterilising/pasteurising effect. As heat penetration during heating in water or steam is well known, this is fairly simple. In order to monitor the heating process, it is necessary to monitor the temperature in the water or steam, and this is normally done continuously, i.e., measuring and recording the temperature at least once every minute. The accuracy of these temperature measurements must be checked regularly. Several countries require that retorts be used for low-acid products, e.g., meat, must be equipped with an accurate indicating thermometer, also called Master Temperature Indicator (MTI). For many years, only mercury-in-glass thermometers were approved, but today other accurate temperature measuring devices, mostly based on platinum resistance, can be used (Berrie, 2001). It may be required that readings of the MTI and the recording thermometer must be compared once per batch. The reading of the recording thermometer must not be more than 0.5 °C above or below the MTI reading. It must not be overlooked that a number of factors may influence the product temperature. The heat distribution in a retort must for example be sufficiently uniform. The following instruments and controls in retorts are normally required:

- a temperature/time recording device;
- water retorts must be equipped with an effective water circulation system and a flow alarm;
- water retorts must be furnished with an automatic water level alarm;
- (water) retorts must be equipped with a pressure recording device;
- in steam retorts, vents and bleeders must ensure adequate removal of air.

This type of temperature monitoring is not applicable in heating systems such as ohmic heating, or heating by microwaves or RF (radio frequency). Monitoring of effect, residence time, etc., may be required, together with checking the product temperature immediately after heating. It may be possible to use different types of temperature loggers or temperature indicators in continuous retorts. In aseptic processing product flow, temperature of the heating medium, residence time, etc., are some of the important parameters.

In conventional heating (water, steam, air), the temperature is higher at the surface and lowest at the centre when the cooling starts, but this may not be the case in non-conventional heating processes such as microwaves and RF. Here, the temperature may be higher at the centre than at the surface, presenting problems in temperature or temperature distribution measurement during and after a non-conventional heating process. Non-invasive methods, most of them based on infra-red (IR) techniques, are available, but have not yet been developed into standard equipment.

Temperature control is not only essential in heating processes. In chilling and freezing it may be necessary to check that the cooling process is performed at an appropriate rate. The temperature around the food products and, at intervals, the product temperature, must be monitored. It is also advisable to check that the products are placed in chilling/freezing facilities in the prescribed way in order to ensure that the process is approximately the same for all products.

### 24.3.2   Container closure

Packaging materials are generally designed to be impermeable to micro-organisms. A foodstuff is often packaged before (in aseptic processes after) the preservation process takes place. In order to maintain the integrity of closed containers in the food chain a good closure, often a hermetic seal, is critical. The different types of closures of cans, bottles, plastic containers, flexible pouches, etc., will not be discussed, but it is evident that the closing or sealing operation is usually a CCP.

Legislation or official guides covering food in metal cases were issued many years ago. Such documents describe the type and frequency of monitoring of double seaming. In order to monitor the heat seal of flexible plastic packages a number of methods are in use, but none of them has been accepted internationally by 2003.

In aseptically processed and packaged food products, the sterility of each package is extremely important, and non-destructive testing of each container for the presence of viable bacteria is highly desirable. One of the methods that is able to perform non-destructive and non-invasive measurement at commercial production speed is MRI (Magnetic Resonance Imaging) based on a pH reduction caused by bacterial proteolysis of proteins and hydrolysis of carbohydrates. (IGC's web site: www.industrialmr.com). Another inspection method is based on ultrasonics (ultrasonic imaging) and requires a transducer to touch each container. A complete control of the closure is also highly desirable for a number of other product groups. Non-destructive on-line methods such as optical, acoustic or pressure-difference methods for package integrity testing are being developed. For MAP (Modified Atmosphere Packaging) foods it is desirable to be able to check the gas composition in each package. This can be done at the processing plant by a gas analyser (sometimes only an $O_2$ analyser) as an integral part of the packaging machine, continuously measuring the concentration of the gases in the gas mixture used in MAP.

### 24.3.3   Other measuring instruments

As discussed in several chapters in this book, pH and water activity ($a_w$) are often very important parameters. Frequently they are CCPs.

**pH**. Effective measurement of pH has been done for many years and should not pose any problems as long as service, calibration, etc., is done as prescribed, for example, in instrument manuals. In principle, pH can be measured very quickly, but measuring pH in foods such as meat is complicated because of large variations between different parts of the animal. pH can be measured continuously in liquid foods.

**Water activity**. This has been measured effectively for more than 40 years. The problem is time as it often takes more than one hour to measure $a_w$ of meat and similar products. In some cases, chemical analyses of salt (NaCl) and water are done instead.

**Ultra high pressure**. A long tradition of measuring very high pressures does not exist in the food industry. But it is necessary for the food manufacturer to have some guarantee that the pressure indicated on a measuring device is the pressure to which the food is exposed.

**Dosimetry**. When irradiation and UV is used it is necessary to measure the dose received by the food. To be sure that the sophisticated instruments required work properly and give proper readings, the operators must trust the instrument company and follow their manual.

**Light intensity/Pulsed electric fields**. The effect on the food and on micro-organisms depends on the number of pulses and their intensity, duration, and wave length. Again, it is necessary to be able to check these parameters.

**Ultrasonics**. It must be possible to check frequency and effect of ultrasound waves.

**Membrane filtration**. It must be possible to check the efficiency of the filtration, and to get some warning when filtration is not functioning properly. An obvious choice is to measure the volume of the flux continuously, as well as measurements of turbidity and optical density.

## 24.4   Monitoring the effectiveness of food preservation during storage and distribution

Quality and safety monitoring is more complicated in the food chain when the food has left the processing line. For unwrapped products such as fruits and vegetables the appearance and even the smell and texture (hardness) may be evaluated. Most foods are packaged and, although the appearance of foods in transparent plastic packs can be evaluated, the general situation is that quality evaluation is impossible for the consumer, and often for food handlers and supermarket personnel!

After the manufacturing process (including the preservation processes) food products are normally stored and distributed before being purchased by the final consumer. Refrigerated foods, i.e., chilled or frozen foods, pass through the chill chain (the cold chain for chilled foods) or the frozen chain (the cold chain for frozen foods). Most preservation techniques, including the new techniques discussed in the previous chapters, are used in combination with other techniques or hurdles such as chilling. Maintaining the correct product temperatures in the entire chill chain is often the most important single factor in ensuring the quality and safety of the food. Several players are involved in the different steps/links in the cold chain. From a food manufacturer or a supermarket point of view it is desirable to be able to detect food products which have been exposed to temperature abuses, especially temperature abuses which could endanger food safety or compromise quality.

### 24.4.1   Temperature monitoring during transport and storage of refrigerated foods

In the 1980s legislation in several countries concentrated more on temperature control of quick-frozen foods than of chilled foods, for example, the EU's quick-frozen food directive (EC/89/108) followed by two directives on measuring temperature of quick-frozen foods (EC/92/1, EC/92/2). Transport temperatures for frozen, quick-frozen and chilled foods in international trade are regulated by means of the ATP agreement (Agreement on the International Carriage of Perishable Foods and on the Special Equipment to be Used for Such Carriage). In the EU different temperature limits are prescribed for the same chilled food items in different member states. There is now greater interest in establishing common (harmonised) rules for chilled foods, e.g., setting maximum temperatures.

It is necessary to use temperature measuring devices (thermometers, recorders) which are sufficiently accurate and which have recently been calibrated. Information on this may be found in legislation, standard documents, etc., and will not be discussed any further in this book. In many cases, control persons have to measure the temperature at the product centre by means of a destructive method. It is generally easier to measure the temperature of chilled than of frozen foods. In storage rooms, during transport, etc., the temperature is monitored by means of temperature recorders. The temperature probe normally measures the temperature of the air surrounding the food product. In storage rooms the temperature is, or should be, fairly constant, meaning that the placement of the temperature probes is not critical. This is especially true in large freezer storage rooms mainly used for long-term storage. In storage rooms the minimum number of temperature recorders (depending on the size of the room) may be laid down in legislation or recommendations (guidelines).

In transport vehicles or containers it is not common to prescribe the number of recorders, but more than one may be recommended in order to improve the possibilities of rejecting lots being transported in unacceptable time-temperature conditions. There may be a temperature difference of some degrees C between the product centre and the air circulating around the product, and there may be temperature variations with time and place in transport vehicles. It is difficult to agree on or prescribe the placement of the temperature probe in transport vehicles where there may be a temperature difference of more than 5 °C between the coldest and warmest air in the air circulation system. Temperature recorders will not indicate the temperature conditions during loading/unloading, or in other cases where refrigerated foods are placed (outside) out of refrigeration during which period product temperatures may rise considerably. Loading/unloading at the different steps of the cold chain is probably the weakest part, together with storage in display cabinets.

It has been known since the 1960s that supermarket display cabinets are a weak link in the cold chain. The centre temperature of a pack in the middle of the upper/outer layer may be several degrees C warmer (6–10 °C for frozen food, 3–5 °C for chilled foods) than the circulating cold air just above the pack. There may be large variations inside a cabinet. Product temperatures will also rise considerably during defrosting. For frozen foods in the outer/upper layers the food product temperature may rise 4 to 5 °C or more. Defrosting may be done twice a day, and the resulting product temperature fluctuations may have serious consequences for product quality, at least if frozen foods spend more than a few days in the upper layers. In chilled cabinets, defrosting periods have less influence on product temperature. On the other hand, if the product temperatures are 5 °C warmer than prescribed, e.g., 10 °C with a legislative limit of 5 °C, this may cause food safety problems. If product temperatures in a freezer cabinet are 5 °C warmer than prescribed, e.g., −13 °C with a legislative limit of −18 °C, this may cause a quality decrease (depending on time), but will not cause food safety problems. Thermographic imaging makes it possible to assess the actual temperatures of the food, or at least the surface of the food packages. A simulated package containing a temperature probe is sometimes placed at one of the warmest locations within the cabinet. The measured temperature may be transmitted to an interface outside the cabinet, making it possible to record product temperatures.

### 24.4.2  Intelligent packaging

The term 'intelligent packaging', also called smart packaging, indicates that the package carries an indicator, which monitors the conditions of packaged foods to give information about the quality of the food during transport and storage. Intelligent package indicators are used to control package integrity and product quality and to help consumers and supermarket personnel choose products with the best quality and remaining storage life, and to identify defective packages. When intelligent packaging involves encapsulation of a material into the packaging material or using a label that cannot be removed, problems with packaging reuse and other legislation in many countries may arise.

*TI or TTI*

Given the temperature problems in the cold chain discussed above, several attempts have been made to monitor the temperature of individual packages. This is not a new technology, and several (more than 100) patents have being issued, using different principles. As early as the 1960s one company in USA placed a TTI in some frozen food packages and asked the consumers who found it, to return the TTI for evaluation. Temperature monitoring devices can be divided into two types.

**TI (Temperature Indicator).** This device reacts when a given temperature is exceeded. It could be above 5 °C for chilled foods, and could be below 0 °C (freezing) for 'fresh' foods or some emulsion-based foods. When the package is exposed to this temperature an irreversible reaction, e.g., a colour change takes place and everybody can see that this package has been temperature abused. A TI does not indicate how long in time the package has been exposed to undesirable conditions.

**TTI (Time-Temperature Indicator or Time-Temperature Integrator).** A TTI is a means of continuously monitoring the temperature of a food product from the point of manufacturing to the consumer's refrigerator or freezer. A TTI is a device which shows an easily measurable time-temperature change that reflects the time-temperature history of the food product to which the TTI is attached. The principle of a TTI is normally a chemical or enzymic (irreversible) reaction, expressed as a visible response in the form of colour change, colour development or other types of colour indication. In most TTIs, the reaction rate can be varied in order to fit the temperature dependent quality changes of different food products. Many types of TI and TTI have been introduced and most of them have been shown to react as described by the manufacturer. It is surprising that the use of TTI or TI is still very limited. A special type of TTI comprises miniature temperature loggers which can measure and record thousands of temperatures, making it possible afterwards to achieve a complete picture of the time-temperature history. Such a temperature record can be used in appropriate shelf life models. The problems with TTI or TI include:

- Who is going to inspect these TTI, and who is going to act if the TTI indicates that a temperature abuse has occurred or that there is no remaining shelf life?
- Who is going to pay if the colour has changed? The manufacturer, the transporter or the supermarket (a TTI does not tell where temperature abuses have occurred)?
- Legal problems – is it permissible to sell food products when a TTI shows that the product is not 'wholesome' (for chilled food the risk of food poisoning will clearly be higher)?
- It will create problems if a consumer buys a product and finds out soon after coming home that the TTI has changed colour, indicating a spoiled (or low quality) product. Have temperatures been too high at the supermarket or

earlier, or has the consumer mishandled the product, e.g., by placing it in a (hot) car for several hours?

- Costs. The price of a TTI is low, but it will be necessary to obtain information on the relation between storage temperature and storage life for each foodstuff.
- A TI or TTI should be readily visible and are normally placed on the package surface, thus reacting quickly to the temperature of the surroundings. Short temperature rises around the food package may not influence the (centre) temperature of the food product itself. Thus, it is necessary to find the relationship between the surface temperature and the temperature of the food product.

One of the purposes of attaching a TTI (or a TI) on retail packages is to transfer information to the final consumer (buyer) on the quality and/or safety of the food. However, in some countries, consumer organisations have expressed opposition to TTIs, claiming that TTIs will reduce the awareness of the food handlers and lead to worse temperature conditions in the cold chain. It has been proposed that a TI or TTI should only be attached to secondary packaging, e.g., be placed on (outside or inside) transport cartons. This is a good (and cheaper) solution provided the supermarket personnel and other food handlers always check and register the state (colour) of the TTI. But it makes it impossible to transfer information on the distribution (time-temperature conditions) to the consumer.

### 24.4.3  Gas concentration indicators in MAP

The increasing use of MAP implies an increasing interest in monitoring the MAP gas concentration. In contrast to vacuum packaging, it is difficult or impossible for the consumer and the supermarket personnel to detect leaking of MAP packages visually. The gas composition in the packaging machine may be monitored at the manufacturer as mentioned above. However, it is also important to secure that no leaks have occurred during distribution as a changed gas composition leads to more rapid spoilage and/or faster growth of pathogenic bacteria. This may be done by measuring the oxygen concentration in the package. An oxygen sensitive indicator is incorporated in flexible packaging materials or can be implemented using labels or direct printing. Many different types of oxygen indicators exist: one is white at low oxygen concentration changing to blue at higher concentrations, another changes from red to blue. In some systems it is possible to measure the colour through the package. An oxygen indicator is mainly a leak detector, as the permeability of the package itself should be sufficiently low to maintain appropriate oxygen content in the storage period. An oxygen indicator is appropriate in MAP where a low oxygen concentration, e.g., less than 1%, is desirable or even necessary. In high oxygen MAP as in retail packed MAP beef and fresh fruit and vegetables in MAP, a suitable $CO_2$ indicator can be used.

### 24.4.4    Spoilage indicators

Spoilage (or freshness) indicators signal product quality (spoilage) directly. The indicators function by detecting the presence of microbial metabolites such as $CO_2$, $SO_2$, ammonia, biogenic amines, hydrogen sulphide and ethanol. The indicator systems include colour change of a dye, formation of colour compounds, a miniature electronic nose and headspace gas detector. Indicators measuring and signalling the development of volatile bases such as ammonia and trimethylamine are also available. The label or tag consists of a plastic chip with a reagent-containing wick. The label is placed on the package and establishes contact with the headspace gases. A colour reaction takes place when the volatile amines get in contact with the wick. Such devices are designed for fishery products such as fresh lean fish. In some fish products, e.g., tuna in MAP, spoilage is due to or accompanied by the formation of biogenic amines such as histamine. A suitable indicator may be fixed to the plastic package indicating when the content of such amines is above a certain level.

Some intelligent packages incorporate indicators which signal the presence of spoilage and/or pathogenic micro-organisms. In one system, immobilised antibodies specific to (pathogenic) micro-organisms are imbedded in plastic film. As the micro-organism or toxin comes into contact with the plastic, it is bound and gives a signal (development of colour). In another system, an immunochemical reaction may take place within a bar code. When a specific organism is present, the bar code changes appearance. It is also possible to incorporate chemicals directly into plastic, e.g., a label or tag, exhibiting a blue colour. In contact with *E. coli* O157:H7 enterotoxin, the colour turns red.

### 24.4.5    Traceability

A special type of smart packaging is to have an electronic chip moulded into the side of plastic containers, thus permitting traceability of the products throughout the distribution chain. The chip may be designed so that stored data can be read by a radio frequency (RF) reader. Other traceability technologies are based on bar codes, memory tags, and RF-emitting tags.

The idea of an intelligent refrigerator getting information from intelligent packages is not new. The output from various intelligent packages or indicators can be converted into electronic signals that may be transmitted as RF or be readable through an interface. It is possible to produce paperboard cartons with printed circuits capable of measuring parameters such as volume and temperature. Based on the measured temperature and time the remaining shelf life can be calculated. This information can be displayed on the carton or be transmitted to a mobile telephone or an intelligent refrigerator. In an intelligent refrigerator, which may be a 'supermarket' or a 'home refrigerator', received signals are transferred into information that may be given on a display or be printed, or lead to direct action, e.g., a message on a screen of a PC that these packages (this lot) should be sold at once or even discarded. The received information could be that the oxygen content is not correct (too high or too low), the amount of metabolites too high, pathogenic micro-organisms are present, or the Time-Temperature history indicates no remaining shelf life.

## 24.5  Future trends

It is self-evident that there are always improvements to be made in instrumentation for surveillance of food processing operations. To mention a few examples: it is still difficult to measure water activity rapidly and precisely or to measure the redox potential exactly in a solid, mixed food. No doubt, there will be improvements in instrumentation in this field in the years to come. Online and inline monitoring will also be much more common than it is today. Another area where there will be new developments is the merger of quality and safety systems. Examples are recorded in this chapter, especially in the fish-commodity field, but there are signs that this trend will be extended to comprise other commodities as well.

Finally, the automation of surveillance systems has also been touched on. This trend is very interesting, since it opens up a new pathway. At the present time only a few attempts have been published in the food field, probably because most foods are so heterogeneous, making modelling and control difficult. Finally it should be mentioned that this new book on food preservation contains no chapter on chemical preservatives. Although chemical preservatives are still used on a limited scale, it is not foreseen that there will be any developments in that area, partly because of the risk for their use generally, but not least because this type of compounds are viewed with suspicion by the consumer.

## 24.6  References

ANTLE, J.M., 1999. 'Benefits and costs of food safety regulation'. *Food Policy*, **24**, 605–623.

APHA (American Public Health Association), 1971, Proceedings of the 1991 National Conference on Food Protection, Washington, USA.

BARENDSZ, 1998. 'Food safety and total quality management'. *Food Control*, **9**, 163–170.

BERRIE, P., 2001. 'Pressure and temperature measurement in food process control', in Kress-Rogers, E. and Brimelow, C. (eds) *Instrumentation and sensors for the food industry: second edition* Woodhead Publishing Ltd, Cambridge.

CODEX ALIMENTARIUS, 1996. 'Hazard analysis and critical control point (HACCP)'. System and guidelines for its application. Annex 1 to Appendix II ALINORM 97/13A, 30–37.

CODEX 2002. Proposed draft code of practice for fish and fishery products, ALINORM 01/18, appendix V. STEP 5.

GOULD, W.A., 1994. CGMP'S/Food Plant Sanitation. CTI Publications, Inc., Baltimore, USA.

JOUVE, J.L., 1997, Personal communication.

KRESS-ROGERS, E. and BRIMELOW, C. (eds), 2001. 'Pressure and temperature measurement in food process control', in Kress-Rogers, E. and Brimelow, C. (eds) *Instrumentation and sensors for the food industry: second edition.* Woodhead Publishing Ltd, Cambridge.

LINKO, S. and LINKO, P., 1998. 'Developments in monitoring and control of food processes'. *Trans IchemeE.*, **76**, Part C, 127–137.

PETERS, R.E., 1998. 'The broader application of HACCP concepts to food quality in Australia'. *Food Control*, **9**, 83–89.

PILLSBURY COMPANY, 1973, Food Safety through the Hazard Analysis and Critical Control Point System. Contract no. FDA 72–59, Pillsbury Company, Research & Development Department, Minneapolis, USA.

ROPKINS, D. and BECK, A.J., 2000. 'Evaluation of worldwide approaches to the use of HACCP to control food safety'. *Trends in Food Science & Technology*, **11**, 10–21.

TOTHILL, I. (ed.), 2003. *Rapid and on-line instrumentation for food quality assurance*, Woodhead Publishing Ltd, Cambridge.

UNNEVEHR, L.J. and JENSEN, H.H., 1999. 'The economic implications of using HACCP as a food safety regulatory standard'. *Food Policy*, **24**, 625–635.

# Index